THE ORIGIN OF SPECIES REVISITED

The Theories of Evolution and of Abrupt Appearance

The marker for Darwin's grave in Westminster Abbey

Originally Published by

Philosophical Library
New York

THE ORIGIN OF SPECIES REVISITED

The Theories of Evolution and of Abrupt Appearance

VOLUME II: PHILOSOPHY OF SCIENCE, PHILOSOPHY OF RELIGION, HISTORY, EDUCATION, AND CONSTITUTIONAL ISSUES

by
W. R. Bird

Regency
Nashville, Tennessee

Published in Nashville, Tennessee, by Thomas Nelson, Inc., and distributed in Canada by Lawson Falle, Ltd., Cambridge, Ontario.

Library of Congress Cataloging-in-Publication Data

Bird, W. R., 1954–
The Origin of Species Revisited: The Theories of
Evolution and of Abrupt Appearance

Includes index (name and subject).
1. Science—Biological Evolution—Biochemical
Evolution—Cosmic Evolution.
2. Philosophy of Science—Philosophy of Religion—History of Science—Educational Theory—Constitutional Law.
I. Title.
QH371.B58 1987, 1988, 1989
ISBN Vol. II 0-8407-6848-6

Printed in the United States of America

1 2 3 4 — 95 94 93 92

TABLE OF CONTENTS

VOLUME I I

Preface
by Dr. Robert M. Augros

In volume one of *The Origin of Species Revisited* W. R. Bird treats the scientific complexities of evolution with admirable scholarship. His dispassionate spirit of inquiry is precisely what is needed at a time when evolution has become so politicized and positions so polarized.

In volume two he brings the same calm and incredible thoroughness to bear on the legal, moral, political, and educational implications of the current crisis in evolutionary theory. This work is not an abstract treatise intended only for specialists. On the contrary, it is a concrete presentation of issues vital not only for biologists and lawyers, but for teachers, students, and parents across the land.

The heart of the matter, amply demonstrated in volume one, is that neo-Darwinian gradualism and natural selection are at odds with much of the evidence and are long overdue for revision or replacement. The majority of the biological community, especially in the United States, however, is tenaciously committed to Darwinism. Recent attacks on this established view by competent scientists, Bird argues, "logically imply the possibility of scientific alternatives." Therefore, there is no reason for the educational monopoly of what Dobzhansky admits is a "mechanistic materialist philosophy explicitly or implicitly shared by most of the present 'establishment' in the biological sciences." Bird delineates the plausible alternatives to what Patterson calls this "entrenched dogma" and presents the evidence favoring a theory of abrupt appearance. Given the scientific legitimacy of such evidence, it only makes sense to offer these scientific alternatives to students in the classroom. Bird thus argues that the teaching of alternative approaches to origins is bona fide science, is educationally desirable, and would not constitute an intrusion of religion into public schools.

I caution the reader not to dismiss this sober two-volume work simply because its author, though thoroughly informed on the issues, is not a biologist. I believe that Bird, in fact, has two distinct advantages in being an "outsider." First, he brings an objectivity to the topic that is rarely found among those trained from their undergraduate days in a narrow speciality and who are often burdened with unexamined presuppositions. And second, he enjoys much more intellectual freedom than most academic biologists. Mr. Bird is able to say what many insiders know but dare not say for fear of ostracism, risk to career, or jeopardy to funding. And Bird is, of course, no outsider when it comes to the legal dimensions of the issues.

In sum, no matter what the reader's perspective and no matter where his allegiances may lie, he will find in this book an incomparable resource. Its fairness and completeness promise to make it a standard reference for years to come.

Robert M. Augros*
Associate Professor of Philosophy
Saint Anselm College
Manchester, New Hampshire

[Dr. Augros*, an evolutionist, is the author of *The New Story of Science* and *The New Biology*, as well as of scientific papers on evolution and on DNA. He teaches philosophy at St. Anselm College, specializing in philosophy of science, and is a consultant in that field. Dr. Augros earned his Ph.D. degree in philosophy at Laval University in Quebec.]

Preface
by Dr. W. Scot Morrow

Scientific things first caught my attention when I was a little boy. The world was a wonderful place; it had a lot of mystery to it, and it invited many questions about which I insisted on answers. Early on, I became convinced that the people called "scientists" provided me with the most satisfactory explanations. Later, it dawned on me that although these authority figures had a good grip on reality, of equal importance was the *way* they told me what they believed to be true about the world. Their ideas had the ring of reasonableness, and were self-correcting. Honesty and fairness made their fabric complete. The noble Hoyle has put it splendidly: "In science and mathematics, the important thing is what is being said, not who is saying it." Perhaps I am still naive, but these are the human qualities that I demand of myself and my colleagues.

To be true to its promises, science must be based on honorable activities, and eschew injustice, intolerance, and the arrogance that all too often accompanies political power. Regrettably, many people who possess technical skill—even genius—especially in writing and speaking, when they find themselves at the top of the intellectual or professional totem pole, cannot resist the temptation to play the role of a despot. Even in the scientific enterprise, we find execrable individuals who would impose their hubristic ideology on the rest of us throught the power of the state.

Fortunately, a supreme irony is being played out in front of us: a brilliant attorney at law, with limited formal training in science, has written *The Origin of Species Revisited*, and brings progress toward saving (at least biological) science from its major totalitarian excess. I say that from my personal perspective as an evolutionist. We evolutionists have swallowed the gradualist party line for far too long; most of us have been taught, and believed as proven fact, that the gradualness of evolution is as obvious as the nose on our face. No other hypothesis need apply; we want no heresy here. And the children should only hear the "truth," since the alternative is unthinkable. Beware, watch out for the "army of the night," or we will find ourselves looking at Torquemada all over again. Well, as W.R. Bird definitively shows, the spawn of the Grand Inquisitor are indeed with us, polluting the scientific and educational landscape, denying employment, tenure, and academic degrees, censoring what is published and taught, etc. And, rubbing salt in the wounds, they discriminate and censor at public expense! What in the world are my fellow evolutionists afraid of? Did Scopes not enjoin us, "I believe in teaching every aspect of every problem or theory"?

With fine analytical scholarship, and a veritable army of solid references, Bird constructs the scientific case for the concept that life appeared abruptly, apparently a "discontinuity," whose mechanisms of origin remain unknown, and whose history of change is far better characterized by the abrupt appearance of new forms rather than by continuous gradual transitions. I am especially impressed with the thoroughness of his treatment of what is meant by "religion" and "science." It is sobering to contemplate just how metaphysical the underpinnings of science are. So much of what we think and know, resolves to a matter of philosophical preference.

By mounting a conclusive scientific and legal attack on the McLean definition of science, Bird demolishes the rationale—if an ethical one ever existed—for allowing only one working hypothesis, on any controversial topic, into a public school classroom.

This outstanding treatise is a masterful defense of intellectual freedom, addressed to the rectification of philosophical and constitutional grievances. This is in the finest legal, moral, and—since many of us scientists have not thought about such a viable philosophical interplay—scientific tradition. Among other apostles of freedom, Kevin Cullinane has suggested that we think of "America" as a concept, not only a country. In this sense, Bird's arguments provide guidance in attempting to answer the question: by what right do we require people to support an activity—in this case educational and scientific—that those same people are sincerely opposed to?

To steal a line from Fiorello H. LaGuardia, this treatise "could run on a laundry ticket" and beat its critics.

W. Scot Morrow*
Associate Professor of Chemistry
Wofford College
Spartanburg, South Carolina

[Dr. Morrow* is an evolutionist biochemist who has long studied the educational issue of freedom for alternative viewpoints and the philosophical issue of manipulation of the definitions of science and religion, and has long taught biochemistry and performed original research on topics including the evolutionary origin of life. He earned his Ph.D. degree in biochemistry at University of North Carolina at Chapel Hill.]

Preface
by Dr. Russell L. French

The time was 1925, the place Dayton, Tennessee—only a few miles from where today I teach teachers at the University of Tennessee, Knoxville. The event was one with which we are vaguely familiar—the Scopes trial. Perhaps that is the problem. We are all *vaguely* familiar with the Scopes trial, its principal players—Clarence Darrow, William Jennings Bryan, John Scopes and its central issue, the teaching of two theories of the origin of the world and man. But, as in so many other areas of knowledge, we are ill-educated in the positions argued in that trial and their implications for our society and educational system today. Further, we have failed to learn over the 63 years since that famous (or infamous) media event the truly important lessons which we could have learned from it.

I believe that few people in 1925 or now realize that the central issue of the Scopes trial was the appropriateness of a law restricting what scientific theories could be taught—*not* the rightness or truth of either the creation or evolution theories. Neither of those theories was then or has been since empirically proven to be fact. Most of us have been acquainted with the oratorial skills of Bryan, the legal brilliance of Darrow, the emotionally charged setting in which their confrontation occurred and the spectacular dynamics of the confrontation itself. However, our teachers have seldom underlined Malone's arguments that all sides of an issue should, indeed, must be taught. I cannot remember ever being introduced to Scopes' attorney Dudley Malone's statement, "For God's sake, let the children have their minds kept open—close no doors to their knowledge; shut no door from them. . ."[1] until my reading of this manuscript. As W.R. Bird so clearly points out, the conditions which gave rise to the

Scopes trial have been completely reversed in only 63 short years. Today, Darrow would find himself voicing the same arguments, but he might well be arguing against the repression of the theory of abrupt appearance from the textbooks and curriculum of our schools. Those segments of society opposed to indoctrination and the limiting of knowledge in 1925 seem to be only too willing now to argue the opposite position.

Like many other students, I was introduced to Darwin and *The Origin of the Species* at several different points in my lengthy educational experience. While I am sure that I missed some, perhaps many, of Darwin's points just as my students fail to see or hear some of what is presented to them, I cannot remember any of those who taught me ever emphasizing Darwin's own comments quoted by Bird in this volume:

> For I am well aware that scarely a single point is discussed in this volume on which facts cannot be adduced, often apparently leading to conclusions directly opposite to those at which I have arrived. A fair result can be obtained only by fully stating and balancing the facts and arguments on both sides of each question; and this is here impossible.

Apparently, neither the Scopes trial, nor Darwin's comments, nor prior and subsequent experience has helped us to differentiate theory from fact. The American College Dictionary defines theory as "a coherent group of general propositions used as principles of explanation for a class of phenomena; a proposed explanation whose status is still conjectural. . ."[2] The scientific information which clearly demonstrates that neither the theory of abrupt appearance nor the theory of evolution has yet been empirically proven to be more than theory is readily available. Bird has assembled that information in this book. Yet, scientists, educators and judges alike have obliterated the distinctions among conjecture, hypothesis, theory and fact, and they have refused to promote the examination of evidence supporting alternate theories. These developments speak volumes about the state of our society, its educational system and the current, educational concern for teaching young people to think.

Having spent 28 years of my life teaching in American public schools and universities, I was struck by John Scopes' statement during his trial:

> Education, you know, means broadening, advancing, and if you limit a teacher to only one side of anything the whole country will eventually have only one thought, be one individual. I believe in teaching every aspect of every problem or theory.[3]

It sounded remarkably similar to a statement by Alan Bloom in the preface of his current best-seller, *The Closing of the American Mind*:

> No real teacher can doubt that his task is to assist his pupil to fulfill human nature against all the deforming forces of convention and prejudice.[4]

Why is it that we educators say we want open-mindness, critical and creative thinking, examination of an issue or idea from all angles; but then are so willing to close out alternate, *supportable* positions, indoctrinate the young and go to court to maintain the right to do so? Is the latter state of affairs the real indicator of human nature? Has our society reached the point where the tremendous expansion of knowledge and human unwillingness to pursue truth rigorously have merged to create the illusion of education but not the reality? Have we become so enamored of empiricism and what we believe to be modern science that we are unable or unwilling to see that values and bias permeate the scientific disciplines as all other disciplines? The continuing controversy over a balanced educational treatment of the theories of evolution and abrupt appearance, when viewed in light of the wealth of information assembled in this book, raises these and a host of other questions for any thinking reader.

I have learned a great deal from reading and pondering W.R. Bird's book. I am not a scientist, and he has done me a great service by bringing before me and sorting so clearly the arguments and positions from many scientific disciplines which are pertinent to the evolution debate. He has forced me to think deeply about the definitions of science and religion and about the interrelationships among the "compartments" which we so often use to pigeonhole education content and human experience. I confess that I either did not know or had forgotten that Marx and Lenin and Hitler had relied heavily on Darwin's theories as support for the social movements which they conceived and propagated, and that even theories of economics cannot be separated from theories of the earth's beginning or man's progress (or lack of it). I had not thought so deeply for a long while about the place and value of bias and belief in inquiry or about the distinction between indoctrination and education. In short, this is a valuable book, but a sobering book, perhaps even a frightening book.

Every serious student of science, of society, of theology, of education and of man should read this book. Bird treats the theories of abrupt appearance versus evolution in depth, but in the process he brings to our consciousness so much more, so much that may be important to the preservation of our society as we have known it.

The reader may see this last statement as overly dramatic. Perhaps it is, but my reactions to the book are filtered through my experience in the heart and heat of the evolution controversy. A few years ago, I was called to serve as an expert educational witness (not an expert scientific witness but an expert witness on educational content and process) in the Louisiana balanced treatment case (Edwards vs. Aguillard). Although I never had to appear in court, I was subjected to six hours of interrogation (more commonly and politely called deposition) by one of the opposition's lawyers. The questions were penetrating. Most of them focused on definitions, positions, documentation and evidence for many of the items covered in this book. It was a humbling experience and one which forced me to realize just how important it is to know what one knows and doesn't know, to know what one believes and why he believes it and to study, to analyze, synthesize and evaluate the information available on a subject as controversial and far-reaching as this one. This book is frightening to me because it clearly demonstrated to me how much I did not know until I had read it. If that was my condition, what about others, perhaps the majority, in our society? And, if we are so ignorant on this subject, what about so many other issues that are before us to "decide"—abortion, civil rights, arms agreements, inclusions and exclusions in other areas of our educational curricula?

As you begin reading, be prepared to think and to be challenged. If you are a teacher of any content at any level, be prepared to face some serious questions: "What have I taught them? What have they gained from spending time with me? What have I contributed to the building up of our society and the principles upon which it was established?"

Russell L. French*
Professor of Education
Department of Curriculum & Instruction
University of Tennessee, Knoxville
Knoxville, Tennessee

[Dr. French* is one of America's leading nonevolutionist educators, and teaches curriculum and instruction at University of Tennessee. He was the executive director of the Tennessee Certification Commission from its establishment in 1983 to 1987; it was the "master teacher program" supported as a national prototype by President Reagan. Dr. French has published more than 35 articles in education journals and books, has spoken at many national education conferences, and earned his Ph.D. degree in educational curriculum and instruction at Ohio State University.]

Notes

[1] Quoted by Bird from the transcript of the Scopes trial.

[2] Clarence L. Barnhart (Editor). *The American College Dictionary.* New York: Random House Publishers.

[3] Quoted by Bird from the transcript of the Scopes trial.

[4] Alan Bloom. *The Closing of the American Mind.* New York: Simon and Schuster, 1987.

Introduction

> *In considering the Origin of Species, it is quite conceivable that a naturalist. . . might come to the conclusion that each species had not been independently created, but had descended, like varieties, from other species. Nevertheless, such a conclusion, even if well founded, would be unsatisfactory, until it could be shown how the innumerable species inhabiting this world have been modified, so as to acquire that perfection of structure and coadaptation which most justly excites our admiration. . . .*
>
> —Charles Darwin*[1]

Volume I addressed the scientific evidence for the theory of evolution and for the theory of abrupt appearance. It found that biological, biochemical, and cosmic evolution are "in crisis,"[2] that dissent is widespread and mounting,[3] and that the challenge comes even more from disillusioned evolutionists than from creationists. Each stage of evolution, and each argument for evolution, has empirical difficulties that are acknowledged by some specialists in the field,[4] as summarized in Chapter 8.

At the same time, the theory of abrupt appearance, in its biological, biochemical, and cosmic aspects, has difficulties and needs further research. However, that theory consists of affirmative lines of scientific evidence, such as the paleontology argument of the widespread abrupt appearance of complex life in the fossil record,

*Scientists and others cited in this introduction, unless otherwise indicated, are not proponents of, and their quoted statements are not intended as endorsements of, either the theory of abrupt appearance or the theory of creation.

the further paleontology argument of the systematic gaps between fossil categories, the information science argument of the vast information content of all living organisms and their component structures, the biogenesis argument that life comes only from life, or the thermodynamics argument that the ordered matter and energy of the universe require a beginning.[5] That evidence is scientific: fossil analysis, information theory, the law of biogenesis, and the laws of thermodynamics are not found in Genesis and do not embody Genesis.

This Volume II discusses whether the theory of evolution and the theory of abrupt appearance are or can be scientific (philosophy of science), whether they are or can be nonreligious (philosophy of religion, history of the evolution controversy, and educational theory on contrasting explanations), and whether they are or can be constitutional (First Amendment concepts of academic freedom and separation of church and state). Its thesis is that the theories of evolution and of abrupt appearance are comparable in aspects that often have been overlooked, and that students should have the opportunity to consider all scientific theories of origins from a strictly scientific standpoint.

Regarding science,[6] no less an authority than Sir Karl Popper* came to "the conclusion that Darwinism is not a testable scientific theory, but a metaphysical research programme . . .."[7] Scores of other philosophers of science and scientists agree that macroevolution is "not subject to test,"[8] that the Darwinian "theory does not allow itself to be tested,"[9] that "Neo-Darwinism. . .is not falsifiable,"[10] or that biochemical evolution or cosmic evolution is not testable or falsifiable.[11]

At the same time, some evolutionists regard the theory of abrupt appearance as at least potentially scientific.[12] Leach* observes that "today it is the conventional neo-Darwinians who appear as the conservative bigots and the unorthodox neo-Sedgwickians [discontinuitists] who rate as enlightened rationalists prepared to contemplate the evidence that is plain for all to see."[13] The theory of creation also "is a kind of science," Dolby* concludes.[14] Patterson*, the senior paleontologist at the British Museum, mused "that evolutionism and creationism seem to have become very hard to distinguish," because "evolution and creation seem to be sharing remarkable parallels."[15]

Regarding religion,[16] the "remarkable parallels" continue. Both the theories of evolution and of abrupt appearance are parallel to—but different from—a number of religious beliefs that include

Protestant, Catholic, Jewish, and nonJudeo-Christian faiths.[17] Both scientific viewpoints are advocated by scientific authors who have written religious materials on origins as well. Each explanation was supported by both scientists and theologians throughout the history of the evolution controversy.[18] It is surprising to some people that the theory of evolution often includes concepts of creation.[19]

Even the theory of creation can be scientific and nonreligious. The theory is testable and falsifiable in a manner comparable to evolution. The term creation itself can mean simply origination by apparently nonnaturalistic means. It was so used by Darwin*, who said that by "the term of creation . . . I really meant 'appeared' by some wholly unknown process,"[20] and was the "conventional practice, . . . using the term creation as a synonym for 'appear' or 'originate'."[21] Today, "the creation idea was. . .applied to the appropriate discontinuity" in cosmic evolution;[22] "cosmologists use the phrase 'creation of the universe' to describe this phenomenon."[23] The term creation is used today to mean sudden origination, by most cosmic evolutionists in connection with the big bang theory (whose fomulator Gamow* described it as "The Creation of the Universe"[24]), the inflationary universe theory (whose foremost spokesman Guth* writes of "creation. . .from absolutely nothing"[25]), the recent steady state theory (whose primary exponent Bondi* described it as the "continual creation" theory about "creation. . .out of nothing"),[26] and quantum and particle creation theories;[27] and by some biochemical evolutionists and biological evolutionists in connection with their proposals.[28] The concept of a creator is not a necessary part of the theory of creation, because that concept is not derived from empirical data in the sense that nonnaturalistic origination is.[29] Several textbooks published by ordinary national publishers describe creation without reference to a creator, and several scientists such as Hoyle, Wickramasinghe, and Ambrose* speak of creation without any creator.[30] Nevertheless, the concept of a creator is not necessarily religious, and in fact was central to the historical origin of modern science.[31]

Regarding constitutionality,[32] the student's right to receive information is furthered by uncensored instruction in both the theory of evolution and in alternative scientific theories of origins, which the U.S. Supreme Court recently indicated is permissible.[33] Teacher academic freedom is a more difficult issue, because forty-two percent of public school teachers conclude that the theory of abrupt appearance in some form should be taught while fifty-three percent disagree,[34] so either course of action is contrary to the professional judgment of nearly half the teachers. This book does not suggest any mandate for teaching all scientific theories of origins at the university level, but suggests the fairness of that sort of uncensored instruction in public secondary and elementary schools that students are legally compelled to attend, that parents are legally forced to finance, and that legislatures have retained authority over for prescribing curriculum. "If there is any fixed star in our constitutional constellation, it is that no official, high or petty, can prescribe what shall be orthodox in politics, nationalism, religion, or other matters of opinion . . .."[35]

Separation of church and state is not violated by objectively teaching scientific evidence.[36] Emerson*, a prominent legal commentator, wrote that "a new theory of the requirements imposed by the first amendment" possibly "may be found in the concept of balanced presentation," where "the obligation of government must be to present a fairly balanced exposition of various relevant theories and points of view, and of alternatives open for action."[37] The Supreme Court has indicated the constitutionality of public school activities in "reciting historical documents such as the Declaration of Independence which contain references to the Deity or by singing officially espoused anthems which include the composer's professions of faith in a Supreme Being, or with the fact that there are many manifestations in our public life of belief in God."[38] The historical test for the Establishment Clause conclusively shows that such references are not proscribed by the First Amendment: the very First Congress that wrote the Clause saw no conflict with dating the Constitution "in the year of our Lord," with a statutory oath for public officials including "so help me God," with a resolution asking for "a Thanksgiving Day to acknowledge 'the many signal favors of Almighty God,' " with chaplains paid with public funds to offer prayers to God, and with Washington's first inaugural address referring to the "Author" of the world.[39] The tripart test that the Supreme Court frequently uses similarly shows the constitutionality of teaching all scientific theories of origins, because the purpose and effect are to offer additional scientific information and thereby to advance students' right to know, while no entanglement results between any religious institution and the state.[40] For similar reasons, a near majority of a U.S. Court of Appeals (seven of fifteen judges) concluded that a requirement for teaching the theory of creation with the theory of evolution "does not infringe the Constitution":[41]

> [I]t has no direct religious reference whatever and merely requires that the whole scientific truth be taught on the subject if any is.
>
> . . ..
>
> I should have thought that requiring the truth to be taught on any subject displayed its own secular warrant, one at the heart of the scientific method itself. . . .[42]

Two of the nine justices on the U.S. Supreme Court agreed.

Strong opposition to the theory of creation is not surprising in view of the widespread scientific bias in favor of evolution,[43] which Patterson* describes as " 'an intellectual fashion, a substitute for religion, an entrenched dogma,' "[44] which Hardin* refers to as "quite remarkable ferocity" toward doubters,[45] and which Grene* sees "as a religion of science that Darwinism chiefly held, and holds men's minds, . . .an orthodoxy preached by its adherents with religious fervor."[46] Pangle* refers to "the bluster and unscientific indignation into which rationalism collapses" when neoDarwinians try to suppress alternative theories,[47] and Provine* acknowledges for example that "most biological scientists are intolerant of creationism."[48]

The determined and adamant opposition of most scientists to scientific alternatives is what is surprising. However, many "imperfect believers" among evolutionists do advocate teaching all scientific theories of origins.[49] Solomon* writes, in connection with "unpopular or minority ideas" particularly of origins, that "[n]othing is so unscientific as the inquisition mentality that served, as it thought, the truth, by seeking to suppress or conceal dissent rather than grappling with it."[50] Provine* writes that "creationism should be taught along with evolutionism in grade schools and high schools. . .in the science classroom," because "creationism is a viable, understandable and plausible theory for the creation point" of view, although it is his "opinion that it is a wrong theory."[51] Stonehouse* of Cambridge says that a recent creationist book "may convince you. . .that there is more in the Creationist argument than scientists are generally willing to concede," and "that uncritical acceptance of Darwinism may be counterproductive."[52] Morrow* writes that teaching even the theory of creation with the theory of evolution is good because "[s]tudents would have available a realistic set of options to explore."[53] Thompson* notes that "[s]tudents should be exposed to both sides of the coin regarding biological change—the doctrine of creation and that of evolution," and that "[c]reationists are now espousing one of the arguments of Clarence Darrow's ardent defense of Scopes: that the theory of the beginning should not be taught to the exclusion of another."[54] Alexander* concurs that "a comparison of the two alternatives can be an excellent exercise in logic and reason."[55] Anderson* and Kilbourn* agree that at least "an argument for teaching special-creation can be made."[56] Black*,[57] Sarich*,[58] and de Grazia*[59] concur. Forty-two percent of public school teachers agree,[60] as does eighty-six percent of the public.[61] The theory of creation differs from the theory of abrupt appearance, of course, and this book only defends the teaching of the latter along with the theory of evolution.

This book agrees with Provine*, Stonehouse*, and those other defenders of students' academic freedom, that all scientific theories should be allowed into the marketplace of ideas. It agrees with Scopes*, who said "I believe in teaching every aspect of every problem or theory," from a scientific standpoint.[62] It concurs with Malone*, Scopes'* attorney, who eloquently pleaded to "let the children have their minds kept open—close no doors to their knowledge; shut no door from them."[63] It joins with Darwin* himself, who looked with confidence to future scientists "who will be able to view both sides of the question with impartiality."[64]

Notes

A note about footnote style that follows *A Uniform System of Citation*: Articles in periodicals are cited by author, title italicized, volume number, journal, first page, relevant page, and date, such as footnote 9 (unless the journal does not use sequential pagination for each volume). Essays collected in books are cited by author, title italicized, book title, first page, relevant page, editor, and date, such as footnote 7. Books are cited by author, title italicized, relevant page, and date, such as footnote 2 (unless unpublished such as footnote 34). Legal cases and statutes are cited in legal style, such as footnote 33.

1 C. Darwin*, *The Origin of Species* 3 (1st ed. 1859, repr. 1964).

2 M. Denton*, *Evolution: A Theory in Crisis* (1985); Ho* & Saunders*, *Preface*, to Beyond Neo-Darwinism ix (M. Ho* & P. Saunders* eds. 1984).

3 Sections 3.2 (d)-(f) & 7.1(b).

4 Chapters 3, 5 & 7.

5 Chapters 2, 4 & 6.

6 Chapters 9-11.

7 Popper*, *Intellectual Autobiography*, in 2 The Philosophy of Karl Popper 3, 134 (P. Schilpp* ed. 1974). Although he has modified his earlier position that natural selection is nonscientific and tautologous, he has not published any modification of his quoted statement. Chapter 10, nn. 19-20.

[8] C. Patterson*, *Evolution* 145 (1978).

[9] Saunders* & Ho*, *Is Neo-Darwinism Falsifiable?—And Does It Matter?*, 4 Nature & System 179, 185 (1982).

[10] *Id.* at 180.

[11] Sections 10.1(b), 10.2(a), 10.3(b) & 10.4(b).

[12] Sections 10.1(a), 10.2(b), 10.3(a) & 10.4(a).

[13] Leach*, *Men, bishops and apes*, Nature, Sept. 3, 1981, at 19, 20.

[14] Dolby*, *Science and Pseudo-Science: The Case of Creationism*, 22 Zygon 195, 208-09 (1987). He views it as a "corrupting" science.

[15] Address of Dr. Colin Patterson at Am. Museum of Natural History, tr. at 3 & 4 (Nov. 5, 1981).

[16] Chapters 12-18.

[17] Sections 14.1-14.2; Scheid*, *Evolution and Creationism in Public Schools*, 9 J. Contemp. Law 51, 106-07 (1983).

[18] Section 14.3.

[19] Sections 13.1-13.3.

[20] 2 *Life and Letters of Charles Darwin* 202-203 (F. Darwin* ed. 1903).

[21] N. Gillespie*, *Charles Darwin and the Problem of Creation* 32 (1979).

[22] J. North*, *The Measure of the Universe* 401 (1965).

[23] Tipler*, *How to Construct a Falsifiable Theory in Which the Universe Came Into Being Several Thousand Years Ago*, 2 Philosophy of Science Assn. 873, 894 (1984).

[24] G. Gamow*, *The Creation of the Universe* (1955).

[25] Guth* & Steinhardt*, *The Inflationary Universe*, Scientific Am., May 1984, at 116, 128.

[26] H. Bondi*, *Cosmology* 143-44 (1968).

[27] Section 13.1(d).

[28] Section 13.1(f)-(g).

[29] Section 13.2.

[30] *Id.*

[31] Section 13.4

[32] Chapters 19-20.

[33] Edwards v. Aguillard, 482 U.S. ..., 96 L. Ed. 2d 510 (1987). The Court struck down the Louisiana "Balanced Treatment for Creation-Science and Evolution-Science Act" on the basis that it had a nonsecular legislative purpose, but said that teachers "already possess" a "flexibility...to supplant the present science curriculum with the presentation of theories, besides evolution, about the origins of life . . .." *Id.*

[34] Austin Analytical Consulting*, Opinion Poll for Biology Teachers question 8 (1986).

[35] West Virginia State Bd. of Educ. v. Barnette, 319 U.S. 624, 642 (1943).

[36] Chapter 21.

[37] Emerson* & Haber*, *The* Scopes *Case in Modern Dress*, 27 U. Chi. L. Rev. 522, 527 (1960) (he is speaking primarily of the university level, but his rationales of a closed forum and governmental involvement apply also to the public school level).

38 Engel v. Vitale, 370 U.S. 421, 435 n. 21 (1962).
39 Section 21.1
40 Section 21.2
41 Aguillard v. Edwards, 778 F. 2d. 225, 226 (5th Cir. 1985) (en banc, Gee, J., dissenting).
42 *Id.* at 227, 228.
43 Section 9.7(a)-(c).
44 C. Patterson*, *Evolution* 150 (1977).
45 G. Hardin*, *Nature and Man's Fate* 216 (1961).
46 Grene*, *The Faith of Darwinism*, Encounter, Nov. 1959, at 48, 48-49.
47 Pangle*, *Introduction*, to L. Strauss, Studies in Platonic Political Philosophy 21-22 (1983).
48 W. Provine*, Theories of Creationism and Evolution from a Historical Perspective (unpub. lecture before Sigma Xi Chapter, Corning, N.Y., Nov. 17, 1981).
49 Section 17.2.
50 P. Davis & E. Solomon*, *The World of Biology* 414 (1974).
51 *Scientists Abandon Evolution*, Contrast, Mar.-Apr. 1982, at 1, 3.
52 Stonehouse*, *Introduction*, to M. Pitman, Adam and Evolution 9, 12 (1984).
53 Letter from Dr. W. Scot Morrow* to Dr. Major Rhodes* (Jan. 1, 1980).
54 A. Thompson*, *Biology, Zoology, and Genetics: Evolution Model vs. Creation Model* 2, 271 (1983).
55 Alexander*, *Evolution, Creation, and Biology Teaching*, in Evolution versus Creationism 90, 91 (J. Zetterberg* ed. 1983).
56 Anderson* & Kilbourn*, *Creation, Evolution, and Curriculum*, 67 Science Education 45, 53-54 (1983).
57 T. Black*, *Straight Talk about American Education* 40, 276 (1982).
58 Lecture by V. Sarich* at Bakersfield, Cal. (May 18, 1986).
59 A. de Grazia*, Quantavolution and Creation in Arkansas 4 (unpub. ms. 1982).
60 Austin Analytical Consulting*, Opinion Poll for Biology Teachers question 8 (1986).
61 NBC News* & Associated Press*, November National Poll 15 (Nov. 24, 1981).
62 Quoted in P. Davis & E. Solomon*, *The World of Biology* 414 (1974).
63 *The World's Most Famous Court Trial* 187 (3d ed. 1925) (transcript of *Scopes* trial).
64 C. Darwin*, *The Origin of Species* 482 (1st ed. 1859, repr. 1964).

PART V

Whether the Theories of Abrupt Appearance and Evolution Are Scientific? The Definitions of Science

The demarcation between science and nonscience has long intrigued philosophers of science and scientists, and the many proposals for demarcation produce a web of intersecting lines without much consensus. Most of the widely-respected definitions of science are comparably satisfied by the theory of evolution and the theory of abrupt appearance.

However, a radical definition has been contrived recently for the obvious purpose of excluding the theory of abrupt appearance by definition. That definition, which requires conformity to natural law, testability, falsifiability, and tentativeness as necessary and apparently sufficient criteria of science, is manifestly incorrect and is not noticeably accepted among philosophers of science. However, the theory of abrupt appearance meets even that definition of science to the same extent as the theory of evolution.

Scientists, unlike philosophers of science, are more often than not apathetic toward the definition of science, as Bloom* notes in *The Closing of the American Mind*:

> The natural scientists are benevolent toward other fields and toward liberal education, if it does not steal away their students and does not take too much time from their preparatory studies. But they themselves are interested primarily in the solution of the questions now important in their disciplines and *are not particularly concerned with discussions of*

> *their foundations*, inasmuch as they are so evidently successful. They are indifferent to Newton's conception of time or his disputes with Leibniz about calculus; Aristotle's teleology is an absurdity beneath consideration. Scientific progress, they believe, *no longer depends on the kind of comprehensive reflection given to the nature of science* by men like Bacon, Descartes, Hume, Kant and Marx. This is merely historical study, and for a long time now, even the greatest scientists have given up thinking about Galileo and Newton. Progress is undoubted. The difficulties about the truth of science raised by postivism, and those about the goodness of science raised by Rousseau and Nietzsche, have not really penetrated to the center of scientific consciousness. Hence, no Great Books, but incremental progress, is the theme for them.[1]

Such a vacuum abhors nature. The great irony of modern science is that so many scientists, who exhaustively study a grand unified theory of physics, the big bang theory of the origin of the universe, or the "unifying" Darwinian theory of biological evolution, totally ignore and generally are totally unaware of the study of the broader grand issue of the meaning of science.

Notes

1 A. Bloom*, *The Closing of the American Mind* 345 (1986) (emphasis added).

CHAPTER 9

Accepted Definitions of Science and the Radical Definition

In questions of science the authority of a thousand is not worth the humble reasoning of a single individual.
—Galileo Galilei[1]

This chapter discusses the definition of science, which must be addressed before anything can be characterized on a principled basis as scientific or nonscientific. The most widely accepted definitions are summarized in Section 9.1. The textbook definition of science, with its tidy sequence of observation, induction, and theory formation, is described in Section 9.2. The radical definition of science offered by a noted philosopher and a federal judge in the *McLean* case, which three anti-creationist philosophers separately analyze as "demonstrably false" and "remote from well-founded opinion in the philosophy of science," is summarized in Section 9.3. The inadequacy as demarcation criteria of natural law, testability and falsifiability, and tentativeness are outlined in Sections 9.4-9.6. Finally, the inconclusiveness of the majority assessment by scientists is suggested by Section 9.7.

*Philosophers and scientists cited in this chapter, unless otherwise indicated, are not proponents of, and their quoted statements are not intended as endorsements of, either the theory of abrupt appearance or the theory of creation.

This chapter does not endorse any of the various definitions of science, but simply calls for a principled definition and fair application. It is easy for philosophy of science to be used for "a clear ideological function" that "gloss[es] over the weaknesses of demarcation proposals exposed by philosophical discussion," as Dolby* of University of Kent warns:

> Philosophy of science is not practiced in a neutral context. The philosophers themselves very often seem to have been concerned to legitimate or to discredit marginal candidates for science, especially from social science. We have noted that Comte was explicitly concerned to legitimate social physics and to deny legitimacy to psychology and political economy. Similarly, in his treatise on induction J.S. Mill was explicitly concerned to set out a sound epistemology and logic of all reasoning that would be adequate as a basis for political and moral theory and action. That is, he wished to find a legitimate basis for social science (Mill [1843] 1975, Book 6). In Popper's autobiographical accounts of the development of his principle of demarcation, he tells us that he wished to provide a principle which would establish the scientific nature of Einstein's general theory of relativity, while denying the same status to Marxism, psychoanalysis, and Adlerian individual psychology (Popper 1974, 34).
>
> *This kind of philosophy of science has a clear ideological function* . . . . [*T*]*hose who wished to make ideological use* of the demarcation criteria tended to mold them into intellectual weapons, to sharpen their cutting edges so that they could be more powerfully used in battles over legitimation. In doing so they have often had to *gloss over the weaknesses of demarcation proposals exposed by philosophical discussion*. Further, because philosophy of science is very often disseminated in this ideologically charged context rather than in the more neutral context of pure philosophy, there has been a tendency for philosophy of science to be *distorted by exaggerations of its claims*.[2]

In particular, the radical definition embodies a number of those "weaknesses of demarcation proposals," and is outside the philosophical mainstream largely because of its ahistoricity, its contrived nature, and its questionable philosophical premises. The theories of evolution and of abrupt appearance are jointly excluded from science by that radical demarcation, but are scientific under virtually all other widely accepted demarcations of science, as Chapter 10 suggests. Some of the points raised by Chapters 9, 10, and 13 have been raised in a provocative book by creationist philosophers (*Origin Science* by Geisler and Anderson), but are here discussed solely in the context of evolutionist and noncreationist thought.

Figure 9.1
Sir Francis Bacon, the father of modern science, who found concepts of abrupt appearance consistent with science

9.1 Prevailing Definitions of Science: Empirical Observations and Logical Interpretations

The definition of science is properly determined by philosophers moreso than by scientists, as Whitehead*,[3] Laudan*[4], Lakatos* and others argue.[5]

Among philosophers of science, "there has been little agreement concerning a universal criterion of the scientific character of theories," as Lakatos* notes.[6] According to Laudan*,

> [P]hilosophy has largely failed to deliver the relevant goods. Whatever the specific strengths and deficiencies of certain well-known efforts at demarcation (several of which will be examined below), it can be said fairly *uncontroversially* that *there is no demarcation line between science and non-science,* or between science and pseudo-science, *which would win assent from a majority of philosophers.*[7]

Most proposed lines for demarcation between science and non-science fail because they include or exclude too much.[8] Further, the lines have a subjective element because they are based on values, as Krausser*[9] and Keller*[10] argue, and as Ruse* also states:

> The final place where I see values entering into biology is in what I like to follow the Kantians in calling "regulative principles" (Ruse 1980). By these I mean the standards and criteria to which theories must conform,

> if they are to be judged "good" science, or indeed if they are to be judged science at all.[11]

To compound the problem, the lines of demarcation themselves shift with paradigm changes in the scientific community, as Kuhn* observes.[12] Several schools of thought explicitly argue that demarcation is not possible, as mentioned below.

The confusion of crisscrossing lines of demarcation "suggests that there are problems about establishing an objective standard," and suggests the need for caution in defining things into or out of science, Dolby* states:

> The fact that so many prescriptive philosophical criteria have been offered for the demarcation of science suggests that there are problems about establishing an objective standard by which we may make our judgments. If there were only one dominant demarcation criterion in philosophy of science, then it might seem quite powerful; but because there are many, each of which is a good basis for criticizing the others, none can be rationally decisive. . . .[13]

A federal judge in the *McLean* case, on the basis of expert witness testimony by Michael Ruse*, a prominent philosopher of science at University of Guelph,[14] listed five "essential conditions of science": that it is "guided by natural law," "explanatory by reference to natural law," "testable," "falsifiable," and "tentative."[15] One philosopher of science has responded that "the criteria which Judge Overton offered [in *McLean*] as 'essential conditions' of science are nothing of the sort," and that the *McLean* opinion made "anachronistic efforts to revive a variety of discredited criteria" and gave "a false stereotype of what science is."[16] Another philosopher of science described the *McLean* criteria as "demonstrably false,"[17] as discussed further below.[18] The one thing that is absolutely clear, in considering the various proposed definitions of science, is that no group of philosophers of science had formulated a definition even remotely resembling the *McLean* definition of science, and no such group subsequently has endorsed anything remotely resembling that definition, except for Ruse* as a courtroom witness for tactical purposes.

The "type of definition favoured by most serious philosophers" builds upon a foundation such as "logical inferences from empirical observations," according to Ziman*:

> Science Arrives at Truth by Logical Inferences from Empirical Observations. This is the standard type of definition favoured by most serious philosophers. It is usually based upon the principle of induction—that what has been seen to happen a great many times is almost sure to

> happen invariably and may be treated as a basic fact or Law upon which a firm structure of theory can be erected.[19]

A similar definition of science is given by the *Oxford English Dictionary*:

> 1. The state or fact of knowing; *knowledge* or cognizance of something specified or implied; also, with wider reference, knowledge (more or less extensive) as a personal attribute. . . .
>
> 2. *Knowledge acquired by study*; acquaintance with or mastery of any department of learning. . . .
>
> 3. A particular *branch* of knowledge or study; a recognized department of learning. . . .
>
> 4. In a more restricted sense: A branch of study which is concerned either with a *connected body of demonstrated truths or with observed facts systematically classified* and more or less colligated by being brought under general laws, and which includes trustworthy methods for the discovery of new truth within its own domain.[20]

Much the same approach is taken by *Encyclopaedia Britannica*,[21] Bertrand Russell*,[22] and others.

Not all of science is identical. Stansfield* distinguishes between "purely descriptive science" (such as classification and systematics) and "experimental science."[23] Gould* notes the legitimate difference between historical and non-historical sciences.[24]

There are nearly as many definitions of science as there are philosophers of science, but those definitions fall into a dozen general categories.

a. Inductivism

The approach of inductivism, initiated by Sir Francis Bacon, and developed by Sir Isaac Newton, was dominant in the seventeenth through the nineteenth centuries and currently still commands a major following. It emphasizes, as the necessary scientific method, "exhaustive induction" based on "empirically observed facts."[25] A modified inductivism is described by Hempel*:

> Scientific knowledge, as we have seen, is not arrived at by applying some inductive inference procedure to antecedently collected data, but rather by what is often called "the method of hypothesis", i.e. by inventing hypotheses as tentative answers to a problem under study, and then subjecting these to empirical test . . .. Hence, while scientific inquiry is certainly not inductive in the narrow sense we have examined in some detail, it may be said to be *inductive in a wider sense*, inasmuch as it involves the acceptance of hypotheses on the basis of data that afford no deductively conclusive evidence for it, but lend it only more or less strong "inductive support", or confirmation. And any "rules of induction" will

> have to be conceived . . . as canons of validation rather than of discovery. . . .[26]

Inductivism has received widespread criticism, ranging from Hume's* problem of induction to more specific analysis of the "general problem of justification," "comparative problem," and "analytical problem."[27]

b. Vocational Approach

The vocational approach defines science as what scientists do. It generally defines scientists as individuals who meet two of the following three factors: (a) a Ph.D. degree or the equivalent in the field, (b) research or study in the field, and (c) membership in professional societies in the field, as discussed later.[28] A related approach is "to think of science as a process" in which certain characteristics are normally present "but not always exclusively so," as Sparkes* suggests.[29]

c. Falsificationism

The falsificationist approach, developed by Sir Karl Popper*, draws the line of demarcation at falsifiability: "the criterion of the scientific status of a theory is its falsifiability, or refutability, or testability."[30] Criticisms typical of the majority of philosophers of science of Popper's* falsification approach are outlined below.[31]

d. Sociological Approach

The Kuhnian or sociological approach, developed by Kuhn* who was formerly of Princeton, involves the initial paradigm of the scientific community engaged in normal science, and the anomalies that sometimes arise from research and increasing theoretical sophistication. A scientific revolution results from persistent anomalies, and a new paradigm arises and goes through the same process.[32] Contrary to Popper*, Kuhn* finds the *lack* of testing, rather than the practice of testing theories, to be the mark of normal science.[53] Criticism of Kuhn's* approach has focused on the artificial or unilluminating nature of his dichotomy between normal science and abnormal science, and the apparent relativism of scientific truth that his approach seems to involve, as Toulmin*[34] and Popper*[35] state.

e. *Empiricism and Other Approaches*

There are many other approaches to defining science. The approach of Norwood Russell Hanson*, influenced by Charles Peirce*,[36] emphasizes that the scientific process (which Hanson* called retroduction), while only quasi-logical, pushes a scientific theory toward more or less intelligibility and explanation.[37] The empiricist approach "argued for a view that made prediction the crucial test of scientific validity," while the rationalist approach "saw coherence and scope as the crucial requirements."[38] Hempel* proposed an empiricist approach centered on verification through testability.[39] The operationalist viewpoint equated science with its procedures, as Bridgman* suggested.[40]

Feigl* offers five criteria for distinguishing science: intersubjective testability, reliability, definiteness and precision, coherence, and comprehensiveness.[41] Klemke* proposes instead four different characteristics: classifications, laws and hypotheses, theories connecting laws, and deductions confirmed by observation and testing.[42]

f. *Anti-Definitional Approaches*

There are several antidefinitional viewpoints. One asserts that it is impossible to define science or to draw a line of demarcation from other disciplines:

> I would like to suggest that *philosophy of science is not at present capable* of providing inescapable arguments on what can or cannot be permitted as science. The fact that it is so often used that way, especially in arguments within social science, has more to do with the great needs of the rival parties to make their views persuasive than it does with the decisiveness of the arguments philosophy of science can offer. I do not wish to draw the conclusion that this means that philosophy of science is useless in discussing the demarcation of science in practical cases. . . .
>
> . . ..
>
> My conclusion is that the academic discussion of the demarcation of science from nonscience tends to find many respects in which science might be thought to be distinctive but *none which is demonstrably decisive*. Some criteria are too severe and exclude apparently successful science; other criteria are too tolerant and allow examples of nonscience. There is no useful way of combining them into a single scale.[43]

Amsterdamski*[44] and Laudan*[45] join in that approach.

Another antidefinitional viewpoint, by Feyerabend* of Berkeley, essentially takes the approach of epistemological anarchy in encouraging the use of hypotheses that are ad hoc, contradictory to accepted experimental results, less persuasive than alternatives, or even refuted by prevailing scientific sentiment.[46] He further claims that scientific progress has actually resulted from the very violation of the accepted rules of scientific method.[47]

g. Radical Approach

Finally, the approaches associated with positivism and materialism assert that true science must be based only on sense experience and verifiable data, excluding any metaphysical, ethical, and other nonmaterial considerations. A description and criticisms of these viewpoints are given below.[48]

Science, however, does not require generation of predictions,[49] cognitive progress,[50] or other such aspirational objectives as prerequisites.

Summary. "[I]t can be said fairly uncontroversially that there is no demarcation line between science and non-science . . . which would win assent from a majority of philosophers" (Laudan* [51]). One reason is that the drawing of a demarcation line involves "values entering into biology" and other sciences (Ruse*[52]). Instead, there are many widely-accepted definitions of science and lines of demarcation from nonscience, and a radical positivist and materialist approach is only one minority viewpoint. The most generally accepted definition, in contrast to the radical definition, is something like that "science arrives at truth by logical inferences from empirical observations" (Ziman*[53]). *Quot homines, tot sententiae.*

9.2 Textbook Definitions of Science: Ubiquitous Presentation and Unanimous Rejection

a. Textbook Description of Science

Textbooks often present a generic description of science by idealized methods. A typical example is as follows:

> A *common characterization of science* (or sometimes of scientific method) runs as follows. Science is knowledge obtained by: (1) making observations as accurate and definite as possible; (2) recording these intelligibly; (3) classifying them according to the subject matter being studied; (4) extracting from them, by induction, general statements (laws) which assert regularities; (5) deducing other statements from these; (6) verifying those statements by further observations; and (7) propounding theories which connect and so account for the largest possible number of

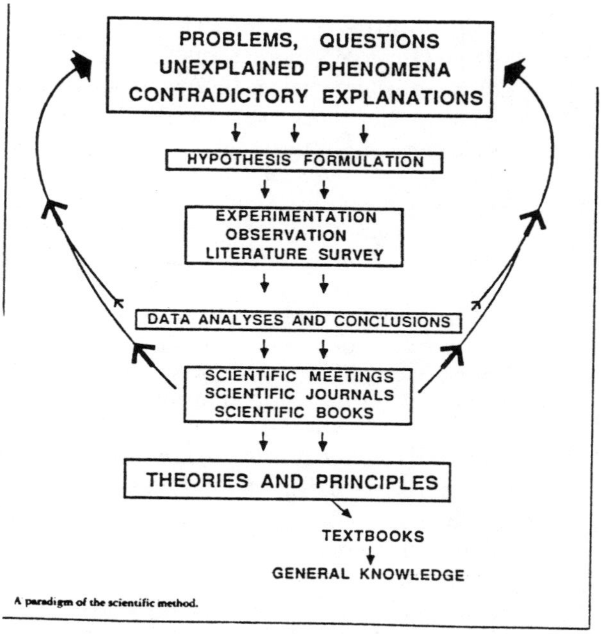

Figure 9.2
"The scientific method" from a typical text: "what passes for scientific methodology is a misrepresentation of what scientists do or ought to do" (Medawar, a Nobel Prize recipient)*

> laws. It is further maintained that this process runs from (1) through (7) *in that order.*
>
> The conception of science has been *challenged* in recent years. Its most severe critic is Sir Karl Popper. . . . Instead we offer a characterization of science . . . free from the *defects* it possesses.[54]

A similar definition can be found in many textbooks, and perhaps in most elementary and secondary school science texts.[55]

b. Repudiation by Philosophers of Science

The one point of agreement among philosophers of science appears to be that this widely-used textbook definition is generally "challenged" and condemned as "defective." For example, Medawar*, a Nobel Prize recipient and director of Britain's National Institute for Medical Research, called the stereotype a "misrepresentation":

> These Lectures began in my mind in the form of a question: why are most scientists completely indifferent to—even contemptuous of—scientific methodology? Put generally, the answer could only be "because what passes for scientific methodology is a misrepresentation of what scientists do or ought to do." . . .[56]

The textbook approach similarly is treated as simplistic or inaccurate by Lakatos*,[57] Laudan*,[58] Eldredge* and Gould*,[59] and Whitehead*.[60] Hempel* even says that the normal method is the exact opposite of observation before law, theory, or hypothesis:

> In sum, the maxim that data should be gathered without guidance by antecedent hypotheses about the connections among the facts under study is *self-defeating*, and it is certainly *not followed* in scientific inquiry. On the contrary, tentative hypotheses are needed to give direction to a scientific investigation. Such hypotheses determine, among other things, what data should be collected at a given point in a scientific investigation.
>
> . . ..
>
> There are, then, *no generally applicable 'rules of induction'*, by which hypotheses or theories can be mechanically derived or inferred from empirical data. The transition from data to theory requires creative imagination. Scientific hypotheses and theories are not *derived* from observed facts, but *invented* in order to account for them. . . .[61]

Cannon*, a historian of science at University of California at Berkeley, reached similar conclusions about the history of science contrasting with the textbook stereotype:

> One is *Darwin's* notorious habit of jumping to conclusions without adequate evidence. He developed his coral reef theory, we remember, before examining coral reefs. The other is that of stubbornly maintaining his theories regardless of the valid arguments and evidence that could be brought against them.
>
> These are procedures to be recommended, of course, only to the great; and I come to the regrettable conclusion that *science takes great strides forward not primarily from laborious objective research*, but rather when some biased person maintains his intuitions in public, and when, thereafter, generations of scientists find that some of these intuitions do actually illuminate whatever work they are doing.[62]

9.3 McLean Case Definition of Science: Tactically Contrived against Discontinuitist Theories

a. Summary of the McLean Definition

The *McLean* opinion, which was a 1982 decision of a federal trial court judge, gave the following definition of science:

> More precisely, the essential characteristics of science are:
> (1) It is guided by natural law;
> (2) It has to be explanatory by reference to natural law;
> (3) It is testable against the empirical world;

Rev. Bill McLEAN, et al., Plaintiffs,
v.
The ARKANSAS BOARD OF EDUCATION, et al., Defendants.
No. LR C 81 322.
United States District Court, E. D. Arkansas, W. D.
Jan. 5, 1982.

Civil rights action was brought to enjoin the enforcement by the Board of Education and its members, the Director of Department of Education, and the State Textbooks and Instructional Materials Selecting Committee of a statute requiring public schools to give balanced treatment to creation science and to evolution science.

Figure 9.3
The McLean court decision: "remote from well-founded opinion in the philosophy of science" (Laudan) and "demonstrably false" (Quinn*)*

(4) Its conclusions are tentative, i.e., are not necessarily the final word; and
(5) It is falsifiable.[63]

That definition is absolutely incorrect as a demarcation of science from nonscience. Each point is discussed in the following sections: the natural law requirements (Section 9.4), the testability and falsifiability requirements (Section 9.5), and the tentativeness requirement (Section 9.6).

The *McLean* definition does not resemble, or come close to resembling, any definition of science existing in the philosophy of science literature, and has not been endorsed subsequently by any philosopher of science, except by certain courtroom witnesses from the *McLean* trial. The witness on whose testimony the judge's opinion was based, Ruse*, later revised his points and offered a six-point list of "major characteristics" of science, apparently for the purpose of demarcation:

> Surveying science and the history of science today, one thing stands out: science involves a search for order. More specifically, science looks for unbroken, blind, natural regularities (*laws*). . . .
>
> A major part of the scientific enterprise involves the use of law to effect *explanation*. . . . The other side of explanations is *prediction*. . . .
>
> Closely connected with the twin notions of explanation and prediction comes *testability* [including confirmation and falsification]. . . .
>
> Science is *tentative*. . . .
>
> Some other features of science should also be mentioned, for instance, the urge for simplicity and unification; however, I have now listed the *major characteristics*. Good science—like good philosophy and good

religion—presupposes an attitude that one might describe as professional *integrity*. . . .[64]

In fact, the *McLean* definition of science was contrived by the American Civil Liberties Union (ACLU) for the tactical purpose of excluding "creation-science" by definition from being scientific (the case was an ACLU challenge to Arkansas' "Act for Balanced Treatment of Creation-Science and Evolution"). Gross*, a philosopher who describes himself as "one of the consultants to Skadden, Arps, Slate, Meagher, and Flom, plaintiffs' attorneys in McLean v. Arkansas," concedes that the *McLean* test is so incorrect as to prevent a favorable recommendation for an undergraduate student—but then defends the test because its requirements are "sufficient to refute Creationism"!

Philosophically, these [*McLean*] criteria may have been acceptable sixty or eighty years ago, but they are not rigorous, they are redundant, and they take no account of many distinctions nor [*sic*] of historical cases. The opinion does not state whether they are singly necessary or jointly sufficient. One would not recommend to graduate school a student who could do no better than this. Fortunately, Judge Overton and the litigators were not applying to graduate school. They were in a court of law. In this forum, confronted with Creationism and religious "know-nothingism" as adversaries, are these criteria so far off the mark? . . . *Are they not sufficient to refute Creationism?*[65]

b. Criticisms of the McLean Definition

The *McLean* definition has been sharply criticized by such philosophers of science as Laudan* of Virginia Polytechnic Institute,[66] Quinn* of Notre Dame University (formerly of Brown University), and Gross* of City University of New York.

Laudan* describes the *McLean* definition as "remote from well-founded opinion in the philosophy of science,"[67] and gives the following general criticism of its definition of science (which should be read in light of his strong opposition to "Creationism"):

Once the dust has settled, however, the trial in general and Judge William R. Overton's ruling in particular may come back to haunt us; for, although the verdict itself is probably to be commended, it was reached *for all the wrong reasons* and by a chain of *argument which is hopelessly suspect*. Indeed, the ruling rests on a host of *misrepresentations of what science is* and how it works.

The heart of Judge Overton's Opinion is a formulation of "the essential characteristics of science." These characteristics serve as touchstones for contrasting evolutionary theory with Creationism; they lead Judge Overton ultimately to the claim, *specious* in its own right, that since Creationism is not "science," it must be religion.

. . . .

. . .The victory in the Arkansas case was hollow, for it was achieved only at the expense of perpetuating and canonizing a *false stereotype of what science is* and how it works. If it goes unchallenged by the scientific community, it will raise grave doubts about that community's intellectual integrity. No one familiar with the issues can really believe that anything important was settled through *anachronistic* efforts to revive a variety of *discredited* criteria for distinguishing between the scientific and the nonscientific.[68]

He adds that the five tests are neither necessary nor sufficient—both underinclusive and overinclusive:

[*McLean*] offered five "essential characteristics of science." I have shown that there are respectable examples of science which violate *each* of Overton's desiderata, and moreover that there are many activities we do not regard as science which satisfy many of them.[69]

Quinn* similarly characterizes the *McLean* definition of science as "demonstrably false," before favorably quoting some of Laudan's* harshest language:[70]

Unfortunately, it is all too clear that it is *unsound*. The problem is that [the *McLean* definition] is *demonstrably false*. None of the characteristics it alleges to be necessary conditions for an individual statement to have scientific status is, in fact, a necessary condition of scientific status of an individual statement.[71]

He similarly treats Ruse's* views as not representative of many philosophers of science, and as "clearly false" in part:

The third risk is that of misrepresentation. If the expert's views are not representative of a settled consensus of opinion in the relevant community of scholars, then policy based on those views will lack credibility within that community, and the members of that community are likely to regard such lack of credibility as discrediting the policy in question. This was the major problem in *McLean v. Arkansas. Ruse's views do not represent a settled consensus of opinion* among philosophers of science. Worse still, *some of them are clearly false* and *some are based on obviously fallacious arguments*. . . . [72]

A similar criticism of the five *McLean* criteria is given by Gross*, who was quoted above conceding that "they are not rigorous, they are redundant, and they take no account of many distinctions nor of historical cases," so that one "would not recommend to graduate schools a student who could do no better than this."[73]

Further, it is not clear whether all or just one of the five *McLean* factors must be met for a concept to be scientific, as Laudan*,[74] Gross*,[75] and Quinn*[76] note. Requiring all would rule out much of modern-day science, and requiring one would rule out very little. Moreover, the five factors are internally inconsistent: natural laws are not tentative, and falsifiability is not separate from (but is an aspect of) testability. For much broader reasons, each element of the *McLean* definition is improper or inadequate, as the following sections demonstrate. *Lucas a non lucendo.*

Figure 9.4
The concept "that the laws of nature . . . have always been true in the past": "a metaphysical construct" and "matter of faith" (Fitch); the "positivist limited scientific knowledge . . . to the laws of nature and . . . 'secondary,' or natural, causes exclusively" (Gillespie*)*

9.4 Natural Laws and the Demarcation of Science: Difference between Existence and Explanation

"Laws" are defined by Ruse* as "unbroken, blind, natural regularities,"[77] and by the *Encyclopedia of Philosophy* as "regularit[ies] of nature."[78] Interestingly enough, the concept of natural laws originated in theology: Bacon, for example, wrote that "the laws of Nature, which now remain and govern inviolably till the end of the world, began to be in force when God first rested from his works and ceased to create; but received a revocation in part by the curse, since which time they change not."[79]

The "*guided* by natural law" and the "*explanatory* by reference to natural law" requirements of the *McLean* opinion have been criticized as "altogether inappropriate" as follows:

> I find the formulation in the Opinion to be rather fuzzy; but the general idea appears to be that it is inappropriate and unscientific to postulate the existence of any process or fact which cannot be explained in terms of

> some known scientific laws . . .. [T]his requirement is an *altogether inappropriate* standard for ascertaining whether a claim is scientific.[80]

Quinn* similarly views the natural laws requirement as "seriously in error."[81] The error of such a natural laws prerequisite is evident in (a) the arbitrary restriction that it imposes on science, and (b) the questionable philosophical presuppositions that it involves, as well as the ahistorical nature of such a requirement (discussed in Section 13.4).

a. Arbitrary Restriction Imposed on Science by Natural Laws Requirement

There are a number of problems arising from the arbitrariness of a natural laws prerequisite to science, which involve the philosophical distinction between existence and explanation, the scientific treatment of singularities and other unique past occurrences, and the internal inconsistency of the requirement.

(1) Distinction between Existence and Explanation[82]. The natural laws requirement is "inappropriate" because it may be scientific to demonstrate the "existence of a phenomenon" even though it cannot necessarily be explained as guided by natural laws.[83] First, that "difference between establishing the existence of a phenomenon and explaining it in a lawlike way" is widely acknowledged:

> For centuries scientists have recognized a difference between establishing the existence of a phenomenon and explaining that phenomenon in a lawlike way. Our ultimate goal, no doubt, is to do both. But to suggest, as the *McLean* Opinion does repeatedly, that an existence claim . . . is unscientific until we have found the laws on which the alleged phenomenon depends is *simply outrageous*. Galileo and Newton took themselves to have established the existence of gravitational phenomena, long before anyone was able to give a causal or explanatory account of gravitation. Darwin took himself to have established the existence of natural selection almost a half-century before geneticists were able to lay out the laws of heredity on which natural selection depended. If we took the *McLean* Opinion criterion seriously, we should have to say that Newton and Darwin were unscientific; and, to take an example from our own time, it would follow that plate tectonics is unscientific because we have not yet identified the laws of physics and chemistry which account for the dynamics of crustal motion.[84]

Second, some scientific phenomena "can have no explanation in terms of laws."[85] Quinn adds,

> If, contrary to fact, there had turned out to be no laws to explain natural selection, Darwin's achievement would still have been scientific. To be

> sure, as Ruse notes, science looks for explanatory laws. But if there are no laws to be found, scientists are prepared to settle for less and can do so without forfeiting the scientific status of their achievements. . . .[86]

In fact, philosophers of science recognize many scientific concerns that are "not lawlike," as Walters* points out in the *Encyclopedia of Philosophy*:

> *Many kinds of statements are recognized as not lawlike*—for example, mathematical statements, explicit definitions, tautologies, and singular or numerical statements restricted to either individual objects or times. The main characteristics of laws that are lacking in singular and numerical statements are the universal quantifier and the timeless present tense. The other kinds of statements fail to be lawlike because they are analytic. Any claim that a statement *p* is a law entails the claim, at least, that *p* is a true, nonanalytic, universal generalization.[87]

(2) Arbitrary Limit on Scientific Inquiry. Such a natural laws prerequisite arbitrarily limits science in several ways.

First, the natural laws requirement rules out the existence or at least the occurrence of nonnaturalistic causes or phenomena, as Buchner* recognizes and defends:

> Natural laws are immutable. . . . The experience of more than a thousand years has pressed on observers the conviction of the immutability of natural laws . . . with such absolute certainty that not the least doubt can remain. . . . With the most absolute truth and with the greatest scientific certainty can we say this day: *There is nothing miraculous in the world.* . . . The ghost of a personal, universal spirit, interfering in natural processes, has long been banished from astronomy, physics, and chemistry. . . . *The ignorant layman may believe in a personal god; but the scientist or educated layman . . . would place his reason below that of the simplest peasant, if he believed in such a one* without foundation. . . . Belief in God is therefore almost confined at the present time to those so-called learned men who know scarcely anything about natural processes. . . . Whatever theological interest or narrow-minded pedantry can urge in opposition to this is controverted by the strength of the facts, which in this respect leave no room for any doubt.[88]

That consequence of definitionally excluding nonnaturalistic causes or phenomena is reaffirmed by Provine*,[89] Mayr*,[90] and others.*[91]

True science, by contrast, cannot by definition alone (not based on scientific data) either always forbid or always require the occurrence of nonnaturalistic causes or phenomena,[92] but must be open to evidence on the issue. Einstein* acknowledged that,[93] and von Braun (the late director of the NASA space program) stated:

> While the admission of a design for the universe ultimately raises the question of a Designer (a subject outside of science), the *scientific method*

> *does not allow us to exclude data* which lead to the conclusion that the universe, life and man are based on design. To be forced to believe only one conclusion—that everything in the universe happened by chance—would violate the very objectivity of science itself. . . .
>
> . . ..
>
> . . .The inconceivability of some ultimate issue (which will always lie outside scientific resolution) should not be allowed to rule out any theory that explains the interrelationship of observed data and is useful for prediction.[94]

Of course, this objection to arbitrary exclusion of nonnaturalistic causes or events does not conflict with, but concurs in, the proper presumption in favor of naturalistic explanations if they are adequate.

Second, the natural laws criterion arbitrarily limits science to some data and explanations even if they are false. It requires science to insist on naturalistic explanations and to suppress nonnaturalistic explanations, even if the naturalistic ones are absolutely improbable and if the excluded nonnaturalistic ones are more plausible, because of the artificially limited field of alternatives. Only faith in the nonexistence of nonnaturalistic causes can so limit science to sometimes false explanations by defining out of the scientific realm what may be more probably true explanations, as Jastrow* points out.[95] An example of events not explainable by laws is some quantum events:

> Certain statements about individual events in the quantum domain are not laws and have no known explanations in terms of laws; moreoever, they can have no explanation in terms of laws if contemporary quantum theory is correct, as it seems to be. But they will remain scientific statements even if contemporary quantum theory is correct. . . .[96]

Thus, many scientists agree with Jastrow*, the founder and director of the Goddard Institute of Space Studies, that science need not blindly follow an absolute natural law limit, and that cosmology in fact has proved the occurrence of nonnaturalistic causes or occurrences:

> [I]t seems to me astronomy has proven that forces are at work in the world that are beyond the present power of scientific description; these are literally supernatural forces, because they are outside the body of natural law. . . .[97]

Note that Jastrow* is an Agnostic, not a Theist.[98]

(3) Distinctive Nature of Past Events. The natural laws prerequisite also fails to account for the distinctive nature of past events, and is inconsistent with the current scientific acceptance of singularities and possible changes in natural laws themselves.

First, the requirement conflicts with the general scientific recognition of singularities, or events that sometimes are simply not explainable by but are instead departures from natural laws. For example, the big bang theory involves "a space-time singularity" in which "it is difficult to say what remains of the conventional laws of physics," according to Pagels*[99] and most cosmologists such as Hawking*,[100] Weisskopf*,[101] Silk*,[102] and Wald*.[103] The inflationary universe theory similarly involves "a cosmological singularity . . . in which the known laws of physics do not apply," Guth* states.[104] The biochemical evolution of life also requires a singularity, as further discussed in the next chapter.[105] Second, that requirement ignores that theories of origins necessarily involve assumed singular events and past causes that are not still operative, and that often can only be presumed but cannot always be proved to have followed natural laws.[106] For example, origin of life experiments can only show "that some of the [natural] processes which they postulate might conceivably have happened, but not that they did actually happen in the real history of the earth," as Dobzhansky* observed[107] and as Hull* and others concur.[108]

Third, it is interesting to note that many evolutionist scientists such as Sagan* will allow for changes in the "laws of nature" at extraordinary times that fit the evolutionary viewpoint:

> Scientists wonder about what happens in an oscillating universe at the cusps, at the transition from contraction to expansion. Some think that the laws of nature are then randomly reshuffled, that the kind of physics and chemistry that orders this universe represent [*sic*] only one of an infinite range of possible natural laws.[109]

Such changes in the laws of nature are inherent in the many universes theory, according to Leslie*,[110] in parts of quantum theory, according to Patton* and Wheeler*,[111] and in the big bang theory, according to Jastrow*,[112] Weisskopf*,[113] and Barrow* and Silk*.[114] Other than for evolutionary singularities, however, they contend for the exclusive rule of natural laws and particularly so for the past times that might have involved nonnaturalistic events according to the abrupt appearance viewpoint.

(4) Internal Inconsistency of the Natural Laws Prerequisite. That requirement also is internally inconsistent in at least two ways.

First, the natural laws criterion itself is based in a nonnatural "faith in the order of nature," as the famous philosopher-mathematician Whitehead* and others* have pointed out:

> Faith in reason is the trust that the ultimate natures of things lie together in a harmony which excludes mere arbitrariness. It is the faith that at the

> base of things we shall not find mere arbitrary mystery. The faith in the order of nature which has made possible the growth of science is a particular example of a deeper faith. This faith cannot be justified by any inductive generalization.[115]

Einstein* agreed that faith in the order of nature is "akin to religious feeling":

> Certain it is that a conviction, akin to religious feeling, of the rationality or intelligibility of the world lies behind all scientific work of a higher order.[116]

Discontinuitist scientists share that underlying belief with evolutionist scientists,[117] but apply it only to the *usual* rule of the "order of nature" rather than to the *exclusive* rule of the order of nature (which rules out by definition any nonnaturalistic causes or phenomena).

The heart of faith in natural laws is faith in uniformitarianism, which indeed is "metaphysical" and a "matter of faith" according to Fitch*:

> By a *metaphysical construct* I mean any unproved or unprovable assumption that we all make and tend to take for granted. One example is the doctrine of *uniformitarianism* that asserts that the *laws of nature*, such as gravity and thermodynamics, have always been true in the past and will always be true in the future. It is the belief in that doctrine that permits scientists to demand repeatability in experiments. I like the word doctrine in this case because it makes clear that *matters of faith* are not restricted to creationists and that in the intellectual struggle for citizen enlightenment we need to be very clear just where the fundamental differences between science and theology lie. It is not, as many scientists would like to believe, in the absence of metaphysical underpinnings in science.[118]

Even Gould* concedes that we "cannot 'prove' the assumption of invariant laws; we cannot even venture forth into the world to gather empirical evidence for it. It is an *a priori* methodological assumption . . . ."[119] Wigner*, a Nobel Prize recipient in physics, concurs that "it is not at all natural that 'natural laws' exist, much less that man is able to discover them."[120] Taylor*,[121] Muelder*,[122] and others agree.

It is ironic that "Cosmology assumes the rationality of the universe, but can give no reason for it short of the creator of the laws of nature being a rational creator," Milne* states.[123] In fact, the historical origin of the natural laws concept was in creationist beliefs, according to Jaki*,[124] Whitehead*,[125] Feuer*,[126] Foster*,[127] Gilkey*,[128] and others discussed in Section 13.4.

A large portion of the scientific community acknowledges the existence of God and the possibility of intervention in nature contrary to natural laws,[129] although a majority denies or questions the existence of God and by that faith rules out any intervention and any breach of natural laws, as discussed in Section 13.3(a). Even the renowned Albert Einstein* wrote that "[t]his firm belief, a belief bound up with deep feeling, in a superior mind that reveals itself in the world of experience, represents my conception of God."[130] The radical approach to natural laws, that they absolutely cannot be suspended at any time regardless of the empirical evidence, is contrary to the views of many modern scientists as well as to the history of science.

Second, the *McLean* criterion of "natural laws" itself does not meet the other three "essential characteristics of science": the requirement is not testable, falsifiable, or tentatively held. Thus, under the *McLean* definition, the natural laws requirement is unscientific.

b. Questionable Philosophical Presuppositions in Positivism and Materialism-Naturalism for a Natural Laws Requirement

Such a natural laws prerequisite, with its limit on scientific inquiry, is rooted in the questionable philosophical grounds of positivism, materialism, and naturalism. One historical impact of positivism was that it "limited scientific knowledge . . . to the laws of nature," Gillespie* states:

> [A] large part of the conflict in Darwin's era arose from the fact that there were, in effect, not one but two major epistemes in natural history . . . positivism and creationism. *The positivist limited scientific knowledge*, which he saw as the only valid form of knowledge, *to the laws of nature* and to processes involving 'secondary,' or natural, causes exclusively.[131]

"The *McLean* opinion testifies to the extent to which a positivistic or scientistic view of the activity of science pervades our society," another commentator observes.[132] Positivism, materialism, and naturalism are not accepted by the majority of philosophers of science, and are far from self-evident or intellectually compelling viewpoints.

(1) Meanings of Positivism, Materialism, and Naturalism. Positivism is defined as follows in the *Encyclopedia of Philosophy*:

> The characteristic theses of positivism are that science is the only valid knowledge and facts the only possible objects of knowledge . . .. Positivism, consequently, denies the existence or intelligibility of forces or substances that go beyond facts and the laws ascertained by science. It

> opposes any kind of metaphysics and, in general, any procedure of investigation that is not reducible to scientific method.[133]

Similar definitions are given by Feigl*,[134] Carlson*,[135] and Passmore*.[136] One of several kinds of positivism is in fact "evolutionary positivism":

> There are two fundamental kinds of positivism: social positivism, with a professedly practicopolitical character, and *evolutionary positivism*, with a professedly theoretical character.... A *materialistic* or spiritualistic metaphysics is often associated with evolutionary positivism.[137]

The historical affinity of positivism and evolution is stressed by Gillespie*, who describes Darwinists as operating within a "positivist" episteme,[138] and by Greene*.[139]

Materialism "asserts that the real world consists of material things, varying in their states and relations, and nothing else."[140] Materialism, or its variety known as naturalism, is defined as follows in *Encyclopaedia Britannica*:

> This modified form of *Materialism* is perhaps better described as *naturalism*. Naturalism holds not that all things consist of matter or its modifications but that *whatever exists can be satisfactorily explained in natural terms*. To explain something in natural terms is to explain it on scientific lines; naturalism is in fact a proclamation of the omnicompetence, or final competence, of science.[141]

(The tie between materialism, naturalism, positivism, and evolution is discussed in Section 13.5.)

Naturalism is described in the *Encyclopedia of Philosophy* in the following terms:

> NATURALISM, in recent usage, is a species of philosophical monism according to which whatever exists or happens is *natural* in the sense of being susceptible to *explanation through methods which, although paradigmatically exemplified in the natural sciences*, are continuous from domain to domain of objects and events. Hence, naturalism is polemically defined as *repudiating the view that there exists or could exist any entities or events which lie, in principle, beyond the scope of scientific explanation*. . . .[142]

Thus, the approach of the radical definition of science, by rigorously limiting science to natural laws, implicitly presupposes positivism, materialism, or naturalism. The radical definition, then, is dependent on the validity of those presuppositions.

(2) Criticisms by Philosophic Majority. Positivism is only one particular school of thought, and is a minority approach rather than the prevailing school among philosophers.[143] It has been criticized by the majority of philosophers of science on various grounds.

First, the basic principle of positivism (that all meaningful scientific statements are verifiable by sense experience) is itself a questionable metaphysical principle that cannot be verified by sense experience, as Ewing* noted[144] and Whitehead* pointed out:

> The *doctrine that science* starts from clear and distinct elements in *experience*, and that it develops by a clear and distinct process of *elaboration, dies hard*. There is a constant endeavor to explain the methodology of science in terms which, by reason of their clarity and distinctness, require no metaphysical elucidation. . . . But when we press the question so as to determine without ambiguity the procedure of science, we become involved in the metaphysical formulations of the speculative Reason.
>
> . . ..
>
> . . . [T]he *claim of science that it can produce an understanding of its procedures* within the limits of its own categories, or that those categories themselves are understandable without reference to their status within the widest categories under exploration by the speculative Reason—that claim is entirely *unfounded*. Insofar as *philosophers* have failed, scientists do not know what they are talking about when they pursue their own methods; and insofar as philosophers have succeeded, to that extent scientists can attain an understanding of science. . . . [145]

Second, the concept of verification by experiences assumes the validity of inductive inferences; yet David Hume* is credited with having posed the induction problem that all attempts to validate inductive inferences depend on inductive reasoning,[146] as was mentioned in Section 9.1(a). Closely related to that, the use of experiences as the basis of inductive reasoning brings a science that "is fundamentally subjective," as Passmore* states:

> The doctrine that both physics and psychology describe "experiences" made such a unification possible. In his earlier writings Carnap tried to show in detail how "the world" could be constructed out of experience, linked together by relations of similarity. But then a new difficulty arose; one about how it is possible to show that one person's experiences are identical with another's. On the face of it, *an experience-based science is fundamentally subjective*; science is verified only at the cost of *losing its objectivity*.[147]

And the use of a verifiability approach was too strong because it "would rule out as meaningless all scientific laws":

> Verifiability. The course taken by the subsequent history of logical positivism was determined by its attempts to solve a set of problems set for it, for the most part, by its reliance on the verifiability principle. The status of that principle was by no means clear, for "The meaning of a proposition is the method of its verification" is *not a scientific proposition*. . . .
>
> The logical positivists themselves were much more concerned about the fact that *the verifiability principle threatened to destroy not only metaphysics but also science*. Whereas Mach had been happy to purge the sciences, the logical positivists ordinarily took for granted the sub-

> stantial truth of contemporary science. Thus, it was a matter of vital concern to them when it became apparent that *the verifiability principle would rule out as meaningless all scientific laws.*
>
> For such laws are, by the nature of the case, not conclusively verifiable; there is no set of experiences such that having these experiences is equivalent to the truth of a scientific law. . . .[148]

However, the modification of the verifiability approach by a confirmability approach was "too weak" because it "admitted . . . metaphysical propositions" into science, Passmore* recounts:

> For these and comparable reasons "verifiability" was gradually replaced by "*confirmability*" or by the rather stronger notion of "*testability.*" . . .
>
> If, however, the original principle proved to be too strong, *the new principle threatened to be too weak.* For, on the face of it, the new principle admitted as meaningful such metaphysical propositions as "Either it is raining or the Absolute is not perfect." Whether the confirmability principle can so be restated as to act as a method of distinguishing between metaphysical statements as meaningless and scientific statements as meaningful remains a question of controversy.[149]

Positivism remained subjective because, while ostensibly casting out all metaphysics, it actually metaphysically objected to "every thought which has not been covered in advance by facts and figures" on the ground of a lack of "evidence," Adorno* adds.[150]

Third, the positivist approach excludes ethical and other nonempirical considerations from science, over the objection of many philosophers,[151] and excludes nonnaturalistic concepts, which bars science from considering some truth or knowledge. One aspect of possible truth that positivist blinders block is the possibility of the nonuniformity of natural laws, and of the past occurrence of abrupt appearance of the universe, first life, or complex plants and animals; which leaves science in the strange position of potentially being limited to something false and not able to embrace something true.[152] Einstein* wrote that the "weak point of positivists" is their failure to acknowledge that scientists have to be resigned to recognizing nonnaturalistic events that cannot be further explained.[153]

Materialism is also widely criticized by philosophers of science, and the following are only a few of the lines of criticism. First, the nature of reason shows a nonmaterial dimension of the real world, as Gunderson* argues.[154] The *Encyclopedia of Philosophy* summarizes his point:

> *Generalized nature of reason.* Keith Gunderson has recently revived an argument of Descartes's to the effect that men are not machines, even cybernetic machines, and therefore not merely material.[155]

Because nonmaterial factors make it incapable of explaining all things, "materialism was from first to last an aspiration rather than an achievement," with the "hope... that with the advance of science we shall find them out"; the "scientific credit of materialism was maintained by drawing very large cheques in its own favour on assets not yet to hand."[155A]

Second, the falsifiability of knowledge of physical items establishes that the real world is not all material, Paulsen* suggests.[156] His analysis is summarized as follows:

> *Incorrigible knowledge of mental states.* It is frequently claimed that:
>
> Introspective knowledge of mental states is logically immune from error.
>
> What I believe about my current mental state cannot be false.
>
> But all knowledge of physical items is corrigible.
>
> Thus, mental states cannot be physical states. Materialists differ in their reply to this objection. . . .[157]

Third, the rationale for epistemic dualism rules out materialism, as Ducasse* contends.[158] His reasoning is outlined by the *Encyclopedia of Philosophy*:

> *Epistemic dualism.* A much more wide-ranging argument has been advanced by some philosophers in the tradition of Kant. They argue that the categories of the *physical and the mental are both necessary to a full understanding of human knowledge; that each presupposes the other*; and that therefore neither can be eliminated in favor of the other. If they are right, the very statement of materialism presupposes its own falsehood. To defend themselves against this claim, materialists are therefore bound to develop a complete epistemology.[159]

Naturalism has encountered substantial criticism as well, much of which overlaps objections to positivism and materialism and so will not be repeated.[160]

Summary. "[E]ither being a natural law or being explainable by a natural law is not a necessary condition for scientific status" (Quinn*[161]), and "is an altogether inappropriate standard for ascertaining whether a claim is scientific" (Laudan*[162]), even though it indeed is a frequent and presumed characteristic of science. An absolute natural laws requirement is "simply outrageous" in overlooking the classic "difference between establishing the existence of a phenomenon and explaining that phenomenon in a lawlike way" (Laudan*[163]), and also is guilty of overlooking that some scientific phenomena "can have no explanation in terms of laws" (Quinn*[164]) or are "not lawlike" such as "mathematical statements, explicit definitions, tautologies, and singular or numerical statements restricted to either individual objects or times" (Walters*[165]). Moreover, such a natural laws requirement may artificially limit science by forbidding it to consider nonnaturalistic events even if true, while compelling it to adopt naturalistic explanations even if totally improbable, because only the latter are left in the limited field. Yet, in quantum theory and elsewhere some events "can have no explanation in terms of laws if contemporary quantum theory is correct" (Quinn*[166]), and in cosmology and perhaps elsewhere science "has proven that forces are at work that... are outside the body of natural law" (Jastrow*[167]). One major category of events excluded by an absolute natural laws requirement is singularities, even though they are widely accepted in connection with theories of origins such as the big bang theory (Pagels*[168]), and even though occasional changes in the laws of nature are widely allowed (Sagan*[169]). Such an absolute natural laws requirement itself is based in a "faith in the order of nature" (Whitehead*[170]), and "it is not at all natural that 'natural laws' exist" (Wigner*[171]). Finally, positivist and materialist presuppositions produce the absolute natural laws requirement (Gillespie*[172]), and are themselves open to a number of philosophical difficulties (Passmore*[173]). (However, the theory of abrupt appearance and the theory of evolution are equally guided by and explanatory under natural laws, as discussed in Section 10.2.) *Felix qui potuit rerum cognoscere causas.*

9.5 Testability and Falsifiability and the Demarcation of Science: Difference between Historical Sciences and Other Sciences

a. Testability as Not an Absolute Criterion of Science

The "testable against the empirical world" concept that was included in the *McLean* definition of science is also proposed by some philosophers of science as an absolute demarcation.[174] However, it has been criticized as not a true distinguishing mark of science by many such as Lakatos*:

> One of the most important points one learns from studying research programmes is that *relatively few experiments are really important.* The heuristic guidance the theoretical physicist receives from tests and 'refutations' is usually so trivial that large-scale testing—or even bothering too much with the data already available—may well be a waste of time. In most cases we need no refutations to tell us that the theory is in urgent

Figure 9.5
"[B]eing testable and being falsifiable are not necessary for individual statements to have scientific status" (Quinn)*

> need of replacement: the positive heuristic of the programme drives us forward anyway. Also, to give a stern 'refutable interpretation' to a fledgling version of a programme is dangerous methodological cruelty. *The first versions may even 'apply' to non-existing 'ideal' cases*; *it may take decades* of theoretical work to arrive at the first novel facts and still more time *to arrive at interestingly testable versions of the research programmes*, at the stage when refutations are no longer forseeable in the light of the programme itself.
>
> . . ..
>
> . . .According to conservative conventionalism, experiments may have sufficient power to refute young theories, but not to refute old, established theories: as science grows, the power of empirical evidence diminishes.[175]

Quinn* similarly suggests that "being testable and being falsifiable are not necessary for individual statements to have scientific status."[176]

Thus, first, testing is not in practice a critical feature of science. This rationale for rejecting the testing criterion is also stressed by Kuhn* and others*:

> To rely on testing as the mark of a science is to miss what scientists mostly do and, with it, the most characteristic feature of their enterprise.[177]

Second, "theories often cannot be tested directly," Riddiford* and Penny* note,[178] in addition to the delay in testing other theories that Lakatos* noted. (Of course, a theory may be testable but not yet tested, and only the former is under discussion here.) Further, many other parts of science are not testable,[179] such as definitions[180] and aspects of all theories of origins.[181]

For example, the testability requirement is a definition, and is not itself testable, falsifiable or tentative (the other *McLean* criteria). As Quinn* adds,

> As a result of the work of Pierre Duhem, it has been known to philosophers of science for three-quarters of a century that many scientific statements are neither testable nor falsifiable individually and in isolation but only conjunctively and in corporate bodies."[182]

Third, historical sciences, including origins, by their nature are only partly testable while being partly nontestable, as described below.[183]

Finally, the testability criterion was proposed by logical positivists, and "was undoubtedly based on the assumptions of radical empiricism."[184] Yet it "does not satisfy the requirements that it imposes on meaningful statements, and is, therefore, itself meaningless," Amsterdamski* observes.[185]

b. Falsifiability as Not an Absolute Criterion of Science

The *McLean* decision listed falsifiability[186] as a prerequisite of science different from testability, and has been advocated as the demarcation of science by Popper* and his followers. Yet falsifiability is a part of testability rather than a separate criterion. Popper*, the philosopher who developed the falsification concept and is its primary proponent, specifies that "[t]estability is falsifiability":

> Every genuine *test* of a theory is an attempt to *falsify* it, or to refute it. *Testability is falsifiability*; but there are degrees of testability; some theories are more testable, more exposed to refutation, than others; they take, as it were, greater risks.[187]

Even Ruse* agrees that falsifiability is an aspect of testability.[188] Thus, in any event falsifiability should not be listed as a separate "essential characteristic of science" as it was in the *McLean* opinion.

Falsifiability is not a prerequisite of science for several reasons, which closely parallel the problems of testability as a demarcation line. In fact, the majority of philosophers of science reject it as an "essential characteristic of science," including Lakatos*,[189] Quine*,[190] Kuhn*,[191] Laudan*,[192] Quinn*,[193] even Ruse*,[194] Sparkes*,[195] and others.[196]

First, many philosophers suggest that falsification, like testing, is unrelated to the real world of practice of science, as Lakatos* argues:

> *Is, then, Popper's falsifiability criterion the solution to the problem of demarcating science from pseudoscience? No.* For Popper's criterion ignores the remarkable tenacity of scientific theories. Scientists have

> thick skins. *They do not abandon a theory merely because facts contradict it.* They normally either invent some rescue hypothesis to explain what they then call a mere anomaly or, if they cannot explain the anomaly, they ignore it, and direct their attention to other problems. Note that scientists talk about anomalies, recalcitrant instances, not refutations. History of science, of course, is full of accounts of how crucial experiments allegedly killed theories. But such accounts are fabricated long after the theory had been abandoned.[197]

The history of physics "refutes the widely held view that scientists necessarily abandon a scientific proposition if a new observation conflicts with it," Polanyi* adds,[198] and Riddiford* and Penny* apply the principle to all of science.[199] One major reason why reality conflicts with falsification theory is that there is "a wide spectrum of scientific theories which, in practice, cannot be rejected as a result of empirical evidence because auxiliary theories can come to the rescue," according to Sparkes* of Open University:

> [Lakatos] described fundamental theories as "core theories" or "touchstone theories" which are "protected" by a layer of auxiliary theories. The importance of this somewhat revised model of the structure of scientific theories is that it explains why it is not so easy to falsify a core theory as Popper's falsifiability criterion implies. For if an experimental result disagrees with the predictions of a theory, scientists are not compelled, *qua* scientists, to reject the theory; they are presented with a choice, the principal elements of which are *either* to reject the core theory *or* to adjust the protective belt of auxiliary theories so that theory and experiment can once more be reconciled. In this way a core theory can be preserved even if, *prima facie*, it seems that the evidence contradicts it.
>
> . . ..
>
> . . .There remains, however, a wide spectrum of scientific theories which, in practice, cannot be rejected as a result of empirical evidence because auxiliary theories can come to their aid. . . .[200]

Instead, second, other critics have argued that the history of science has generally been one of the confirmation of proposed explanations rather than the falsification of conjectures, as Harré* notes.[201] In addition, critics of Popper's* position have argued that there is no logical difference between supporting a theory through confirming occurrences or through absence of falsifying occurrences, Quinton* points out.[202]

Third, some concepts that are universally viewed as scientific are simply not falsifiable. Lakatos* observes that core theories are seldom if ever falsifiable,[203] and Kuhn* states that "[a]ll theories can be modified by a variety of *ad hoc* adjustments."[204] Laudan* notes that definitions and existential statements are not falsifiable either:

> Karl Popper's 'falsificationist' criterion ... fares no better. Apart from the fact that it leaves ambiguous the scientific status of virtually every singular existential statement, however well supported (e.g., the claim that there are atoms, that there is a planet closer to the sun than the earth, that there is a missing link), it has the untoward consequence of countenancing as 'scientific' every crank claim which makes ascertainably false assertions.[205]

Other nonfalsifiable scientific concepts include "all probabilistic statements," Amsterdamski* notes,[206] and quantification, atomistic discreteness, hierarchical structure, and the principle of uniformity in nature itself, Holton*[207] and Quinn*[208] point out. Both falsifiability and testability "may be criticized because they exclude logic and mathematics from the realm of science."[209]

Fourth, although much of science does involve falsifiable occurrences, scientific study of origins involves nonrecurring past events with incomplete records, and the very nature of nonrecurring past events and limited records means that explanations of origins may only be partially falsifiable just as they are only partially testable.[210] Incidentally, Popper*, the architect of falsification analysis, argued that Darwinian evolution is "not falsifiable" but is instead a "metaphysical research programme".[211]

Fifth, the falsification requirement of course is itself neither a natural law nor tentative. And it has been falsified by the many instances in science of "contrary empirical evidence failing to falsify" theories, Sparkes* argues:

> The willingness with which scientists cling to Popper's criterion of falsifiability, as a demarcation between science and non-science, is a nice illustration of Lakatos's thesis. If any instance can be found in science of contrary empirical evidence failing to falsify a theory then Popper's criterion has failed. *But despite the existence of such instances it continues to have a good following*. It can be protected, just like many other good theories. The exception does not so much prove, as improve, the rule![212]

Amsterdamski* concurs: "falsificationism is also incompatible with the fact that the empirical falsification of the claims of science is neither a sufficient nor a necessary condition for their elimination."[213]

Summary. Thus, "being testable and being falsifiable are not necessary for individual statements to have scientific status" (Quinn*[214]), and are not "essential characteristics of science" in the view of many specialists. "To rely on testing as a mark of science is to miss what scientists mostly do" (Kuhn*[215]), particularly in relation to origins where limited testing is possible.[216] "It is now widely acknowledged that many scientific claims are not testable in isolation, but only when imbedded in a larger system of statements, *some* of whose consequences can be submitted to test"—and some of which cannot be (Riddiford* and Penny*[217]).

Falsifiability is probably less widely accepted as a demarcation criterion, and less related to the real world of science, than testability. Scientists, instead of "reject[ing] the core theory," more often "adjust the protective belt of auxiliary theories" (Sparkes*[218]). Many parts of science, such as "virtually every singular existential statement" and definition, are not falsifiable (Laudan*[219]). Finally, the falsifiability criterion itself may have been falsified (Sparkes*[220])! *Teneas non aurum totum quod splendet ut aurum.* (In any event, the theories of evolution and of abrupt appearance are to the same extent testable and falsifiable, as discussed later.[221])

A CIVIC BIOLOGY

Presented in Problems

BY

GEORGE WILLIAM HUNTER, A.M.

AMERICAN BOOK COMPANY

NEW YORK CINCINNATI CHICAGO

Figure 9.6
The "dogmatism of normal science" (Lakatos): best exemplified in the textbooks, including the one used by Scopes**

9.6 Tentativeness and the Demarcation of Science: Difference between Science and Scientists

The "tentativeness" requirement of the *McLean* decision has similarly been criticized as "completely irrelevant" and as not an "essential characteristic" of science. Quinn* calls it an "untenable view that being . . . held tentatively by its adherents" is a condition "necessary for a statement to be scientific."[222] Tentativeness in fact is not a characteristic at all of most of modern science.

a. Nontentativeness of Normal Science

First, science is ordinarily characterized by "the 'dogmatism'of 'normal science' " rather than by tentativeness, as Lakatos* and Popper* explicitly recognize:

> Popper is right in stressing that 'the *dogmatic attitude* of sticking to a theory as long as possible is of considerable significance. Without it we could never find out what is in a theory—we should give the theory up before we had a real opportunity of finding out its strength; and in consequence no theory would ever be able to play its role of bringing order into the world, of preparing us for future events, of drawing our attention to events we should otherwise never observe'. Thus the 'dogmatism' of 'normal science' does not prevent growth as long as we combine it with the Popperian recognition that there is good, progressive normal science and that there is bad, degenerating normal science, and as long as we retain the determination to eliminate, under certain objectively defined conditions, some research programmes.[223]

Kuhn* adds that "[n]ormal science, for example, often suppresses fundamental novelties because they are necessarily subversive of its basic commitments."[224] Laudan*,[225] Kerkut*,[226] Opik*,[227] and others note the same characteristic dogmatism.

Second, that dogmatism is normally appropriate as scientists "try to work around the falsifying data" rather than prematurely abandoning their theories, as Ruse* argues:

> [S]cientists have not thrown out their theories, simply because some of the facts were against them. They refused to let their theories be falsified. And indeed, they ought to have so refused. If a scientist threw out his (or her) theory as soon as something went wrong, as soon as the facts told against the theory, very little science would get done. *Often, if not normally, the proper scientific strategy is to continue with the theory, and to try to work around the falsifying data*—by showing the data not to be at all what it appears, by inventing ad hoc hypotheses to explain away the data, or if worse comes to worst, by ignoring the data and hoping that some day it will go away.[228]

That is consistent with Lakatos'* analysis.[229] Dogmatism "may prove correct," and if not "may serve a useful purpose as a stimulant to research," Opik* adds:

> DOGMATISM IN SCIENCE
>
> While religious—or antireligious—abstract dogma stands beyond the reach of science, in science the dogmatic approach has played, and is still

> playing, a *conspicuous role*, but with a difference: the preconceived ideas in science are subject to verification or rejection through further research. They remain "dogma" only as their adherents refuse to consider alternatives to their doctrines, rejecting criticism beforehand. . . .
>
> Scientific dogma as here defined *may prove correct*; and even when ultimately disproved, it *may serve a useful purpose*, as a stimulant to research and the accumulation of facts. Often it may also be harmful, as an obstacle to freedom of research, especially when influencing editors and reviewers of scientific magazines or directors of institutions.

b. Irrelevance of Tentativeness or Dogmatism

Tentativeness is not only atypical but irrelevant to science.

First, "whether a body of reasoning is scientific or not should be decided independently of the question of whether the adherents are committed to one ideology or another," as Raup* argues,[231] and as Laudan* concurs.[232] That is part of the generally accepted Reichenbach* distinction between the "context of discovery" and the "context of justification."[233] The point is made even more strongly by Quinn*:

> [T]entativeness is not a structural or methodological condition on the content of a body of beliefs but is a psychological condition on the attitudes of believers. But whether a belief is held tentatively or dogmatically is *completely irrelevant* to whether or not it is scientifically or in any other way epistemically respectable. . . .[234]

Finally, the tentativeness criterion contradicts the natural laws criterion, because natural laws are never tentatively held (or they would not be "laws"), and theories are also not tentatively held (or they would be hypotheses instead). It also contradicts the falsifiability criterion, because falsified concepts normally are not merely tentatively rejected. Similarly, the tentativeness criterion is not itself tentative, much less falsifiable or testable.

Summary. Thus, tentativeness is not an "essential characteristic"—or a characteristic at all—of science. "Numerous historians and philosophers of science (e.g., Kuhn, Mitroff, Feyerabend, Lakatos) have documented the existence of a certain degree of dogmatism about core commitments in scientific research and have argued that such dogmatism plays a constructive role in promoting the aims of science. . . . [O]ne does not even begin to get at those differences by pretending that science is characterized by an uncompromising open-mindedness" (Laudan*[235]). In fact, normal science is characterized by "dogmatism" rather than tentativeness (Lakatos*[236]). Nevertheless, "whether a belief is held tentatively or dogmatically is completely irrelevant to whether or not it is scientifically or in any other way epistemically respectable" (Quinn*[237]). (However, if it is, the theory of abrupt appearance meets a tentativeness requirement more than the theory of evolution does, as discussed below.[238])

* * *

The radical definition of science, and particularly its embodiment in the *McLean* definition, is incorrect and rejected by most philosophers of science in virtually every point, as Quinn* summarizes:

> This was the major problem in *McLean v. Arkansas*. Ruse's views do *not represent a settled consensus* of opinion among philosophers of science. Worse still, *some of them are clearly false* and some are based on obviously fallacious arguments.[239]

"If [*McLean's* definition] goes unchallenged by the scientific community, it will raise grave doubts about that community's intellectual integrity," in the assessment of a noted philosopher of science.[240] However, even if the *McLean* definition is accepted, the theories of evolution and of abrupt appearance comparably conform to it, as discussed in Chapter 10. *De omni re scibili et quibusdam aliis?*

9.7 Majority Assessment by Scientists: Inconclusive Criterion of Science

With the various definitions of science in mind, an important question is who is to apply those definitions. The most frequent answer is the "community of philosophers of science" or the "community of scientists."

The scientific community has been defined as follows by Kuhn*:

> A scientific community consists, in this view, of the practitioners of a scientific specialty. . . . For these major communities group membership is readily established, except at the [disciplines'] fringes. [1] Subject of highest degree, [2] membership in professional societies and [or] [3] journals read are ordinarily more than sufficient.[241]

Satisfaction of two of these three factors is ordinarily sufficient to place an individual in the philosophic or scientific community, according to Reingold*:

> Today, in the twentieth century, we define a scientist as anyone who meets at least two and usually three of the following characteristics: (1) he or she possesses a *suitable educational degree* (e.g., a Ph.D. or M.S.); (2) he or she is in an *occupation or has an occupational title that requires*

Figure 9.7
Galileo and his non-geocentric theory of the universe: persecuted by "the astronomer-scientists of the time, as well as by the Pope" (Barber)*

> the possession of that degree or at least of the knowledge supposedly entailed by obtaining that degree (e.g., professor of chemistry); (3) he or she belongs to a *professional association* of people who supposedly have the knowledge for which the degree was acquired and who, as a group, are presumably interested in advancing it (let us say, the American Chemical Society). . . .[242]

The philosophical community would be identified by a parallel definition.

The next question is what part of that community makes the determination if the community is not unanimous. The answer should not be a numerical majority, for several reasons. The following sections discuss the (a) significance of minority opinions in the scientific community, (b) bias of the scientific community in general, (c) bias of that community in favor of the theory of evolution, and (d) bias of the scientific community against the theory of abrupt appearance and the theory of creation.

a. Significance of Minority Opinions in the Scientific Community

The scientific nature and correctness of a concept cannot properly be decreed by the majority in the philosophic or scientific community, Margolis* observes:

> This truly democratic principle has led to the fallaciously democratic

practice of determining the validity of a scientific view by finding how many other scientists agree with it. Voting in this context is so much influenced by past training and indoctrination that it tends to reject the new and to reaffirm the old.[243]

A majority rule of scientists is not only "fallacious" but "has no bearing," Brady* adds:

Unless we assume scientists to be infallible, the fact that a theory has been adopted does not justify that adoption. . . . This standard [of how many people believe a theory] works fine for historians who are estimating the historical importance of this or that theory, but it has no bearing on the problem at hand.[244]

Scientific unity sometimes arises from very nonscientific factors, according to Feyerabend*:

There are, of course, areas in which scientists agree—but this cannot raise our confidence. Unity is often the result of a political decision. On other occasions, it is the result of shared prejudices. Or it may indicate a decrease in critical consciousness; criticism remains faint if only one point of view is considered.[245]

"[S]cientific knowledge is not objective," Bartels* flatly states:

One can predict that pressure for societal implementation could have the effect of *"hardening" the scientific claims*, raising their status so that their objectivity and accuracy are not questioned. . . .

. . ..

. . .And it is recognized that scientific knowledge represents not a true depiction of reality, but rather is shaped by and for certain political objectives.

. . .It must be recognized generally that *scientific knowledge is not objective*, and hence cannot serve as the undisputed, rock-hard base upon which potentially discriminatory political decisions may be erected.[246]

Instead, the professional opinions of the minority are important and should be expressed rather than suppressed, even if they are "scientific heresies," Kerkut* stresses:

It would seem a good principle to *encourage the study of 'scientific heresies*.' There is always the danger that a reader might be seduced by one of these heresies but the danger is neither as great nor as serious as the danger of having scientists brought up in a type of mental straitjacket or of taking them so quickly through a subject that they have no time to analyse and digest the material they have 'studied.'[247]

It is a good thing to "try to construct alternative theories—alternatives even to those theories which appear to you inescapable: for only in this way will you understand the theories you hold," Popper* adds.[248]

Nearly every current scientific majority view was once a minority view, and most past majority viewpoints in the history of science have been abandoned.[249] Examples are given by Rosen*:

> One need hardly point out that popularity was also a characteristic of the phlogiston theory, Ptolemaic cycles and epicycles, the ether as an explanation for wave transmissions in a vacuum, and those ideas of 19th-century Europe that preceded natural selection theory—the miasma or noxious vapors (Rogers, 1973)—to explain evolutionary change.[250]

Thus, a definition of science by consensus was rejected by Bridgman*:

> Some people go so far as to define science as the consensus of all competent observers. This, it seems to me, goes too far and misplaces the emphasis.... 'Competent persons' at any epoch means those who at that epoch have been subjected to a definite preconditioning. . . . It does not preclude the possibility that all competent persons are reacting incorrectly because of some feature of contemporary culture, and there are examples, as Weierstrass in mathematics, where consensus was ultimately shown to have been wrong.[251]

b. "Bias" of the Scientific Community in General

The scientific (and philosophic) community has always had strong majority biases, which make it even more improper to apply the definitions of science to particular concepts by a philosophic or scientific majority vote. Several sources of bias are discussed, and then some more outrageous examples are given.

(1) Sources of Bias. One source of bias is scientism, which Jaki* of Seton Hall University describes:

> The scientific community will hardly take a look at the difference between science as a form of knowledge, which is always imperfect and always limited, and the systematic deification of science which is scientism. Scientism is a cultural blindfold which prevents its wearers from appraising in its true weight. . . .[252]

Another major form of bias is that any theory colors perceptions of fact, as Eldredge* and Gould* stress:

> (1) The expectations of theory color perception to such a degree that new notions seldom arise from facts collected under the influence of old pictures of the world. New pictures must cast their influence before facts can be seen in different perspective.[253]

Darwin* himself suggested that scientists "let theory guide [their] observations"—and conceal that guidance:

> I would suggest to you the advantage, at present, of being very sparing in introducing theory in your papers (I formerly erred much in Geology that way); *let theory guide your observations*, but till your reputation is well established, be sparing of publishing theory. It makes persons doubt your observations.[254]

Others, such as Robinson*,[255] Kuhn*,[256] and Hein*,[257] have emphasized the lens of some theory through which all scientists and philosophers view their fields. Ruse* tackles the "myth" that science is value-free:

> There is a popular opinion among analytic philosophers, at least there was until very recently, that science is value-free or neutral. . . .
>
> I can only say bluntly that study of the history of science has shown me that this position is *totally mistaken*. It is as much a *myth* as in Pegasus, the Loch Ness monster, and the proposed solution of the Ruse children to the mystery of the missing cookies.
>
> As I read into the science of the nineteenth-century, it became more and more apparent to me that everyone—creationist or evolutionist—had every one of the values or prejudices of his fellow Victorians. . . .
>
> I found, very quickly, that they were indeed quite wrong. *Today's science drips with as many hopes and aspirations, as did yesterday's science.* I have an embarrassment of riches from which to make my case, so let me simply choose one example, drawn from a controversy which much interests and excites evolutionists today. I refer to the row going on at present about the *nature of the fossil record and the process of macroevolution.*[258]

Bohm* answers the scientist who claims that he has no bias:

> It seems clear that everybody has got some kind of metaphysics, even if he thinks he hasn't got any. Indeed, the practical "hard-headed" individual who "only goes by what he sees" generally has a very dangerous kind of metaphysics, i.e., the kind of which he is unaware. . . . Such metaphysics is dangerous because, in it, assumptions and inferences are being mistaken for directly observed facts, with the result that they are effectively riveted in an almost unchangeable way into the structure of thought.[259]

The impact of a widely held theory is often to foster intolerance of minority scientific views, as Brady* points out:

> When a theory becomes part of the common working knowledge of an entire community *it becomes the context* within which that community understands the world. *Doubt comes to be regarded as something less than legitimate*, and critics find themselves talking only to each other. The critic is, in a certain sense, self-exiled, for he or she is trying to question what the common language of the field takes for granted, and this linguistic hurdle is a difficult one to overcome. Yet for the critic, the task is merely one of clarification. The other side, however, must deal with a condition which may turn out, in the end, to be far more debilitating, i.e. belief.[260]

There is a "dangerous tendency" to form a herd "among researchers" that shuts off successful development, Solzhenitsyn adds.[261] "Normal science, for example, often suppresses fundamental novelties because they are necessarily subversive of its basic commitments," as Kuhn* observes.[262]

Another source of scientific bias is "the resistance on the part of scientists themselves to scientific discovery," as Barber* shows:

> In the study of the history and sociology of science, there has been a relative lack of attention to one of the interesting aspects of the social process of discovery—the resistance on the part of scientists themselves to scientific discovery. . . .
>
> Moving to the early 19th century, we learn that the scientists of the day resisted Thomas *Young's wave theory of light* because they were, as Gillispie says, faithful to a corpuscular model. By the end of the century, when scientists had swung over to the wave theory, the validity of Young's earlier discovery was recognized. Substantive scientific theory was also one of the sources of resistance to *Pasteur's discovery of the biological character of fermentation processes.* The established theory that these processes are wholly chemical was held to by many scientists, including Liebig, for a long time. The same preconceptions were also the source of the resistance to *Lister's germ theory of disease*, although in this case, as in that of Pasteur, various other factors were important.[263]

A pervasive form of bias is the "mechanistic materialist philosophy explicitly or implicitly shared by most of the present 'establishment' in the biological sciences," as Dobzhansky* acknowledged.[264] That is extensively discussed in Section 13.5(a).[265] Another such bias is evolution, as discussed in Section 9.7(c).

Another widespread bias is against religion, as Jaki* points out:

> This certainly holds true of the scientific community, a part of our civilization in which sympathy for positive Christianity, let alone for a dogmatic Catholicism riveted in the supernatural, is the exception. That community is part of a civilization which is largely ignorant of the hollowness of most of its reasons for that lack of sympathy. . . .[266]

Others have noted that anticlerical bias too.[267]

(2) Examples of Bias. Numerous examples exist of scientific bias and intolerance toward a minority scientific viewpoint, besides those just mentioned. The famous Galileo incident [268] is one where "the astronomer-scientists of the time," as well as the pope, opposed and censured a scientific advance, as Barber* recounts:

> In his magisterial discussion of the Copernican revolution, Kuhn tells us not only about the nonscientific opposition to the heliocentric theory but also about the *resistance from the astronomer-scientists of the time.* Even after the publication of *De Revolutionibus*, the belief of most astronomers in the stability of the earth was unshaken. The idea of the earth's motion was either ignored or dismissed as absurd. Even *the great astronomer-observer Brahe remained a life-long opponent* of Copernican-

ism; he was unable to break with the traditional patterns of thought about the earth's lack of motion. And his immense prestige helped to postpone the conversion of other astronomers to the new theory. Of course, religious, philosophical, and ideological conceptions were closely interwoven with substantive scientific theories in the culture of the scientists of that time, but it seems clear that *the latter as well as the former played their part in the resistance* to the Copernican discoveries.[269]

A twentieth-century example is the ridicule directed at continental drift, which Gould* describes:

> During the period of nearly universal rejection, *direct evidence* for continental drift—that is, the data gathered from rocks exposed on our continents—*was every bit as good* as it is today. It was dismissed because no one had devised a physical mechanism that would permit continents to plow through an apparently solid oceanic floor. In the absence of a plausible mechanism, the idea of continental drift was rejected as absurd. The data that seemed to support it could always be *explained away*. . . . In short, we now accept continental drift because it is the expectation of a new orthodoxy.[270]

That bias, including by the leaders of the profession, is further described by Broad* and Wade*, who discount the typical excuse of lack of a mechanism:

> For any who might suppose that the twentieth century is immune to such foibles, consider the concept of continental drift, proposed by the German meteorologist Alfred Wegener in 1922. . . . But it took geologists and geophysicists *almost forty years*, from 1922 to about 1960, to accept that the continents are in motion. Sometimes the excuse is offered that geologists knew of no mechanism by which the continents could be moved, but this is not so; a well-known article written by geologist Arthur Holmes in 1928 correctly advocated convection currents as the force that moves the continents.
>
> It was the *leaders of their profession*, Harold Jeffreys in England and Maurice Ewing in the United States, who *spearheaded the opposition*. . . .[271]

A second example from this century is active supression of the minority scientific viewpoint expressed by Velikovsky*, which de Grazia* *et al.* summarize:

> What must be called the *scientific establishment rose in arms*, not only against the new Velikovsky theories but against the man himself. Efforts were made to *block* dissemination of Dr. Velikovsky's ideas, and even to punish supporters of his investigations. Universities, scientific societies, publishing houses, the popular press were approached and threatened; *social pressures and professional sanctions* were invoked to control public opinion.
>
> . . . .

> Prominent American scientists, roused to indignation even before the book was published, greeted it with a remarkable demonstration of ill will that included a partially successful *attempt to suppress* the work by imposing a boycott on its first publisher's textbooks. The reading public witnessed the unique spectacle of a scientific debate staged not in the semi-privacy of scientific meetings and journals, but in the popular press, with scientists—in rare accord—on one side and lay champions of free speech on the other. . . . Velikovsky and his book were discredited in the public eye.
>
> From the start there was more to the controversy than the simple question of a dissenting scholar's right to be published and read; the atmosphere generated by scientific consternation was charged with a *peculiar emotion* that Newsweek termed "a highly unacademic fury."[272]

That storm of emotional fury included attempts to prevent publication of his book and article:

> Velikovsky was summoned to Brett's office and told that *professors in certain large universities were refusing to see Macmillan salesmen*, and *letters demanding cessation of publication* were arriving from a number of *scientists*. Brett beseeched Velikovsky to save him from disaster by approving an arrangement that had been tentatively worked out with Doubleday & Company, which had no textbook department. . . . Brett showed Velikovsky a letter from Michigan astronomer Dean B. MacLaughlin, who insisted Velikovsky's book was nothing but lies. On the same page McLaughlin averred *he had not read* and never would read the book.[273]

Censorship did not cease with book publishers, but extended to science periodicals such as *Science*, the journal of the American Association for the Advancement of Science:

> Velikovsky sought to publish a paper showing that the points brought out in that letter were but a few among many other ideas set forth in his books that have already been supported by independent research. The attempt was in vain; Philip Abelson, the editor of *Science*, *returned* Velikovsky's paper *without reading it* and *published instead a facetious letter* from a Poul Anderson. . . .[274]

A third example from the twentieth century is Lysenko* genetics in the Soviet Union, as described by Stansfield*:

> His name was Trofim D. Lysenko. In one of the most bizarre incidents in the history of biology, this man gained the confidence and backing of the Central Committee of the Communist Party through his association with Premier Stalin. It was decreed that the Lysenko style of biology, genetics, and especially agriculture be adopted throughout the country. Needless to say, the folly of pursuing an erroneous theory led to disastrous effects on Russia's agricultural productivity and thoroughly disrupted its progress in basic biological research for almost two decades. In

1965 Lysenko was demoted from his positions of authority and genetics once again became a respectable science.[275]

Part of Stalin's "backing" was that the "Central Committee of the Soviet Communist Party in 1949 declared Mendelian genetics pseudoscientific and had its advocates, like Academician Vavilov, killed in concentration camps," Lakatos* adds.[276] The sixteen years of Lysenko* genetics are chronicled by Joravsky*[277] and Graham*.[278] Unfortunately, science in the Soviet Union is still "manipulated," Popovsky* writes.[279]

Many other examples from recent years can be given, such as rejection of "relativity theory—an aberration as far as the Nobel Committee was concerned at least until Einstein's death," of "Boltzmann's constant,"[280] of theories of heat and gases,[281] and of catastrophism. Catastrophism has been the casualty of presuppositions that "restrict the range of hypotheses that scientists are willing to entertain," specifically the presupposition of gradualism that "has operated for the past one hundred and fifty years as a serious constraining bias in the history of geology," Gould* states.[282]

In the past centuries "history is replete with instances," as Broad* and Wade* illustrate:

> But history is replete with instances where openmindedness and objectivity have failed. Tycho Brahe, the greatest observational astronomer of his time, resisted the theory of *Copernicus* to his dying day, and encouraged many other astronomers to do likewise. In the nineteenth century, Thomas *Young's* wave theory of light, *Pasteur's* discovery of the biological nature of fermentation, and *Mendel's* theory of genetics all met with dismissal or resistance from the professional scientists of the specialties concerned.
>
> . . ..
>
> George *Ohm*, the nineteenth-century German who discovered the law of electrical resistance, was a math teacher at the Jesuit Gymnasium in Cologne; his ideas were ignored by scientists at German universities. *Mendel's* genetic laws were ignored by professionals in his field for thirty-five years, in part because, as an abbé with an experimental plot in his backyard, he seemed to be a mere amateur. . . .
>
> . . ..
>
> . . .Louis *Pasteur* met with violent resistance from doctors when he advanced his germ theory of disease; they regarded him as a mere chemist poaching on their scientific preserves. Joseph *Lister's* discovery of antisepsis was initially ignored in both England and the United States, in part because Lister, a doctor working in Glasgow and Edinburgh, was regarded as a provincial.
>
> Few episodes in the illustrious annals of scientific progress are more

> striking than that of the nineteenth-century Hungarian physician Ignaz *Semmelweis*. He discovered that puerperal, or childbed, fever, then causing typically 10 to 30 percent mortality in maternity hospitals throughout Europe, could be virtually abolished by the simple expedient of having doctors wash their hands in a chlorine solution before examining the mother. . . .
>
> The book was almost universally ignored by the medical profession, even though throughout Europe puerperal fever continued to ravage maternity hospitals. . . .[283]

Probably the most heated example, the bias in favor of the theory of evolution and against the theory of creation, is discussed in the remainder of this section.

c. *"Bias" of the Scientific Community in Favor of the Theory of Evolution*

The majority of the scientific community is strongly biased in favor of evolution, as paleontologist Colin Patterson* observes:

> Popper warns of a danger: 'A theory, even a scientific theory, may become an intellectual fashion, a substitute for religion, an entrenched dogma'. This has certainly been true of evolutionary theory.[284]

Brady* concurs:

> What is at stake is not the validity of the Darwinian theory itself, but of the approach to science that it has come to represent. The peculiar form of consensus the theory wields has produced a premature closure of inquiry in several branches of biology, and even if this is to be expected in 'normal science', such a *dogmatic* approach does not appear healthy.[285]

The dogmatism (rather than tentativeness) of this majority position[286] is described in Section 10.5(b).

Many scientists and philosophers have described evolution as effectively a "scientific religion," such as philosopher Grene*:

> It is as a *religion of science* that Darwinism chiefly held, and holds, men's minds. . . .
>
> . . ..
>
> . . . The modified, but still characteristically Darwinian theory has itself become an orthodoxy, preached by its adherents with religious fervor and doubted, they feel, only by a few muddlers imperfect in scientific faith. . . .[287]

Lipson* calls evolution "a scientific religion,"[288] Jaki* terms it "a creed . . . with scientists committed to document the all-purpose role of natural selection,"[289] Midgley* writes of "evolution as a religion,"[290] Macbeth* concludes that "Darwinism has itself become a religion,"[291] and Conklin* said that for many biologists evolution "is an object of genuinely religious devotion . . .."[292]

The consequence of questioning evolution is that the dissenter "inevitably attracts the speculative psychiatric eye to himself,"[293] according to Hardin*, as well as an "attack with quite remarkable ferocity," in the words of biologists Saunders* and Ho*:

> [T]he work of those who are less cautious in this regard is sometimes *attacked* with quite *remarkable ferocity* by critics who see in it nothing but a perverse refusal to accept a theory whose validity they believe has been established beyond any reasonable doubt.[294]

One openminded scientist wrote that certain conclusions mean "you are really not an evolutionist, and therefore your views deserve little serious consideration"![295] The same intolerance has been noted by others.[296]

This evolutionary bias has caused paleontologists to wear "blinders" and to "ignore" data in conflict with neo-Darwinian biological evolution, Gould* and Eldredge* state,[297] with the following sort of result:

> But for years the apparent lack of progressive change within fossil species has been ignored or else the evidence—not the theory—has been attacked.[298]

It has caused researchers of human origins to reject some molecular biology findings, Zihlman* and Lowenstein* say,[299] and in fact there "data are still so scarce that theory heavily influences interpretations," Pilbeam* adds.[300] Evolutionary dogmatism has produced "virulence" in opposition to the transformed cladist approach, which Patterson* describes:

> Yet whenever and wherever cladistics is discussed, there is controversy. The *virulence of this controversy* and the partisan feelings evoked are *remarkable* in so old and apparently harmless a discipline as systematics; there has hardly been such bad temper in biology since the violent arguments provoked 120 years ago by Darwin's theory of evolution by natural selection.[301]

In general, "a strong positive evolutionary pressure is brought to bear upon all of us to maintain the paradigm" of neo-Darwinism, Schwabe* notes.[302]

At the same time, "[t]hose who believe the Darwinian theory apply it, or parts of it, to their observations," so that "[t]heir results are artifacts of their belief, but this fact can hardly be visible to them until they are willing to question what they have previously taken for granted," in Brady's* assessment.[303] He continues:

> Once we have become convinced by our theory, for whatever reason, artifacts of that belief are bound to emerge, for *we see the world in the context of our belief*. . . .
>
> If we are in the position of saying "Since we now know the theory is

correct, what follows?", the item under investigation here is not the world of experience, *but the theory*, for experience no longer has the power to question that belief. The addition of empirical evidence at this point changes nothing, because whatever *evidence we include will be interpreted by our theory*, producing such artifacts as the *illusory 'confirmation'* and 'correction' above. There should be no confusion about this. A firm conviction precludes any possibility of learning from experience—learning, that is, about the relation of the idea to evidence, or to empirical support. By treating the theory as a known parameter we *approximate tautology* by a means I did not specifically describe in the first section, although it is a failure of empirical specification. *The theory is unbeatable because it is allowed to interpret our observations* while they are being made or being recorded. Once this has been done, it is only logical that the data so collected cannot be used to question the interpretation, being a product of it. . . .[304]

Evolutionary bias also applies to cosmic and biochemical origins. In seeing evidence that the universe had a beginning, astronomers "become irritated, . . . pretend the conflict does not exist, or . . . paper it over with meaningless phrases," Jastrow* observes.[305] There is a "deep seated hostility by both observers and theoreticians in the astronomical community toward the steady state theory," Burbidge* says.[306] Origin of life researchers "may be prone to ignore or to underemphasize logical difficulties," Simon* notes.[307] Meanwhile, philosophers of science remind us "that the mathematical probability of all theories . . . given any amount of evidence is zero," as Lakatos* says.[308] Others such as Laudan*[309] and Sullivan*[310] agree.

d. "Intolerance" of the Scientific Community against the Theories of Abrupt Appearance and of Creation

Most of the scientific community is "intolerant" of the theory of creation, as Provine* (a noted historian of science at Cornell) observes:

> [M]ost biological scientists are intolerant of creationism and do not understand the reasons for the great attraction of the creationist's position.[311]

Ruse* states flatly that "orthodox scientists loathe scientific creationism and do all in their power to oppose it:

> I must point out that orthodox scientists loathe scientific creationism and do all in their power to oppose it. I am afraid that one of the problems with living in a democracy is that sometimes crazy ideas do influence a

> number of people for a period of time. Fortunately, in a democracy we do have the means at hand to oppose such ideas, and this is what many evolutionists are doing.[312]

For example, Ruse* elsewhere says that "American biologists have only contempt for so-called 'Scientific Creationism'," in an editorial in a new journal,[313] and refers to creationist concepts as "lunatic ideas."[314] Asimov* calls creationists "the army of the night" and a "frightening force, impervious to, and immunized against, the feeble lance of mere reason."[315] Geissler* calls them "not merely a curiosity but also a real danger," so that "we have to oppose creationism actively."[316] Strike* agrees that the "referee system has rejected creationism."[317]

Pangle* (a philosopher) concurs:

> The attempts by neo-Darwinians to limit the claims to knowledge, and hence the access to the education of the young, of so-called "Creationists" are painfully stark contemporary examples of the bluster and unscientific indignation into which rationalism collapses in these cases.[318]

Ellis* adds that "the very concept of the creation of the Universe at such a singular beginning is philosophically objectionable to some scientists."[319]

That prejudice actually reaches the point of discrimination against creationist scientists or students in universities and schools, and by science publications, as Sections 18.2 discusses. For example, Patterson* concedes that "their chances of achieving or retaining prestigious academic positions would be greatly undermined,"[320] while Shafersman* argues that " 'creationists' with legitimate postgraduate degrees and other appropriate credentials are not scientists" because of disqualification by their creationist conclusions.[321]

The theory of abrupt appearance, along with other nonDarwinian explanations, faces much of the intolerance and bias that the theory of creation encounters. Dobzhansky* concedes that the acceptance of Darwinian evolution "is nevertheless so wide that its opponents complain of inability to get a hearing for their views."[322] The points about evolutionary bias in Section 9.7(c) reflect obstacles to the theory of abrupt appearance.

Summary. A large majority of scientists today embrace the theory of evolution, but the number of scientists who believe a theory "has no bearing on the problem" of whether a theory is scientific (Brady*[323]). Despite widespread popular beliefs to the contrary, "scientific knowledge is not objective" (Bartels*[324]). There are many benefits from "try[ing] to construct alternative theories" (Popper*[325]), particularly because every majority theory now was once a minority theory, while nearly every majority theory of the past is now a discarded theory. Yet a majority scientific theory readily "becomes the context within which that community understands the world," and "[d]oubt comes to be regarded as something less than legitimate" (Brady*[326]). General scientific biases, besides theory coloring perception, include "resistance on the part of scientists themselves to scientific discovery" (Barber*[327]), and a "mechanistic materialist philosophy explicitly or implicitly shared by most of the present 'establishment' in the biological sciences" (Dobzhansky*[328]). Twentieth-century examples of scientific bias include hostility to continental drift for forty years (Broad* and Wade*[329]), suppression of Velikovsky's* proposals (de Grazia* *et al.*[330]), Soviet enforcement of Lysenko* genetics (Joravsky*[331]), and many others.

"[E]volutionary theory" has become "an entrenched dogma" (Patterson* [332]) and "a dogmatic approach" (Brady*[333]). Neo-Darwinians "see the world in the context of our belief," and "evidence . . . will be interpreted by our theory," so that the "theory is unbeatable because it is allowed to interpret our observations" (Brady*[334]). Questioning of neo-Darwinian evolution brings an "attack with quite remarkable ferocity" (Saunders* and Ho*[335]), and "complain[ts] of inability to get a hearing for their views" (Dobzhansky*[336]). Thus, "orthodox scientists loathe scientific creationism and do all in their power to oppose it" (Ruse* [337]), and "the very concept of the creation of the Universe at such a singular beginning is philosophically objectionable to some scientists" (Ellis*[338]). *Igni et aqua interdictus.* The pervasiveness of that strong bias reaffirms the philosophic principle that applying a definition of science should not be done by majority vote of scientists.

* * *

Science is difficult to define, as reflected in the large number of proposed lines of demarcation, but probably is best delineated by a number of proposals whose common denominator is Ziman's* "logical inferences from empirical observations." The definition of science that should be rejected forthrightly is the radical definition based on positivist, materialist, and/or naturalistic presuppositions, and particularly the *McLean* definition that has been described by the only philosophers of science publishing assessments as "demonstrably false" and a "false stereotype." The definition of science must be broad enough to include at least some minority theories that may someday be majority viewpoints, and to overcome the "dogmatism of normal science" and its majority theories.

Notes

[1] Quoted in Vaucouleurs*, *The Case for a Hierarchical Cosmology*, 167 Science 1203, 1203 (1970) (italics in original).

[2] Dolby*, *Science and Pseudo-Science: The Case of Creationism*, 22 Zygon 195, 201-02 (1987) (italics added).

[3] A. Whitehead*, *The Function of Reason* 48 (1929).

[4] *See* Laudan*, *The Demise of the Demarcation Problem*, in 2 Working Papers in Science and Technology 7, 9 (R. Laudan* ed. 1983).

[5] 1 I. Lakatos*, *The Methodology of Scientific Research Programmes* 124 (J. Worrall* & G. Currie* eds. 1978). Of course, some scientists have ventured into the field of philosophy to write on the definition of science.

[6] *Id.* at 124 (Lakatos* notes that there has been agreement on the scientific nature of many single achievements).

[7] Laudan*, *The Demise of the Demarcation Problem*, in 2 Working Papers in Science and Technology 7, 9 (R. Laudan* ed. 1983) (italics added). *See also id.* at 7, 30 ("For most of this century, numerous scientists and some philosophers have acted, especially in their more public pronouncements, as if there were clear conceptions of the 'scientific' and the 'pseudoscientific.' Various forms of intellectual activity (ranging from the so-called social sciences to even less respectable matters like Velikovsky and psychokinesis) have been repeatedly labelled by many scientists and philosophers as 'unscientific' or 'pseudoscientific.' Such pejorative accusations have generally been issued with a confidence and an air of authority that is completely out of character with the *murkiness which actually afflicts our conception of the 'scientific.'*") (italics added); Laudan*, *Commentary: Science at the Bar—Causes for Concern*, Science, Technology & Human Values, Fall 1982, at 16, 18 ("few authors can even agree on what makes an activity scientific").

[8] Laudan*, *The Demise of the Demarcation Problem*, in 2 Working Papers in Science and Technology 7, 20 (R. Laudan* ed. 1983) ("Without conditions which are both necessary and sufficient, we are never in a position to say 'this is scientific: but that is unscientific.' Hence a demarcation criterion which fails to provide both sorts of conditions simply will not perform the tasks expected of it.").

[9] Krausser*, *A Cybernetic Systems Theoretical Approach to Rational Understanding and Explanation . . .*, Ratio, Dec. 1973, at 22 ("It is much more likely that explanations may be shown to be special forms or cases of *verstehen*").

10 E. Keller*, *Reflections on Gender and Science* 126 (1985) ("Ideology makes itself felt principally in the process by which particular styles, methodologies, and theories come to be legitimated as 'good science.' . . . Inevitably, the question is not simply which theory offers the fullest explanation, the best prediction, but also which theory best satisfies a host of unspecified 'aesthetic' criteria . . .—including which theory is most consonent with one's implicit ideological and emotional expectations.").

11 Ruse*, *The Ideology of Darwinism*, in Darwin Today 233, 249 (E. Geissler* & W. Scheler* eds. 1983).

12 T. Kuhn*, *The Structure of Scientific Revolutions* 103 (2d ed. 1970) ("As a result, the reception of a new paradigm often necessitates a redefinition of the corresponding science. Some old problems may be relegated to another science or declared entirely 'unscientific.' Others that were previously non-existent or trivial may, with a new paradigm, become the very archetypes of significant scientific achievement. And as the problems change, so, often, does the standard that *distinguishes* a real scientific solution from a mere metaphysical speculation, word game, or mathematical play.") (italics added).

13 Dolby*, *Science and Pseudo-Science: The Case of Creationism*, 22 Zygon 195, 201 (1987).

14 Ruse*, *Creation-Science Is Not Science*, in Creationism, Science, and the Law: The Arkansas Case 150, 151-53 (M. La Follette* ed. 1983).

15 McLean v. Arkansas Bd. of Educ., 529 F. Supp. 1255, 1267 (E.D. Ark. 1982).

16 Laudan*, *More on Creationism*, in Science, Technology & Human Values, Winter 1983, at 36, 36; Laudan*, *Commentary: Science at the Bar—Causes for Concern*, Science, Technology & Human Values, Fall 1982, at 16, 19.

17 Quinn*, *The Philosopher of Science as Expert Witness*, in Science and Reality: Recent Work in the Philosophy of Science 32, 41-42 (J. Cushing*, C. Delaney* & G. Gutting* eds. 1984).

18 Sections 9.3 & 10.2-10.5.

19 Ziman*, *What is Science?*, in Introductory Readings in the Philosophy of Science 35, 37 (E. Klemke*, R. Hollinger* & A. Kline* eds. 1980) (italics added).

20 9 *Oxford English Dictionary* 221 (1971) (italics added).

21 *Science*, 10 New Encyclopaedia Britannica: Micropaedia 552, 552 (15th ed. 1974).

22 Russell*, *The Scientific Outlook*, in Basic Problems of Philosophy 268 (D. Bronstein*, Y. Kriorian* & P. Weiner* eds. 1955) ("science is that sort of knowledge which gives causal understanding").

23 W. Stansfield*, *The Science of Evolution* 8 (1977).

24 Gould*, *The promise of paleobiology as a nomothetic, evolutionary discipline*, 6 Paleobiology 96, 113 (1980); Section 10.3 (b).

25 S. Toulmin*, *Science, Philosophy of*, 16 Encyclopaedia Britannica: Macropaedia 375, 378-79 (15th ed. 1974).

[26] C. Hempel*, *Philosophy of Natural Science* 17-18 (1966) (italics in original).

[27] Black*, *Induction*, 4 Encyclopedia of Philosophy 169, 170 (P. Edwards* ed. 1967). *See also* Lakatos*, *History of Science and Its Rational Reconstructions*, 8 Boston Studies in the Philosophy of Science 1 (1971).

[28] *See* T. Kuhn*, *The Structure of Scientific Theories* 459, 461-62 (2d ed. 1970); Section 9.7.

[29] Sparkes*, *What is this thing called science?*, 89 New Scientist 156, 157 (1981) (italics deleted).

[30] Popper*, *Science: Conjectures and Refutations*, in Introductory Readings in the Philosophy of Science 23 (E. Klemke*, R. Hollinger* & A. Kline* eds. 1980) (original in italics). *See also id.* at 22; K. Popper*, *Conjectures and Refutations* 33-37 (1963) ("4. A theory which is not refutable by any conceivable event is nonscientific. Irrefutability is not a virtue of a theory (as people often think) but a vice.").

[31] Section 9.5(b). *E.g.*, 1 I. Lakatos*, *The Methodology of Scientific Research Programmes* 3-4 (J. Worrall* & G. Currie* eds. 1978); Laudan*, *The Demise of the Demarcation Problem*, in 2 Working Papers in Science and Technology at 7, 23 (R. Laudan* ed. 1983); Kuhn*, *Logic of Discovery or Psychology of Research?*, in Criticism and the Growth of Knowledge 13 (I. Lakatos* & A. Musgrave* eds. 1970); P. Duhem*, *The Aim and Structure of Physical Theory* (2d ed. P. Weiner* trans. 1954).

[32] T. Kuhn*, *The Structure of Scientific Revolutions* 92, 94, 97 (2d ed. 1970).

[33] Watkins*, *Against 'Normal Science'*, in Criticism and the Growth of Knowledge 25, 29 (I. Lakatos* & A. Musgrave* eds. 1970) (Kuhn* states: "it is normal science, in which Sir Karl's sort of testing does not occur, rather than extraordinary science which most nearly distinguishes science from other enterprises."). *See also* Kuhn*, *Logic of Discovery or Psychology of Research?*, in *id.* at 1, 10.

[34] S. Toulmin*, *Human Understanding* 76, 98-119 (1972).

[35] Popper*, *Normal Science and Its Dangers*, in Criticism and the Growth of Knowledge 51, 56-58 (I. Lakatos* & A. Musgrave* eds. 1970).

[36] Black*, *Induction*, 4 Encyclopedia of Philosophy 169, 176-77 (P. Edwards* ed. 1967).

[37] N. Hanson*, *Patterns of Discovery: An Inquiry into the Conceptual Foundations of Science* 72-90 (1972).

[38] S. Toulmin*, *Science, Philosophy of*, 16 Encyclopaedia Britannica: Macropaedia 375, 387-88 (15th ed. 1974). The constructivist viewpoint likewise held that "the essential test of a science is that it should provide coherent, consistent, and wide-ranging theoretical organizations." *Id.* at 388.

[39] C. Hempel*, *Philosophy of Natural Science* 30-32 (1966); C. Hempel*, *Aspects of Scientific Explanation* ch. 4 (1965).

[40] Ziman*, *What Is Science?*, in Introductory Readings in the Philosophy of Science 35, 37 (E. Klemke*, R. Hollinger* & A. Kline* eds. 1980). *See also*

P. Bridgman*, *The Logic of Physics* 5 (1927) ("In general, we mean by any concept nothing more than a set of operations; the concept is synonymous with the corresponding set of operations.") (emphasis omitted).

41 Klemke*, *Introduction,* to Introductory Readings in the Philosophy of Science 1, 14 (E. Klemke*, R. Hollinger* & A. Klein* eds. 1980); *id.* at 16 ("many writers have rejected some (or all) o[f] those criteria").

42 *Id.* at 16-17.

43 Dolby*, *Science and Pseudo-Science: The Case for Creationism,* 22 Zygon 195, 202, 205 (1987) (italics added).

44 S. Amsterdamski*, *Between Experience and Metaphysics* 28 (1975).

45 Laudan*, *The Demise of the Demarcation Problem,* in 2 Working Papers in Science and Technology 7 (R. Laudan* ed. 1983).

46 P. Feyerabend*, *Against Method: Outline of an Anarchistic Theory of Knowledge* 20-31, 49, 65, 68 (1978). Several reasons are given for using unconventional hypotheses: that evidence allegedly supporting the majority theory may be theory-contaminated while potentially refuting evidence may be improperly excluded, that no single interesting theory agrees with all known facts in its domain, that no idea has ever been examined in all its ramifications, that critical assessment of a prevailing theory can best be made from outside that theory, and that criticism based on abandoned explanations has often led to innovative developments. *Id.*

47 *Id.* at 304.

48 Section 9.4(b).

49 Section 9.5(c).

50 Laudan*, *The Demise of the Demarcation Problem,* in 2 Working Papers in Science and Technology 7, 27 (R. Laudan* ed. 1983) ("Similarly, cognitive progress is not unique to the 'sciences.' Many disciplines (e.g., literary criticism, military strategy, and perhaps even philosophy) can claim to know more about their respective domains than they did 50 or 100 years ago. By contrast, we can point to several 'sciences' which, during certain periods of their history, exhibited little or no progress. Continuous, or even sporadic, cognitive growth seems neither a necessary nor a sufficient condition for the activities we regard as scientific."). Finally, the majority of philosophers have rejected proposed requirements for well testedness, high rates of growth, success of predictions, and consilience of inductions. *Id.* at 28.

51 Note 7.

52 Note 11.

53 Note 19.

54 Klemke*, *Introduction,* in Introductory Readings in the Philosophy of Science 11, 16 (E. Klemke*, R. Hollinger* & A. Kline* eds. 1980) (italics added).

55 *E.g.,* R. Oram* *et al.*, *Biology: Living Systems* 23-31 (1979); A. Kluge*, *Chordate Structure and Function* 1 (2d ed. 1977).

56 P. Medawar*, *Induction and Intuition in Scientific Thought* vii (1969).

[57] I. Lakatos*, *The Methodology of Scientific Research Programmes* 2-3 (J. Worrall* & G. Currie* eds. 1978) ("One can today easily demonstrate that there can be no valid derivation of a law of nature from any finite number of facts; but we still keep reading about scientific theories being proved from facts. Why this stubborn resistance to elementary logic?").

[58] Laudan*, *The Demise of the Demarcation Problem*, in 2 Working Papers in Science and Technology 7, 15 (R. Laudan* ed. 1983) ("At first blush, this program of identifying science with a certain technique of inquiry is not a silly one; indeed, it still persists in some circles even in our time.").

[59] *See* Eldredge* & Gould*, *Punctuated Equilibria: An Alternative to Phyletic Gradualism*, in Models in Paleobiology at 82, 85 (J. Schopf* ed. 1972) ("(1) We do not encounter facts as data (literally "given") discovered objectively. All observation is colored by theory and expectation . . .. (2) Theory does not develop as a simple and logical extension of observation; it does not arise merely from the patient accumulation of facts.").

[60] A. Whitehead*, *The Function of Reason* 60 (1929).

[61] C. Hempel*, *Philosophy of Natural Science* 13, 15 (1966) (italics added, original italics deleted).

[62] Cannon*, *The Bases of Darwin's Achievement: A Revaluation*, 5 Victorian Studies 109, 134 (1961) (italics added).

[63] McLean v. Arkansas Bd. of Educ., 529 F. Supp. 1255, 1267 (E. D. Ark. 1982).

[64] Ruse*, *Creation-Science Is Not Science*, in Science, Technology & Human Values, Fall 1982, at 19 (italics in original except penultimate italics).

[65] Gross*, *Commentary: Philosophers at the Bar—Some Reasons for Restraint*, in Science, Technology & Human Values, Fall 1983, at 30, 36.

[66] Laudan* writes:

> [S]everal scientists and philosophers have *opportunistically suspended their usual critical faculties* in order to act as if the demarcation between science and non-science is virtually unproblematic. As Henry Bauer's studies of Velikovsky and the Loch Ness Monster graphically illustrate, the idea seems to be that if one is dealing with a 'crank,' or even with the general public, one can expediently ignore the problematicity of the distinction and haul out whatever dogmatic obiter dicta about science are convenient for imposing a preferred solution on the situation. (Witness further the *unconscionable behavior of many recent critics of 'creation science*,' whose testimony persuaded a federal judge that we know what 'the essential characteristics of science' are.) . . .

Laudan*, *The Demise of the Demarcation Problem*, in 2 Working Papers in Science and Technology 7, 30-31 (R. Laudan* ed. 1983) (italics added).

[67] Laudan*, *Commentary: Science at the Bar—Causes for Concern*, Science, Technology & Human Values, Fall 1982, at 16, 19.

[68] *Id.* (italics added).

[69] Laudan*, *More on Creationism*, in Science, Technology & Human

Values, Winter 1983, at 36, 37 (italics added). Laudan* is not correct in accepting the definition of "creation-science" from the *McLean* decision.

Laudan* also states that the "invocation of such labels as 'scientific' or 'unscientific' runs the grave risk of intellectual dishonesty—unless it is made quite clear that such labels are nothing more than short-hand allusions to a thorough epistemic critique of the doctrines so labelled." *Id.*

70 Quinn*, *The Philosopher of Science as Expert Witness*, in Science and Reality: Recent Work in the Philosophy of Science 32, 42, 50 (J. Cushing*, C. Delaney* & G. Gutting* eds. 1984) (italics added).

71 *Id.* at 42.

72 Quinn*, *The Philosopher of Science as Expert Witness*, in Science and Reality: Recent Work in the Philosophy of Science 32, 51 (J. Cushing*, C. Delaney* & G. Gutting* eds. 1984) (italics added).

73 Gross*, *Commentary: Philosophers at the Bar—Some Reasons for Restraint*, in Science, Technology & Human Values, Fall 1983, at 30, 36. However, he turns around and defends the five criteria on pragmatic and tactical grounds. *Id.*

74 Laudan*, *More on Creationism*, Science, Technology & Human Values, Winter 1983, at 36, 37.

75 Gross*, *Commentary: Philosophers at the Bar—Some Reasons for Restraint*, in Science, Technology & Human Values, Fall 1983, at 30, 36.

76 Quinn*, *The Philosopher of Science as Expert Witness*, in Science and Reality: Recent Work in the Philosophy of Science 32, 40 (J. Cushing*, C. Delaney* & G. Gutting* eds. 1984).

77 Ruse*, *Creation-Science Is Not Science*, in Creationism, Science, and the Law 150, 151 (M. LaFollette* ed. 1983).

78 Kim*, *Explanation in Science*, 3 Encyclopedia of Philosophy 159, 159 (P. Edwards* ed. 1967).

79 Bacon, *A Confession of Faith*, in 7 Works of Francis Bacon 221 (J. Spalding* ed. 1858-74).

80 Laudan*, *Commentary: Science at the Bar—Causes for Concern*, Science, Technology & Human Values, Fall 1982, at 16, 17-18 (italics added).

81 Quinn*, *The Philosopher of Science as Expert Witness*, in Science and Reality: Recent Work in the Philosophy of Science 32, 47 (J. Cushing*, C. Delaney* & G. Gutting* eds. 1984).

82 H. Reichenbach*, *Experience and Prediction* 6-7, 382-84 (1938); F. Suppe*, *The Search for Philosophic Understanding of Scientific Theory*, in The Structure of Scientific Theories 1, 125 (1974) (Hans Reichenbach's* widely quoted distinction between the "context of discovery" and the "context of justification").

83 Quinn*, *The Philosopher of Science as Expert Witness*, in Science and Reality: Recent Work in the Philosophy of Science 32, 42 (J. Cushing*, C. Delaney* & G. Gutting* eds. 1984) ("scientists have for a long time understood the difference between establishing the existence of phenomena and explaining them by natural laws").

[84] Laudan*, *Commentary: Science at the Bar—Causes for Concern*, Science, Technology & Human Values, Fall 1982, at 16, 17-18 (italics added).

[85] Quinn*, *The Philosopher of Science as Expert Witness*, in Science and Reality: Recent Work in the Philosophy of Science 32, 43 (J. Cushing*, C. Delaney* & G. Gutting* eds. 1984) (italics added).

[86] *Id.* at 42. *See also* Section 10.3 (b).

[87] Walters*, *Laws of Science and Lawlike Statements*, 4 Encyclopedia of Philosophy 410, 411 (P. Edwards* ed. 1967) (italics added).

[88] L. Buchner*, *Force and Matter* (P. Eckler* trans. 1891).

[89] Provine*, *Implications of Darwin's Ideas on the Study of Evolution*, 32 BioScience 501, 506 (1982) ("Here are the implications of this mechanistic view of life as I see them. First, except for purely mechanistic ones, no organizing or purposive principles exist in the world. There are no gods and no designing forces. The frequently made assertion that modern biology and the assumptions of the Judeo-Christian tradition are fully compatible is false. Second, there exist no inherent moral or ethical laws, no absolute guiding principles for human society.").

[90] Mayr*, *The Nature of the Darwinian Revolution*, 176 Science 981, 988 (1972) (" The natural causes postulated by the evolutionists completely separated God from his creation, for all practical purposes. The new explanatory model replaced planned teleology by the haphazard process of natural selection. This required a new concept of God and a new basis for religion. . . . It is now clear why the Darwinian revolution is so different from all other scientific revolutions. It required not merely the replacement of one scientific theory by a new one, but, in fact, the rejection of at least six widely held basic beliefs . . ..").

[91] G. Chesterton, *Orthodoxy* 68 (1908) ("If a man believes in an unalterable natural law, he cannot believe in any miracle in any age."). This is further discussed in Section 13.3.

The argument that science and theology or metaphysics are mutually exclusive realms, so that scientific conclusions can have no implications for theology or metaphysics, is rejected by most scientists and is based on a particular theology (NeoOrthodoxy and other existential theology). Section 13.3(b).

[92] In other words, science cannot properly conclude either that nonnaturalistic causes or phenomena never occur *or* always are responsible for events, although it can properly prefer explanation by law and can properly decide for particular events which explanation is more plausible (natural laws or nonnaturalistic causes or phenomena). This discussion does not equate nonnaturalistic events with miracles, but recognizes that categories of nonnaturalistic events exist other than miracles.

[93] S. Jaki*, *Cosmos and Creator* (1982) (Einstein* said science must be resigned to recognize nonnaturalistic events even though it cannot study their cause further).

[94] Letter from Dr. Wernher von Braun to Dr. Vernon Grose (Sept. 14, 1972)

(Braun was Director of NASA's Marshall Space Flight Center and a creationist physicist) (italics added). Macbeth* makes a similar observation:

> Therefore it is important to note how [G.G. Simpson] excludes design as a matter of scientific principle and method: "... the progress of knowledge rigidly requires that no non-physical postulate ever be admitted in connection with the study of physical phenomena. We do not know what is and what is not explicable in physical terms, and the researcher who is seeking explanations must seek physical explanations only. . . . " If a Watchmaker is thus carefully excluded at the beginning, we need not be surprised if no Watchmaker appears at the end. The dice have been loaded against him.

N. Macbeth*, *Darwin Retried* 126 (1971), quoting G. Simpson*, *Tempo and Mode in Evolution* 76 (1944). *See also* G. Simpson*, *This View of Life* 131 (1964).

95 Jastrow* states:

> [Scientists] believe that every event that takes place in the world can be explained in a rational way as the consequence of some previous event. If there is a *religion in science*, this statement can be regarded as its main article of *faith*.

R. Jastrow*, *Until the Sun Dies* 11 (1977) (italics added).

96 Quinn*, *The Philosopher of Science as Expert Witness*, in Science and Reality: Recent Work in the Philosophy of Science 32, 42-43 (J. Cushing*, C. Delaney* & G. Gutting* eds. 1984).

97 Jastrow*, *The Astronomer and God*, in The Intellectuals Speak Out About God 15, 19 (R. Varghese* ed.) (1984) (italics deleted). However, non-naturalistic forces need not be supernatural.

98 R. Jastrow*, *God and the Astronomers* 11 (1978).

99 H. Pagels*, *Perfect Symmetry: The Search for the Beginning of Time* 338 (1985).

100 Hawking*, *The edge of spacetime*, New Scientist, Aug. 16, 1984, at 10, 13 ("This showed that singularities *could* occur in general solutions of general relativity but it did not answer the question of whether they necessarily *would* occur. However, between 1965 and 1970, physicists proved several theorems which showed that any model of the Universe which obeyed general relativity, satisfied one or two other reasonable assumptions and contained as much matter as we observe in the Universe, must have a big-bang singularity.") (italics in original).

101 Weisskopf*, *The Origin of the Universe*, 71 Am. Scientist 473, 476 (1983).

102 J. Silk*, *The Big Bang* 322-24 (1979).

103 R. Wald*, *Space, Time and Gravity: The Theory of the Big Bang* 51 (1971).

104 Guth* & Steinhardt*, *The Inflationary Universe*, Scientific Am., May 1984, at 116, 128.

105 Section 10.2(a).

[106] Section 10.3.

[107] T. Dobzhansky*, *The Biology of Ultimate Concern* 46, 46 (1967).

[108] Hull*, *Thermodynamics and Kinetics of Spontaneous Generation*, 186 Nature 693, 694 (1960).

[109] C. Sagan*, *Cosmos* 260 (1980).

[110] Leslie*, *Cosmology, Probability, and the Need To Explain Life*, in Scientific Explanation and Understanding 53, 54, 58 (N. Rescher* ed. 1983) ("The hypothesis, remember, is that laws and/or initial conditions (a distinction which may be hard to draw) vary from universe to universe.").

[111] Patton* & Wheeler*, *Is Physics Legislated by Cosmogony*, in Quantum Gravity: An Oxford Symposium 538 (C. Isham* ed. 1974) (Oxford U. Press).

[112] R. Jastrow*, *God and the Astronomers* 113-14 (1978) ("the world had a beginning under conditions in which the known laws of physics are not valid").

[113] Weisskopf*, *The Origin of the Universe*, 71 Am. Scientist 473, 479 (1983) ("not know at all what the laws of nature were").

[114] Barrow* & Silk*, *The Structure of the Early Universe*, Scientific Am., Apr. 1980, at 118, 118 ("unfamiliar physical principles").

[115] A. Whitehead*, *Science and the Modern World* 18 (1925).

[116] A. Einstein*, *Essays in Science* 11 (1955). *See also* A. Einstein*, *Lettres a' Maurice Solovine* 114 (1956) ("I regard the intelligibility of the world (in the measure that we are authorized to speak of such an intelligibility) as a miracle or an eternal mystery."); Frank*, *Einstein, Mach, and Logical Positivism*, in 1 Albert Einstein: Philosopher-Scientist 269, 285 (P. Schilpp* ed. 1959) (Einstein* said "To this [sphere of religion] there also belongs the *faith* in the possibility that the regulations valid for the world of existence are rational, that it is comprehensible to reason. I cannot conceive of a genuine scientist without that profound *faith*.")

[117] Kaufman*, *Luminous Reputations*, Science Digest, Jan. 1981, at 8, 8 ("Like most scientists, Einstein included, I have an almost religious belief in a basic underlying order—a belief that natural forces are just manifestations of some deeper thing.").

[118] Fitch*, *The Challenges to Darwinism Since the Late Centennial and the Impact of Molecular Studies*, 36 Evolution 1138-39 (1982).

[119] Gould*, *Toward the Vindication of Punctuational Change*, in Catastrophes and Earth History: The New Uniformitarianism 9, 11 (W. Berggren* & J. Van Couvering* eds. 1984).

[120] E. Wigner*, *The Unreasonable Effectiveness of Mathematics in the Natural Sciences*, 13 Communications in Pure and Applied Mathematics 227 (1960).

[121] Taylor*, *A Scientist Questions The Philosophers*, 35 Thought 255 (1960) ("The existence and nature of reality as it is given and as the scientist sees it cannot but prompt further discussion of the old philosophical question of the nature of reality. The very possibility of science, of that concordance which becomes obvious through science, between our thoughts and

nature, is not a scientific question but a philosophical one. All scientific demonstrations presuppose the existence of science and that about which the science is. Thus the very existence of science calls for metaphysical explanation.").

122 *The Development of American Philosophy* 333 (W. Muelder* & L. Sears* eds. 1940) ("The special *sciences* are obliged to take for granted a number of most important propositions, because their ways of working afford no means of bringing these propositions to the test. In short, they always *rest upon metaphysics*.") (italics added).

123 E. Milne*, *Modern Cosmology and the Christian Idea* (1952).

124 S. Jaki*, *Science and Creation* viii (1974).

125 A. Whitehead*, *Science and the Modern World* 12-13 (1925).

126 Feuer*, *Noumenalism and Einstein's Argument for the Existence of God*, 26 Inquiry 251, 259 (1983).

127 Foster*, *The Christian Doctrine of Creation and the Rise of Modern Natural Science*, 43 Mind 446, 448, 453, 465 (1934).

128 L. Gilkey*, *Maker of Heaven and Earth* 110 (1959).

129 *E.g.*, *The Intellectuals Speak Out About God* (R. Varghese* ed. 1984).

130 A. Einstein*, *Essays in Science* 11 (1955) (he was pantheistic).

131 N. Gillespie*, *Charles Darwin and the Problem of Creation* 3 (1979) (U. of Chicago Press) (italics added).

132 Caudill, *Law and Worldview: Problems in the Creation-Science Controversy*, 3 J. Law & Religion 1, 44 (1985) (discontinuitist author).

133 Abbagnano*, *Positivism*, 6 Encyclopedia of Philosophy 414, 414 (P. Edwards* ed. 1967).

134 Feigl*, *Positivism and Logical Empiricism*, 14 Encyclopaedia Britannica: Macropaedia 877, 877 (15th ed. 1974).

135 Carlson*, *Science and the Supernatural*, 73 Science 217, 218-19 (1931) ("What is the method of science? In essence it is this—the rejection in toto of all non-observational and non-experimental authority in the field of experience.... The scientist tries to rid himself of all faiths and beliefs. He either knows or he does not know. If he knows, there is no room for faith or belief. If he does not know, he has no right to faith or belief.").

136 Passmore*, *Logical Positivism*, 5 Encyclopedia of Philosophy 52 (P. Edwards* ed. 1967). Positivism is further discussed in Section 13.5.

137 Abbagnano*, *Positivism*, 6 Encyclopedia of Philosophy 414, 415 (P. Edwards* ed. 1967) (italics added).

138 N. Gillespie*, *Charles Darwin and the Problem of Creation* 3 (1979).

139 Philosopher John Greene* notes the following:

> A final ingredient in the world view that came to be called *Darwinism* was the stream of Lockean epistemology and sensationalist psychology that ran strong in the English-speaking world and taught all whom it influenced to reject notions of innate ideas, intuition, and the like and to rely upon *sense experience* as the source of all knowledge. In the nineteenth century this intellectual tendency was powerfully reinforced and

given new expression by a growing *positivistic faith* in the methods of natural science as man's sole means of gaining knowledge of reality. Since science was increasingly conceived as the search for the laws governing the phenomena presented in sense experience, the hope of discovering or knowing a reality behind the veil of sense experience diminished as the prestige of science grew. Positivism led to agnosticism.

J. Greene*, *Science, Ideology, and World View* 133 (1981) (italics added).

[140] Campbell*, *Materialism*, 5 Encyclopedia of Philosophy 179, 179 (P. Edwards* ed. 1967).

[141] Wilshire*, *Metaphysics*, 12 Encyclopaedia Britannica: Macropaedia 10, 26 (15th ed. 1974) (italics added).

[142] Danto*, *Naturalism*, 5 Encyclopedia of Philosophy 448, 448 (P. Edwards* ed. 1967) (italics added).

[143] *See* Abbagnano*, *Positivism*, 6 Encyclopedia of Philosophy 414 (P. Edwards* ed. 1967); Passmore*, *Logical Positivism*, 5 *id.* 52.

[144] Ewing*, *Meaninglessness*, in 5 Encyclopedia of Philosophy 705 (P. Edwards* ed. 1972); A. Ewing*, *The Fundamental Questions of Philosophy* 44-47 (1962).

[145] A. Whitehead*, *The Function of Reason* 53-54, 58-59 (1929) (italics added).

[146] *See* W. Salmon*, *The Foundation of Scientific Inference* 5-56 (1967) (summary of problem of induction and proposed solutions).

[147] Passmore*, *Logical Positivism*, 5 Encyclopedia of Philosophy 52, 55 (P. Edwards* ed. 1967) (italics added).

[148] *Id.* at 54-55 (italics added).

[149] *Id.* at 55 (italics added).

[150] Adorno*, *Introduction*, to The Positivist Dispute in German Sociology 58 (1976).

[151] *See* L. Laudan*, *Progress and Its Problems* 132 (1977)("Far from viewing the introduction of philosophical, religious and moral issues into science as the triumph of prejudice, superstition and irrationality, this model claims that the presence of such elements may be entirely rational; further, that the suppression of such elements may itself be irrational and prejudicial.").

[152] Section 9.4(a)(2).

[153] Quoted in S. Jaki*, *Cosmos and Creator* 53 (1982).

[154] Gunderson*, *Descartes, La Mettrie, Language and Machines*, 39 Philosophy 193 (1964).

[155] Campbell*, *Materialism*, 5 Encyclopedia of Philosophy 179, 186 (P. Edwards* ed. 1967) (italics in original).

[155A] R. Collingwood*, *The Idea of Nature* 105 (1945) (Oxford U. Press).

[156] F. Paulsen*, *An Introduction to Philosophy* (F. Thilly* trans. 1895).

[157] Campbell*, *Materialism*, 5 Encyclopedia of Philosophy 179, 187 (P. Edwards* ed. 1967) (italics in original).

[158] C. Ducasse*, *Nature, Mind and Death* (1951).

159 Campbell*, *Materialism*, 5 Encyclopedia of Philosophy 179, 187 (P. Edwards* ed. 1967) (italics in original).
160 *E.g.*, Bouwsma*, *Naturalism*, 45 J. Philosophy 12 (1948); Aiken*, *Notes on the Categories and Naturalism*, 43 J. Philosophy 517 (1946); Murphy*, *Book Review of Naturalism and the Human Spirit*, 42 J. Philosophy 400 (1945).
161 Quinn*, *The Philosopher of Science as Expert Witness*, in Science and Reality: Recent Work in the Philosophy of Science 32, 43 (J. Cushing*, C. Delaney* & G. Gutting* eds. 1984).
162 Note 80.
163 Note 84.
164 Note 85.
165 Note 87.
166 Note 96.
167 Note 97.
168 Note 99.
169 Note 109.
170 Note 115.
171 Note 120.
172 Note 138.
173 Note 143.
174 *E.g.*, Ayala*, *Scientific hypotheses, natural selection and the neutrality theory of protein evolution*, in The Role of Natural Selection in Human Evolution 19, 19-20 (F. Salzano* ed. 1975) (geneticist).
175 1 I. Lakatos*, *The Methodology of Scientific Research Programmes* 65, 105 (J. Worrall* & G. Currie* eds. 1978) (italics added). *See also id.* at 6 ("The history of science refutes both Popper and Kuhn: on close inspection both Popperian crucial experiments and Kuhnian revolutions turn out to be myths: what normally happens is that progressive research programmes replace degenerating ones.").
176 Quinn*, *The Philosopher of Science as Expert Witness*, in Science and Reality: Recent Work in the Philosophy of Science 32, 43 (J. Cushing*, C. Delaney* & G. Gutting* eds. 1984).
177 Kuhn*, *Logic of Discovery or Psychology of Research?*, in Criticism and the Growth of Knowledge 1, 10 (I. Lakatos* & A. Musgrave* eds. 1970).
178 Riddiford* & Penny*, *The scientific status of modern evolutionary theory*, in Evolutionary Theory: Paths into the Future 1, 32 (J. Pollard* ed. 1984) (suggesting instead, "It is predictions that can be tested rather than the theories themselves.").
179 Laudan*, *Commentary: Science at the Bar—Causes for Concern*, Science, Technology & Human Values, Fall 1982, at 16,17 ("It is now widely acknowledged that many scientific claims are not testable in isolation, but only when imbedded in a larger system of statements, some of whose consequences can be submitted to test.").
180 1 I. Lakatos*, *The Methodology of Scientific Research Programmes* 144 (J. Worrall* & G. Currie* eds. 1978).

[181] Section 10.3(b).
[182] Quinn*, *The Philosopher of Science as Expert Witness*, in Science and Reality: Recent Work in the Philosophy of Science 32, 43 (J. Cushing*, C. Delaney* & G. Gutting* eds. 1984).
[183] Section 10.3(b).
[184] S. Amsterdamski*, *Between Experience and Metaphysics* 26 (1975).
[185] *Id.* at 31.
[186] "Falsifiability" is "refutability, or testability." Popper*, *Science: Conjectures and Refutations*, in Introductory Readings in the Philosophy of Science 23 (E. Klemke*, R. Hollinger* & A. Kline* eds. 1980).
[187] *Id.* at 22 (italics added). *See also* F. Ayala* & J. Valentine*, *Evolving: The Theory and Processes of Organic Evolution* 3 (1979) ("testing by attempted falsification"); T. Dobzhansky*, F. Ayala*, G. Stebbins* & J. Valentine*, *Evolution* 476 (1977).
[188] Ruse*, *Creation-Science Is Not Science*, in Creationism, Science, and the Law: The Arkansas Case 150, 152 (M. LaFollette* ed. 1983).
[189] 1 I. Lakatos*, *The Methodology of Scientific Research Programmes* 3-4, 30 (J. Worrall* & G. Currie* eds. 1978).
[190] Quine*, *Two Dogmas of Empiricism*, in From a Logical Point of View 20-46 (W. Quine* ed. 1963).
[191] He writes:

> But Sir Karl describes as 'falsification' or 'refutation' what happens when a theory fails in attempted application, and these are the first of a series of related locutions that again strike me as *extremely odd*. Both 'falsification' and 'refutation' are antonyms of 'proof'. They are drawn principally from logic and from formal mathematics; the chains of argument to which they apply end with a 'Q.E.D.'; invoking these terms implies the ability to compel assent from any member of the relevant professional community. No member of this audience, however, still needs to be told that, where a whole theory or often even a scientific law is at stake, *arguments are seldom so apodictic. All experiments can be challenged*, either as to their relevance or their accuracy. *All theories can be modified* by a variety of *ad hoc* adjustments without ceasing to be, in their main lines, the same theories.

Kuhn*, *Logic of Discovery or Psychology of Research?*, in Criticism and the Growth of Knowledge 1, 13 (I. Lakatos* & A. Musgrave* eds. 1970) (italics added).
[192] Laudan*, *The Demise of the Demarcation Problem*, in 2 Working Papers in Science and Technology 7, 23 (R. Laudan* ed. 1983). He states about the *McLean* decision:

> It simply will not do for the defenders of science to invoke philosophy of science when it suits them (e.g., their much-loved principle of falsifiability comes directly from the philosopher Karl Popper) and to dismiss it as "arcane" and "remote" when it does not. However noble the motivation, bad philosophy makes for bad law.

Laudan*, *Commentary: Science at the Bar—Causes for Concern*, Science,

Technology & Human Values, Fall 1982, at 16, 19.

193 Quinn*, *The Philosopher of Science as Expert Witness*, in Science and Reality: Recent Work in the Philosophy of Science 32, 42 (J. Cushing*, C. Delaney* & G. Gutting* eds. 1984).

194 Ruse*, *A Philosopher at the Monkey Trial*, 93 New Scientist 317, 319 (1982) ("I myself am not really that keen on falsifiability as a mark of science in the first place."). Ruse* also concedes that "[s]imple criteria that supposedly give a clear answer to every case—for example, Popper's single stipulation of falsifiability—will not do." Ruse*, *Response*, in Science, Technology & Human Values, Fall 1982, at 19, 20.

195 Sparkes*, *What is this thing called science?*, 89 New Scientist 156, 157 (1981).

196 Riddiford* & Penny*, *The scientific status of modern evolutionary theory*, in Evolutionary Theory: Paths into the Future 1, 10 (J. Pollard* ed. 1984) ("The major criticism of Popper's work is that Popper fails to describe how scientists actually work. Kuhn (1970), Lakatos (1970, 1974, 1976), and Feyerabend (1970a, 1970b, 1975) are some of the authors . . .."); *id.* at 14 ("We do not accept the criterion that a theory must be directly falsifiable. In its place we propose to use the ability of a theory to lead to testable predictions as the criterion of a theory's scientific adequacy."); Hull*, *Karl Popper and Plato's Metaphor*, in 2 Advances in Cladistics 177, 189 (N. Platnick* & V. Funk* eds. 1983).

197 1 I. Lakatos*, *The Methodology of Scientific Research Programmes* 3-4 (J. Worrall* & G. Currie* eds. 1978) (italics added). *See also id.* at 30 ("Their *falsification* as it occurs in actual history is prima facie irrational by the standards of our falsificationist. By his standards, *scientists frequently seem to be irrationally slow*: for instance, eighty-five years elapsed between the acceptance of the perihelion of Mercury as an anomaly and its acceptance as a falsification of Newton's theory, in spite of the fact that the ceteris paribus clause was reasonably well corroborated. On the other hand, scientists frequently seem to be irrationally rash; for instance, ...") (italics added).

198 M. Polanyi*, *Science, Faith and Society* 11 (1946).

199 Riddiford* & Penny*, *The scientific status of modern evolutionary theory*, in Evolutionary Theory: Paths into the Future 1, 10 (J. Pollard* ed. 1984).

200 Sparkes*, *What is this thing called science?*, 89 New Scientist 156, 156 (1981) (italics in original).

201 R. Harré*, *The Philosophies of Science: An Introductory Survey* 50 (1972). When a scientific concept is partially falsified, it need not be and historically has not been abandoned, but instead has been modified, as discussed in Section 9.6.

202 Quinton*, *Karl Raimund Popper*, in 6 Encyclopedia of Philosophy 398, 399 (1972); W. Salmon*, *The Foundation of Scientific Inference* 26-27 (1967).

203 He says:

The basic unit of appraisal must not be an isolated theory or conjunction of theories but rather a "research programme" with a conventionally accepted (and thus by provisional decision "irrefutable") "hard core" and with a "positive heuristic" which defines problems, outlines the construction of a belt of auxiliary hypotheses, forsees anomalies and turns them victoriously into examples, all according to a preconceived plan.

Lakatos*, *History of Science and Its Rational Reconstructions*, in Method and Appraisal in the Physical Sciences 9 (C. Hawson* ed. 1976) (Cambridge U. Press).

[204] Kuhn*, *Logic of Discovery or Psychology of Research?*, in Criticism and the Growth of Knowledge 13 (I. Lakatos* & A. Musgrave* eds. 1970).

[205] Laudan*, *The Demise of the Demarcation Problem*, in 2 Working Papers in Science and Technology 7, 23 (R. Laudan* ed. 1983).

[206] S. Amsterdamski*, *Between Experience and Metaphysics* 27 (1975).

[207] G. Holton*, *Thematic Origins of Scientific Thought: Kepler to Einstein* 29, 63 (1973).

[208] Quinn*, *The Philosopher of Science as Expert Witness*, in Science and Reality: Recent Work in the Philosophy of Science 32, 43 (J. Cushing*, C. Delaney* & G. Gutting* eds. 1984) ("many scientific statements are neither testable nor falsifiable individually and in isolation but only conjunctively").

[209] S. Amsterdamski*, *Between Experience and Metaphysics* 27 (1975).

[210] Section 10.4(b).

[211] Popper*, *Intellectual Autobiography*, in 2 The Philosophy of Karl Popper 3, 134, 137 (P. Schilpp* ed. 1974). Although Popper* has "changed [his] mind about the testability and the logical status of the theory of natural selection," Popper*, *Natural Selection and the Emergence of Mind*, 32 Dialectica 339, 344-45 (1978), he has not published any change in his conclusions about other aspects of Darwinian evolution. *See* ch. 10, notes 19-20, 306.

[212] Sparkes*, *What is this thing called science?*, 89 New Scientist 156, 157 (1981) (italics added).

[213] S. Amsterdamski*, *Between Experience and Metaphysics* 27 (1975).

[214] Note 176.

[215] Note 177.

[216] Section 10.3 (b)

[217] Note 178.

[218] Note 200.

[219] Note 205.

[220] Note 212.

[221] Sections 10.3 & 10.4.

[222] Quinn*, *The Philosopher of Science as Expert Witness*, in Science and Reality: Recent Work in the Philosophy of Science 32, 48 (J. Cushing*, C. Delaney* & G. Gutting* eds. 1984).

[223] 1 I. Lakatos*, *The Methodology of Scientific Research Programmes* 89-90 (J. Worrall* & G. Currie* eds. 1978) (italics added).

[224] T. Kuhn*, *The Structure of Scientific Revolutions* 5 (2d ed. 1970).

225 He states:

> But historical and sociological researches on science strongly suggest that the *scientists of any epoch likewise regard some of their beliefs as so fundamental as not to be open to repudiation or negotiation.* Would Newton, for instance, have been tentative about the claim that there were forces in the world? Are quantum mechanicians willing to contemplate giving up the uncertainty relation? Are physicists willing to specify circumstances under which they would give up energy conservation? Numerous historians and philosophers of science (e.g., Kuhn, Mitroff, Feyerabend, Lakatos) have documented the existence of a certain degree of dogmatism about core commitments in scientific research and have argued that such dogmatism plays a constructive role in promoting the aims of science. . . . [O]ne does not even begin to get at those differences by pretending that science is characterized by an uncompromising open-mindedness.

Laudan*, *Commentary, Science at the Bar—Causes for Concern*, Science, Technology & Human Values, Fall 1982, at 16, 17 (italics added). Kuhn's* position is the same:

> The dogmatic attitude in science—which would explain its stable periods—was described by Kuhn as a prime feature of "normal science."

1 I. Lakatos*, *The Methodology of Scientific Research Programmes* 90 (J. Worrall* & G. Currie* eds. 1978).

226 G. Kerkut*, *Implications of Evolution* viii (1960) ("It is very depressing to find that many subjects are becoming encased in scientific *dogmatism.* The basic information is frequently overlooked or ignored and opinions become repeated so often and so loudly that they take on the tone of Laws.") (italics added).

227 Opik*, *About Dogma in Science, and Other Recollections of an Astronomer*, 15 Ann. Rev. Astronomy & Astrophysics 1, 5 (1977).

228 Ruse*, *Falsifiability, Concilience and Systematics*, 28 Systematic Zoology 530, 531 (1979) (italics added).

229 1 I. Lakatos*, *The Methodology of Scientific Research Programmes* 48 (J. Worrall* & G. Currie* eds. 1978) ("Instead, we must use our ingenuity to articulate or even invent '*auxiliary* hypotheses', which form a protective belt around this core, and we must redirect the modus tollens to these. It is this protective belt of auxiliary hypotheses which has to bear the brunt of tests and get adjusted and re-adjusted, or even completely replaced, to defend the thus-hardened core.") (italics added).

230 Opik*, *About Dogma in Science, and Other Recollections of an Astronomer*, 15 Ann. Rev. Astronomy & Astrophysics 1, 5 (1977) (italics added).

231 Raup*, *The Geological and Paleontological Arguments of Creationism*, in Scientists Confront Creationism 147, 159 (L. Godfrey* ed. 1983).

232 Laudan*, *Commentary: Science at the Bar—Causes for Concern*, Science, Technology & Human Values, Fall 1982, at 16, 17 ("Even worse, the charge of dogmatism . . . egregiously *confuses doctrines with the proponents*

of those doctrines. . . . [I]t is quite irrelevant whether they themselves are closeminded.") (speaking of creationists).

[233] Section 14.3(b).

[234] Quinn*, *The Philosopher of Science as Expert Witness*, in Science and Reality: Recent Work in the Philosophy of Science 32, 44 (J. Cushing*, C. Delaney* & G. Gutting* eds. 1984) (italics added).

[235] Note 225.

[236] Note 223.

[237] Note 234.

[238] Section 10.5.

[239] Quinn*, *The Philosopher of Science as Expert Witness*, in Science and Reality: Recent Work in the Philosophy of Science 32, 51 (J. Cushing*, C. Delaney* & G. Gutting* eds. 1984) (italics added).

[240] Laudan*, *Commentary: Science at the Bar—Causes for Concern*, Science, Technology & Human Values, Fall 1982, at 16, 19. *See also* Quinn*, *The Philosopher of Science as Expert Witness*, in Science and Reality: Recent Work in the Philosophy of Science 32, 50 (J. Cushing*, C. Delaney* & G. Gutting* eds. 1984) ("Scientists and their friends should derive little comfort from the outcome of McLean v. Arkansas. Victory was indeed achieved at the wholly unneccessary 'expense of perpetuating and canonizing a false stereotype of what science is and how it works.' ").

[241] Kuhn*, *Second Thoughts on Paradigms*, in The Structure of Scientific Theories 459, 461-62 (F. Suppe* 2d ed. 1977).

[242] Reingold*, *Definitions and Speculations: The Professionalization of Science in America in the Nineteenth Century*, in The Pursuit of Knowledge in the Early American Republic: American Scientific and Learned Societies 36 (A. Oleson* & S. Brown* eds. 1976).

[243] L. Margolis*, *The Origin of Eukaryotic Cells* (1970)

[244] Brady*, *Natural Selection and the Criteria by Which a Theory Is Judged*, 28 Systematic Zoology 600, 617 (1979).

[245] Feyerabend*, *The Expert as Con Man*, 92 Science Digest 83 (1983).

[246] Bartels*, *Commentary: It's Good Enough for Science, but Is It Good Enough for Social Action?*, Science, Technology & Human Values, Fall 1985, at 69, 72-73 (italics added).

[247] G. Kerkut*, *Implications of Evolution* 157 (1960) (italics added).

[248] K. Popper*, *Objective Knowledge* 266 (1972).

[249] E. Radl*, *The History of Biological Theories* (1930).

[250] Rosen*, *Book Review*, 27 Systematic Zoology 370, 371 (1978).

[251] P. Bridgman*, *The Way Things Are* 129 (1959).

[252] Jaki*, *The Case for Galileo's Rehabilitation*, Fidelity, Mar. 1986, at 37, 40-41.

[253] Eldredge* & Gould*, *Punctuated Equilibria: An Alternative to Phyletic Gradualism*, in Models in Paleobiology 82, 83 (J. Schopf* ed. 1972).

[254] 2 *More Letters of Charles Darwin* 323 (F. Darwin* ed. 1903).

[255] J. Robinson*, *Early Hominid Posture and Locomotion* 212 (1972)("The

conceptual framework within which a student works shapes the viewpoint from which he approaches the material being studied and *powerfully influences the conclusions* that he draws.") (italics added).

[256] T. Kuhn*, *The Structure of Scientific Revolutions* 97 (2d ed. 1970) ("Paradigms provide all phenomena except anomalies with a theory determined place in the scientist's field of vision.").

[257] H. Hein*, *On the Nature and Origin of Life* 93 (1971) ("on the whole our metaphysical commitment has priority over our scientific and commonsense beliefs such that, if challenged, they will yield to it rather than the reverse.").

[258] Ruse*, *The New Dualism: "Res Philosophica" and "Res Historica,"* in Nature Animated 3, 13, 17 (M. Ruse* ed. 1983).

[259] Bohm*, *Some Remarks on the Notion of Order*, in 2 Towards a Theoretical Biology 41, 42 (C. Waddington* ed. 1969).

[260] Brady*, *Dogma and doubt*, 17 Biological J. Linnean Society 79, 79 (1982) (italics added).

[261] A. Solzhenitsyn, *A World Split Apart* (1979) (commencement address at Harvard University).

[262] T. Kuhn*, *The Structure of Scientific Revolutions* 5 (2d ed. 1970).

[263] Barber*, *Resistance by Scientists to Scientific Discovery*, 134 Science 596, 596, 597 (1961) (italics added, footnotes omitted).

[264] Dobzhansky*, *A Biologist's World View*, 175 Science 49, 49 (1972).

[265] W. Dampier-Whetham*, *A History of Science* 445 (1951) ("At the beginning of the twentieth century the majority of men of science held unconsciously a naive materialism"); N. Gillespie*, *Charles Darwin and the Problem of Creation* 155-56 (1979) (U. of Chicago Press) ("Darwin's progress toward positivism in science must have been duplicated in other scientists and scientifically inspired laymen: . . . to a general acceptance of *positivism* as a tool for such work and as a world view.") (italics added); *id.* at 9 ("the growth of positivism throughout science, during the period in question, [is] a historical given").

[266] Jaki*, *The Case for Galileo's Rehabilitation*, Fidelity, Mar. 1986, at 37, 40-41.

[267] F. Hoyle, *The Intelligent Universe* 238 (1983) ("the anticlerical bias of modern science"); Watkins*, *Against 'Normal Science'*, in Criticism and the Growth of Knowledge 33 (I. Lakatos* & A. Musgrave* eds. 1970) ("a significant parallelism between science, especially Normal Science, and theology").

[268] T. Kuhn*, *The Copernican Revolution* (1957) (Harvard U. Press).

[269] Barber*, *Resistance by Scientists to Scientific Discovery*, 134 Science 596, 597 (1961) (italics added except title, footnote omitted).

[270] Gould*, *The Continental Drift Affair*, Natural History, Feb. 1987, at 12, 12 (italics added).

[271] W. Broad* & N. Wade*, *Betrayers of the Truth: Fraud and Deceit in the Halls of Science* 134-35 (1982) (italics added).

[272] *The Velikovsky Affair: Scientism vs. Science* 1, 7 (A. de Grazia*, R. Juergens* & L. Stecchini* eds. 1966) (italics added).

[273] *Id.* at 26 (italics added).
[274] *Id.* at 46-47 (italics added except title).
[275] W. Stansfield*, *The Science of Evolution* 31 (1977).
[276] 1 I. Lakatos*, *The Methodology of Scientific Research Programmes* 7 (J. Worrall* & G. Currie* eds. 1978).
[277] D. Joravsky*, *The Lysenko Affair* (1970) (Harvard U. Press); Joravsky*, *The Lysenko Affair*, Scientific Am., Nov. 1962, at 41.
[278] L. Graham*, *Science and Philosophy in the Soviet Union* (1972).
[279] M. Popovsky*, *Manipulated Science: The Crisis of Science and Scientists in the Soviet Union Today* xiii (1979).
[280] Schwabe*, *On the validity of molecular evolution*, 11 Trends in Biochemical Sciences 280, 280 (1986).
[281] Brush, *Should the History of Science Be Rated X?*, 183 Science 1164, 1168 (1974).
[282] Gould*, *Toward the Vindication of Punctuational Change*, in Catastrophes and Earth History: The New Uniformitarianism 9, 15-16 (W. Berggren* & J. Van Couvering eds. 1984).
[283] W. Broad* & N. Wade*, *Betrayers of the Truth: Fraud and Deceit in the Halls of Science* 134, 136-37 (1982) (italics added).
[284] C. Patterson*, *Evolution* 150 (1977).
[285] Brady*, *Dogma and doubt*, 17 Biological J. Linnean Society 79, 95-96 (1982) (italics added).
[286] T. Dobzhansky*, *Evolutionary and Population Genetics*, 142 Science 1131, 1134 (1963) ("Its acceptance is nevertheless so wide that its opponents complain of inability to get a hearing for their views."); F. Hoyle, *The Intelligent Universe: A New View of Creation and Evolution* 25 (1983) (evolution is a "new dogma").
[287] Grene*, *The Faith of Darwinism*, Encounter, Nov. 1959, at 48, 48-49 (italics added).
[288] Lipson*, *A Physicist Looks at Evolution*, 31 Physics Bulletin 138, 138 (1980) ("In fact, evolution became in a sense a scientific religion; almost all scientists have accepted it and many are prepared to 'bend' their observations to fit in with it.").
[289] S. Jaki*, *Cosmos and Creator* 115 (1982) ("Darwinism is a creed not only with scientists committed to document the all-purpose role of natural selection. It is a creed with masses of people who have at best a vague notion of the mechanism of evolution as proposed by Darwin, let alone as further complicated by his successors.")
[290] M. Midgley*, *Evolution as a Religion* (1985).
[291] N. Macbeth*, *Darwin Retried* 126-27 (1971).
[292] E. Conklin*, *Man Real and Ideal* 147 (1943) ("The concept of organic evolution is very highly prized by biologists, for many of whom it is an object of genuinely religious devotion, because they regard it as a supreme integrative principle. This is probably the reason why severe methodological criticism employed in other departments of biology has not yet been brought to bear on evolutionary speculation.").

293 G. Hardin*, *Nature and Man's Fate* 216 (1961).
294 Saunders* & Ho*, *Is Neo-Darwinism Falsifiable?—And Does It Matter?*, 4 Nature & System 179, 192 (1982) (italics added).
295 Hall*, *The Inheritance of Emotionality*, Sigma Xi Q., Mar. 1938, at 19.
296 *E.g.*, J. Rifkin*, *Algeny* 119-20 (1983) ("The *ferocity* with which many evolutionists set forth their views and the high level of *intolerance* they demonstrate toward alternative frames of reference should be cause enough for pause, if not alarm.") (italics added).
297 Gould* & Eldredge*, *Punctuated equilibria: the tempo and mode of evolution reconsidered*, 3 Paleobiology 115, 116, 117 (1977) ("[*P*]*aleontologists have worn blinders* that permit them to accumulate cases in one category only; they have sought evidence of slow, steady and gradual change as the only true representation of evolution in the fossil record (Eldredge and Gould 1972). Two other *classes of information were explained away or simply ignored*: 1) morphological *gaps* in stratigraphic sequences—which might have suggested a punctuational view of evolution—were attributed to imperfections of the fossil record; 2) evolutionary *stasis*, though recognized by all and used by stratigraphers in the practical work of our profession, was ignored by evolutionists as 'no data.' ") (italics added).
298 Eldredge*, *An Extravagance of Species*, Natural History, July 1980, at 47, 50.
299 Zihlman* & Lowenstein*, *False Start of the Human Parade*, Natural History, Aug. 1979, at 86, 90 ("But these same scholars have almost universally, and sometimes emotionally, rejected the findings of molecular evolution, primarily because these challenges, indeed, refute, the claim that Ramapithecus was the ancestral human.").
300 Pilbeam*, *Rearranging Our Family Tree*, Human Nature, June 1978, at 39, 45 ("I know that, at least in paleoanthropology, data are still so sparse that theory heavily influences interpretations. Theories have, in the past, clearly reflected our current ideologies instead of the actual data . . ..").
301 Patterson*, *Cladistics*, 27 Biologist 234, 234, (1980) (italics added).
302 Schwabe*, *On the validity of molecular evolution*, 11 Trends in Biochemical Sciences 280, 282 (1986).
303 Brady*, *Dogma and doubt*, 17 Biological J. Linnean Society 79, 90 (1982).
304 *Id.* at 91-92.
305 R. Jastrow*, *God and the Astronomers* 16 (1978) ("Theologians generally are delighted with the proof that the Universe had a beginning, but astronomers are curiously upset. Their reactions provide an interesting demonstration of the response of the scientific mind—supposedly a very objective mind—when evidence uncovered by science itself leads to a conflict with the articles of faith in our profession. It turns out that the scientist behaves the way the rest of us do when our beliefs are in conflict with the evidence. We become irritated, we pretend the conflict does not exist, or we paper it over with meaningless phrases.").

[306] Burbidge*, *Was there really a Big Bang?*, Nature, Sept. 3, 1971, at 36, 36.
[307] M. Simon*, *The Matter of Life* 166 (1971) ("Scientists can become so impressed by the possibilities of building up a hypothetical historical picture of the origins of life at all that they may be prone to ignore or to underemphasize logical difficulties and matters of detail.").
[308] 1 I. Lakatos*, *The Methodology of Scientific Research Programmes* 3 (J. Worrall* & G. Currie* eds. 1978).
[309] Laudan*, *The Demise of the Demarcation Problem*, in 2 Working Papers in Science and Technology at 7, 27 (R. Laudan* ed. 1983) ("There seems good reason, drawn from the history of science, to suppose that most scientific theories are false; under the circumstances, how plausible can be the claim that science is the repository of all and only well-confirmed theories?").
[310] J. Sullivan*, *The Limitations of Science* 141-62 (1933) ("it is highly probable that all scientific theories are wrong").
[311] W. Provine*, Theories of Creationism and Evolution from a Historical Perspective (unpublished lecture before Sigma Xi Chapter, Corning, N.Y., Nov. 17, 1981).
[312] Ruse*, *The Ideology of Darwinism*, in Darwin Today 233, 255 (E. Geissler* & W. Scheler* eds. 1983).
[313] Ruse*, *Editorial*, 1 Biology & Philosophy 1 (1986).
[314] M. Ruse*, *Darwinism Defended* xvi (1982).
[315] Asimov*, *The "Threat" of Creationism*, N.Y.T. Magazine, June 14, 1981, at 90, 100.
[316] Geissler*, *Discussion*, in Darwin Today 251 (E. Geissler* & W. Scheler* eds. 1983)
[317] Strike*, *The Status of Creation-Science: A Comment on Siegel and Hahn*, 63 Phi Delta Kappan 555, 556 (1982).
[318] Pangle*, *Introduction*, to L. Strauss, Studies in Platonic Political Philosophy 21-22 (1983) (U. of Chicago Press).
[319] Ellis*, *Alternatives to the Big Bang*, 22 Ann. Rev. Astronomy & Astrophysics 157, 162 (1984).
[320] *E.g.*, Patterson*, *An Engineer Looks at the Creationist Movement*, 89 Proc. Iowa Academy of Sciences 57 (1982) ("Were biologists, geologists, or paleontologists to endorse publicly a pseudoscience such as creationism *their chances of achieving or retaining prestigious academic positions would be greatly undermined*, as would their chances for high office in professional societies. Only in Bible colleges, seminaries, and creationist ministries can the latter succeed as outspoken creationists.") (Dr. John Patterson).
[321] Shafersman*, the president of the anti-creationist Committee on Education in Evolutionary Biology (formerly Committees of Correspondence) for Texas, has written and a geological journal has published the following:

> I dispute Henry Morris's claim that thousands of scientists are creationists. No scientist today questions the past and present occurrence of evolution in the organic world .... Those 'thousands of creationists' with

legitimate post-graduate degrees and other appropriate credentials are *not scientists*, precisely because they have abandoned the scientific method and the scientific attitude, criteria far more crucial to the definition of scientist than the location or duration of one's training or the identity of one's employer.

Schafersman*, *Letter*, Geotimes, Aug. 1981, at 11, 11 (italics added). *See also* Deposition of Michael Ruse*, Keith v. Louisiana Dep't of Educ., 553 F. Supp. 295 (M.D. La. 1982).

322 Dobzhansky*, *Evolutionary and Population Genetics*, 142 Science 1131, 1134 (1963).

323 Note 244.

324 Note 246.

325 Note 248.

326 Note 260.

327 Note 263.

328 Note 264.

329 Note 271.

330 Note 272.

331 Note 277.

332 Note 284.

333 Note 285.

334 Note 304.

335 Note 294.

336 Note 322.

337 Note 312.

338 Note 319.

CHAPTER 10

Theories of Evolution and Abrupt Appearance and Various Definitions of Science

Therefore, either the demarcation criteria of philosophy of science should accept creationism as genuine science or they should include some provision for changes over time in the standards of what is to count as science.

My own preference is, as I have made clear, that creationism is a kind of science. Science is not simply whatever the dominant mode of culture declares to be science. Science must be organized knowledge that meets rational standards, and scientific procedure must be capable of generating new knowledge by those standards.

—R.G.A. Dolby*,
Senior Lecturer in Philosophy of Science, University of Kent[1]

*Philosophers and scientists cited in this chapter, unless otherwise indicated, are not proponents of, and their quoted statements are not intended as endorsements of, either the theory of abrupt appearance or the theory of creation. However, their quoted statements are acknowledging concepts that support the scientific nature of one or both theories.

The various definitions of science are comparably met by the theory of evolution and the theory of abrupt appearance (Section 10.1). The *McLean* definition, although "demonstrably false"[2] and "remote from well-founded opinion in the philosophy of science,"[3] itself is equally met by those theories. The theory of evolution and the theory of abrupt appearance are to the same incomplete extent guided by and explainable by natural laws (Section 10.2). They are comparably although incompletely testable and falsifiable, and nearly twenty testable claims and falsifiable claims are listed that are central to the theory of abrupt appearance, while many nontestable and nonfalsifiable elements are listed for the theory of evolution (Sections 10.3 and 10.4). Moreover, the theory of evolution is less tentatively held than the theory of abrupt appearance (Section 10.5), and the two theories comparably meet other criteria (Section 10.6). Nonetheless, the radical definition and the *McLean* test are not defensible demarcations of science.

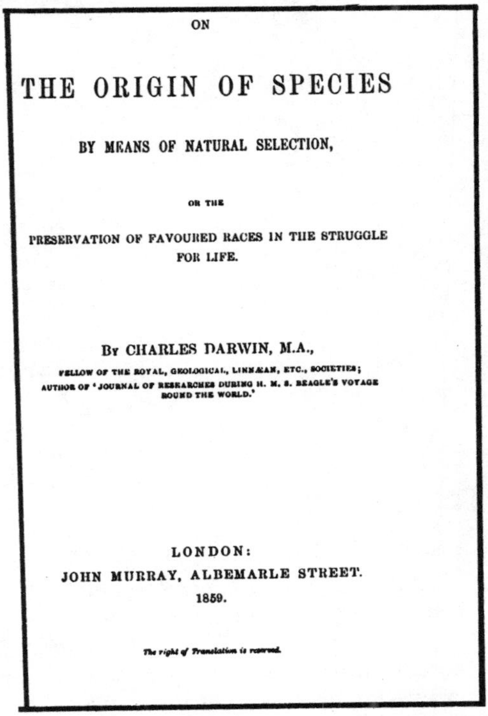
ON

THE ORIGIN OF SPECIES

BY MEANS OF NATURAL SELECTION,

OR THE

PRESERVATION OF FAVOURED RACES IN THE STRUGGLE FOR LIFE.

BY CHARLES DARWIN, M.A.,

FELLOW OF THE ROYAL, GEOLOGICAL, LINNÆAN, ETC., SOCIETIES;
AUTHOR OF 'JOURNAL OF RESEARCHES DURING H. M. S. BEAGLE'S VOYAGE ROUND THE WORLD.'

LONDON:
JOHN MURRAY, ALBEMARLE STREET.
1859.

The right of Translation is reserved.

Figure 10.1
Darwin's Origin of Species (title page of first edition): regarded the "theory of creation" as scientific, testable, and falsifiable, because "[a]gain and again, he describes phenomena that do not fit the creation theory" (Mayr*)*

10.1 Comparable Satisfaction of Prevailing Definitions by the Theories of Abrupt Appearance and Evolution

a. The Theory of Abrupt Appearance

The theory of abrupt appearance meets most of the various definitions of science summarized in Section 9.1 as well as does the theory of evolution: It involves empirical data and scientific interpretation (as the theory of abrupt appearance is defined in Chapters 2, 4, and 6, and summarized in Chapter 8). That interpretation involves Baconian induction as well as hypothesis and deduction,[4] qualified scientists under the vocational approach,[5] and falsifiability comparable to evolution under Popper's* approach.[6] The theory of abrupt appearance incorporates a new paradigm that seeks to explain anomalies in the old Darwinian and macroevolutionary paradigm consistent with Kuhn's* sociological approach,[7] involves testability comparable to evolution under the Hempel* and other empiricist approaches,[8] and in general conforms to the various definitions of science to a degree comparable to the theory of evolution's conformity.[9]

The "theory of creation," which is Darwin's* term and so is here used,[10] was scientific in Darwin's* estimation, in that he constantly argued that it conflicted with empirical evidence or with the better interpretation of the data.[11] Bacon himself employed his inductivist approach to embrace a theory of creation,[12] and other leading scientists found that theory a satisfactory scientific explanation of the evidence (as discussed in Sections 13.4 and 15.2(a)).

The same is true of the *McLean* definition. Laudan*, professor of philosophy of science at Virginia Polytechnic Institute (and an ardent opponent of the theory of creation), concludes that the theory of creation "manifestly does"[13] meet the definition of science in the *McLean* opinion:

> At various key points in the Opinion, Creationism is charged with being untestable, dogmatic (and thus non-tentative), and unfalsifiable. All three charges are of dubious merit.
>
> . . ..
>
> . . .[I]t can be argued that creationism already satisfies these requirements . . ..[14]

Quinn* similarly concludes that "[c]reation science . . . clearly satisfies these conditions" of testability and falsifiability,[15] and Dolby* suggests "that creationism is a kind of science" in the quotation beginning this chapter. In so describing the theory of creation, neither those authors nor this author is referring to a religious theory that appeals to arbitrary acts of a creator or to the authority of a religious text,[16] but instead to a scientific theory that relies on regularities of nature unless scientific evidence reflects singularities or singular events, and then relies on empirical evidence to describe those singularities or singular events.

Some creationist scientists have expressed their individual opinions that "neither creation nor evolution is a scientific *theory*." Those statements have been frequently misquoted as concessions that the theory of creation cannot be scientific. However, nothing of the kind is meant. Instead, the opinions (which are not shared by most creationist and discontinuitist scientists) mean either that neither creation nor evolution is a scientific "theory" (although each is a scientific hypothesis or scientific model or scientific research program),[17] or that "biblical" creationism (as distinguished from the theory of creation) is not a scientific theory.

b. The Theory of Evolution

On the other hand, Popper*, the internationally famous philosopher of science, and others have concluded that evolution itself does *not* meet the testability-falsifiability criterion that in its most rigorous form was added to the radical definition and pulled into the *McLean* test:

> 37. *Darwinism as a Metaphysical Research Programme*
>
> From this point of view the question of the scientific status of Darwinian theory—in the widest sense, the theory of trial and error elimination—becomes an interesting one. I have come to the conclusion that Darwinism is *not a testable scientific theory*, but a *metaphysical research programme*—a possible framework for testable scientific theories.
>
> . . ..
>
> Now to the degree that Darwinism creates the same impression, it is not so very much better than the theistic view of adaptation; it is therefore important to show that Darwinism is *not a scientific theory, but metaphysical*.[18]

Although Popper* has modified his earlier position that natural selection is nonscientific and almost tautologous,[19] he has *not* published any modification of his statement that in significant part "Darwinism is not a testable scientific theory."[20] Scores of other philosophers and scientists have agreed in applying Popper's* criteria, to Darwinism and to macroevolution, as discussed in Sections 10.3 and 10.4, such as Patterson*[21] and Cartmill*.[22] In either case, the theory of abrupt appearance and the theory of evolution are parallel in relation to the various definitions of science, including the radical definition and *McLean* test.

When rival scientific explanations exist, the newer research program perhaps "should be sheltered for a while from [its] powerful established rival," Lakatos* notes:

> All this suggests that we must not discard a budding research programme simply because it has so far failed to overtake a powerful rival. We should not abandon it if, supposing its rival were not there, it would constitute a progressive problemshift. And we should certainly regard a newly interpreted fact as a new fact, ignoring the insolent priority claims of amateur fact collectors. As long as a budding research programme can be rationally reconstructed as a progressive problemshift, *it should be sheltered for a while from a powerful established rival.*
>
> . . ..
>
> . . .One must *never allow a research programme to become a Weltanschauung*, or *a sort of scientific rigour*, setting itself up as an arbiter between explanation and non-explanation, as mathematical rigour sets itself up as an arbiter between proof and non-proof.[23]

Perhaps, for a theory that "is not yet a fully formed body of scientific belief, then demarcation criteria which are applied to systems of claimed knowledge are not appropriate," Dolby* adds.[24]

As with any theory, evolution should not be allowed to become the test between scientific explanation and scientific nonexplanation or nonscience, with the effect of excluding nonevolutionary research programs by definition. And the same standards for demarcation and for persuasion should be applied to all theories of origins; the theory of evolution should not be subject to a requirement of mere plausibility while the theory of abrupt appearance is subject to a requirement of logically compelling force to be admitted into the realm of science and considered fairly.

10.2 Comparable Explanation with Natural Laws by the Theories of Abrupt Appearance and Evolution

The theories of abrupt appearance and evolution are to the same incomplete extent "guided by natural law" and "explanatory by

Figure 10.2 Evolution departing from natural laws: in the "big bang singularity when... we expect general relativity to break down" (Wald), in abiogenesis of the first life by means "so extremely improbable that nothing can 'explain' why it originated" (Popper*)*

reference to natural law," under the first criterion of the radical definition and *McLean* test for science.[25] This section applies the natural laws requirement, which has been shown to be erroneous above,[26] to (a) the theory of evolution and then (b) the theory of abrupt appearance.

a. Natural Laws and the Theory of Evolution

Evolution is not fully guided by natural laws and not fully explanatory by reference to natural laws in central areas.

(1) Non-Guidance by Natural Laws. Evolution is not guided by natural laws, in critical areas, because it has the following aspects that are breaks in natural laws:

(a) Cosmic evolution:	(1) Origin of matter and energy (2) Singularity of big bang (3) Singularities in black holes
(b) Biochemical evolution:	(1) Abiogenesis (origin of life from nonlife) (2) Origin of vast information content (3) Overcoming of massive improbability
(c) Biological evolution:	(1) Occurrence of macroevolution (2) Origin of vast information content and overcoming of massive improbability (3) Irreducibility of life and consciousness.

(a) Cosmic Evolution. First, cosmic evolution breaches natural laws in significant ways. (1) It includes "the primary origin of

matter or energy," for which "science cannot account," in Stansfield's* words.[27] That origin was a singularity, in the sense that it contradicted the natural law of conservation of matter and energy (the first law of thermodynamics), according to Silk*,[28] Shapley*,[29] Krauskopf*,[30] Einstein*,[31] and North*.[32] The inflationary universe theory adds the singularity of "creation ex nihilo" of the universe, and various quantum creation and particle creation theories involve similar singularities of various amounts of matter and energy.[33] (2) Cosmic evolution also involves a "big bang singularity when . . . we expect general relativity to break down," as Wald* says.[34] A big bang event is also termed a singularity by Weisskopf*,[35] Silk*,[36] Ellis*,[37] Patton* and Wheeler*,[38] and Narlikar*.[39] Such a singularity would have been "a beginning under conditions in which the known laws of physics are not valid," Jastrow* notes,[40] and Barrow* and Silk*,[41] Weisskopf*,[42] and Tipler*[43] concur. (3) Cosmic evolution also faces other singularities in each black hole (assuming black holes exist), because at the center the curvature of space-time becomes sharper and sharper, under the theory of Hawking*. Thus, natural laws of physics do not govern a critical aspect of black holes.[44]

(b) Biochemical Evolution. Biochemical evolution also partly conflicts with natural laws. (1) It is centered around abiogenesis (the generation of life from nonlife),[45] which contradicts the natural law of biogenesis (that life comes only from prior life).[46] (2) Biochemical evolution also includes the origin of vast information content, contrary to its implausibility under the natural laws measured by information science,[47] as Hoyle concludes:

> the combinatorial arrangement of *not* even one among the many thousands of biopolymers on which life depends could have been arrived at by *natural processes* here on the Earth.[48]

(3) Furthermore, it assumes the overcoming of an extreme improbability, which Ambrose* calculates to be in the range of 1 chance in $10^{2,000,000}$ (as discussed above),[49] contrary to the natural laws reflected in statistical probabilities.[50] Wald*, a Nobel Prize recipient, calls that "impossible" except for a scientific "miracle."[51] Popper* thus denies "that Darwinism can explain the origin of life":

> I do not think that Darwinism can explain the origin of life. I think it quite possible that life is so extremely improbable that nothing can "explain" why it originated; for statistical explanation must operate, in the last instance, with very high probabilities.[52]

He instead sees a singularity—"an impenetrable barrier to science":

> *Monod's suggestion is that life emerged from inanimate* matter by an

> extremely improbable combination of chance circumstances, and that this may not merely have been an event of low probability but of zero probability—in fact, a *unique* event.
>
> . . ..
>
> Thus we may be faced with the possibility that the origin of life (like the origin of the universe) becomes an *impenetrable barrier to science*, and a residue to all attempts to reduce biology to chemistry and physics. For even though Monod's suggestion of the uniqueness of life's origin is refutable—by attempts at reduction, to be sure—if true, it would amount to a denial of any fully successful reduction. With this suggestion Monod, who is a reductionist for reasons of method, arrives at the position . . ..[53]

(c) Biological Macroevolution. Finally, biological evolution in part similarly violates natural laws. (1) It is centered in macroevolution, yet no plausible mechanism exists to generate macroevolution and the fossil record generally contradicts it, as Grassé*[54] and Kerkut*[55] lament, and as was assessed in Volume 1.[56] (2) Biological evolution also involves an extreme improbability, which has been calculated to be so small that "an adequate scientific theory of [macro]evolution must await the discovery of new natural laws," in the view of Eden* of MIT, leaving biological macroevolution contrary to natural laws or mathematical laws reflected in statistical probability.[57] Related to that is an information content of every higher organism, with "genetic programmes of . . . close to a thousand million bits of information, equivalent to the sequence of letters in a small library of one thousand volumes," which could not plausibly have been generated by Darwinian or other natural processes according to Denton*.[58] Finally, biological evolution confronts the problems of life and consciousness, which "biology cannot explain . . . by the current workings of physical and chemical laws,"[59] as Polanyi* points out:

> But again, once it is recognized, on other grounds, that *life transcends physics and chemistry*, there is no reason for suspending recognition of the obvious fact that *consciousness* is a principle that fundamentally transcends not only physics and chemistry but also the mechanistic principles of living beings.[60]

Thus, each major stage of evolution is not "guided by natural law" in central areas, although it is partially guided by natural laws.

(2) Non-Explanation by Natural Laws. Evolution is also not "explanatory by reference to natural laws" in important areas, not only because of the previously discussed breaks in natural laws, but because of many critical elements that are not "explanatory."

(a) Macroevolution Generally. The failure of biological macroevo-

lution in general to provide sufficient explanation is indicted by Grassé*:

> Their success among certain biologists, philosophers, and sociologists notwithstanding, the *explanatory* doctrines of biological evolution do *not stand up* to an objective, in-depth criticism. They prove to be either in conflict with reality or else incapable of solving the major problems involved.[61]

A similar indictment has been issued by Popper*, who suggests that the theory "cannot . . . explain any particular evolutionary change":

> While we can explain a particular eclipse by predicting it, we *cannot* predict or *explain* any particular evolutionary change (except perhaps certain changes in the gene population within one species); all we can say is that if it is not a small change, there must have been some intermediate steps—an important suggestion for research: a research programme.[62]

"One can, therefore, use those macroscopic [phenomena] to describe the biological reality, *but not to explain it*," Hoffman* states in reference to macroevolution.[63] Evolution's explaining mechanism is fundamentally inadequate," Erbrich* adds.[64] Others agree.[65]

Although macroevolution may not provide a true explanation for most phenomena, it offers a superficial explanation for any phenomenon—"for any property of living beings," Lipson* observes.[66] Yet, as Sparkes* points out,

> If for example, a theory is so all-embracing that it can explain any outcome, and so is wholly non-predictive, it must be regarded as an *unscientific explanation*.[67]

Macroevolution even has been called merely a tautology, meaning that it has no explanatory power,[68] by Eden* of M.I.T.:

> In consequence the theory has been modified to the point that virtually every formulation of the principles of evolution is a *tautology*.[69]

Manser* similarly applied the tautology concept to macroevolution generally.[70]

(b) Darwinism. Darwinism similarly has been criticized widely as "little more than a tautology providing no real predictive or explanatory power," as Steele* says,[71] and as Scriven* concurs.[72] Adaptation has been severely characterized as nonexplanatory, by Manser*,[73] Lewontin*,[74] and Macbeth*;[75] and as tautologous by Saunders* and Ho*[76] and by Eden*:

> As an instance, the statement that species *adapt* to changes in an environment by a variation in the properties of phenotypes and by the consequent process of natural selection is clearly *vacuous*. . . . Since these are the only possibilities, the original statement is *tautologous*.[77]

Popper* came close to agreeing before his recent change:

> Take 'adaptation.' At first sight natural selection appears to explain it, and in a way it does, but it is *hardly a scientific way*. To say that a species not living is adapted to its environment is, in fact, *almost tautological*.[78]

Population genetics "comes perilously close" to "explain[ing] nothing" according to Lewontin* of Harvard:

> If one simply cannot measure the stated variables or the parameters with which the theory is constructed, or if their measure is so laden with error that no discrimination between alternative hypotheses is possible, the theory becomes a *vacuous* exercise in formal logic that has no point of contact with the contingent world. The theory *explains nothing* because it explains everything. It is my contention that a good deal of the structure of *evolutionary genetics* comes perilously close to being of this sort.[79]

Roughgarden* agrees in his leading treatise.[80] Classifications similarly are nonexplanatory, Kitts* adds:

> *Classifications are not meant to explain*. They are meant to be explained. The joint attributes of taxa and the gaps separating taxa are not explained by a classification. They are stated by means of a classification.[81]

Migration (part of the mechanism) and other ecological claims "are actually tautologies" and "are not scientific theories at all" in the words of Peters:*

> I argue that the 'theory of evolution' does not make predictions, so far as *ecology* is concerned, but is instead a logical formula which can be used only to classify empiricisms and to show the relationships which such a classification implies. Similar criticisms are then made of several ecological concepts. The essence of the argument is that these 'theories' are actually *tautologies* and, as such, *cannot make empirically testable predictions*. They are *not scientific theories* at all.[82]

At the same time that it adequately "explains nothing," Darwinism inadequately "explains everything," as Lewontin* said. It allows "virtually any observation within its conceptual purview" and "inevitably results in accepting virtually any data as being 'consistent' with the theory," Cracraft* observes:

> For example, Ho and Saunders identify *neutral mutation theory* and the challenge to Darwinian gradualism by "punctuated equilibrium" as seminal contributions to the erosion of neo-Darwinism, yet both have been interpreted as entirely consistent with that view (not only by the defenders of neo-Darwinism itself but also by some of the chief advocates of neutralism and punctuated equilibrium). This points up the *difficulty of chipping away at a theory having few hard-core theoretical statements* and *allowing virtually any observation within its conceptual purview*. If the critics are correct to spurn this state-of-affairs, and I think they are, then they would do well to rid themselves of one of the primary attributes of this new "emerging paradigm of evolution," which accord-

> ing to Ho and Saunders is its "pluralism." To them, evolution is a complex phenomenon, with a variety of processes operating at different hierarchical levels, and thus a pluralistic viewpoint is not only necessary but "leads to a fundamentally different approach" (pp. x, 5). "Pluralism"—or virtually anything goes—is a predicament for neo-Darwinism and, as far as I can see, will not serve any competing worldview well. The goal of a general theory of evolution should not be to account for any and all observations; that is too much to demand. Such a theory must describe, in contrast, what generally is the rule. *Neo-Darwinism*, as usually conceived by most contemporary biologists, has *failed as a rigorous theory* because it does not present us with a narrow, precise set of statements about how most of the world is organized. Instead, it tries to tell us how all the world is consistent with a "pluralistic" worldview called neo-Darwinism. *Old-fashioned Darwinism, in contrast to our present mutation of it, would find difficulty reconciling neutralism and pervasive morphological stasis* through time with the notion of directional natural selection relentlessly sculpturing the phenotype along the path of environmental change. A "pluralistic" philosophy toward the structure of scientific theories inevitably *results in accepting virtually any data as being "consistent"* with the theory. . . .[83]

Similarly for neo-Darwinism, "with a little ingenuity any observation can be made to appear consistent with it," Saunders* and Ho* conclude.[84] Even Mayr* admitted that "Popper is right; this model is so good that it can explain anything, as Popper has rightly complained."[85] Gould* has compared it "to the 'Blob,' of movie fame," in that "it could be manipulated to account for all data in its path,"[86] and Leith* lists some of its victims:

> Before continental drift was discovered, the Darwinians explained the distribution of life on earth in terms of dispersal; *after* the discovery of drift they explained the same distribution without such heavy reliance on dispersal. In the 19th century, when the fossil record was seen as a history of gradual change, the Darwinians explained evolution as a *gradual* adaptive process; now that many palaeontologists interpret the fossils as a history of 'fits and starts,' the Darwinians see evolution as a *variable-rate* adaptive process. *One is tempted to ask what observations the Darwinians can't explain.*[87]

(c) Natural Selection. Furthermore, natural selection has received the most widespread and vehement criticism (by evolutionists) as being nonexplanatory and tautologous (as well as unfalsifiable, as discussed below[88]). That is no small matter, because natural selection "remains the fundamental process directing evolutionary change," according to Dobzhansky* *et al.*[89] and Mayr*.[90] Yet it remains as nonexplanatory as the most religious approaches, according to Ho* and Saunders*:

And as Darwinists and neo-Darwinists have become ever more adept at finding possible selective advantages for any trait one cares to mention, explanation in terms of the all-powerful force of *natural selection* has come more and more to resemble explanation in terms of the conscious design of the omnipotent Creator.[91]

Natural selection is called nonexplanatory by Rosen* (then of the American Museum of Natural History):

> Although natural selection theory *fails to explain* the origin of evolutionary novelties, its greatest shortcoming in terms of evolutionary theory is that it *fails to explain* evolutionary diversity.[92]

Lewontin* concludes that "[n]atural selection explains nothing because it explains everything."[93] O'Grady* suggests that it only describes and does not explain:

> [T]hose data were being *described*, not *explained*. . . .
>
> . . ..
>
> . . . If evolution is caused by something other than organism-environment interactions, then the concepts of natural selection and survival of the fittest are *descriptions* of effects they did not cause. As such, their range of application is enormous, while their *causal explanatory power is practically non-existent.* [94]

Hughes* and Lambert* emphasize that natural selection "is not necessarily real" and does not "explain" biological evolution:

> We should remember that *natural selection is not necessarily real* (*sensu* Thom, 1972; Bhaskar, 1978) *just because biologists and mathematicians have been talking about it for over 100 years*. As Lewontin (1976) commented: "It cannot be assumed that any behaviour or institution to which a name can be given necessarily has an existence as a real thing subject to the laws of nature".
>
> . . ..
>
> *We are certainly not arguing here that differential survival of whole organisms does not occur*. This must inevitably happen. The question that we must ask is, *does this represent the controlling dynamic* of organic evolution (Hailman, 1982)? *Cannot a similar argument be equally well constructed to "explain" any frequency distribution*? For example, consider *rocks* which vary in hardness and also persist through time. Clearly the harder rocks are better "adapted" to survive harsh climatic conditions. As Lewontin (1976) points out, a similar story can be told about political parties, rumours, jokes, stars and discarded soft drink containers.[95]

Thus, Bradie* and Gromko* conclude that natural selection "resides in that nether region between science and metaphysics."[96]

The conclusion that natural selection is nonexplanatory is reached by a number of biologists and philosophers such as the following:

Rosen*
Lewontin*
O'Grady*
Hughes*
Lambert*
Bradie*
Gromko*
Hempel*[97]
Macbeth*[98]
Brady*[99]
Cannon*[100]
Hairston*[101]
Little*[102]
Løvtrup*[103]
Medawar*[104]
Platnick*[105]
Polanyi*[106]
Wassermann*.[107]

Natural selection also confronts the "most frequent criticism" that it "is a tautology," as Riddiford* and Penny* recount:

> The most frequent criticism of the synthetic theory is that the principle of natural selection (see Figure 2) is a *tautology*. A tautologous statement is necessarily true because it expresses a repetition of the same idea such as, bachelors are unmarried men, or triangles are three-sided figures. Stated either as 'the survival of the fittest' or as 'the differential survival and reproduction of a genotype,' the critics feel that the principle is, like a tautology, a repetition conveying no information about the empirical world. Writers who have described the principle in this way include: Brady, 1979; Barker, 1969; Bethell, 1976; Bohm, 1968; Cannon, 1958; Dobzhansky, 1968; Grene, 1974; Haldane, 1935; Macbeth, 1971; Manser, 1965; Peters, 1976; Platnick, 1977; Popper, 1972, 1976; Stebbins, 1974; Waddington, 1960.[108]

The reason why it is a tautology is summarized by Waddington* of Oxford:

> Darwin's major contribution was, of course, the suggestion that evolution can be explained by the natural selection of random variations. *Natural selection*, which was at first considered as though it were a hypothesis that was in need of experimental or observational confirmation, turns out on closer inspection to be a *tautology*, a statement of an inevitable although previously unrecognized relation. It states that the fittest individuals in a population (defined as those which leave most offspring) will leave most offspring.[109]

The tautology criticism of natural selection, or of its "survival of the fittest" component, in fact has been made in published articles by literally dozens of scientists and philosophers of science such as the following:

Stanley* of Johns Hopkins[110]
Rosen* of the American Museum[111]
Patterson* of the British Museum[112]
Stebbins*[113]
Platnick*[114]

Eden*[115]
Hoyle[116]
Grene*[117]
Brady*[118]
Peters*[119]
Himmelfarb*[120]
Harris*[121]
Haldane*[122]
Barker*[123]
Krimbas*[124]
Koestler*[125]
Smart*[126]
Flew*[127]
Manser*[128]
Bohm*[129]
Cannon*[130]
Macbeth*[131]
Bethell*[132]
Rifkin*[133]
Roszak*[134]
Lerner*[135]
Saunders* and Ho*[136]
Riddiford* and Penny*
Waddington*.

Gould* has disputed the tautology criticism on the ground that natural selection explains by the independent criterion of good engineering design. Rosen* disagrees and reaffirms the tautology in natural selection:

> The real problem with Darwinian selection theory, however, is that *it can explain everything, and therefore, nothing*. By logical necessity what survives (or what produces more offspring) is more fit than what doesn't, what is more it is therefore better adapted, and what is better adapted is therefore selected for (or in other words, survives). When *Gould* (1976) recently responded to continuing criticism of selection theory by using goodness of human engineering design as an independent criterion of animal and plant fitness, he was, in effect, rejecting not only Waddington's logic, but neo-Darwinism as well: ". . . let me admit that Bethell's criticism applies to much of the technical literature in evolutionary theory, especially to the abstract mathematical treatments . . . [i.e., population genetics]. These studies do assess fitness only in terms of differential survival . . . Nature, however, is not limited by the calculations of theoretical geneticists." Gould is *unable* to tell us how to recognize a successful organism apart from its existence, or what exactly is the reason for its existence as compared with others which have died off, or which attribute of the organism shall be compared with human engineering achievements, or even how such comparisons can be rendered objective. In short, he has provided no reason not to reject the *tautology* other than what he believes is its popularity: "I maintain, perhaps naively, that [selection's] current unabated popularity must have something to do with its success in explaining the admittedly imperfect information we now possess about evolution." Of course *selection* is successful in explaining nature, since the characteristic of *tautologies* is that they explain everything. And, of course, that is the true measure of selection's appeal. But is Gould asking us to believe that the true measure of a scientific theory is decided in a popularity contest regardless of its internal logical structure? Gould does, indeed, "maintain naively."[137]

(d) Absence of Laws. Even if evolution were explanatory, "the evolutionary hypothesis is not a universal law of nature,"[138] Popper* concludes, and in fact "there can be no evolutionary laws":

> The nature of evolutionary laws has been questioned by a number of critics of the synthetic theory, including Goudge (1961), Scriven (1958), and Smart (1963), all of them claiming that *there can be no evolutionary laws.* They have, for the most part, felt that this is so because the theory describes a unique, historical process . . ..[139]

In fact, "a connection with (1) natural physical laws . . . has not been established" according to Brooks* and Wiley*,[140] "neo-Darwinism is like a cosmological theory in physics without the context of physical law" in the view of Hughes*,[141] and Darwinians do not " 'explain' in the sense that they enable events to be deduced from a set of initial conditions together with universal laws, in the way that physics and chemistry explain their respective fields" in the estimation of Manser*.[142] Abbagnano*,[143] Smart*,[144] Scriven*,[145] and Goudge*[146] concur.

b. Natural Laws and the Theory of Abrupt Appearance

The theories of abrupt appearance and evolution are comparable in their degree of guidance and explanation by reference to natural laws.

(1) Guidance by Natural Laws. The theory of abrupt appearance is guided by natural laws to the same partial degree that the theory of evolution is.

(a) Affirmative Evidence and Natural Laws. First, its various lines of affirmative evidence all involve scientific data and scientific interpretations that are natural laws or are based on natural laws, as the discussion of the theory of abrupt appearance shows in Volume I.[147] This can be seen in a listing of the affirmative evidence:

Aspect of Theory of Abrupt Appearance	*Affirmative Evidence Applying a Natural Law*	*Affirmative Evidence Interpreting Empirical Data by a Natural Law or Law-Based Theory*
(a) Biological abrupt appearance:	Information content argument —Information science laws [148] Probability argument —Natural laws measured by probability laws	Paleontology argument —Fossil data Comparative morphology argument —Fossil and morphology data Comparative discontinuity argument —Classification, anatomy, and biochemistry data

	Genetics argument —Genetic laws	
(b) Biochemical abrupt appearance:	Information content argument —Information science laws Probability argument —Biochemical laws measured by probability laws Biogenesis argument —Biogenesis law Thermodynamics argument —Thermodynamic law	Isomers argument —Organic molecular data
(c) Cosmic abrupt appearance:	Thermodynamics argument —Thermodynamic laws Information content argument —Information science laws	Anthropic principle argument —Cosmic suitability data Heterogeneity argument —Matter distribution data Galaxy and star formation argument —Gravitational and other force data Radiohalos argument —Polonium halo data

Second, the theory of abrupt appearance does not postulate any more singularities (primeval suspensions of natural laws) than the theory of evolution requires, and bases its assumption that singularities have occurred (that natural laws may have been suspended) in the past on scientific evidence that is best explained by such a suspension. The singularities required by cosmic evolution, biochemical evolution, and biological evolution were described above.

Third, the theory of abrupt appearance accepts and incorporates the current formulation of virtually all natural laws. Cosmic abrupt appearance accepts the laws of thermodynamics, gravity, electromagnetism, weak and strong nuclear forces, light, and matter and energy, etc.; and agrees that those laws have governed development and change of the universe after the singularity (as most evolutionists term it) of the origin of the universe. Biochemical abrupt appearance accepts the laws of chemistry, molecular structure, probability, etc., and similarly agrees that those laws have guided change and development after the singularity or singular event (as many or most evolutionists describe it) of the origin of the first life. Biological abrupt appearance similarly accepts the data and principles of genetic laws, probability laws, information theory, natural selection (rightly understood), classification theory, comparative anatomy and biochemistry, migration and genetic drift, cell structure, organ structure, energy transport, etc., to the extent those are not biased by unsupported evolutionary assumptions. Moreover, the theory of abrupt appearance concurs that such processes as natural selection (rightly understood), mutation and genetic recombination, migration and genetic drift, and species selection (rightly understood) and other factors have led to change and development of organisms, including microevolutionary change, after the singularities or singular events of the origin of natural groups of organisms.

(b) Abrupt Appearance as a Natural Law. Because scientific evidence does indeed point to abrupt appearances of the universe, first life, and natural groups of organisms, if those are not characterized as permissible singularities or singular events, then those abrupt appearances may be properly summed up in a natural law of the abrupt appearances in complex form of the universe, the first life, and the natural groups of organisms.[149]

First, a parallel concept of nomothetic creation was widely held by creationist scientists during the time of Darwin*, as Gillespie* acknowledges:

> Accordingly, these creationists usually denounced the miraculous creation of new species with appropriate scientific fervor. Their talk of law, however, should not mislead one into thinking that their explanation of the origin of new species was naturalistic, that is, positive or nontheological. This variety of the concept of creation by law, or nomothetic creation, as I shall call it, appealed to naturalists who leaned toward a *law-bound biological science*. Charles Lyell, for instance, in the Principles of Geology (1830) spoke in the Newtonian manner of "general laws which may regulate the first introduction of species. . . [and] may limit their duration on the earth."[150]

Examples include Sir Richard Owen*,[151] director of the Natural History Department of the British Museum and "the leading comparative anatomist of his time,"[152] and Adam Sedgwick, geology professor at Cambridge and possibly "the best geologist who ever lived,"[153] whose position is typical:

> The hypothesis does not suspend or interrupt an established law of Nature. It does suppose the introduction of a new phenomenon unac-

> counted for by the operation of any known law of Nature; and it appeals to a power above established laws, and yet acting in harmony and conformity with them.[154]

The early catastrophists similarly proposed scientific laws of catastrophe without miracles, Gould* states.[155]

The modern theory of creation is "very similar to some of the doctrines proclaimed in the name of science in the century after the scientific revolution, in particular in the early eighteenth century," according to Dolby*.[156] Although he is critical, he cannot characterize even the theory of creation as pseudo-science:

> *I do not wish to say that those eminent natural philosophers of the seventeenth and eighteenth centuries who produced syntheses like those of modern creationism were doing pseudo-science.* Further, if such an activity was describable as science then, there is a case for describing it as science now. *So whatever may be wrong with creationism, I do not wish to say that it is pseudo-science, either.* I am inclined to the view that it is archaic science functioning as a framework for criticism of science.[157]

Second, although a natural law of abrupt appearance would involve a natural law different from those visibly operating today, the same is necessarily true of each phase of evolution. That is, if natural laws govern the key points of evolution, they must be natural laws different from those operating today in the cases of cosmic evolution (the origin of matter and energy contrary to the second law of thermodynamics and the big bang through or preceded by different natural laws), of biochemical evolution (the origin of life contrary to the laws of biogenesis and statistical probability), and of biological macroevolution (the origin of higher categories of organisms contrary to the capacity of natural selection and other mechanisms and contrary to the laws of genetics and statistical probability).[158] Although that natural law of abrupt appearance would involve initial singularities, the same is true of the initial singularities of cosmic evolution (the origin of matter and energy and the big bang), of biochemical evolution (abiogenesis and statistical impossibilities), and of biological macroevolution (the origin of higher categories and of incredible information content).[159]

Those who argue that such abrupt appearances could not have happened are basing their argument on an unsupported faith that present natural laws have constantly and exclusively operated (except when evolution requires otherwise), so that no additional natural laws have ever operated (except when evolution requires otherwise). Those who argue that such abrupt appearances cannot be considered by science are saying that empirical data (abrupt appearances in the fossil record etc.) and laws (appearances required by the laws of thermodynamics etc.) somehow cannot be considered by science except with certain approved theories (biological evolution and cosmic evolution), and are thereby excluding by faulty definition what may be an additional natural law and what may be true. Moreover, they are applying a different standard than for the theory of evolution.

The possibility of a law of abrupt appearance, or at least of a scientific allowance for abrupt appearance, is reluctantly recognized by Good*:

> If a new biological type is not the result *of transformism it must, as far as we are capable of judging, arise in some way within the meaning of the words de novo*, and that is something quite beyond our experience. *That we have no such experience, however, is not in itself a reason for excluding the possibility of an origin of this sort in all cases*, though it does afford reasonable grounds for doubting whether this has ever been a general and wide-spread phenomenon, because if this had been the case the less likely that we should continue to be without any evidence of it. On this argument then the very numbers of the Flowering Plants tend to support the opinion that they are, at least in all essentials, the result of biological transformism. At the same time we cannot totally ignore the *possibility* that occasionally in time and space, if no more frequently, *there may have been involved an event of a different kind.*[160]

(2) Explanation by Natural Law. The theory of abrupt appearance is also "explanatory by reference to natural laws" to the same partial extent as evolution is.

(a) Affirmative Evidence and Natural Laws. First, the theory of abrupt appearance is scientific in "establish[ing] the existence of a phenomenon" (abrupt appearance in complex form) whether or not it does "explain that phenomenon in a lawlike way."[161] Riddiford* and Penny* make that distinction as follows:

> These two aspects of *description and explanation (mechanism) are usually distinguished in science, and* in most areas for historical reasons they are clearly identified. For instance, the theory of continental drift was proposed long before plate tectonics was suggested as the mechanism for continental drift; Kepler's laws described the motion of the planets but again it was many years before Newton was able to show that his proposed gravitational force would account for these observations. . . .[162]

Brady* warns against losing "the distinction between the detection of pattern and its explanation by a process hypothesis," and observes that demonstration of existence must precede explanation:

> *We do not, or should not, advance explanatory or process theories prior to the discovery of a particular order in appearances to which the theory is addressed.* After all, we do not perceive causality in any direct sense, but we do perceive effects, and we have no guide to the operation of any particular causal power until we find a regularity, or pattern, within these effects. Indeed, it would seem to be our ability to find a representation of the general within the particular that sets us looking for a generative cause in the first place. The very idea of causal law may take its origin in this characteristic of experience, since it is but the projection of this relation—of the constant within change—into the realm of power. *If we lose the distinction between the detection of pattern and its explanation by a process hypothesis, we lose the reason for our inquiry, not merely historically, but logically.*[163]

Quinn*[164] and Laudan*[165] similarly criticize a natural laws requirement.

It is in fact not necessary to discover a "mechanism" or cause in order to discover scientifically the "patterns of nature", Brady* states:

> The actual discovery of the patterns of nature may *not necessitate a theory of their mechanism.* The discovery of the *natural system in taxonomy* did not depend upon a speculation on the mechanism by which the system came about, but Darwin's speculation on mechanism drew heavily on what was already known of that system. . . . But this represents *an advantage*, for we are not so likely to generate a pattern from our theoretical mechanism, rather than from our observations, if we have no theoretical mechanism.[166]

Not only is it unnecessary, but it is impossible according to Cracraft*: "The causal process is outside the realm of analysis for those investigating historically-based events."[167] A science limited to description without explanation is scientific, as is evident in Goethe's* example:

> *Goethe did not advance hypotheses* in the sense that the term is applied to an explanatory account added to the phenomena by a speculative act. *His science was entirely descriptive*, its concepts derived from the phenomena. But 'description' for him was not a simple abstraction of regularities. . . .[168]

At present, transformed cladists and some other systematists carry on descriptive classification without attempting explanation,[169] as do many other scientists in various fields. The reason is that there are many aspects of science besides causation, and even for those studying laws "causal laws do not exhaust the class of scientific laws," as Danto* states:

> Not every law used in prediction has explanatory force if we think of

> explanations as causal explanations, for causal laws do not *exhaust the class* of scientific laws, which also includes functional expressions of covariation among magnitudes, statistical laws, and so on, all of which are used in predicting. Even so, it has been questioned whether even causal explanation requires the use of causal laws, either in science or in history or the social sciences, where this controversy has been chiefly focused. . . .[170]

The absence of a mechanism is peculiarly a part of central aspects of origins. Tipler* notes that origin events encounter barriers to explanation by a mechanism:

> By the word "*origin*" cosmologists generally mean that *either* an all-encompassing *singularity* formed a boundary to spacetime at this past time, or else the density of matter becomes so great at this time that it makes *no sense to retrodict via known physical laws any further into the past*. In both cases an origin to the Universe is inferred because *there is a barrier to further retrodiction*. Thus the existence of such a retrodiction barrier defines the "origin" of the Universe. The Universe is said to come into existence at the retrodiction barrier.[171]

North* concurs that views of origins (which he calls "creation") cannot be explanations in a causal sense, and are not required to be causal theories:

> On the other hand, a recurrent theme of so *many discussions* of this topic is that of the *impossibility of explaining creation scientifically*, some rather *outmoded views on causation being usually called in as evidence*. Creation, the Beginning, the First Event—not all have the same meaning, but *all involve a discontinuity* which has often been said to constitute a limit to that which may be known. *Scientific explanations of them, in the old causal sense, are out of the question*. But cosmology might be said to have *explained* the beginning of the universe once it has decided that the occurrence of such a state of affairs in the past follows from *a theory which finds support in current observations*. . . .
>
> . . ..
>
> . . .*Both the belief that science deals with causes and the requirement that any event must be preceded by a cause, are misleading*.[172]

McCrea* agrees.[173] That causal limit is simply another way of saying that the origin of the universe, the first life, and perhaps the various plants and animals involves singularities, or breaks in the regularity of natural laws, as discussed earlier in this section. Of course, if there is a law of abrupt appearance, then that law provides the theory of abrupt appearance with a mechanism, although the mechanism would not yet have been integrated with other theories. But in that sense the theory of abrupt appearance is no different from the theory of continental drift for its first few decades, or from any theory in its earlier years. And some theories, as the theory of gravity, exist for centuries as a description of real physical phenomena without a mechanism of their cause. Moreover, the nonintegration of the theory of abrupt appearance would not be its fault or reflect its weakness, but would be the fault of other theories that refuse to allow integration.

In fact, the absence of a mechanism for explanation by natural laws is as true of the theory of evolution as it has been alleged to be for the theory of abrupt appearance. In biological macroevolution, the mechanism is subject to great debate (and is currently insufficient), as Patterson* observes:

> Now as you all know there is somewhat of a revolution going on in evolutionary theory at the moment. . . . It concerns the possible mechanisms that are responsible for transformations. . . . Well, here is Gillespie again on creationism in the 1850s. He says:
>
> > 'Frequently, those holding creationist ideas could plead ignorance of the means and affirm only the facts.'
>
> That seems to summarize the feeling I get in talking to evolutionists today. They plead *ignorance of the means* of transformation but affirm only the facts, knowing that it has taken place. Again the two points do seem *hard to distinguish*.[174]

In biochemical evolution, the proposed mechanism again falls vastly short (particularly in view of statistical improbability and information content problems).[175] In cosmic evolution, the mechanism of the big bang cannot even be studied (other than by conjecture), as Jastrow* acknowledges:

> [F]or the astronomical evidence proves that the Universe was created twenty billion years ago in a fiery explosion, and in the searing heat of that first moment, all the *evidence* needed for a scientific study of the cause of the great explosion *was melted down and destroyed*.[176]

Similarly, the origin of matter and energy must be assumed to result either from eternal existence, a vacuum fluctuation, or a discontinuous appearance.[177] Thus, North* describes the big bang theory as involving "a discontinuity which has often been said to constitute a limit to that which may be known" and which cannot be explained causally,[178] and Weisskopf* states that "the question of what happened before has no concrete content" so that "[s]cientific description and explanation apply only to the events that happened afterwards."[179] Jastrow* argues that, because "an infinite or nearly infinite pressure, temperature and density . . . must necessarily have melted down and eradicated any material evidence left over from a pre-existing Universe," then "science will not be able to decipher the cause of the cosmic explosion . . .."[180]

Second, the theory of abrupt appearance consists of scientific laws, empirical data, and their scientific interpretation, as described in Volume 1.[181] It would be highly unscientific "to exclude data which lead to the conclusion that the universe, life and man" appeared abruptly, just because the theory allegedly cannot "explain that phenomenon in a lawlike way," as von Braun (the late Director of the NASA space program) argued:

> [T]he scientific method does not allow us to exclude data which lead to the conclusion that the universe, life and man are based on design. To be forced to believe only one conclusion—that everything in the universe happened by chance—would violate the very objectivity of science itself. . . .
>
> . . ..
>
> . . .The inconceivability of some ultimate issue (which will always lie outside scientific resolution) should not be allowed to rule out any theory that explains the interrelationship of observed data and is useful for prediction.[181A]

(b) Abrupt Appearance as a Natural Law. To the extent evolutionary singularities are viewed as involving natural laws that operated in the past, discontinuitist singularities can be viewed as involving natural laws of abrupt appearance as discussed earlier.

Summary. Most of the various definitions of science are satisfied comparably by the theory of abrupt appearance and the theory of evolution. That is true even under the *McLean* test and radical definition. The following quotations should be read in their full context above.

The natural laws requirement is partially met by both the theory of evolution and the theory of abrupt appearance. (a) Evolution is not guided by natural law in its critical origin events, because cosmic evolution includes the singularity of "the primary origin of matter or energy" (Stansfield*[182]) and the "big bang singularity when . . . we expect general relativity to break down" (Wald*[183]). Biochemical evolution similarly centers around a singularity of the origin of life "so extremely improbable that nothing can 'explain' why it originated" (Popper*[184]), and is a "unique event" that possibly "becomes an impenetrable barrier to science" (Popper*[185]). Biological evolution also confronts such information theory and probability problems that "an adequate scientific theory of [macro]evolution must await the discovery of new natural laws" (Eden*[186]).

Evolution is also not explanatory by natural laws in several basic senses. Macroevolution "cannot . . . explain any particular evolutionary change" in a plausible sense (Popper*[187]), although at the same time it "is so all-embracing that it can explain any outcome, and so is . . . an unscientific explanation," only explaining in a superficial sense (Sparkes*[188]). Darwinism similarly "explains nothing because it explains everything" (Lewontin*[189]). Natural selection shares the same fault in that it "fails to explain the origin of evolutionary novelties" and "fails to explain evolutionary diversity" (Rosen*[190]), so that many scientists and philosophers criticize it as nonexplanatory; and "[n]atural selection . . . turns out on closer inspection to be a tautology" that "the fittest individuals in a population (defined as those which leave the most offspring) will leave most offspring" (Waddington*[191]), as dozens of others criticize it. Not only is evolution nonexplanatory in critical areas, but "a number of critics" have claimed "that there can be no evolutionary laws" (Riddiford* and Penny*[192]), and that Darwinian theories do not " 'explain' in the sense that they enable events to be deduced from a set of initial conditions together with universal laws, in the way that physics and chemistry explain their respective fields" (Manser*[193]).

(b) The theories of abrupt appearance and of evolution are comparable in their extent of guidance and explanation by natural laws. The theory of abrupt appearance is guided by natural laws in that it explains certain natural processes and empirical evidence. Biological abrupt appearance rests on the natural laws of information science, those measured by probability laws, and the laws of genetics; and it builds on the empirical evidence of paleontology, comparative morphology, classification, comparative anatomy, and comparative biochemistry. Biochemical and cosmic abrupt appearance similarly are founded on the natural laws of information science, probability, biogenesis, and thermodynamics; and on the empirical evidence of isomers, anthropic considerations, galaxy and star formation, and polonium halo origin. The theory of abrupt appearance does not involve any more singularities than, but all the regularities of, the theory of evolution. Furthermore, a natural law of abrupt appearance may well exist, and that concept has a venerable history in the nomothetic theories of creation of Owen*, Sedgwick, and other great scientists (Gillespie*[194]). Thus, Good* concludes that "new biological type[s]" may "arise in some way within the meaning of the words *de novo*," and that there is a "possibility that occasionally in time and space, if no more frequently, there may have been involved an event of a different kind" from biological evolution (Good*[195]).

The theory of abrupt appearance also explains by natural laws, beyond the possibility of nomothetic abrupt appearances and beyond the scientific evidence of which the theory consists. Thus, "aspects of description and explanation (mechanism) are usually distinguished in science" (Riddiford* and Penny*[196]), and the "discovery of the patterns of nature may not necessitate a theory of their mechanism" (Brady*[197]). The theory of evolution lacks a mechanism to the same extent as does the theory of abrupt appearance, in that biologists "plead ignorance of the means of transformation" (Patterson*[198]), while cosmologists concede that a big bang involved "a discontinuity which has often been said to constitute a limit to that which may be known" or explained causally (North*[199]). In the field of origins, singularities pose "a barrier to further retrodiction" (Tipler*[200]), and "[s]cientific explanations . . ., in the old causal sense, are out of the question" (North*[201]). Even where singularities need not be posited, singular events generally limit investigation and proof.

On each point, the theories of evolution and abrupt appearance are parallel, incompletely guided by natural laws and not fully explainable by natural laws. The incomplete aspects arise from singularities, singular events, and possibly other features inherent in origin events, which also are parallel for the two theories. *Eivsdem farinae.*

Figure 10.3
"A strict application of a criterion of testability might rule out both," but "loose application will include both" (Strike) (a Mt. Wilson Observatory telescope)*

10.3 Comparable Testability of the Theories of Abrupt Appearance and Evolution

Any absolute requirement of testability as a demarcation of science, which has been criticized above in connection with the *McLean* test and the radical approach,[202] is also equally met by the theories of abrupt appearance and evolution. This section discusses (a) the testability of the theory of abrupt appearance, (b) the incomplete testability of some scientific concepts, and (c) the limited testability of evolution.

a. Testability of the Theory of Abrupt Appearance

The theory of abrupt appearance is testable in substantial part, as is the theory of creation.

(1) Testability of Numerous Central Elements. The affirmative lines of scientific evidence for the theory of abrupt appearance, in each of its three aspects, are testable. They involve the following testable aspects that are in fact central claims:

Aspect of Theory of Abrupt Appearance	*Affirmative Evidence*	*Testable Claim*
(a) Biological abrupt appearance:	(1) Paleontology argument of abrupt appearances:	The fossil record is characterized by generally systematic abrupt appearances of natural groups and of higher categories.
	(2) Paleontology argument of gaps:	The fossil record is characterized by systematic gaps between natural groups and between higher categories.
	(3) Comparative morphology argument:	The structure of fossilized organisms generally is systematically similar to their modern-day counterparts if nonextinct, and generally exhibits systematic stasis until the present or their extinction.
	(4) Information content argument:	The information content of all organisms, including their complex features and molecules, is sufficiently vast to render biological abrupt appearance more plausible and biological macroevolution extremely implausible.

	(5) Probability argument:	The mathematical probability is higher for biological abrupt appearance and vastly low for biological macroevolution of complex features, complex organs, and symbiotic relationships.
	(6) Genetics argument:	Genetic limits on the scope and frequency of viable mutations generally restrict viable variation or microevolution, provide genetic barriers between natural groups, and prevent biological macroevolution.
	(7) Comparative discontinuity argument:	Anomalies in classification, comparative anatomy, and comparative biochemistry are sufficiently extensive as to point more plausibly to discontinuous ancestry than common ancestry of various natural groups.
(b) Biochemical abrupt appearance:	(1) Information content argument:	The information content of the least complex organisms and their genetic coding systems is sufficiently vast to render biochemical abrupt appearance more plausible and biochemical evolution extremely implausible.
	(2) Probability argument:	The mathematical probability is higher for biochemical abrupt appearance and vastly low for biochemical evolution of the least complex organisms and of their enzymes, other proteins, and DNA.
	(3) Isomers argument:	The isomers in protein amino acids and nucleic acid sugars that are necessary to life are explained more plausibly by biochemical abrupt appearance and would not have arisen plausibly in a primordial soup or pond.
	(4) Biogenesis argument:	Life comes only from prior life and the general chemical tendency outside of a living organism is away from life and away from molecules necessary for life rather than toward life.
	(5) Thermodynamics argument:	The thermodynamic probability of the first life is higher for biochemical abrupt appearance and vastly low for biochemical evolution.

(c) Cosmic abrupt appearance:	(1) Thermodynamics argument:	The first and second laws of thermodynamics require a beginning for the universe and preclude its eternal existence.
	(2) Information content argument:	The information content of the universe is sufficiently vast to render cosmic abrupt appearance more plausible and cosmic evolution extremely implausible.
	(3) Anthropic principle argument:	The suitability of the universe for life is intricate and leaves cosmic abrupt appearance more plausible and cosmic evolution implausible.
	(4) Heterogeneity argument:	The heterogeneity of the universe is implausible under the big bang theory, and is more plausibly explained by cosmic abrupt appearance.
	(5) Star and galaxy formation argument:	The formation of galactic clusters, galaxies, stars, and the solar system requires extremely improbable conditions, and is more plausibly explained by cosmic abrupt appearance.
	(6) Radiohalos argument:	The polonium halos in the earth's crust require an abruptly appearing and initially cool earth, in the absence of uranium or thorium halos.

Each of these important parts of the theory of abrupt appearance is testable at least to the extent that the theory of evolution is.

The argument that the theory of abrupt appearance is false necessarily presupposes that it is testable and falsifiable. In other words, if empirical evidence can be brought against the truth of a proposition of the theory of abrupt appearance, then the theory must make empirical claims, and it must be theoretically possible to bring scientific evidence in support of those same empirical claims. The further argument that the theory of abrupt appearance is false in central or nonperipheral areas necessarily presupposes that it makes central or nonperipheral empirical claims, and that it is testable and falsifiable in central or nonperipheral areas. It is clearly special pleading to argue that the theory of abrupt appearance is just empirical enough to be tested and falsified, but not empirical enough to be sufficiently testable and falsifiable to be scientific. The scientific evidence in Chapters 2, 4, and 6 shows the contrary.

(2) Testability of the Theory of Creation. Not only is the theory of abrupt appearance testable, but even the scientific theory of creation is testable. Quinn* observes that "[c]reation-science as defined in [the Arkansas law even] clearly satisfies these conditions" of testability and falsifiability.[203] Laudan* similarly acknowledges its testability (while also strongly opposing the theory of creation):

> At various key points in the [*McLean*] Opinion, Creationism is charged with being untestable, dogmatic (and thus nontentative), and unfalsifiable. *All three charges are of dubious merit.* For instance, to make the inter-linked claims that Creationism is neither falsifiable nor testable is to assert that Creationism makes no *empirical assertions* whatever. That is surely *false. Creationists make a wide range of testable assertions about empirical matters of fact. . . .*
>
> In brief, these claims are *testable*, they have been tested, and they have failed those tests. Unfortunately, the logic of the Opinion's analysis precludes saying any of the above. . . . The correct way to combat Creationism is to confute the empirical claims it does make, *not to pretend that it makes no such claims at all.*[204]

Several leading evolutionists have acknowledged the testability of at least significant parts of the theory of creation (while believing that it has failed the tests), such as Gould*:

> Creationists do offer some *testable* statements, and these are amenable to scientific analysis. Why, then, do I continue to claim that creationism isn't science? Simply because these relatively few statements have been tested and conclusively refuted.[205]

Raup* concurs that the theory of creation makes a few testable arguments:

> In my view, a few of the arguments used by the creationists are "scientific" in the sense that they use the basic methods of *testing* hypotheses normally considered to be scientific. This does not mean, of course, that the conclusions are correct.[206]

(Section 10.3(c) discusses how the theory of evolution is not testable in most of its claims.[207])

The frequently made contention by evolutionists that the theory of creation is scientifically false, or contrary to scientific evidence, necessarily presupposes that the theory is testable by scientific data. For example, the National Academy of Sciences* published a booklet arguing as follows:

> Moreover, when the evidence for creationism has been subjected to the *tests* of the scientific method, it has been found invalid.[208]

To be subjected to "tests," the theory of creation must be testable, and Quinn* says so explicitly though disdainfully:

> The trouble with this claim is not that it is untestable or unfalsifiable. Its problem is rather that it has been *repeatedly tested* and is so highly

> disconfirmed that, for all practical purposes, it has been falsified.
>
> Unfortunately, the *patently false claim* that creation science is neither testable nor falsifiable seems well on its way to becoming, for some evolutionary biologists, a rhetorical stick with which to belabor their creationist opponents. . . .[209]

Darwin* himself clearly viewed the theory of creation as testable; Mayr* notes that, "[a]gain and again, he describes phenomena that do not fit the creation theory":

> Darwin himself had subscribed to this [creation] when he shipped on the "Beagle," and he was converted to his new ideas only after he had made *numerous observations that were to him quite incompatible with creation.* He felt strongly that he must establish this point decisively before his readers would be willing to listen to the evolutionary interpretation. *Again and again, he describes phenomena that do not fit the creation theory. Three sets of observations, in particular, impressed Darwin*: that fossils from South America are related to the living fauna of that continent rather than to contemporaneous fossils from elsewhere; that the faunas of the different climatic zones of South America are related to each other, rather than to animals of the same climatic zone on different continents; and, most important, that the faunas of islands (Falkland, Galapagos) are related to those of the nearest mainland and that related species occur on different islands of the same archipelago. Chapter 13 (pp. 349-387) is devoted largely to such evidence. Other cases are mentioned on page 95 (fossil lineages), page 129 (the order of the natural system), page 139 (the similarity of cave animals on all continents), page 167 (homologous variation in related species and genera), page 352 (disjunct distributions), pages 355 and 396-399 (the relationship of island species to those of the nearest continents), page 390 (the vulnerability of island species), page 394 (the unbalanced biota of volcanic and other oceanic islands), and pages 473-474 (rudimentary characters), to single out the more important instances. *All these observations were to Darwin incompatible with any creationist explanation*, yet were entirely consistent with an evolutionary interpretation.[210]

Obviously "numerous observations" can contradict an explanation only if it is testable and falsifiable, and surely Darwin* was not mistaken in thinking that his "one long argument" against the theory of creation was a scientific contest.

Contrary to Gould's* argument, the testable and falsifiable aspects of the theory of creation are not "peripheral" and minor,[211] at least in the estimation of Darwin*, his fellow anticreationists such as Huxley* and Haeckel*, or modern anticreationists such as Quinn* and the National Academy of Sciences* spokesmen. If the allegedly false aspects are nonperipheral, then the testable and falsifiable aspects are nonperipheral. Of course, if the theory of creation is subject to disproof by testing, then it is logically subject to confirmation by testing if supporting evidence exists. If its disproof is in central areas, its potential confirmation would be in central areas.

b. Incomplete Testability of Some Scientific Concepts

The existence of parts of the theory of abrupt appearance and of the theory of evolution that are not testable does not render either nonscientific. Incomplete testability is true of scientific theories generally, of the historical sciences generally, and of theories of origin as well.

(1) Nontestable Aspects of Science Generally. There are many nontestable aspects of science. There is a spectrum of scientific theories ranging from the "well-testable" to the "hardly testable," as Popper* states:

> There will be well-testable theories, hardly testable theories, and non-testable theories. Those which are non-testable are of no interest to empirical scientists. They may be described as metaphysical (Popper, 1965, p. 257).[212]

There is often a "protective belt of auxiliary theories" around the "core theory," and only the former is testable under Lakatos's* approach.[213] Brooks* and Wiley* agree:

> Scientific conceptual frameworks are often constructed as a core hypothesis and associated auxiliary hypotheses. The core hypothesis tends to be a simple and concise statement tendered as the fundamental truth encompassed by the conceptual framework. Two examples are "$E = MC^2$" from relativity theory and "earth and life evolve together" from panbiogeographical and vicariance biogeographical theory. . . . On the other hand, the simplicity of *core hypotheses* makes them *difficult to test directly*, and the research programs unified by the core hypothesis form a set of auxiliary hypotheses that tend to "buffer" the core hypothesis from direct testing. Since the auxiliary hypotheses are drawn from research programs, they should be highly amenable to direct testing. Thus, most of the testing of any new general theory involves the auxiliary hypotheses. . . .[214]

Furthermore, "many scientific claims are not testable in isolation," as Laudan* adds:

> It is now widely acknowledged that *many scientific claims are not testable in isolation*, but only when embedded in a larger system of statements, some of whose consequences can be submitted to test.[215]

Quinn* makes a similar point.[216] Finally, "theories often cannot be tested directly," Riddiford* and Penny* state.[217]

(2) Nontestable Aspects of the Historical Sciences. Nontestable

aspects are common to the historical sciences. "[W]e should treasure the legitimate difference between historical and non-historical science,"[218] which include "not just evolution but a suite of fundamental disciplines ranging from geology, to cosmology, to linguistics,"[219] to paleontology, to abiogenesis, Gould* points out.[220] Others too have distinguished historical sciences from other sciences, such as Simpson*,[221] Popper*,[222] and Ruse*.[223]

The basic distinction is that historical sciences involve "nonrepeatable events"[224] and "unique occurrences," whether singularities or singular events, according to Gould*:

> [T]he historical sciences try to explain unique occurrences—immensely complex historical accidents. Evolutionary biologists, as historical scientists, do not expect detailed repetition and cannot use the actual results of history to establish probabilities for recurrence (would a Caesar again die brutally in Rome if we could go back to *Australopithecus* in Africa and start anew? . . . Thus the improbabilities of history proclaim that each species is unique and unrepeatable in detail. . . .[225]

Dobzhansky* and others concur.[226] A related distinction is that historical sciences involve incomplete evidence.[227] Unique occurrences and incomplete evidence necessarily lead to incomplete testability.

One consequence of the inherent difference between historical sciences and other sciences is "the different methods used by all historical sciences" that "don't match stereotypes of '*the* scientific method',"[228] Gould* observes:

> We learn in high school about *the* scientific method—a cut-and-dried procedure of simplification to essential components, experiment in the controlled situation of a laboratory, prediction and replication. But the science of history—not just evolution but a suite of fundamental disciplines ranging from geology, to cosmology, to linguistics—can't operate by this stereotype. We are charged with explaining events of extraordinary complexity that occur but once in all their details. We try to understand the past, but don't pretend to predict the future. We can't see past processes directly, but learn to infer their operation from preserved results.
>
> Science is a pluralistic enterprise with a rich panoply of methods appropriate for different kinds of problems. Past events of long duration don't lie outside the realm of science because we cannot make them happen in a month within our laboratory. Direct vision isn't the only, or even the usual, method of inference in science. We don't see electrons, or quarks, or chemical bonds, any more than we see small dinosaurs evolve into birds, or India crash into Asia to raise the Himalayas.
>
> William Whewell, the great English philosopher of science during the early nineteenth century, argued that historical science can reach con-

> clusions, as well confirmed as any derived from experiment and replication in laboratories, by a method he called "consilience' (literally "jumping together") of inductions. . . .[229]

Thus, theories in historical sciences must be evaluated by analogy and circumstantial evidence rather than by normal direct and substantial testing, Ruse* states.[230] In doing so, "[t]he causal process is outside the realm of analysis for those investigating historically-based events," Cracraft* adds.[231] That of course opens historical sciences up to alternative scientific interpretations on a scale far greater than other sciences.

(3) Nontestable Aspects of Origins Theories. Beyond the partial nontestability of the historical sciences, nontestable aspects are endemic to theories of origin. Whereas the singular events of the historical sciences lead to incomplete testability, the singularities of events of origin even more strongly involve nonrepeatable events, fragmentary evidence, causation subject to different interpretations, and also different natural laws and nonuniformitarian processes.[232]

That incomplete testability is comparably characteristic of all theories of origin, because they are alternative explanations of the same singularities, singular events, and incomplete evidence. Specifically, incomplete testability is a parallel characteristic of the theory of abrupt appearance, the theory of creation, and the theory of evolution, not only because they involve historical sciences and incomplete evidence but because they involve origin events that included singularities. The parallel status of those theories is noted by Strike*:

> Siegel understands scientific claims to be statements that are empirically testable. They can be confirmed or falsified by observation or experiment. Other statements are metaphysical or religious in character. According to this test, Siegel claims, creationism is religion, not science. . . .
>
> . . ..
>
> But Siegel's test is problematic. It is a variation on a theme developed earlier in this century by philosophers whose goal was to find a way to distinguish science from metaphysics. Many modern philosophers have argued that such tests are unworkable. I agree. In this context, Siegel's test will not do the work that he wishes it to do. *Neither creationism nor evolution is rigorously testable.* Very general scientific theories usually do not generate numerous sharp predictions. Rather they generate approaches to investigating some class of phenomena. *A strict application of a criterion of testability might rule out both evolution and creation. A loose application will include both.*[233]

Gould* points out that "[e]volutionary biology is a quintessentially historical discipline," sharing the characteristics discussed above.[234] Bradie* and Gromko* conclude that biological evolution is partially testable in that it contains "testable and refutable empirical hypotheses" as well as hypotheses "relatively immune to the slings and arrows of experimental fortune."[235] Brady* distinguishes between "a testable part of the theory" and the "untested central thesis."[236]

c. *Limited Testability of the Theory of Evolution*

Evolution is not testable in critical aspects. These include the aspects that conflict with natural laws (as discussed above[237]), and also (1) several central parts of biological macroevolution or of Darwinism including natural selection and adaptation, as well as (2) critical parts of biochemical evolution and cosmic evolution.

(1) Partial Nontestability of Biological Macroevolution. The nontestability of one or more critical parts either of biological macroevolution or of Darwinism has been acknowledged by the following scientists and philosophers, who are discussed in this section (as well as by the others who call natural selection tautologous):

Popper*	Bradie*
Patterson*	Gromko*
Birch*	Harris*
Ehrlich*	Bethell*
Brady*	Stanley*
Cracraft*	Wassermann*
Macbeth*	O'Grady*
Saunders*	Cartmill*
Ho*	Bush*
Forey*	Peters*
Bertalanffy*	Whitfield*

For example, Popper* (the philosopher of science who developed the testability-falsifiability requirement) states of evolution: "It is metaphysical because it is not testable."[238] Patterson* finds evolution incompletely testable,[239] while Birch* and Ehrlich* find it nontestable.[240]

The limited testability of macroevolution has been noted by Brady*:

> But until the organism can be theoretically reduced to determinate laws, the theory is too incomplete to be testable.[241]

The "abundance of untestable statements in the literature" is described, in connection with axiomatic evolutionist reasoning, by Cracraft*:

> First, axiomatic reasoning, as it is employed by functional evolutionary morphology, simply does not increase our knowledge about process. It seduces investigators (particularly students) into thinking they are working on questions of general importance when they are not. Second, this form of axiomatic reasoning leads to an abundance of *untestable* statements in the literature.[242]

The primary reason is that macroevolution is "a historical theory, about unique events, and unique events are, by definition, . . . unrepeatable and so not subject to test."[243]

The limited testability of Darwinism has drawn much of the fire,[244] as Saunders* and Ho* note:

> In this section we consider in detail a number of tests of the theory that have been proposed, and we shall see how each of them fails. It is not just a question of lack of imagination on the part of neo-Darwinists. By its very nature, [the] *theory does not allow itself to be tested.*[245]

The central element, natural selection, has been most criticized as untestable, and Forey* is representative:

> Suffice it to say that there have been recent views (Løvtrup 1977; Macbeth 1973; Rosen 1978) expressing serious doubts about the theory of natural selection, or at least the ways in which it may be *tested* and placed on a scientific plane. I confess *sympathy* with these views.[246]

Brady* concurs in a thorough philosophy of science article:

> I shall argue, in the following discussion, that the real difficulty behind the recent criticisms is the *inconclusive empirical status of the theory* [*of natural selection*], and that the belief with which the theory is embraced by the defenders makes that empirical inconclusiveness all but invisible to them.[247]

The nontestability of natural selection is acknowledged by Bertalanffy*,[248] Bradie* and Gromko*,[249] and all the authors such as Harris*[250] and Bethell*[251] who target the tautology and nontestability problem of identifying the "fit" organisms for "survival of the fittest." In addition, the dual mechanism of natural selection and genetic drift renders each "no longer testable," Patterson* notes:

> When these two theories [natural selection and genetic drift] are combined, as a general explanation of evolutionary change, that general theory is *no longer testable.* Take natural selection: no matter how many cases fail to yield to a natural selection analysis, the theory is not threatened, for it can always be said that these failures of selection theory are explained by genetic drift. And no matter how many supposed examples of genetic drift are shown to be due, after all, to natural selection, the neutral theory is not threatened, for it never pretended to explain all evolution.[252]

Gould* has replied that the tautology criticism, and implicitly the nontestability criticism, is unjustified because an organism's fitness can be measured by the independent criterion of engineering design. Just as Rosen* found Gould's* response inadequate on the tautology criticism (as quoted in the last section), Brady* finds it inadequate on the nontestability criticism:

> Gould suggests that the crucial aspect is an integrated adaptive scheme, a design which is superior *a priori* to those other individuals in the population examined that do not possess it (superior, of course, in terms of its probability of survival in the selected environment). But if we allow nature to do the summing for us, after Hull's example, we never calculate the probability of survival, but simply identify the superior designs after the fact of survival, and then speculate on what led to this survival. *No test can be forthcoming if we act in this manner*, and this is the basis of Bethell's complaint. . . . Gould's reply . . . correctly shows that Darwin's theory was not tautologically formulated, . . . [but] I cannot see that Gould has answered Bethell at all. *He has never even mentioned the problem of testing. . . .*[253]

The leading alternative mechanism, punctuated equilibria, shares the problem of testability, because species selection shares the criticism "that natural selection operated with greatest effect exactly where it was least likely to be documented—in small, localized, transitory populations—would have seemed to render Darwin's new theory nontestable . . . ."[254]

The related concept of adaptation has similarly been criticized by Wassermann* as nontestable:

> The fact that numerous biologists have indulged in untestable *ad hoc* speculations about the manner in which specific adaptations could have been attained by natural selection does not vindicate their enterprise as being 'scientific'. Popper's attacks on such abuses of the concept of natural selection are fully justified.[255]

Brady* carries the point further:

> I have argued within it that until the organism is reduced to a determinate system, we have *not* the knowledge to mount a good *test* of optimalization theory—that is, we cannot question it. If that is so, it follows that the theory *has no empirical support*. Its strength comes from its logical power to generate explanations for every manner of organic *adaptation* rather than from the evidence, which, as we have seen, contains no potential for falsification. The theory may be true, but whether it is or not, it cannot be said to have shown evidence of this truth, and the widespread acceptance of the theory must rest on some other grounds.[256]

He is joined in that assessment by Popper*,[257] O'Grady*,[258] and others.[259] The widespread speculations about adaptation of specific organisms are "thoroughly untestable" and "an article of faith rather than a scientific statement," in the assessment of Cracraft*;[260] and are simply " 'just so' stories because the possibilities are limited only by imagination."[261]

There are other nontestable elements of macroevolution and Darwinism. One is phylogenies (one of the lines of alleged evidence for macroevolution),[262] as Cartmill* describes:

> A single phylogenetic hypothesis forbids nothing to happen, and therefore it *cannot be tested* (at least in Popper's sense). . . . Popperian phylogenetic reconstruction apparently is not [possible]. It follows that the study of phylogeny is not, by Popper's criteria, a science at all.[263]

Another nontestable area is speciation, as Bush* points out:

> Evolutionary biologists have not even been able to agree on a suitable definition of a species, a factor that in some respects has hindered our progress in unraveling the details of how speciation occurs in nature. . . . Ultimately, all our models must be recast in a molecular context; also, we must describe gene flow, selection, drift, and competition (and their consequences) in more exact terms. Only then can we formulate *testable* hypotheses of speciation. Until we know more about the molecular machinery of adaptation—that is, what is and is not possible at the molecular level—our models of speciation must remain little more than speculation based on the subjective interpretation of equivocal data.[264]

A further area is ecology in its relationship to evolution, which Peters* says "cannot make empirically testable predictions."[265] Among the other examples is the evolution of eukaryotes, which Whitfield* suggests incorporates enough "special pleading" that little "could be tested unambiguously against experimental findings."[266]

(2) Partial Nontestability of Biochemical and Cosmic Evolution. Similarly, the critical element of biochemical evolution—abiogenesis—is not fully testable, Green* and Goldberger* conclude:

> [T]he macromolecule-to-cell transition is a jump of fantastic dimensions, which lies *beyond the range of testable hypothesis*. In this area *all is conjecture*. The available facts do not provide a basis for postulating that cells arose on this planet.[267]

The same is true of an important element of cosmic evolution—the origin of matter and energy, Simpson* notes:

> Yet the *origin of that cosmos* and the causal principles of its history remain unexplained and *inaccessible* to science. Here is hidden the first cause sought by theology and philosophy.[268]

The big bang theory is also nontestable in part, both because the big bang would have been a singularity and because it destroyed all evidence of its first fractional second and of the prior state of the universe.[269]

Summary. The theories of abrupt appearance and of evolution are comparably testable: Strike* notes that "[a] strict application of a criterion of testability might rule out both," but "[a] loose application will include both" (Strike*[270]).

(a) The theory of abrupt appearance is testable in central elements that correspond to the eighteen lines of affirmative scientific evidence described in Chapters 2, 4, and 6. Those evolutionists who claim that the theory of abrupt appearance is false or falsified thereby concede that it makes central empirical claims and is testable in regard to those claims. Even the theory of creation "clearly satisfies" the requirement of testability (Quinn*[271]), "make[s] a wide range of testable assertions about empirical matters of fact" (Laudan*[272]), "offer[s] some testable statements" (Gould*[273]), makes "a few . . . arguments" that "are 'scientific' in the sense that they use the basic methods of testing hypotheses" (Raup*[274]), and was viewed by Darwin* as testable in numerous areas (Mayr*[275]).

(b) A scientific theory or model need not be, and rarely is, completely testable. The "core theory" often cannot be tested directly or even indirectly, while the "protective belt of auxiliary theories" typically is testable (Sparkes*[276]). "[M]any scientific claims are not testable in isolation, but only when embedded in a larger system of statements" (Laudan*[277]). Incomplete testability is typical of the historical sciences, because "the historical sciences try to explain unique occurrences" or singular events (Gould*[278]) and use "different methods" that "don't match stereotypes of 'the scientific method' " (Gould*[279]). Partial nontestability is particularly typical of theories of origin, because they involve singularities as well as singular events that not only are nonrepeatable but were governed by potentially different laws (Section 9.4(a)(3)).

(c) The theory of evolution is "a historical theory, about unique events, and unique events are, by definition, . . . unrepeatable and so not subject to test" (Patterson*[280]). It has an "untested central thesis" as well as "testable part[s] of the theory" (Brady*[281]). As for Darwinism, the "theory does not allow itself to be tested" (Saunders* and Ho*[282]), and "there have been recent views expressing serious doubts about the theory of natural selection, or at least the ways in which it may be tested and placed on a scientific plane" (Forey*[283]). For neo-Darwinism, there is "an abundance of untestable statements in the literature" (Cracraft*[284]). For punctuated equilibria and species selection just as for neo-Darwinism and natural selection, the argument that "selection operated with greatest effect exactly where it was least likely to be documented—in small, localized, transitory populations—would have seemed to render [the] new theory nontestable" (Stanley*[285]). Other evolutionary elements such as adaptation involve "untestable *ad hoc* speculations" (Wassermann*[286]) and " 'just so' stories because the possibilities are limited only by the imagination" (Brady*[287]). *Maior e longinquo reverentia.*

Figure 10.4
Karl Popper, the formulator of falsification: "Darwinism is not a testable scientific theory, but a metaphysical research programme"*

10.4 Comparable Falsifiability of the Theories of Abrupt Appearance and Evolution

The falsifiability requirement, which has been criticized above,[288] is also equally met by the theories of abrupt appearance and evolution. Both are in large part falsifiable, and both are partially unfalsifiable. This section first addresses (a) the central falsifiable aspects of the theory of abrupt appearance, (b) the partial falsifiability of some scientific concepts, and then (c) the significant unfalsifiable elements of the theory of evolution.

a. *Falsifiability of the Theory of Abrupt Appearance*

(1) Falsifiability of Numerous Central Elements. Each of the

affirmative lines of scientific evidence for the theory of abrupt appearance is falsifiable, just as each is testable. For example, the theory of biological abrupt appearance includes the paleontology arguments about the systematic abrupt appearances of complex organisms in the fossil record and the systematic gaps between those organisms. Those aspects of the theory could be falsified by fossil evidence of a systematically nonabrupt appearance of complex life and of systematic transitional forms between fossil natural groups and higher categories. Similarly, each of the other affirmative arguments for the theory of abrupt appearance, which were described in Volume 1, is clearly falsifiable as follows:

Aspect of Theory of Abrupt Appearance	*Affirmative Evidence*	*Falsification Method*
(a) Biological abrupt appearance:	(1) Paleontology argument of abrupt appearances:	By fossils showing a systematically nonabrupt appearance of complex natural groups and higher categories.
	(2) Paleontology argument of gaps:	By fossils showing systematic transitional forms between such fossil categories.
	(3) Comparative morphology argument:	By morphology analysis showing a systematic dissimilarity between fossil organisms and their modern-day counterparts if not extinct, and a systematic progressive change rather than stasis.
	(4) Information content argument:	By showing that the information content of organisms plausibly could have evolved under natural laws within the generally accepted time available.
	(5) Probability argument:	By showing that the probability of macroevolution of complex organisms, of all complex features and organs, and of symbiotic relations is plausibly high under natural laws within the generally accepted time available.

	(6) Genetics argument:	By showing that viable mutations of a scope and frequency sufficient to cross genetic barriers between natural groups and higher categories could with a high probability have occurred within the generally accepted time available.
	(7) Comparative discontinuity argument:	By showing that anomalies in classification, comparative anatomy, and comparative biochemistry are statistically insignificant or sufficiently nonextensive to be better explained by common ancestry than by discontinuous ancestry of natural groups.
(b) Biochemical abrupt appearance:	(1) Information content argument:	By showing that the information content of the least complex organisms and their genetic coding systems could plausibly have evolved during the generally accepted time available.
	(2) Probability argument:	By showing that the probability of evolution of the least complex living organisms including their enzymes, proteins, and DNA is plausibly high within the generally accepted time available.
	(3) Isomers argument:	By showing that isomers of protein amino acids and nucleic acid sugars are not generally necessary to life, or could plausibly have arisen in a primordial soup or other evolutionary scenario.
	(4) Biogenesis argument:	By showing a plausible method of overcoming the vast gulf between nonlife and life and of overcoming the cross-reaction, isomer, dilution, radiation, and investigator interference problems and improbable conditions.
	(5) Thermodynamics argument:	By showing a high thermodynamic probability of evolution of a first life.

(c) Cosmic abrupt appearance:	(1) Thermodynamics argument:	By showing that the quantities of matter and antimatter are equal and that both could have come into existence and remained separate by natural means, and by showing either that an eternal universe would not have burned up most of its hydrogen and dissipated most of its complex order or that a mechanism exists for reducing entropy in the universe.
	(2) Information content argument:	By showing that the vast information content in the universe could plausibly have evolved by natural laws.
	(3) Anthropic principle argument:	By showing that the suitability of the universe to life is statistically probable, or that other forms of life can and do exist under various other conditions.
	(4) Heterogeneity argument:	By showing that the heterogeneity or uneven distribution of the universe plausibly could have arisen from the big bang or other phenomenon.
	(5) Star and galaxy formation argument:	By showing that the formation of galactic clusters, galaxies, stars, and solar systems could plausibly have occurred under natural laws within the generally accepted time available, and is still occurring on a significant scale in the universe.
	(6) Radiohalos argument:	By showing a plausible method for a polonium halo either to form in molten rock, to form on a cool earth other than from radioactive decay, or to be incorporated in nonfractured granites and cordierites, all without uranium or thorium traces.

That chart makes it clear that the theory of abrupt appearance is falsifiable to the same extent as is the theory of evolution. An example of the falsifiability of those lines of evidence involves the radiohalos argument, in connection with which the primary researcher has publicly stated in published letters in a science journal the specific method of falsifying his findings and interpretations.[289]

Evolutionists who wish to argue that the theory of abrupt appearance is false thereby concede that it is falsifiable, as well as empirical and testable. Those who suggest that disproved aspects are significant thereby identify the falsifiable aspects as significant ones. It is simply not logical or honest to argue both that the theory of abrupt appearance is false in central claims and yet is not falsifiable in central claims. (The falsity or verity of its scientific claims are discussed in Chapters 2, 4, and 6.)

(2) Falsifiability of the Theory of Creation. The theory of creation also is substantially falsifiable, as an ideological opponent, Laudan*, concedes:

> [W]e discover both (a) that creation-science is *testable and falsifiable*, and (b) that creation-science has been tested and falsified—insofar as any theory can be said to be falsified.[290]

Another opponent, Quinn*, similarly acknowledges that the theory of creation "clearly satisfies" the falsifiability requirement.[291]

The argument that the theory of creation is false amounts to a concession that it is falsifiable in the allegedly false areas. Quinn* thus objects to Gould's* contradictory position as unfair "verbal abuse":

> In a recent collection of essays, Stephen Jay Gould claims that " 'scientific creationism' is a self-contradictory nonsense phrase precisely because it cannot be falsified".... Ironically, in the next sentence Gould goes on to contradict himself by asserting that "the individual claims are easy enough to refute with a bit of research." Indeed, some of them are! But since they are easily refuted by research, *they are after all falsifiable and, hence, testable.* This glaring inconsistency is the tip-off to the fact that talk about testability and falsifiability functions as *verbal abuse and not as a serious argument* in Gould's anti-creationist polemics.[292]

A similar objection is raised to Ruse's* argument that some advocates of the theory of creation erect "protective belts of auxiliary hypotheses" around that theory (as Lakatos* says most scientists do):

> Ruse goes on to say, even if creation scientists do expose their theories to tests, "when new counter-empirical evidence is discovered, creation

> scientists appear to pull back, refusing to allow their positions to be falsified." This remark too, even if accurate, is *utterly beside the point.* The requirement is that a theory *be* falsifiable by empirical evidence, not that its adherents *admit* that it has been falsified if and when it has been. Once creation scientists make testable assertions, as they have, it is up to the evidence and not to them whether those assertions are disconfirmed to the point of being falsified. Hence, Ruse's main reasons for considering creation science untestable and unfalsifiable turn out to be, upon inspection, nothing more than two irrelevant *ad hominem* arguments.[293]

Sparkes* notes that both the theory of evolution and the theory of creation "can be protected, if we so choose," from falsification by virtue of those auxiliary hypotheses.[294]

b. Partial Falsifiability of Some Scientific Concepts

The existence of unfalsifiable parts does not make either the theory of abrupt appearance or the theory of evolution nonscientific, because partial unfalsifiability is possible for scientific explanations.[295] For example, "[t]here is no way that the Cell Theory can be falsified," Moore* concedes.[296] Lakatos* described the unfalsifiable core and partially or fully falsifiable auxiliary hypotheses of a research program:

> Lakatos has started from a position similar to that of Popper but like Kuhn has again developed the idea that scientific theories are protected from conflicting empirical data. Accordingly he claims *Popper's [falsifiability] criterion for demarcation must be altered.* Lakatos describes how scientific theories are arranged in hierarchies in which core theories, presumably equivalent to Kuhn's paradigms, are *protected from refutation by the presence of auxiliary hypotheses.*
>
> The basic unit of appraisal must not be an isolated theory or conjunction of theories but rather a "research programme" with a conventionally accepted (and thus by provisional decision *"irrefutable")* *"hard core"* and with a "positive heuristic" which defines problems, outlines the construction of a *belt of auxiliary hypotheses*, foresees anomalies and turns them victoriously into examples, all according to a preconceived plan (Lakatos, 1976, p. 9).[297]

Frequently "the general formula itself is not subject to falsification although its concrete interpretations are," Bradie* and Gromko* add.[298]

Partial falsifiability particularly applies to the historical sciences and theories of origin, as does the related concept of partial testability. Gould* describes "historical sciences" as the opposite of "falsifiable sciences."[299] Riddiford* and Penny*, in discussing theories of origin, "do not accept the criterion that a theory must be directly falsifiable," as long as it can lead to some testable predictions.[300] The reason is that historical sciences involve incomplete evidence and singular events, and origins events involve singularities. That is quite evident in connection with the theory of evolution.

c. Limited Falsifiability of the Theory of Evolution

Evolution is only partially falsifiable. That is true of (1) biological macroevolution, and also of (2) biochemical evolution and cosmic evolution.

(1) Partial Unfalsifiability of Biological Macroevolution. The criticism has been widely made that all or part of macroevolution, Darwinism, and critical aspects are unfalsifiable. The critics include the following philosophers and scientists:

Sparkes*	Cartmill*
Patterson	Schwabe*
Popper*	Warr*
Cracraft*	Peters*
Wald*	Løvtrup* (Darwinism)
Saunders*	Brady* (central claims)
Ho*	Bethell*
Weisskopf*	Bradie*
Birch*	Gromko*
Ehrlich*	Nelson*
	Platnick*

Their specific positions are described in the following paragraphs.

Macroevolution has been questioned, in terms of its falsifiability, by Sparkes*:

> If then, as seems reasonable, science is to be thought of as an adaptive or feedback process, why is it that another adaptive process, *evolution, seems to have difficulty in establishing its scientific credentials*? . . .
>
> . . ..
>
> . . . This unpredictability, of course, makes *experimental falsification of the theory very difficult*, and so, by Popper's criterion, *leaves the scientific status of the theory unsure*. . . .[301]

Patterson*[302] and apparently Gould*[303] concur.

Darwinism has drawn more criticism because of partial or total unfalsifiability. Popper*, the philosopher of science who developed the falsification concept, has argued that Darwinian evolution is unfalsifiable at least in large part,[304] although he has written subsequently to clarify that he is not questioning its scientific status,[305] as Miller* and Fowler* correctly state:

> Popper has since stated publicly that such a use of this quote to deny the scientific status of evolutionary theory is improper. Nevertheless, his words seem to lend credence to the view that evolutionary theory is not science but metaphysics . . ..[306]

Cracraft* summarizes the problem of Darwinism:

> As critics have already discovered, neo-Darwinism is a resilient bugger; but it is not so greatly resistant to conceptual challenge as are *neo-Darwinists liberal in their willingness to accept virtually anything within their paradigm*. Of course, defenders of the faith thereby weaken their main claim: *how can neo-Darwinism be considered a meaningful theoretical construct if all presumptive conflicting observations are immediately considered to be part-and-parcel of the theory*? This ever-widening scope of neo-Darwinism is both a boon and a bane for its critics. A boon, because if neo-Darwinism continues to *swallow up any and all challenges*, then *eventually it will forfeit any claim to be taken seriously as a scientific theory*; a bane, because critics have an increasingly difficult time focusing on the core of neo-Darwinism as it *becomes more and more amorphous*. . . .[307]

Similar criticisms have been made by Wald*,[308] Saunders* and Ho*,[309] Weisskopf*,[309] Birch* and Ehrlich*,[310] Cartmill*,[311] Schwabe* and Warr*,[312] and Peters*.[313] For example, Saunders* and Ho* state that neo-Darwinism is unfalsifiable:

> Neo-Darwinism, the theory that evolution can be adequately explained in terms of the natural selection of random variations, is *not falsifiable*. Many of the potential falsifiers that have been suggested turn out to be tests not of Neo-Darwinism but of something else, frequently of the hypothesis that evolution has occurred. Others, such as those having to do with non-adaptedness and gradualism, are inherently incapable of providing conclusive tests. The remainder . . . are so hedged about with qualifications as to make the theory invulnerable.
>
> . . ..
>
> . . . The synthetic theory possesses a remarkable elasticity: when under attack it expands to include almost anything, but once the pressure is relaxed it contracts to the definition given by Maynard Smith.[315]

Løvtrup* concludes that neoDarwinism "is either falsified, or else it is an unfalsifiable, hence metaphysical theory."[316]

Natural selection in particular has been criticized as unfalsifiable, as Brady* describes:

> [M]ost recent critics have already understood this and are actually arguing that the theory is *not falsifiable* in its operational form. Under examination, the operational forms of the concepts of adaptation and fitness turn out to be too indeterminate to be seriously tested, for they are protected by ad hoc additions drawn from an indeterminate realm. . . .[317]

Others making the unfalsifiability criticism include Eldredge* and Gould* (in connection with phyletic gradualism),[318] Wald*,[319] Bethell*[320] (whose criticism by Gould*[321] has been rejected by Brady*[322]), Bradie* and Gromko*,[323] and Wassermann*.[324] Furthermore, because "tautologies are not subject to empirical falsification,"[325] most of the scientists who argue that natural selection or Darwinism is a tautology[326] would conclude that one or both is unfalsifiable.

Other aspects of Darwinian evolution confront the same problem. In connection with the systematics or classification argument, "Nelson and . . . Platnick lodge a frontal assault on Darwinism in systematics by claiming it to be falsified."[327] In reference to functional morphology arguments, Gould* finds that "the premise of good design . . . used as an a priori assumption rather than a hypothesis to be accepted or rejected . . . is unfalsifiable since failure of one adaptive story merely calls forth the invention of an alternative—and scientists have never been short on imagination."[328] Wassermann* agrees.[329] In reference to the phylogeny argument, Cartmill* concludes "that phylogenetic hypotheses are not falsifiable . . . ."[330] In connection with the biochemistry argument, Schwabe* finds that the excuse of "faster and slower rates of evolution" make it "unfalsifiable" and "eliminate[] a paradigm from the roster of hypotheses of science."[331] He and Warr* find monophyletic molecular evolution equally unfalsifiable.[332]

(2) Partial Unfalsifiability of Biochemical and Cosmic Evolution. Biochemical evolution and cosmic evolution also are in part unfalsifiable, both because they involve singularities[333] and because they involve fragmentary evidence. That fragmentary evidence results not only from macroevolution leaving fossils only of a small percentage of organisms, but from evolution of the first life not leaving fossil or other remains, and the evolutionary big bang destroying some of its own manifestations. For the big bang and similar explanations, "in the nature of the case neither group can be verified or falsified in any observationally direct manner."[334]

Summary. The theory of abrupt appearance and the theory of evolution are comparably falsifiable, as would be expected from their comparable testability.

(a) The theory of abrupt appearance, which consists of at least eighteen empirical lines of evidence, is falsifiable on each point. For example, its paleontology argument of abrupt appearances of natural groups and higher categories can be falsified by fossils showing systematic nonabrupt appearances of natural groups and of higher taxons. Those who argue that the theory is false in significant parts thereby concede that it is falsifiable in significant aspects. Even the theory of creation, which is different from the theory of abrupt appearance, is "falsifiable and, thence, testable" (Quinn*[335]), and is "testable and falsifiable" (Laudan*[336]), although those authors regard it as false.

(b) Partial unfalsifiability is as permissible for a scientific theory or hypothesis as partial testability. The core of many scientific research programs is unfalsifiable, while the belt of auxiliary hypotheses is falsifiable (Lakatos*[337]), and "the general formula is not subject to falsification although its concrete interpretations are" (Bradie* and Gromko*[338]). Partial unfalsifiability is particularly characteristic of historical sciences and origins.

(c) The theory of evolution is only partially falsifiable. Macroevolution "seems to have difficulty in establishing its scientific credentials" because "experimental falsification of the theory [is] very difficult" (Sparkes*[339]). "Neo-Darwinism . . . is not falsifiable," because "[m]any of the potential falsifiers that have been suggested turn out to be tests not of Neo-Darwinism but of something else," while "[o]thers, such as those having to do with non-adaptedness and gradualism, are inherently incapable of providing conclusive tests," and "[t]he remainder . . . are so hedged about the qualifications as to make the theory invulnerable" (Saunders* and Ho*[340]). Natural selection is widely criticized as unfalsifiable (Wassermann*[341]), as are other elements of Darwinism, biochemical evolution, and cosmic evolution. *Probitas laudatur et alget?*

10.5 Comparable Tentativeness of the Theories of Abrupt Appearance and Evolution

The tentativeness requirement of the *McLean* test and radical definition of science, which has been criticized earlier as erroneous and as simply not a normal characteristic of science,[342] is at least equally met by the theory of abrupt appearance and the theory of evolution. In fact, a strong argument can be made that the theory of abrupt appearance is generally far more tentatively held by most supportive scientists than the theory of evolution is held by most advocates, in view of the insistence of many leading evolutionists on calling evolution a "fact" and in view of the emotional zeal of many

Figure 10.5
Tentativeness: "today it is the conventional neo-Darwinians who appear as the conservative bigots and the unorthodox neo-Sedgwickians who rate as enlightened rationalists prepared to contemplate the evidence" (Leach) (picture of Adam Sedgwick of Cambridge, Darwin's* teacher and opponent)*

evolutionists in defending evolution and attacking alternatives. Leach* makes that observation (Sedgwickians were early creationist scientists):

> [T]oday it is the conventional *neo-Darwinians* who appear as the conservative *bigots* and the unorthodox neo-*Sedgwickians* who rate as *enlightened rationalists* prepared to contemplate the evidence that is plain for all to see.[343]

This is discussed in reference to (a) the tentativeness of the theory of abrupt appearance and then (b) the dogmatism of many advocates of evolution.

a. Tentativeness of the Theory of Abrupt Appearance

(1) Tentativeness and the Theory of Abrupt Appearance. The tentativeness normally accompanying the theory of abrupt appearance is evident in its scientific content that does not conduce to religious fervor (Chapters 2, 4, and 6), its ability to discard any lines of empirical argument that are disproved, and its historical background that involved dispassionate analysis (Section 15.2(a)).

(2) Tentativeness and the Theory of Creation. The comparable tentativeness (or revisability) of the theories of creation and evolution has been noted by Professor Laudan*:

> Judge Overton's third worry about Creationism centers on the issue of revisability. Over and over again, he finds Creationism and its advocates "unscientific" because they have "refuse[d] to change it regardless of the evidence developed during the course of the[ir] investigation." In point of fact, the charge is *mistaken*. If the claims of modern-day creationists are compared with those of their nineteenth-century counterparts, *significant shifts* in orientation and assertion are evident. One of the most visible opponents of Creationism, Stephen Gould, concedes that creationists have modified their views about the amount of variability allowed at the level of species change. *Creationists do, in short, change* their minds from time to time. Doubtless they would credit these shifts to their efforts to adjust their views to newly emerging evidence, in what they imagine to be a scientifically respectable way.
>
> . . . .
>
> Even worse, the *ad hominem* charge of dogmatism against Creationism egregiously *confuses doctrines with the proponents of those doctrines*. . . . What counts is the epistemic status of Creationism, not the cognitive idiosyncrasies of the creationists. Because many of the theses of Creationism are testable, the mindset of creationists has no bearing in law or in fact on the merits of Creationism.[344]

An example of tentativeness is the general questioning or rejection by creationists of the earlier position that tracks in the Paluxy River area were of dinosaurs and humans contemporaneously.[345] In fact, Eldredge* notes that "none other than a creationist . . . has blown the whistle on these tracks."[346] Thus, the theory of creation has indeed been tentative enough to change, and the faults of creationist scientists are a different issue from its scientific nature.[347]

b. Nontentativeness and Dogmatism of the Theory of Evolution

By contrast, evolution is generally or at least often proclaimed dogmatically and nontentatively.

(1) Insistence on Evolution as Fact. That is evident in the many strong affirmations of the most committed evolutionists, such as Sagan*, that "evolution is a fact, not a theory,"[348] and Ruse*, that "Evolution is a fact, *fact, FACT!*" (his emphasis).[349] Asimov* writes that "the evidence in favor of evolution is so strong that no reputable biologist doubts the fact . . .,"[350] and Thomas* says "[t]here can no longer be any question at all, in any educated mind, that the species in today's world evolved from precursor creatures in a line stretching all the way back to the bacteria-like fossils," "[n]or can the central role played by Darwinian natural selection be held in question. These are matters of scientific fact, as solid as any available to

mankind."[351] Those remarks would surprise the reputable biologists and educated minds, summarized in Section 3.2(f), who reject macroevolution as well as creation, and the reputable biologists, summarized in Sections 3.2(d), 3.3(a), and 10.2(a), who deny the "central role played by Darwinian natural selection."

Examples of evolutionist dogmatism abound. Lewontin* recently called for evolutionists "to state clearly that evolution is a *fact*, not theory," while deriding the "creationist know-nothings."[352] The administrative office of the National Association of Biology Teachers (comprising mostly public high school teachers) published a list of assertions by notable scientists that evolution is a "fact,"[353] while public high school textbooks often make assertions that there is "no longer any reasonable doubt that evolution occurs."[354] Many other things have been scientific "facts" too; for example, Haeckel* stated that the "existence of ether (or cosmic ether) as a real element is a positive fact."[354A] Einstein* and subsequent scientists disagreed.

Nonetheless, when terms are properly defined, biological macroevolution and Darwinism are *not* generally regarded as fact, as discussed in Section 3.1(c). For Darwinian evolution and biochemical evolution, "its explanation on the basis of recognized processes is still in the stage of *partly demonstrated* theory or, in the case of the origin and early differentiation of the first cellular organisms, a *working hypothesis*," in the words of leading evolutionists Dobzhansky*, Ayala*, Stebbins*, and Valentine*.[355] Moreover, "[b]y calling evolution fact, the process of evolution is removed from dispute" on its merits and "becomes a sacred archetype."[356]

The origin of dogmatism about evolution can be traced to Darwin* himself, and Cannon* with regret finds such dogmatism beneficial to science:

> Here I think we will eventually find the secret of Darwin's greatness, in two traits not always praised in theories of 'how to conduct yourself scientifically.' One is *Darwin's notorious habit of jumping to conclusions without adequate evidence*. He developed his coral reef theory, we remember, before examining coral reefs. The other is that of *stubbornly maintaining* his theories regardless of the valid arguments and evidence that could be brought against them. . . .
>
> These are procedures to be recommended, of course, only to the great; and I come to the regrettable conclusion that *science takes great strides forward* not primarily from laborious research, but rather *when some biased person maintains his intuitions in public*, and when, thereafter, generations of scientists find that some of these intuitions do actually illuminate whatever work they are doing.[357]

Brady* joins in that analysis.[358]

(2) Religious Fervor of Faith in Evolution. That dogmatism has led many evolutionists and noncreationists to criticize the "religious fervor" of some outspoken evolutionists, as Grene* says:

> To-day the tables are turned. The modified, but still characteristically Darwinian theory has itself become an orthodoxy, preached by its adherents with *religious fervour*, and doubted, they feel, only by a few muddlers imperfect in scientific faith.[359]

Those concurring that evolution too often involves religious faith include Midgley* in the recent book *Evolution as a Religion*,[360] Lipson*,[361] Jaki*,[362] Patterson*,[363] Macbeth*,[364] and Jastrow*.[365] Lessl* notes the "inherent religiosity of *Cosmos*," the leading book by Sagan*.[366] For example, Burton*, a former president of the American Physiological Society, describes "worship of the principle of natural selection":

> The facts must mold the theories, not the theories the fact. . . . I am most critical of my biologist friends in this matter. It seems to me that they have allowed what is a most useful *working hypothesis* in a limited field in the whole of biology, to become "*dogma*," in their *worship* of the principle of natural selection as the only and sufficient operator in evolution. If they have done this, they no longer can act as true scientists when examining evidence that might not fit into this frame of concepts. If you do not believe me, try telling a biologist that, impartially judged along with other accepted theories of science, such as the theory of relativity, it seems to you that the theory of natural selection has a very uncertain, hypothetical status, and watch his reaction. I'll bet you that he gets red in the face. *This is "religion" not "science" with him.*[367]

Evolutionary "dogmatism" has been criticized by Brady* and others:

> What is at stake is not the validity of the Darwinian theory itself, but of the approach to science that it has come to represent. The peculiar form of consensus the theory wields has produced a premature closure of inquiry in several branches of biology, and even if this is to be expected in 'normal science,' such a *dogmatic* approach does not appear healthy.[368]

It has led Stansfield* to state in his college evolution textbook that "[p]erhaps the greatest contribution creationists are currently making to science is their recognition of 'creeping dogmatism' in the science of evolution."[369] Gould* finds "that gradualism has acted as a restrictive dogma,"[370] and Scott* laments that origin of life researchers sometimes exhibit a similar attitude.[371]

Summary. The theory of abrupt appearance is generally more tentatively held than the theory of evolution: "today it is the conventional neo-Darwinians who appear as the conservative bigots and the unorthodox neo-Sedgwickians who rate as enlightened rationalists prepared to contemplate the evidence" (Leach*[372]). Many evolutionists proclaim that "Evolution is a fact, *fact*, *FACT*!" (Ruse*[373]), without forthrightly proclaiming that only microevolution is a fact (accepted by discontinuitists too) while macroevolution and Darwinism are theories subject to reasonable dispute (Section 3.1(c), Dobzhansky* *et al.*[374]). Further, "Darwinism is a creed not only with scientists committed to document the all-purpose role of natural selection," but "with masses of people who have at best a vague notion of the mechanism of evolution as proposed by Darwin, let alone as further complicated by his successors" (Jaki*[375]).

10.6 Other Comparable Characteristics of the Theories of Abrupt Appearance and Evolution

Many other characteristics of science have been proposed, and generally are comparably exhibited by the theories of abrupt appearance and of evolution. This section focuses on (1) comparable limits on prediction, (b) comparable integrity of scientific work, and (c) comparable descriptive criteria of science.

a. Comparable Limitations on Prediction

Although generation of predictions is not properly a requirement of science,[376] it is an area of parallels between the theories of abrupt appearance and evolution. For any "sciences of history," scientists "don't pretend to predict the future,"[377] and "eschew[] prediction while seeking explanation" of "immensely complex and nonrepeatable events,"[378] Gould* states. For the field of origins, singularities and singular occurrences are critical events, and they are not subject to prediction because they have occurred and will occur only once.[379] It is important to note that theories "simply cannot be given predictive credit for everything they agree with," as Brady* says:

> Theories, qua theories, simply cannot be given predictive credit for everything they agree with. They can never be uniquely responsible for an entire canon (of known facts in field) but share this with any number of possible contenders. We are speaking here, of course, of theories as postulations whose relation to the world is yet to be determined. Once we are convinced that we know that relation, however, and that the theory in question is true, we may indeed assign it complete responsibility for the canon, discarding all other explanations, for it is now identified with

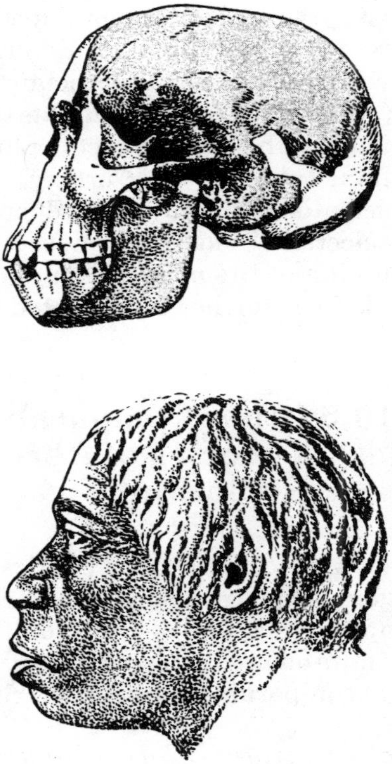

Figure 10.6
Piltdown Man: "the exposure . . . does, in fact, weaken [Darwinists'] position" because of the "zeal with which eminent scientists defended it . . . and the way in which the most respected scientific techniques were soberly and painstakingly applied" (Himmelfarb)*

reality. Since Maynard Smith argues that to postulate counter-examples to his understanding of neo-Darwinism we should have to imagine the world quite otherwise than it is, he has evidently taken the step in question. Predictably, any audience sharing his belief will be unlikely to notice that no empirical support can result from the procedure.[380]

Macroevolution does not make meaningful predictions, according to Peters*:

> The essence of the argument is that these 'theories' are actually tautologies and, as such, cannot make empirically testable predictions. They are not scientific theories at all.[381]

"The evolutionary development of a particular species or population as such cannot be predicted with any reasonable degree of certainty," Hull* adds.[382]

Similarly, "modern evolutionists admit that Darwinism has no predictive power," Macbeth says.[383] "None of the elements within the [evolutionary] feedback loop (e.g. the form of the surviving species) is reliably predictable," Sparkes* states.[384] The inability to make predictions is also true of natural selection, according to Mayr*:

> The theory of natural selection can describe and explain phenomena with considerable precision, but it cannot make reliable predictions.[385]

The same is true of the concept of adaptation, Brady* states.[386] And it is true of many steps in evolution, such as the evolution of eukaryotes: "All hypotheses in this area of speculation are so multifaceted that it is extraordinarily difficult to set predictive tests . . . ."[387]

b. Comparable Integrity of Scientific Work

Although scientific integrity is a characteristic of individual scientists rather than a line of demarcation between science and nonscience, it is comparably met by the theories of abrupt appearance and evolution.

(1) Irrelevance of Professional Integrity to Demarcation. As part of his proposed demarcation between science and nonscience, Ruse* offers a criterion of "professional integrity":

> Good science . . . presupposes an attitude that one might describe as professional integrity. A scientist should not cheat or falsify data or quote out of context or do any other thing that is intellectually dishonest. Of course, as always, some individuals fail; but science as a whole disapproves of such actions. Indeed, when transgressors are detected, they are usually expelled from the community. . . .[388]

There is no question that dishonesty or other unethical conduct is reprehensible and should not be tolerated by either evolutionists or discontinuitists.

However, few if any other philosophers of science regard a professional integrity requirement for scientists as relevant to the scientific nature of theories. For example, Quinn* rejects the Ruse* requirement of professional integrity as "having no bearing on the scientific status" of ideas:

> [I]t should be tolerably clear that integrity, like tentativeness, is a characteristic of persons either individually or as groups. As such, it has *no bearing on the scientific status of their ideas* or assertions. I have no wish to defend, mitigate or excuse the intellectual dishonesty one finds in the writings of some creationists. But I do detect a certain unctuous tone in Ruse's praise of the intellectual honesty of scientists in general at a time when *scientific fraud has become something of a national scandal* in the United States. . . .[389]

Moreover, as Quinn* notes, those ideals have historically been broken by many scientists generally, as well as by many evolutionists particularly. In fact, the irony is that those ideals have perhaps been violated most in evolutionary works.

(2) Scientific Fraud by Many Evolutionists. Professional integrity has been breached by major evolutionary "frauds." One example is Darwin's* appropriation of Blyth's* work, which Eiseley* chronicled:

> According to anthropologist Loren Eiseley, Darwin appropriated the work of Edward Blyth, a little-known British zoologist who wrote on natural selection and evolution in two papers published in 1835 and 1837. Eiseley points to similarities in phrasing, the use of rare words, and the choice of examples.[390]

Another example is Haeckel's* use of fraudulent drawings, which Rager* describes:

> Haeckel was not prudish in the selection of tools for his fight. In order to pro[ve] the validity of the law of biogenesis, he published several figures, the originals and legends of which were *faked* up.
>
> This fake is now shown in a few examples. . . . For this purpose he used the same printing stock three times and invented a different legend for each copy.
>
> There are a number of other figures the originals of which were changed by Haeckel in order to demonstrate that human ontogeny successively passes through stages of development which repeat phylogeny. . . .
>
> This is not the first time that Haeckel's *fake* has been revealed. . . . [T]he well known zoologist Ludwig Rütimeyer (1868) protested against it (see also W. His, 1874). . . .
>
> The law of biogenesis had to use *cheating tricks* in order to fit data to the theory. . . .[391]

Further examples of evolutionist frauds are the once universally accepted "Piltdown Forgery" (the title of a book published by Oxford University Press)[392] that consisted of a filed down ape jaw planted with fossil human teeth,[393] and a more recent fraud involving a dolphin's rib offered as a hominid collarbone.[394] Teilhard de Chardin* is described by Miller* and Fowler* as "a scientist whose science was questionable, a theologian whose theology was suspect," because he "has been charged with scientific fraud, theological heresy, and cosmological anthropocentrism."[395]

Fraud in science is so widespread that one book categorizes different forms,[396] another book describes and documents scores of instances under the title *Betrayers of the Truth: Fraud and Deceit in the Halls of Science*,[397] and a new book supplements the list with the title *False Prophets*.[398] The situation is described by Quinn*:

> All over the country institutions are busy putting in place formal and explicit policies for dealing with dishonesty in research, and clearly the

impetus to do so comes mainly from the numerous and well-publicized cases of scientific fraud that have occurred in recent years. The fact that institutions find it necessary to make formal policy on such matters is a good indication that the informal self-policing mechanisms of the scientific community are not doing their job.[399]

(3) Scientific Lack of Integrity by Many Evolutionists. Many examples of scientific dishonesty with data and observation also exist.[400] These include many instances of evolutionist suppression or discounting of unfavorable data, according to Lipson*:

> In fact, evolution became in a sense a scientific religion; almost all scientists have accepted it and many are prepared to 'bend' their observations to fit in with it.[401]

Eiseley*[402] and Romer*[403] mention casual discarding of anomalous fossils; Weidenreich* described how "paleontological facts are disregarded and replaced with purely speculative constructions" on the evolution of man;[404] and Keith* recounts arbitrary rejection of human remains mixed with alleged prehuman remains.[405]

Another category of concerns is ideological suppression of disfavored views (Section 9.7(b)) and particularly of the theory of creation (Sections 9.7(d) and 18.2).

Some evolutionists have been guilty of serious misquotations, such as Haldane*, who "misquoted Velikovsky, then ridiculed the misquotation":

> Evolutionist J. B. S. Haldane, author of *Science and Ethics*, reviewed the [Velikovsky] book in the *New Statesman and Nation* for November 11, 1950. Haldane *misquoted* Velikovsky, then ridiculed the misquotation; he mismatched dates and the events Velikovsky had associated with them; he concluded that the book was "equally a degradation of science and religion.[406]

Hyman* quoted Darwin* out of context in defending him, on the question whether Darwin* proposed that man descended from monkeys.[407] Neugebauer* misquoted Velikovsky* without remorse.[408]

Scientists' tests are often not susceptible to duplication or verification by others, as in the cases of Galileo,[409] Dalton,[410] and Mendel*.[411] A "fudge factor" was used by Einstein* in his initial theory of relativity: "In order to arrive at this consistent view, we admittedly had to introduce an extension of the field equations of gravitation which is not justified by our actual knowledge of gravitation."[412] Scientists have used and do use outdated or repudiated information in order to support a preferred result, or disregard meaningful information because it conflicts with a preferred result,[413] such as Newton,[414] Millikan*,[415] and others.[416] Scientists sometimes do alter scientific theory or change scientific terminology to meet legal or political advantage, whether pursuant to the Marxist beliefs of many modern biologists or the Victorian economic views of many early Darwinians.[417]

However, methodology is generally not viewed by philosophers of science as part of the demarcation between science and non-science, as Klemke* notes:

> Second , nothing is said in this characterization about the method of obtaining knowledge or of obtaining laws. It may be induction, but it may also be a guess, intuition, hunch or whatever.[418]

The "scientific method" is [o]ne of the most misunderstood—and thereby overrated—procedures yet devised," "perpetuating the myth that [scientists] are privy to some form of higher mental processes," Eldredge* concludes.[419] That is not to question careful research, only its apotheosis.

c. *Comparable Conformity to Descriptive Criteria*

Various descriptive criteria for science have been proposed. A recent article by Dolby*, a philosopher of science at University of Kent, summarizes nine such factors, cautioning that "[n]one of them can be regarded as either necessary or sufficient for the status of science," and concludes that the theory of creation meets most:

> These criteria are important in the sense that good science strives to satisfy each in a sensibly balanced way. None of them can be regarded as either necessary or sufficient for the status of science.
>
> 1. Scientific knowledge is, or strives to be explicit and open to public scrutiny. . . . (*Creationism seems to meet this criterion.*)
>
> 2. It is coordinated, rather than fragmentary, bringing consistency, coherence, order, and simplicity to its content. (*So is creationism.*)
>
> 3. Although there are also formal sciences, the empirical sciences at least should be based on and seek to explain experience. . . . (*This applies to creationism.*)
>
> 4. The observations and measurements made should strive to maximize their precision and the range they cover. (Creationism is too immature and too limited in its resources to have made much progress on this criterion.)
>
> 5. The science should seek some generality of understanding. (*Creationism does.*)
>
> 6. The concepts used and the relationships constructed among them should be as rigorously formulated as possible, so as to minimize ambiguity and to facilitate checking the inference drawn. (It is easy to be

highly suspicious of the apparent obscurantism of creationism on this criterion.)

7. The science so constructed should have explanatory and predictive power. . . . Modern science (and quantum theory in particular) has moved away from causal determinism as a scientific ideal. (*Creationism seeks to explain and predict much*, but it allows only a *limited range* of evidence to carry weight in criticism.)

8. Successful sciences should be capable of practical application to other sciences and to the rest of human practice. (The distinctive features of creationism do not seem to have any application, except in a religious context.)

9. There are some kinds of subject matter which successful science should avoid, in particular matters which have proved to be socially divisive, such as the theologically contentious or the politically divisive. Perhaps metaphysical, mystical, and nonnaturalistic approaches should also be excluded. (Creationism clearly fails to meet this criterion, but, as I have noted, none of these requirements can be regarded as necessary for science.)[420]

The theory of abrupt appearance appears to meet most of the desiderata for which, whether rightly or wrongly, Dolby* finds the theory of creation to score low.

Summary. Thus, the demarcation between science and nonscience should not be based on generation of predictions, personal characteristics of scientists, or descriptive criteria at least as necessary factors. Nevertheless, each such criterion is comparably met by the theory of abrupt appearance and the theory of evolution.

* * *

Thus, even if the criteria of science are used that were criticized in Chapter 9, those criteria are comparably satisfied by the theories of abrupt appearance and evolution. Those theories are significantly but incompletely governed by natural law, significantly but incompletely testable and falsifiable, and significantly but incompletely tentative. The criteria are even comparably satisfied by the theories of creation and evolution; and if fixed criteria are used the theory of creation "might well be a science by the standards of the early eighteenth century," while "if the standards of science can vary with time, then it is possible that they will vary again" to make the theory of creation scientific or the theory of evolution nonscientific.[421] Whatever demarcation is chosen, it should be chosen dispassionately and applied fairly.

Notes

[1] Dolby*, *Science and Pseudo-Science: The Case of Creationism*, 22 Zygon 195, 208-09 (1987)(italics added). Dolby* goes on to argue that the theory of creation is an "archaic" science and a "corrupting" science.

[2] Quinn*, *The Philosopher of Science as Expert Witness*, in Science and Reality: Recent Work in the Philosophy of Science 32, 42 (J. Cushing*, C. Delaney* & G. Gutting* eds. 1984).

[3] Laudan*, *Commentary: Science at the Bar—Causes for Concern*, Science, Technology & Human Values, Fall 1982, at 16, 19.

[4] Each affirmative line of evidence for the theory of abrupt appearance combines induction and deduction. This can be seen in the paleontology, comparative morphology, information content, genetics (heavily deductive), and comparative discontinuity (heavily inductive) arguments of biological abrupt appearance (Chapter 2); the information content, isomers (heavily inductive), biogenesis (highly deductive), and thermodynamics (highly deductive) arguments of biochemical abrupt appearance (Chapter 4); etc.

[5] Section 15.2(c).

[6] Section 10.4(a).

[7] Each affirmative line of evidence for the theory of abrupt appearance builds on evolutionary anomalies, addresses underemphasized data, or reinterprets acknowledged data. *See* Chapters 2, 4 & 6.

[8] Section 10.3(a).

[9] *See* Section 9.1.

[10] *E.g.*, C. Darwin*, *The Origin of Species* 471 (1st ed. 1859, repr. 1964).

[11] *E.g.*, *id.* at 55, 129, 152, 155, 167, 470, 471, 473, 475, 478, 480, 482, 483.

[12] F. Bacon, *Novum Organum* cxxix (1902).

[13] Laudan*, *More on Creationism*, in Science, Technology & Human Values, Winter 1983, at 36, 36. The definition of creation that Laudan* accepts from the *McLean* decision is not correct. *See* Chapters 2, 4 & 6.

[14] Laudan*, *Commentary: Science at the Bar—Causes for Concern*, Science, Technology & Human Values, Fall 1982, at 16, 16, 18 (1982).

[15] Quinn*, *The Philosopher of Science as Expert Witness*, in Science and Reality: Recent Work in the Philosophy of Science 32, 43 (J. Cushing*, C. Delaney* & G. Gutting* eds. 1984).

[16] R. Shapiro*, *Origins* 263 (1986).

[17] Similarly, an evolutionist scientist explains his parallel statement about evolution:

> I made no such claim. I sought to distinguish between theories and other scientific statements, not between science and non-science. And I made myself very clear about my view of the relationship of explanatory theories to biological classifications. I said (1977:190), "*In denying that classifications are scientific theories I do not mean to deny that classifications can be scientific.*

Kitts*, *Theories and Other Scientific Statements: A Reply to Settle*, 29 Systematic Zoology 190, 191 (1980).

[18] Popper*, *Intellectual Autobiography*, in 2 The Philosophy of Karl Popper 3, 134, 137 (P. Schilpp* ed. 1974) (italics added). *See* note 306.

[19] Popper* modified his prior position on natural selection in 1978:

> I have in the past described the theory [of natural selection] as "almost tautological", and I have tried to explain how the theory of *natural selection* could be untestable (as is a tautology) and yet of great scientific interest. My solution was that the doctrine of *natural selection* is a most useful metaphysical research programme. . . .
>
> I still believe that *natural selection* works in this way as a research programme. Nevertheless, I have changed my mind about the testability and the logical status of the theory of *natural selection*; and I am glad to have an opportunity to make a recantation.

Popper*, *Natural Selection and the Emergence of Mind*, 32 Dialectica 339, 344-45 (1978) (italics added).

[20] He also published a letter saying that "hypotheses" of the historical sciences such as evolution "can *in many cases* be tested":

> I here wish to affirm that these and other historical sciences have in my opinion scientific character: their hypotheses can *in many cases* be tested. It appears as if some people would think that the historical sciences are untestable because they describe unique events. However, the description of unique events can *very often* be tested by deriving from them testable predictions or retrodictions.

Popper*, *Letter*, 87 New Scientist 611, 611 (1980) (italics added). This clarification does *not* say that all of macroevolution or Darwinism is testable and falsifiable, but *only* parts. *See* text accompanying note 306.

[21] Patterson* reaches the same conclusion:

> 12.4 A metaphysical research programme.
>
> So, at present, we are left with neo-Darwinian theory: that evolution has occurred, and has been directed mainly by natural selection, with random contributions from genetic drift, and perhaps the occasional hopeful monster. In this form, the theory is not scientific by Popper's standards. Indeed, Popper calls the theory of evolution not a scientific theory but 'a metaphysical research programme'.

C. Patterson*, *Evolution* 149 (1978).

[22] Cartmill*, *Hypothesis Testing and Phylogenetic Reconstruction*, in Zeitschrift für Zoologische Systematik und Evolution 73, 90 (1981) ("Phylogenetic reconstruction is possible. However, Popperian phylogenetic reconstruction apparently is not. It follows that the study of phylogeny is *not*, by Popper's criteria, a *science* at all."); Ghiselin*, On *Paradigms and the Hypermodern Species Concept*, 27 Systematic Zoology 437, 437-38 (1978) ("He read a work by Smart (1968), which asserted that biology is *not a science* because there are no laws for any particular species.").

[23] 1 I. Lakatos*, *The Methodology of Scientific Research Programmes* 68, 70-71 (J. Worrall* & G. Currie* eds. 1978) (italics added).

[24] Dolby*, *Science and Pseudo-Science: The Case of Creationism*, 22 Zygon 195, 206 (1987).
[25] McLean v. Arkansas Bd. of Educ., 529 F.Supp. 1255, 1267 (E.D. Ark. 1982).
[26] Section 9.4.
[27] W. Stansfield*, *The Science of Evolution* 53 (1977).
[28] J. Silk*, *The Big Bang* 144 (1979) ("the singularity, when creation of matter possibly occurred").
[29] Shapley*, *On the Evolution of Atoms, Stars and Galaxies*, in Adventures in Earth History 77, 79 (P. Cloud* ed. 1970) ("What preceded their appearance, if anything? That is perhaps a question for metaphysics. The origin of origins is beyond astronomy.").
[30] K. Krauskopf* & K. Beiser*, *The Physical Universe* 645 (3d ed. 1973) ("Where did the matter come from in the first place?").
[31] *The Universe and Dr. Einstein* 104 (L. Barnett* ed. 1948) ("[T]he problem of initial origin remains. It merely pushes the time of Creation into the infinite past.").
[32] J. North*, *The Measure of the Universe* 401 (1965) ("the origins of prime matter").
[33] Section 13.1(b)-(d).
[34] R. Wald*, *Space, Time, and Gravity: The Theory of the Big Bang* 51 (1971).
[35] Weisskopf*, *The Origin of the Universe*, 71 Am. Scientist 473, 476 (1983) ("the event of infinite density, that so-called singularity, must have occurred less than 20 billion years ago").
[36] J. Silk*, *The Big Bang* 322-24 (1979) ("The pioneers of the Big Bang theory were not greatly concerned about the *singularity* in space-time that was apparently required by the Friedmann equation. The open models possess a singularity at the finite past, and the closed model has both a past and a future singularity (Figure 18.2).") (italics added).

Because the big bang would have destroyed much of the evidence, "what happened before has no concrete content." Weisskopf*, *The Origin of the Universe*, 71 Am. Scientist 473, 480 (1983).
[37] Ellis*, *Alternatives to the Big Bang*, 22 Ann. Rev. Astronomy & Astrophysics 157, 180 (1984).
[38] Patton* & Wheeler*, *Is Physics Legislated by Cosmogony?*, in Quantum Gravity: An Oxford Symposium 538, 540-43 (C. Isham*, R. Penrose* & D. Sciama* eds. 1975).
[39] Narlikar* & Padmanabhan*, *Creation-field cosmology: A possible solution to singularity, horizon, and flatness problems*, 32 Physical Rev. D 1928, 1928 (1985).
[40] R. Jastrow*, *God and the Astronomers* 113-114 (1978) ("the world had a beginning *under conditions in which the known laws of physics are not valid*, and as a product of forces or circumstances we *cannot* discover.") (italics added).
[41] Barrow* & Silk*, *The Structure of the Early Universe*, Scientific Am.,

Apr. 1980, at 118, 118 ("What happened at the precise moment of creation is not yet known because *unfamiliar physical principles* unique to the immense densities and temperatures of that moment mask the initial structure of the universe.") (italics added).

[42] Weisskopf*, *The Origin of the Universe*, 71 Am. Scientist 473, 478 (1983) ("do not know at all what the laws of nature were").

[43] Tipler*, *How to Construct a Falsifiable Theory in Which the Universe Came Into Being Several Thousand Years Ago*, 2 Philosophy of Science Association 873, 880 (1984).

[44] *See* Kazmann*, *Time: In Full Measure*, 60.E.O.S. 21, 22-23 (1979); Section 6.6.

[45] *See* Wald*, *The Origin of Life*, in Physics and Chemistry of Life 3 (Scientific Am. eds.* 1956) ("spontaneous generation"); Section 5.3.

[46] *See* Abelson*, *Chemical Events on the Primitive Earth*, 55 Proc. National Acad. of Sciences 1365, 1369 (1966); Section 4.4.

[47] Yockey*, *Self Organization Origin of Life Scenarios and Information Theory*, 91 J. Theoretical Biology 13, 13 (1981) ("The information content of amino acid sequences cannot increase until a genetic code with an adaptor function has appeared. Nothing which even vaguely resembles a code exists in the physico-chemical world. One must conclude that no valid scientific explanation of the origin of life exists at present."). *See also* Section 4.1.

[48] Hoyle, *The Big Bang in Astronomy*, 92 New Scientist 521, 526 (1981) (italics added).

[49] E. Ambrose*, *The Nature and Origin of the Biological World* 135 (1982). *See also* Sections 4.2 & 5.4.

[50] Lafont*, *Book Review*, Permanences, Nov. 1972, at 7, 8, quoting G. Salet*, *Chance and Certainty: Evolution in the Light of Modern Biology* (1972). *See also* E. Borel*, *Probabilities and Life* 28 (1962); E. Borel*, *Elements of the Theory of Probability* 57 (1965).

[51] Wald*, *The Origin of Life*, in Physics and Chemistry of Life 3, 9, 12 (Scientific Am. eds.* 1956). *See also* Section 4.2.

[52] Popper*, *Intellectual Autobiography*, in 2 The Philosophy of Karl Popper 3, 134-35 (P. Schilpp* ed. 1974).

[53] Popper*, *Reduction and the Incompleteness of Science*, in Studies in the Philosophy of Biology 259, 270 (1974)(italics added except first).

[54] P. Grassé*, *The Evolution of Living Organisms* (trans. 1977).

[55] G. Kerkut*, *Implications of Evolution* (1960).

[56] Sections 3.3 & 2.1-2.2.

[57] Eden*, *Inadequacies of Neo-Darwinian Evolution as a Scientific Theory*, in Mathematical Challenges to the Neo-Darwinian Interpretation of Evolution 109, 110 (P. Moorhead* & M. Kaplan* eds. 1967). *See also* T. Roszak*, *Unfinished Animal* 101-02 (1975) ("The irony is devastating. The main purpose of Darwinism was to drive every last trace of an incredible God from biology. But the theory replaces the old God with an even more incredible deity—omnipotent chance."); note 50.

[58] M. Denton*, *Evolution: A Theory in Crisis* 351 (1985); Section 2.4.

[59] Polanyi*, *Life Transcending Physics and Chemistry*, Chemical & Engineering News, Aug. 21, 1967, at 54, 55, 64-65 ("The description of a living system therefore transcends the chemical and physical laws which govern its atomic constituents. . . . But the problem of evolution lies beyond my subject here. When I say that life transcends physics and chemistry, I mean that biology *cannot explain life* in our age by the current workings of physical and chemical *laws*.") (italics added).

[60] Polanyi*, *Life's Irreducible Structure*, 160 Science 1308, 1310 (1968) (italics added).

[61] P. Grassé*, *The Evolution of Living Organisms* 202 (trans. 1977) (italics added).

[62] Popper*, *Intellectual Autobiography*, in 2 The Philosophy of Karl Popper 3, 138 (P. Schilpp* ed. 1974) (italics added).

[63] Hoffman*, *Paleobiology at the crossroads: a critique of some modern paleobiological research programs*, in Dimensions of Darwinism 241, 263 (M. Grene* ed. 1983) (italics added).

[64] Erbrich*, *On the Probability of Emergence of a Protein with a Particular Function*, 34 Acta Biotheoretica 53, 78 (1985).

[65] N. Macbeth*, *Darwin Retried* 147 (1971) ("Unfortunately, in the field of exvolution most explanations are not good. As a matter of fact, they *hardly qualify as explanations* at all; they are suggestions, hunches, pipe dreams, hardly worthy of being called hypotheses.") (italics added).

[66] Lipson*, *A Physicist Looks at Evolution*, 31 Physics Bul. 138, 138 (1980) ("I have always been slightly *suspicious* of the theory of *evolution* because of its ability to account for any property of living beings (the long neck of the giraffe, for example). I have therefore tried to see whether biological discoveries over the last thirty years or so fit in with Darwin's theory. I do not think that they do. . . . To my mind, the theory does not stand up at all.").

[67] Sparkes*, *What is this thing called science?*, 89 New Scientist 156, 156 (1981) (italics added).

[68] Popper*, *Natural Selection and the Emergence of Mind*, 32 Dialectica 339 (1978); *see* Riddiford* & Penny*, *The Scientific Status of Modern Evolutionary Theory*, in Evolutionary Theory: Paths into the Future 1, 19 (J. Pollard* ed. 1984).

[69] Eden*, *Inadequacies of Neo-Darwinian Evolution as a Scientific Theory*, in Mathematical Challenges to the Neo-Darwinian Interpretation of Evolution 109, 109 (P. Moorhead* & M. Kaplan* eds. 1967) (italics added).

[70] Manser*, *The Concept of Evolution*, 40 Philosophy 18, 26-27 (1965) ("As in the case of '*adaptation*', other key terms of the theory, such as '*variation*' and 'environment,' suffer from circular definitions. . . . Hence I think that much of what is said by those who defend the *theory of evolution* in its present form is *only a redescription* of the phenomena, though this does not mean that such a redescription was not worth carrying out. . . . Because the *normal scientific way* of doing this is to give a *causal explanation*, the

presumption is that such an account is also given by the theory of evolution. But what has rather been done is to produce a terminology in which the phenomena can be set, and at the same time an *illusion of explanation*.") (italics added).

[71] E. Steele*, *Somatic Selection and Adaptive Evolution* 1 (2d ed. 1981).

[72] Scriven*, *Explanation and Prediction in Evolutionary Theory*, 130 Science 477, 481 (1959) ("It is not surprising, therefore, that when we turn to the attempts of Darwin and the Mendelians to *formulate some laws* of the traditional kind, or to make predictions, we find the results to be very unsatisfactory. As Waddington says, even the modern attempt to develop a mathematical approach to evolution has not 'led to any noteworthy quantitative statements about evolution. . . . The formulae involve parameters . . . most of which are still too inaccurately known to enable quantitative predictions to be made or verified' (13). And if this is the case for the mathematical theory, the case is much worse for exact statements which do not involve the flexibility of mathematical relationships. . . . Tendency statements like this are *explanation-indicators*; they justify no more than *very weak* hypothetical predictions with unspecified conditions ('if everything else was the same, then . . .'), for they tell us nothing about the likelihood of conditions of struggle or the strength of the tendency.").

[73] Manser*, *The Concept of Evolution*, 40 Philosophy 18, 26-27 (1965).

[74] Lewontin*, *Sociobiology as an Adaptionist Programme*, 24 Behavioural Science 5 (1979).

[75] N. Macbeth*, *Darwin Retried* 77 (1971) ("When the most learned evolutionists can give neither the how nor the why, the marvels seem to show that *adaptation* is inexplicable. Yet those who cannot explain it *will not admit that it is inexplicable*. This is a strange situation, only partly ascribable to the rather unscientific conviction that evidence will be found in the future. It is due to a psychological quirk . . ..") (italics added); *id.* at 104 ("We agree that Darwinism cannot predict, but we must remind Professor Mayr that it also *cannot explain* . . ..") (italics added).

[76] Saunders* & Ho*, *Is Neo-Darwinism Falsifiable?—And Does It Matter?*, 4 Nature & System 179 (1982) ("The neoDarwinist claim to sufficiency is of great importance in evolutionary biology for it *completely delimits the type of explanation* that is either desired or even acceptable, and therefore the sort of research that is to be carried out. Forty years ago, Huxley (1942, p. 23) criticized research devoted to 'the paper demonstration that such and such a character was or might be *adaptive*,' but the synthetic theory of which he was one of the founders is now serving as the justification for precisely this kind of work.") (italics added).

[77] Eden*, *Inadequacies of Neo-Darwinian Evolution as a Scientific Theory*, in Mathematical Challenges to the Neo-Darwinian Interpretation of Evolution 109, 109 (P. Moorhead* & M. Kaplan* eds. 1967) (italics added).

[78] Popper*, *Intellectual Autobiography*, in 2 The Philosophy of Karl Popper 3, 137 (P. Schilpp* ed. 1974).

[79] R. Lewontin*, *The Genetic Basis of Evolutionary Change* 11-12 (1974) (italics added).

[80] J. Roughgarden*, *The Theory of Population Genetics and Evolutionary Ecology* (1979).

[81] Kitts*, *Karl Popper, Verifiability, and Systematic Zoology*, 26 Systematic Zoology 185, 189 (1977) (italics added).

[82] Peters*, *Tautology in Evolution and Ecology*, 110 Am. Naturalist 1, 1 (1976) (italics added).

[83] Cracraft*, *Book Review of Beyond Neo-Darwinism*, 1 Cladistics 300, 301 (1985) (italics added).

[84] Ho* & Saunders*, *Preface*, to Beyond Neo-Darwinism ix, ix (M. Ho* & P. Saunders* eds. 1984).

[85] Mayr*, *Evolutionary Challenges to the Mathematical Interpretations to Evolution*, in Mathematical Challenges to the Neo-Darwinian Interpretation of Evolution 47, 47 (P. Moorhead* & M. Kaplan* eds. 1967).

[86] O'Grady*, *Evolutionary Theory and Teleology*, 107 J. Theoretical Biology 563, 575 (1984) (quoting Gould*).

[87] Leith*, *Letter*, Listener, Nov. 5, 1981, at 539 (italics added).

[88] Section 10.4(c).

[89] T. Dobzhansky*, F. Ayala*, G. Stebbins* & J. Valentine*, *Evolution* 32, 504 (1977).

[90] Mayr*, *Prologue*, in The Evolutionary Synthesis 1, 24 (E. Mayr* & W. Provine* eds. 1980) ("second of the two principal components of Darwin's theory of evolution"). Punctuated equilibria proponents question the centrality of natural selection but generally do not discard it.

[91] Ho* & Saunders*, *Preface*, to Beyond Neo-Darwinism ix, x (M. Ho* & P. Saunders* eds. 1984).

[92] Rosen*, *Darwin's Demon*, 27 Systematic Zoology 370, 372 (1978) (italics added).

[93] Lewontin*, *Testing the theory of natural selection*, 236 Nature 181, 181 (1972).

[94] O'Grady*, *Evolutionary Theory and Teleology*, 107 J. Theoretical Biology 563, 575, 567 (1984) (italics added).

[95] Hughes* & Lambert*, *Functionalism, Structuralism, and "Ways of Seeing,"* 111 J. Theoretical Biology 787, 796-97 (1984) (italics added).

[96] Bradie* & Gromko*, *The Status of the Principle of Natural Selection*, 3 Nature & System 3, 8 (1981).

[97] S. Toulmin*, *Science, Philosophy of*, 16 Encyclopaedia Britannica 375, 389 (15th ed. 1974) ("[O]ne distinguished Empiricist philosopher, Carl Hempel, has drawn a somewhat extreme conclusion, viz., that the theory of natural selection is *not really an explanation of organic evolution* at all—not even a bad one—but is merely an elaborate redescription of the historical episodes concerned.").

[98] N. Macbeth*, *Darwin Retried* 44 (1971) ("Natural selection is almost always handled in general terms. . . . This means that it has no *explanatory power* when specific problems arise. . . . [Deevey] says: 'Of course these

things are marvels, and of course, the fossil record being what it is, no one can say with confidence exactly how any one of them came about.' Note the word exactly. The Darwinians contend that any given result must have been produced by natural selection working on small changes, but when asked to be exact they are helpless.") (italics added).

[99] Brady*, *Dogma and doubt*, 17 Biological J. Linnean Society 79 (1979).

[100] H. Cannon*, *The Evolution of Living Things* (1958).

[101] Hairston*, *Fitness, Survival and Reproduction*, 28 Systematic Zoology 392 (1979).

[102] Little*, *Evolution: Myth, Metaphysics, or Science*, 87 New Scientist 708 (1980).

[103] Løvtrup*, *On the Falsifiability of Neo-Darwinism*, 1 Evolutionary Theory 267 (1976).

[104] Medawar*, *Comment on "On Chance and Necessity"*, in Studies in the Philosophy of Biology 363 (F. Ayala* & T. Dobzhansky* eds. 1974)

[105] Platnick*, *Adaptation, Selection and Falsifiability*, 27 Systematic Zoology 347 (1978).

[106] Polanyi*, *Genius in Science*, in Methodological and Historical Essays in the Natural and Social Sciences 57 (R. Cohen* & M. Wartofsky* eds. 1974).

[107] Wassermann*, *Testability of the Role of Natural Selection within Theories of Population Genetics and Evolution*, 29 British J. Philosophy of Science 223 (1978).

[108] Riddiford* & Penny*, *The scientific status of modern evolutionary theory*, in Evolutionary Theory: Paths into the Future 1, 19 (J. Pollard* ed. 1984) (italics added).

[109] Waddington*, *Evolutionary Adaptation*, in 1 Evolution After Darwin 381, 385 (S. Tax* ed. 1960) (italics added).

[110] S. Stanley*, *Macroevolution* 192-93 (1979) ("I tend to agree with those who have viewed natural selection as a *tautology* rather than a true theory (see review by Peters, 1976). It is essentially a description of what has happened . . ..") (italics added).

[111] Rosen*, *Darwin's Demon*, 27 Systematic Zoology 370, 370-71 (1978).

[112] C. Patterson*, *Evolution* 146-47 (1978).

[113] Stebbins*, *Adaptive Shifts and Evolutionary Novelty: A Compositionalist Approach*, in Studies in the Philosophy of Biology, Reduction and Related Problems 285 (F. Ayala* & T. Dobzhansky* eds. 1974).

[114] Platnick*, *Book Review*, 26 Systematic Zoology 224 (1976).

[115] Eden*, *Inadequacies of Neo-Darwinian Evolution as a Scientific Theory*, in Mathematical Challenges to the Neo-Darwinian Interpretation of Evolution 5, 5 (P. Moorhead* & M. Kaplan* eds. 1967) ("Concepts such as *natural selection* by the survival of the fittest are *tautologous*; that is, they simply restate the fact that only the properties of organisms which survive to produce offspring, or to produce more offspring than their cohorts, will appear in succeeding generations.") (italics added).

[116] F. Hoyle, *The Intelligent Universe: A New View of Creation and Evolu-*

tion 32, 244 (1983) ("the idea of natural selection is little more than a trivial tautology").

[117] Grene*, *Bohm's Metaphysics and Biology*, in Toward a Theoretical Biology 61, 66 (C. Waddington* ed. 1969) ("It must then, and is usually said to, be survival that adaptation is 'for.' But in that case the whole 'theory' becomes a tautology, a complicated way of saying simply that what survives survives."); M. Grene*, *The Knower and the Known* 193-95 (1974).

[118] Brady*, *Natural Selection and the Criteria by Which a Theory Is Judged*, 28 Systematic Zoology 600, 607 (1979) ("some versions of the theory—i.e., differential reproduction—are tautological"). Brady* argues that the real problem is the unfalsifiability rather than tautology of macroevolution.

[119] Peters*, *Tautology in Evolution and Ecology*, 110 Am. Naturalist 1, 11 (1976) ("Instead they consist of the logical elaboration of certain axioms. Consequently, they must be termed tautologies.").

[120] G. Himmelfarb*, *Darwin and the Darwinian Revolution* 316 (1959) ("The survivors, having survived, are thence judged to be the fittest.").

[121] C. Harris*, *Evolution, Genesis and Revelations: Readings from Empedocles to Wilson* 189-90 (1981) ("This is a circular argument—a tautology. 'Survival of the fittest' may thus be taken as an untestable truism—an axiom.").

[122] Haldane*, *Darwinism under Revision*, Rationalist Ann., 1935, at 19.

[123] Barker*, *An Approach to the Theory of Natural Selection*, 44 Philosophy 271 (1969).

[124] Krimbas*, *On Adaptation*, 17 Evolutionary Biology 1, 6 (1984).

[125] A. Koestler*, *Janus: A Summing Up* (1978).

[126] J. Smart*, *Philosophy and Scientific Realism* (1963).

[127] Flew*, *'The Concept of Evolution': A Comment*, 41 Philosophy 70, 70 (1966).

[128] Manser*, *The Concept of Evolution*, 40 Philosophy 18 (1965).

[129] Bohm*, *Addendum on Order and Neo-Darwinism*, in 2 Towards a Theoretical Biology (C. Waddington* ed. 1968).

[130] W. Cannon*, *The Evolution of Living Things* (1958).

[131] N. Macbeth*, *Darwin Retried* 62-63 (1971) ("[S]omeone asked how we determine who are the fittest. The answer came back that we determine this by the test of survival; there is no other criterion. But this means that a species survives because it is the fittest and is the fittest because it survives, which is circular reasoning and equivalent to saying that whatever is, is fit. The gist is that some survive and some die, but we knew this at the outset. Nothing has been explained."); *id.* at 47 ("If we say that evolution is accomplished largely by natural selection and that natural selection consists of differential reproduction, what have we done? Differential reproduction means that some species multiply by leaving more offspring than one-for-one, while others leave one-for-one and remain stable, and others leave less than one-for-one and dwindle or die out. Thus we have as Ques-

tion: Why do some multiply, while others remain stable, dwindle, or die out? To which is offered as Answer: Because some multiply, while others remain stable, dwindle, or die out. The two sides of the equation are the same. We have a *tautology*. The definition is meaningless.") (italics added).

132 Bethell*, *Darwin's Unfalsifiable Theory*, Kronos, Summer 1982, at 33, 33-34 ("Darwin proposed no criterion of fitness other than that of survival itself. . . . [I]t follows that 'the survival of the fittest' is not a testable theory, but a *tautology*. Which one survives? The fittest. Who are they? Those that survive.") (italics added); Bethell*, *Darwin's Mistake*, Harper's Magazine, Feb. 1976, at 70, 72 ("tautology").

133 J. Rifkin*, *Algeny* 143 (1983) ("tautology").

134 T. Roszak*, *Unfinished Animal* 101 (1975) ("at key points, Darwin's theory boiled down to empty *tautologies* and unproven assumptions").

135 I. Lerner*, *The Genetic Basis of Selection* 10 (1958).

136 Saunders* & Ho*, *Is Neo-Darwinism Falsifiable?—And Does It Matter?*, 4 Nature & System 179, 183 (1982) ("the principle of natural selection is tautological").

137 Rosen*, *Darwin's Demon*, 27 Systematic Zoology 370, 370-71 (1978). *See* text accompanying note 253 & note 261.

138 K. Popper*, *The Poverty of Historicism* 107 (2d ed. 1960) (He continues that evolution is "a particular (or more precisely, singular) historical statement about the ancestry . . ..").

139 Quoted in Riddiford* & Penny*, *The scientific status of modern evolutionary theory*, in Evolutionary Theory: Paths into the Future 1, 30 (J. Pollard* ed. 1984).

140 D. Brooks* & E. Wiley*, *Evolution as Entropy* 23 (1986).

141 Hughes* & Lambert*, *Functionalism, Structuralism, and "Ways of Seeing,"* 111 J. Theoretical Biology 787, 797 (1984).

142 Quoted in Riddiford* & Penny*, *The scientific status of modern evolutionary theory*, in Evolutionary Theory: Paths into the Future 1, 1-2 (J. Pollard* ed. 1984).

143 Abbagnano*, *Positivism*, 6 Encyclopedia of Philosophy 414, 418 (P. Edwards* ed. 1967).

144 J. Smart*, *Philosophy and Scientific Realism* (1963).

145 Scriven*, *Explanation and Prediction in Evolutionary Theory*, 130 Science 477 (1959).

146 T. Goudge*, *The Ascent of Life: A Philosophical Study of the Theory of Evolution* (1961).

147 Chapters 2, 4 & 6.

148 Brooks* and Wiley* recognize that information theory "provide[s] a connection between biological processes and natural physical laws." D. Brooks* & E. Wiley*, *Evolution as Entropy* x (1986) (U. of Chicago Press).

149 Similarly, the inflationary universe theory of Guth*, Steinhardt*, and Tryon* proposes that an appearance of the universe "from absolutely nothing" is "describable by physical laws." Guth* & Steinhardt*, *The*

Inflationary Universe, Scientific Am., May 1984, at 116, 128; Section 13.1(c).

[150] N. Gillespie*, *Charles Darwin and the Problem of Creation* 21 (1979) (U. of Chicago Press) (italics added).

[151] *Id.* at 91 ("After 'extensive, patient, and unbiased inductive research,' he had rejected 'the principle of direct or miraculous creation' as violating the scientific idea of 'natural law or secondary cause' in nature. He denounced the 'miracle theory of creation' as a 'theological notion' and even censured Darwin for supposedly invoking a miracle to originate life. Like so many others, Owen had been swayed by the uniformitarian logic that if species died out gradually (as paleontology showed), and because of natural causes such as the struggle for existence, analogy suggested that they had come in the same way. In other words, if they did not go out as a result of sudden miraculous catastrophes, they did not so come in. So far, Owen might seem to be on his way to a positive theory of evolution. But this interpretation would be a mistake. 'Derivation,' as he called his theory, relied on a 'creative power' which possessed a 'grandeur . . . which is manifested daily, hourly, in calling into life many forms, by conversion of physical and chemical into vital modes of force, under as many diversified conditions of the requisite elements to be so combined."); Owen, *Book Review*, 11 Edinburgh Rev. 487-532 (1860) (anonymous), reprinted in D. Hull*, *Darwin and His Critics* 175, 212 (1973) (U. of Chicago Press) ("Owen has long stated his belief that some preordained law or secondary cause is operative in bringing about the change [in species]; but our knowledge of such law, if such exists, can only be acquired on the prescribed terms.") (quoting Baden Powell).

[152] D. Hull*, *Darwin and His Critics* 213 (1973).

[153] Cannon*, *The Bases of Darwin's Achievement: A Revaluation*, 5 Victorian Studies 109, 132 (1961).

[154] Sedgwick, *Book Review*, The Spectator, Apr. 7, 1860, at 334-35, reprinted in D. Hull*, *Darwin and His Critics* 154, 161 (1973).

[155] Gould*, *Toward the Vindication of Punctuational Change*, in Catastrophes and Earth History 9, 13 (W. Berggren* & J. Van Couvering* eds. 1984).

[156] Dolby*, *Science and Pseudo-Science: The Case of Creationism*, 22 Zygon 195, 206 (1987).

[157] *Id.* at 207 (italics in original).

[158] Section 10.2(a)(1).

[159] *Id.*

[160] R. Good*, *Features of Evolution in the Flowering Plants* 384 (1974) (italics added except Latin).

[161] Laudan*, *Commentary: Science at the Bar—Causes for Concern*, Science, Technology & Human Values, Fall 1982, at 16, 18.

[162] Riddiford* & Penny*, *The scientific status of modern evolutionary theory*, in Evolutionary Theory: Paths into the Future 1, 4 (J. Pollard* ed. 1984).

[163] Brady*, *On the Independence of Systematics*, 1 Cladistics 113, 125

(1985) (italics added).

[164] Quinn*, *The Philosopher of Science as Expert Witness*, in Science and Reality: Recent Work in the Philosophy of Science 32, 42 (J. Cushing*, C. Delaney* & G. Gutting* eds. 1984).

[165] Laudan*, *Commentary: Science at the Bar—Causes for Concern*, Science, Technology & Human Values, Fall 1982, at 16, 18.

[166] Brady*, *Natural Selection and the Criteria by Which a Theory Is Judged*, 28 Systematic Zoology 600, 620 (1979) (italics added).

[167] Cracraft*, *The Use of Functional and Adaptive Criteria in Phylogenetic Systematics*, 21 Am. Zoologist 21, 31-32 (1981).

[168] Brady*, *Form and Cause in Goethe's Morphology*, in Goethe and the Sciences: A Re-appraisal 257, 290-91 (F. Amrine* *et al.* eds. 1983).

[169] Section 3.4(c).

[170] Danto*, *Philosophy of Science, Problems of*, 6 Encyclopedia of Philosophy 298, 299 (P. Edwards* ed. 1967).

[171] Tipler*, *How to Construct a Falsifiable Theory in Which the Universe Came Into Being Several Thousand Years Ago*, 2 Philosophy of Science Association 873, 874-75 (1984).

[172] J. North*, *The Measure of the Universe* 400-01 (1965) (italics added).

[173] McCrea*, *The steady-state theory of the expanding universe*, 9 Endeavor 3, 6-7 (1950).

[174] Address of Dr. Colin Patterson* at Am. Museum of Natural History, tr. at 3-4 (Nov. 5, 1981) (italics added).

[175] Section 10.2(a)(2).

[176] R. Jastrow*, *God and the Astronomers* 12 (1978) (italics added). *See also* Section 10.2(a) (1).

[177] *See* Sections 13.1(b)-(d) & 7.3(a).

[178] J. North*, *The Measure of the Universe* 400 (1965) (italics deleted).

[179] Weisskopf*, *The Origin of the Universe*, 71 Am. Scientist 473, 480 (1983).

[180] Jastrow*, *The Astronomer and God*, in The Intellectuals Speak Out About God 15, 16 (R. Varghese* ed. 1984).

[181] Chapters 2, 4 & 6; Sections 8.2, 8.4 & 8.6.

[181A] Letter from Dr. Wernher von Braun to Dr. Vernon Grose (Sept. 14, 1972) (creationist scientist). *See also* Section 9.4(a)(2).

[182] Note 27.

[183] Note 34.

[184] Note 52.

[185] Note 53.

[186] Note 57.

[187] Note 62.

[188] Note 67.

[189] Note 79.

[190] Note 92.

[191] Note 109.

[192] Note 139.

[193] Note 142.

[194] Note 150.
[195] Note 160.
[196] Note 162.
[197] Note 166.
[198] Note 174.
[199] Note 178.
[200] Note 171.
[201] Note 172.
[202] Section 9.5.
[203] Quinn*, *The Philosopher of Science as Expert Witness*, in Science and Reality: Recent Work in the Philosophy of Science 32, 43 (J. Cushing*, C. Delaney* & G. Gutting* eds. 1984). He finds the theory of creation to have failed other tests. *Id.* at 43.
[204] Laudan*, *Commentary: Science at the Bar—Causes for Concern*, Science, Technology & Human Values, Fall 1982, at 16, 16-17 (italics added). *See also* Laudan*, *The Demise of the Demarcation Problem*, in 2 Working Papers in Science and Technology 7, 25 (R. Laudan* ed. 1983). The definition of the theory of creation used by Laudan* in his former article is incorrect.
[205] Gould*, *Creationism: Genesis v. Geology*, Atlantic, Sept. 1982, at 10, 13 (italics added). *See also* Laudan*, *Commentary: Science at the Bar—Causes for Concern*, Science, Technology & Human Values, Fall 1982, at 16, 17 (This author does not agree that the abrupt appearance of organisms is necessarily "supernatural.").
[206] Raup*, *The Geological and Paleontological Arguments of Creationism*, in Scientists Confront Creationism 147, 159 (L. Godfrey* ed. 1983) (italics added).
[207] Brady*, *Dogma and doubt*, 17 Biological J. Linnean Society 79, 89 (1982) ("These are, in the order of discussion, the transference of empirical support from a *testable part* of the theory to the untested central thesis, a claim of confirmation that cannot be credited to the theory at all, and a general claim of 'fruitfulness'."); Dobzhansky*, *On Methods of Evolutionary Biology and Anthropology*, 45 Am. Scientist 381, 388 (1957) ("The *applicability of the experimental method* to the study of such unique historical processes is *severely restricted* before all else by the time intervals involved, which far exceed the lifetime of any human experimenter."); Section 9.5.
[208] Committee on Science and Creationism*, *Science and Creationism: A View from the National Academy of Sciences* 26 (1984) (italics added).
[209] Quinn*, *The Philosopher of Science as Expert Witness*, in Science and Reality: Recent Work in the Philosophy of Science 32, 43 (J. Cushing*, C. Delaney* & G. Gutting* eds. 1984) (italics added).
[210] Mayr*, *Introduction*, to C. Darwin*, The Origin of Species xii, xiii (1st ed. 1859, repr. 1964) (italics added).
[211] Gould*, *Creationism: Genesis vs. Geology*, Atlantic Monthly, Sept. 1982, at 10, 12.

[212] Quoted in Riddiford* & Penny*, *The scientific status of modern evolutionary theory*, in Evolutionary Theory: Paths into the Future 1, 9 (J. Pollard* ed. 1984).
[213] Sparkes*, *What is this thing called science?*, 89 New Scientist 156, 156 (1981).
[214] D. Brooks* & E. Wiley*, *Evolution as Entropy* x (1986) (U. of Chicago Press) (italics added).
[215] Laudan*, *Commentary: Science at the Bar—Causes for Concern*, Science, Technology & Human Values, Fall 1982, at 16, 17.
[216] Quinn*, *The Philosopher of Science as Expert Witness*, in Science and Reality: Recent Work in the Philosophy of Science 32, 43 (J. Cushing*, C. Delaney* & G. Gutting* eds. 1984) ("it has been known to philosophers of science for three-quarters of a century that many scientific statements are neither testable nor falsifiable individually and in isolation but only conjunctively").
[217] Riddiford* & Penny*, *The scientific status of modern evolutionary theory*, in Evolutionary Theory: Paths into the Future 1, 32 (J. Pollard* ed. 1984).
[218] Gould*, *The promise of paleobiology as a nomothetic, evolutionary discipline*, 6 Paleobiology 96, 113 (1980).
[219] Gould*, *Darwinism Defined: The Difference Between Fact and Theory*, Discover, Jan. 1987, at 64, 69.
[220] Gould*, *The promise of paleobiology as a nomothetic, evolutionary discipline*, 6 Paleobiology 96, 113 (1980).
[221] G. Simpson*, *The Major Features of Evolution* 338 (1953) ("historical biologists" are persons in such fields as paleontology and paleobotany).
[222] Popper*, *Letter*, 87 New Scientist 611 (1980) ("the historical sciences, such as palaeontology, or the history of the evolution of Life on Earth"—"their hypotheses can in many cases be tested").
[223] M. Ruse*, *Darwinism Defended* 45-46 (1982).
[224] Gould*, *Balzan Prize to Ernst Mayr*, 223 Science 255, 255 (1984) ("An entire set of disciplines, . . . often subjected to ridicule because they do not follow this pathway of 'hard' science, is thereby ignored: the historical sciences, treating immensely complex and nonrepeatable events . . . . Evolutionary biology is a quintessential historical discipline.").
[225] Gould*, *The Wisdom of Casey Stengel*, Discover, Mar. 1983, at 62, 64-65 (italics in original).
[226] Dobzhansky*, *On Methods of Evolutionary Biology and Anthropology*, 45 Am. Scientist 381, 388 (1957) (The "evolutionary happenings" of paleontology and paleobiology are "unique, unrepeatable, and irreversible."); *see also* T. Dobzhansky*, F. Ayala*, G. Stebbins* & J. Valentine*, *Evolution* 8 (1977).
[227] R. Jastrow*, *God and the Astronomers* 12 (1978).
[228] Gould*, *Darwinism Defined: The Difference Between Fact and Theory*, Discover, Jan. 1987, at 64, 65 (italics in original).
[229] *Id.* at 69-70 (italics in original).

[230] M. Ruse*, *Darwinism Defended* 45-46 (1982).
[231] Cracraft*, *The Use of Functional and Adaptive Criteria in Phylogenetic Systematics*, 21 Am. Zoologist 21, 31-32 (1981).
[232] Section 9.4.
[233] Strike*, *The Status of Creation-Science: A Comment on Siegel and Hahn*, 63 Phi Delta Kappan 555, 555-56 (1982) (italics added) (he proposes a process test instead that he believes the theory of creation fails and the theory of evolution meets, at least in their current form).
[234] Gould*, *Balzan Prize to Ernst Mayr*, 223 Science 255, 255 (1984).
[235] Bradie* & Gromko*, *The Status of the Principle of Natural Selection*, 3 Nature & System 3, 11 (1981).
[236] Brady*, *Dogma and doubt*, 17 Biological J. Linnean Soc. 79, 89 (1982).
[237] Section 10.2(a) (1).
[238] Popper*, *Intellectual Autobiography*, in 2 The Philosophy of Karl Popper 3, 136 (P. Schilpp* ed. 1974). Popper* has not abandoned this conclusion. Notes 18-20; text accompanying note 306.
[239] C. Patterson*, *Evolution* 147 (1978) ("evolutionary theory is *not testable* in the same way as a theory in physics, or chemistry, or genetics . . ..") (italics added).
[240] Birch* & Ehrlich*, *Evolutionary History and Population Biology*, 214 Nature 349, 352 (1967) ("Our theory of evolution has become . . . one which cannot be refuted by any possible observations. It is thus '*outside of empirical science*' . . ..") (italics added).
[241] Brady*, *Natural Selection and the Criteria by Which a Theory Is Judged*, 28 Systematic Zoology 600, 621 (1979).
[242] Cracraft*, *The Use of Functional and Adaptive Criteria in Phylogenetic Systematics*, 21 Am. Zoologist 21, 34 (1981).
[243] C. Patterson*, *Evolution* 145-46 (1978). *See also* N. Macbeth*, *Darwin Retried* 93 (1971).
[244] N. Macbeth*, *Darwin Retried* 99 (1971) ("Let us now apply all this to classical Darwinism. Anyone familiar with the literature knows how everything is taken as a confirmation. Also, there is no way to *test* large parts of the theory by experiment.") (italics added).
[245] Saunders* & Ho*, *Is Neo-Darwinism Falsifiable?—And Does It Matter?*, 4 Nature & System 179, 185 (1982) (italics added).
[246] Forey*, *Neontological Analysis Versus Palaeontological Stories*, in Problems of Phylogenetic Reconstruction 119, 124 (K. Joysey* & A. Friday* eds. 1982) (italics added).
[247] Brady*, *Dogma and doubt*, 17 Biological J. Linnean Society 79, 79 (1982) (italics added).
[248] A. Koestler*, *Janus: A Summing Up* 179 (1978) (quoting L. von Bertalanffy*) (" 'I think the fact that a theory so vague, so insufficiently verifiable and so far from the criteria otherwise applied in 'hard' science, has become a dogma, can only be explained on sociological grounds.' ").
[249] Bradie* & Gromko*, *The Status of the Principle of Natural Selection*, 3 Nature & System 3, 11 (1981) (for general forms but not specific forms).

[250] C. Harris*, *Evolution, Genesis and Revelations: Readings from Empedocles to Wilson* 189-90 (1981) (" 'Survival of the fittest' may thus be taken as an *untestable* truism—an axiom.") (italics added); Harris*, *An Axiomatic Interpretation of the Neo-Darwinian Theory of Evolution*, 18 Perspectives in Biology & Medicine 179, 182 (1975) ("It could be argued that the neo-Darwinian theory can be stated in such a way that it is testable and that experimental proof of the theory in that form would therefore prove the axioms. Fisher's fundamental theorem, which states that 'the rate of increase in fitness of any organism at any time is equal to its genetic variance in fitness at that time' [6, chap. 1] perhaps comes closest to stating a theory of evolution in testable form. But in fact, the theorem is not uniquely neo-Darwinian because it does not specify the means by which mutations arise. Hence, it does *not afford a test* of the first axiom. Fisher also defined fitness in terms of the number of offspring per parent, that is, survival of the lineage. Therefore, the theorem also fails to provide a test of the second axiom.") (italics added).

[251] Bethell*, *Darwin's Unfalsifiable Theory*, Kronos, Summer 1982, at 33, 33-34 (" 'the survival of the fittest' is not a *testable* theory, but a *tautology*") (italics added); Bethell*, *Darwin's Mistake*, Harper's Magazine, Feb. 1976, at 70, 75; Section 10.2(a) (2).

[252] C. Patterson*, *Evolution* 70 (1978) (italics added).

[253] Brady*, *Dogma and doubt*, 17 Biological J. Linnean Soc. 79, 86 (1982) (italics added, original italics deleted). *See* notes 137 & 261.

[254] S. Stanley*, *Macroevolution* 6 (1979) (speaking of natural selection). *See* Section 3.3(f).

[255] Wassermann*, *Testability of the Role of Natural Selection within Theories of Population Genetics and Evolution*, 29 British J. Philosophy of Science 223, 240 (1978) (italics in original).

[256] Brady*, *Dogma and doubt*, 17 Biological J. Linnean Society 79, 88 (1982) (italics added).

[257] Popper*, *Intellectual Autobiography*, in 2 The Philosophy of Karl Popper 3, 137 (P. Schilpp* ed. 1974) ("Adaptation or fitness is defined by modern evolutionists as survival value, and can be measured by actual success in survival; there is hardly any possibility of *testing* a theory as feeble as this.") (italics added). Popper's* shift on natural selection does not appear to alter this point. Notes 18-20.

[258] O'Grady*, *Evolutionary Theory and Teleology*, 107 J. Theoretical Biology 563, 576 (1984) ("Many of its [neo-Darwinism's] components (e.g. adaptation status, evolutionary scenarios) are virtually untestable, and thus appear irrefutable.").

[259] Wassermann*, *Testability of the Role of Natural Selection within Theories of Population Genetics and Evolution*, 29 British J. Philosophy of Science 223, 223-24 (1978) ("The second kind of explanation, which relies on natural selection, is found in attempts to 'explain' the genesis and maintenance of specific evolutionary adaptations by resort to existentially quantified ad hoc hypotheses, which sometimes may be linked hypothetically to

theories of population genetic mechanisms. As neither these *ad hoc* hypotheses nor their specially postulated linkage with theories of general mechanisms are *falsifiable*, the hypotheses as well as the linkages are *not testable*. Such 'explanations' of adaptations are therefore metaphysical.") (italics added).

[260] Cracraft*, *The Use of Functional and Adaptive Criteria in Phylogenetic Systematics*, 21 Am. Zoologist 21, 31-32 (1981) ("The *causal process is outside the realm of analysis* for those investigating historically-based events. The critical factor in the scientific study of any phenomenon is that explanatory hypotheses should be susceptible to criticism, that explanations should be evaluated by empirical tests of some sort. As far as I can see, statements of the type that 'phenotype x is an adaptation, evolved via the agency of natural selection' are thoroughly *untestable*. The necessary data needed to refute such an assertion cannot be gathered, and we are more or less forced to accept it as an article of *faith* rather than as a scientific statement.") (italics added).

[261] Brady*, *Dogma and doubt*, 17 Biological J. Linnean Society 79, 88 (1982) ("When we try to understand adaptation we are reduced to 'just so' stories because the possibilities are limited only by imagination. It is this very indeterminacy that caused Lewontin (1977) to worry about the nature of the ceteris paribus clause in any engineering analysis: 'In order to make the argument that a trait is an optimal solution to a particular problem, it must be possible to view the trait and the problem in isolation, all other things being equal. If other things are not equal, if a change in a trait as a solution to one problem changes the organism's relation to other problems of the environment, it becomes impossible to carry out the analysis part by part, and we are left in the hopeless position of seeing the whole organism as being adapted to the whole environment.' ").

[262] Platnick*, *Cladograms, Phylogenetic Trees, and Hypothesis Testing*, 27 Systematic Zoology 438, 441 (1978) (some "pheneticists or nonevolutionary biologists" so argue, although Platnick* does not).

[263] Cartmill*, *Hypothesis Testing and Phylogenetic Reconstruction*, in Zeitschrift für Zoologische Systematik und Evolutions forshung 73 (1981) (italics added).

[264] Bush*, *What Do We Really Know about Speciation?*, in Perspectives on Evolution 119, 119-20 (R. Milkman* ed. 1982) (italics added).

[265] Peters*, *Tautology in Evolution and Ecology*, 110 Am. Naturalist 1, 1 (1976) ("I argue that the 'theory of evolution' does not make predictions, so far as ecology is concerned, but is instead a logical formula which can be used only to classify empiricisms and to show the relationships which such a classification implies. *Similar criticisms are then made of several ecological concepts*. The essence of the argument is that these 'theories' are actually tautologies and, as such, cannot make empirically *testable* predictions. They are not scientific theories at all.").

[266] Whitfield, *Book Review*, 18 Biological J. Linnean Society 77, 78 (1982).

[267] D. Green* & R. Goldberger*, *Molecular Insights into the Living Process*

407 (1967) (italics added). *See* Section 5.4.
[268] G. Simpson*, *The Meaning of Evolution* 278 (1950) (italics added). *See also* Section 7.3(a).
[269] Section 10.2(a) (1).
[270] Note 233.
[271] Note 203.
[272] Note 204.
[273] Note 205.
[274] Note 206
[275] Note 210.
[276] Note 213.
[277] Note 215.
[278] Note 225.
[279] Note 229.
[280] Note 239.
[281] Note 236.
[282] Note 245.
[283] Note 246.
[284] Note 242.
[285] Note 254.
[286] Note 255.
[287] Note 256.
[288] Section 9.5(b).
[289] Gentry, *Letter*, Physics Today, Oct. 1982, at 13, 13; Gentry, *Letter*, Physics Today, Apr. 1983, at 13, 13.
[290] Laudan*, *More on Creationism*, in Science, Technology & Human Values, Winter 1983, at 36, 38 (italics added).
[291] Quinn*, *The Philosopher of Science as Expert Witness*, in Science and Reality: Recent Work in the Philosophy of Science 32, 43 (J. Cushing*, C. Delaney* & G. Gutting* eds. 1984). He believes that the theory of creation, as defined in the Arkansas law, "is so highly disconfirmed that, for all practical purposes, it has been falsified." *Id.*
[292] *Id.* at 43-44 (italics added).
[293] *Id.* at 47 (first italics in original, other italics added).
[294] Sparkes*, *What is this thing called science?*, 89 New Scientist 156, 158 (1981).
[295] *See* Moore*, *Science as a Way of Knowing—Evolutionary Biology*, 23 Am. Zoologist 1, 8-9 (1983); Laudan*, *Commentary: Science at the Bar—Causes for Concern*, Science, Technology & Human Values, Fall 1982, at 16, 17 ("It is now widely acknowledged that many scientific claims are not testable in isolation, but only when imbedded in a larger system of statements, some of whose consequences can be submitted to test."); Section 10.3(a).
[296] Moore*, *Science as a Way of Knowing—Evolutionary Biology*, 23 Am. Zoologist 1, 8-9 (1983) ("Thus, the Cell Theory would be taken to consist of the many sorts of observations—morphological and physiological—relating

to the basic units of structure and function of most living creatures. Used this way, a theory cannot be disproven. There is *no way* that the Cell Theory can be *falsified*.") (italics added).

297 Riddiford* & Penny*, *The scientific status of modern evolutionary theory*, in Evolutionary Theory: Paths into the Future 1, 11 (J. Pollard* ed. 1984) (italics added, original italics deleted).

298 Bradie* & Gromko*, *The Status of the Principle of Natural Selection*, 3 Nature & System 3, 9 (1981).

299 Gould*, *One's Approach to a Course in Geology*, 30 J. Geological Educ. 120 (1984).

300 Riddiford* & Penny*, *The scientific status of modern evolutionary theory*, in Evolutionary Theory: Paths into the Future 1, 14 (J. Pollard* ed. 1984).

301 Sparkes*, *What is this thing called science?*, 89 New Scientist 156, 158 (1981) (italics added).

302 C. Patterson*, *Evolution* 147 (1978) ("Using Popper's criterion, we must conclude that evolutionary theory is not testable in the same way as a theory in physics, or chemistry, or genetics, by experiments designed to *falsify* it.") (italics added).

303 Gould*, *One's Approach to a Course in Geology*, 30 J. Geological Educ. 120 (1984).

304 Popper*, *Intellectual Autobiography*, in 2 The Philosophy of Karl Popper 3, 134, 137 (P. Schilpp ed. 1974). Popper* has not abandoned this conclusion. *See* notes 18-20.

305 Note 20.

306 Miller* & Fowler*, *What's Wrong with the Creation/Evolution Controversy?*, CTNS Bulletin, Autumn 1984, at 1, 5 (footnote omitted).

307 Cracraft*, *Book Review of Beyond Neo-Darwinism*, 1 Cladistics 300, 300-01 (1985) (italics added).

308 Wald*, *The Problems of Vicarious Selection*, in Mathematical Challenges to the Neo-Darwinian Interpretation of Evolution 71, 71 (P. Moorhead* & M. Kaplan* eds. 1967) ("It can, indeed, explain anything. You may be ingenious or not in proposing a mechanism which looks plausible to human beings and mechanisms which are consistent with other mechanisms which you have discovered, but it is still an unfalsifiable theory.").

309 Saunders* & Ho*, *Is Neo-Darwinism Falsifiable?—And Does It Matter?*, 4 Nature & System 179 (1982).

310 Weisskopf*, *Discussion*, in Mathematical Challenges to the Neo-Darwinian Interpretation of Evolution 62, 64 (P. Moorhead* & M. Kaplan* eds. 1967) ("I think it was Medawar who said that one thing about the theory of evolution is (and he quoted Popper) that is it *not falsifiable*, that whatever happens you can always explain it.") (italics added).

311 Birch* & Ehrlich*, *Evolutionary history and population biology*, 216 Nature 349, 352 (1967)("Our theory of evolution has become . . . one which *cannot be refuted* by any possible observations. It is thus 'outside of empirical science,' but not necessarily false.") (italics added).

312 Cartmill*, *Hypothesis Testing and Phylogenetic Reconstruction*, in Zeitschrift für Zoologishe Systematik und Evolutionsforschung 73, 90 (1981).
313 Schwabe* & Warr*, *A Polyphyletic View of Evolution: The Genetic Potential Hypothesis*, 27 Perspectives in Biology & Medicine 465, 467 (1984) ("This liberal spread of rules, each of which can be observed in use by scientists, does not just sound facetious but also, in our opinion, *robs* monophyletic molecular evolution of its vulnerability to *disproof*, and thereby of its entitlement to the status of a scientific theory.").
314 Peters*, *Tautology in Evolution and Ecology*, 110 Am. Naturalist 1 (1976).
315 Saunders* & Ho*, *Is Neo-Darwinism Falsifiable?—And Does It Matter?*, 4 Nature & System 179, 180, 191 (1982) (italics added).
316 S. Løvtrup*, *Darwinism: The Refutation of a Myth* 422 (1987).
317 Brady*, *Natural Selection and the Criteria by Which a Theory Is Judged*, 28 Systematic Zoology 600, 600 (1979) (italics added).
318 Eldredge* & Gould*, *Punctuated Equilibria: An Alternative to Phyletic Gradualism*, in Models in Paleobiology 82, 90 (J. Schopf* ed. 1972) ("We have all heard the *traditional response* so often that it has become imprinted as a catechism that brooks no analysis: the fossil record is extremely imperfect. . . . This traditional approach to morphological breaks merely underscores what Feyerabend meant (see above) in comparing theories to party lines, for it renders the picture of phyletic gradualism *virtually unfalsifiable*.") (italics added).
319 Wald*, *Discussion*, in Mathematical Challenges to the Neo-Darwinian Interpretation of Evolution 62, 71 (P. Moorhead* & M. Kaplan* eds. 1967) ("It can, indeed, explain anything. You may be ingenious or not in proposing a mechanism which looks plausible to human beings . . . but it is still an unfalsifiable theory.").
320 Bethell*, *Darwin's Unfalsifiable Theory*, Kronos, Summer 1982, at 33, 34 ("Once this point is clarified, we can see that the analogy between biology and engineering breaks down, because evolutionary biology as currently set forth by such experts as Gould himself does not recognize the idea that animals have any ultimate function other than to survive and leave offspring. It can plausibly be argued from an engineer's standpoint that various birds are badly designed—ostriches and flamingoes, for example—but if they succeed in surviving and leaving offspring, as they do, who is to say that they are defective from an engineer's point of view?").
321 *Id.* at 34, 36 ("The scientist, or the philosopher of science, might put the problem with Darwin's theory this way. No event, or observation in nature, could conceivably demonstrate that the theory was false. To some this might at first seem to be a strength rather than a weakness of the theory, but in fact of course a theory that cannot be falsified in principle is not 'true' but rather a semantically disguised statement of the type 'all apples are apples'. . . . Darwin's theory is immune—logically immune—to falsification. . . .[T]he theory of natural selection is so vacuous that no experiment

can in principle either verify or falsify it. . . .").

[322] He says the following about the optimalization approach:

> If that is so, it follows that *the theory has no empirical support.* Its strength comes from its logical power to generate explanations for every manner of organic adaptation rather than from the evidence, which, as we have seen, contains *no potential for falsification.* The theory may be true, but whether it is or not, it cannot be said to have shown *evidence* of this truth, and the widespread acceptance of the theory must rest on some other grounds.

Brady*, *Dogma and doubt*, 17 Biological J. Linnean Society 79, 88 (1982) (middle italics added, other italics in original).

[323] Bradie* & Gromko*, *The Status of the Principle of Natural Selection*, 3 Nature & System 3, 8-9 (1981) ("the general formula itself is not subject to falsification although its concrete interpretations are").

[324] Wassermann*, *Testability of the Role of Natural Selection Within Theories of Population Genetics and Evolution*, 29 British J. Philosophy of Science 223, 223-24 (1978).

[325] Peters*, *Tautology in Evolution and Ecology*, 110 Am. Naturalist 1, 2 (1976).

[326] Section 10.2(b)(2).

[327] Cracraft*, *Book Review of Beyond Neo-Darwinism*, 1 Cladistics 300, 302 (1985).

[328] Gould*, *The promise of paleobiology as a nomothetic, evolutionary discipline*, 6 Paleobiology 96 (1980).

[329] G. Wassermann*, *Testability of the Role of Natural Selection within Theories of Population Genetics and Evolution*, 29 British J. Philosophy of Science 223, 223-24 (1978) ("neither these ad hoc hypotheses nor their specially postulated linkage with theories of general mechanisms are falsifiable.").

[330] Cartmill*, *Hypothesis Testing and Phylogenetic Reconstruction*, in Zeitschrift für Zoologishe Systematik und Evolutionsforschung 73, 90 (1981) ("We may, I think, conclude from all this that phylogenetic hypotheses are not falsifiable in Popper's sense of the word.").

[331] Schwabe*, *On the validity of molecular evolution*, 11 Trends in Biochemical Sciences 280, 280, 281 (1986).

[332] Schwabe* & Warr*, *A Polyphyletic View of Evolution: The Genetic Potential Hypothesis*, 27 Perspectives in Biology & Medicine 465, 467 (1984).

[333] Section 10.2(a)(1).

[334] Hepburn*, *Creation, Religious Doctrine of: Creation in the Context of Scientific Cosmological Theories*, 2 Encyclopedia of Philosophy 255, 255 (P. Edwards* ed. 1967).

[335] Note 292.

[336] Note 290.

[337] Note 297.

[338] Note 298.

[339] Note 301.

340 Note 315.
341 Note 324.
342 Section 9.6.
343 Leach*, *Men, bishops and apes*, Nature, Sept. 3, 1981, at 19, 20 (italics added).
344 Laudan*, *Commentary: Science at the Bar—Causes for Concern*, Science, Technology & Human Values, Fall 1982, at 16, 17 (italics added). *See also* Quinn*, *The Philosopher of Science as Expert Witness*, in Science and Reality: Recent Work in the Philosophy of Science 32, 44 (J. Cushing*, C. Delaney* & G. Gutting* eds. 1984). Laudan* also states:

> Well, that tells us something interesting about the psychology of creationists, but it has no bearing whatever on an assessment of their doctrines. After all, when confronted by comparable problems in other walks of life, we proceed exactly as I am proposing, that is, by distinguishing beliefs from believers. When, for instance, several experiments turn out contrary to the predictions of a certain theory, we do not care whether the scientist who invented the theory is prepared to change his mind. We do not say that his theory cannot be tested, simply because he refuses to accept the results of the test. . . . In just the same way, the soundness of creation-science can and must be separated from all questions about the dogmatism of creationists.

Laudan*, *More on Creationism*, in Science, Technology & Human Values, Winter 1983, at 36, 37-38.
345 Newfeld, *Dinosaur Tracks and Giant Men*, 2 Origins 64 (1975) (rejecting); Kuban, *The Taylor Site "man tracks,"* Origins Research, Spring-Summer 1986, at 1 (rejecting); Morris, *The Paluxy River Mystery*, Acts & Facts, Jan. 1986, at i, iii, iv ("none of the four trails at the Taylor site can today be regarded as unquestionably of human origin"; "it would now be improper for creationists to continue to use the Paluxy data as evidence against evolution").
346 N. Eldredge*, *The Monkey Business: A Scientist Looks at Creationism* 131 (1982).
347 *Id. See also* Alexander*, *Evolution, Creation, and Biology Teaching*, in Evolution versus Creationism 90, 92, 102 (P. Zetterberg* ed. 1983) (admitting that "[c]reationist arguments can also be shown to involve significant retreats," while interpreting that to indicate untenable hypotheses).
348 C. Sagan*, *Cosmos* 27 (1980) (emphasis in original).
349 M. Ruse*, *Darwinism Defended* 58 (1982).
350 I. Asimov*, *In the Beginning* 40 (1981).
351 Thomas*, *On the Nature of Cooperation*, Discover, Nov. 1981, at 58, 59.
352 Lewontin*, *Evolution/Creation Debate: A Time for Truth*, 31 BioScience 559 (1981).
353 Those are as follows:

> *Sir Julian Huxley* (1960): . . . The evolution of life is no longer a theory; it is a *fact* and the basis of all our thinking.
>
> *Ernst Mayr* (1976): . . . That evolution is a *fact* and that the astonishing

diversity of animals and plants evolved gradually was accepted quite universally soon after 1859.

George Gaylord Simpson (1951): . . . he finally and definitely established evolution as a *fact*, no longer speculation or an alternative hypothesis for scientific investigation. . . .

G. Ledyard Stebbins (1977): The origins of races and species by evolution is a demonstrated *fact* supported by experimental evidence as strong as the evidence for the existence of atoms, electrons, protons, and other particles of matter.

Theodosius Dobzhansky (1951): Evolution as a historical process is established as thoroughly and completely as science can establish *facts* of the past witnessed by no human eyes.

Donald C. Johanson [*sic*] (1981): Evolution is, I believe, firmly established as a scientific *fact*.

Ashley Montagu (1981): . . . the truth is that evolution is an *irrefutable fact* . . .."

Hughes*, *The Fact and the Theory of Evolution*, 44 Am. Biology Teacher 25, 27 (1982) (italics in original).

354 Biological Sciences Curriculum Study*, *Biological Science: Molecules to Man* (1st ed. 1961) (very significant textbook series).

354A E. Haeckel*, *The Riddle of the Universe* 238 (1900) (italics in original).

355 T. Dobzhansky*, F. Ayala*, G. Stebbins* & J. Valentine*, *Evolution* 5 (1977) (italics added).

356 Lessl*, *Science and the Sacred Cosmos: The Ideological Rhetoric of Carl Sagan*, 71 Quarterly J. Speech 175, 178 (1985) ("By calling evolution fact, the process of evolution is removed from dispute; it is no longer merely a scientific construct, but now stands apart from humankind and its perceptual frailties. Sagan apparently wishes to accomplish what Peter Berger calls "objectification," the attribution of objective reality to a humanly produced concept. . . . With evolution no longer regarded as a mere human construct, but now as a part of the natural order of the cosmos, evolution becomes a sacred archetype against which human actions can be weighed. Evolution is a sacred object or process in that it becomes endowed with mysterious and awesome power . . ..").

357 Cannon*, *The Bases of Darwin's Achievement: A Revaluation*, 5 Victorian Studies 109 (1961) (italics added).

358 Brady*, *Dogma and doubt*, 17 Biological J. Linnean Soc. 79, 95 (1982).

359 Grene*, *The Faith of Darwinism*, Encounter, Nov. 1959, at 48, 49 (italics added).

360 M. Midgley*, *Evolution as a Religion* (1985).

361 H. Lipson*, *A Physicist Looks at Evolution*, 31 Physics Bull. 138, 138 (1980) ("In fact, evolution became in a sense a scientific religion; almost all scientists have accepted it and many are prepared to 'bend' their observations to fit in with it.").

362 S. Jaki*, *Cosmos and Creator* (1982) ("*Darwinism is a creed* not only with scientists committed to document the all-purpose role of natural selec-

tion. It is a *creed* with masses of people who have at best a vague notion of the mechanism of evolution as proposed by Darwin, let alone as further complicated by his successors.") (italics added).

[363] C. Patterson*, *Evolution* 150 (1977) ("Popper warns of a danger: 'A theory, even a scientific theory, may become an intellectual fashion, a substitute for religion, an entrenched dogma.' This has certainly been true of evolutionary theory.").

[364] N. Macbeth*, *Darwin Retried* 126-27 (1971) ("Darwinism itself has become a religion.").

[365] R. Jastrow*, *God and the Astronomers* 113 (1978) ("There is a kind of *religion in science*; it is the religion of a person who believes there is order and harmony in the Universe, and every event can be explained in a rational way as the product of some previous event; every effect must have its cause; there is no First Cause.") (italics added).

[366] Lessl*, *Science and the Sacred Cosmos: The Ideological Rhetoric of Carl Sagan*, 71 Q. J. Speech 175, 183 (1985).

[367] Burton*, *The Human Side of the Physiologist: Prejudice and Poetry*, 1 Physiologist 2 (1957) (italics added).

[368] Brady*, *Dogma and doubt*, 17 Biological J. Linnean Society 79, 95-96 (1982) (italics added). *See also* F. Hoyle, *The Intelligent Universe* 25 (1983) (chapter 2: "The Gospel According to Darwin . . . A New Dogma").

[369] W. Stansfield*, *The Science of Evolution* 11 (1977).

[370] Gould*, *Toward the Vindication of Punctuational Change*, in Catastrophes and Earth History: The New Uniformitarianism 9, 17 (W. Berggren* & J. Van Couvering* eds. 1984).

[371] Scott*, *Update on Genesis*, New Scientist, May 2, 1985, at 30, 33.

[372] Note 343.

[373] Note 349.

[374] Note 355.

[375] Note 362.

[376] Section 9.1.

[377] Gould*, *Darwinism Defined: The Difference Between Fact and Theory*, Discover, Jan. 1987, at 64, 69-70.

[378] Gould*, *Balzan Prize to Ernst Mayr*, 223 Science 255, 255 (1984).

[379] Section 9.4(a)(3).

[380] Brady*, *Dogma and doubt*, 17 Biological J. Linnean Soc. 79, 91 (1982).

[381] Peters*, *Tautology in Evolution and Ecology*, 110 Am. Naturalist 1, 1 (1976).

[382] D. Hull*, *Philosophy of Biological Science* 68 (1974).

[383] N. Macbeth*, *Darwin Retried* 103 (1971).

[384] Sparkes*, *What is this thing called science?*, 89 New Scientist 156, 158 (1981).

[385] Mayr*, *Cause and Effect in Biology*, 134 Science 1501, 1504 (1961).

[386] Brady*, *Dogma and doubt*, 17 Biological J. Linnean Soc. 79, 86 (1982).

[387] Whitfield, *Book Review*, 18 Biological J. Linnean Society 77, 78 (1982).

[388] Ruse*, *Creation-Science Is Not Science*, in Creationism, Science, and

the Law 150, 153 (M. La Follette* ed. 1983). *See also* Ruse*, *Creation-Science Is Not Science*, Science, Technology & Human Values, Fall 1982, at 73, 74.

389 Quinn*, *The Philosopher of Science as Expert Witness*, in Science and Reality: Recent Work in the Philosophy of Science 32, 48 (J. Cushing*, C. Delaney* & G. Gutting* eds. 1984) (italics added).

390 W. Broad* & N. Wade*, *Betrayers of the Truth* 30-31 (1982). *See also* L. Eiseley*, *Darwin and the Mysterious Mr. X* (1979); A. Brackman*, *A Delicate Arrangement: Untold Story of the Darwinian Conspiracy* (1980); *but see* Gould*, *Darwin Vindicated*, N.Y. Rev. of Books, Aug. 16, 1979, at 36.

391 Rager*, *Human embryology and the law of biogenesis*, 79 Rivista di Biologia (Biology Forum) 449, 451-52 (1986) (italics added, names decapitalized).

392 J. Weiner*, *The Piltdown Forgery* (1955).

393 It was offered and accepted as a "missing link" between an ape-like ancestor and man. Straus*, *The Great Piltdown Hoax*, 119 Science 265 (1954); Oxnard*, *Human Fossils: New Views of Old Bones*, 41 Am. Biology Teacher 264 (1979).

394 Anderson*, *Hominid collarbone exposed as dolphin's rib*, 98 New Scientist 199 (1983) ("He puts the incident on a par with two other embarrassing faux pas by fossil hunters: *Hesperopithecus*, the fossil pig's tooth that was cited as evidence of very early man in North America, and *Eoanthropus* or "Piltdown Man," the jaw of an orangutan and the skull of a modern human that were claimed to be the 'earliest Englishman'.").

395 Miller* & Fowler*, *What's Wrong with the Creation/Evolution Controversy?*, CTNS Bulletin, Autumn 1984, at 1, 9.

396 C. Babbage*, *Reflections on the Decline of Science in England* 174-83 (1970).

397 W. Broad* & N. Wade*, *Betrayers of the Truth: Fraud and Deceit in the Halls of Science* at 22-37, 212-24, 226-32 (1982) (chapters on "Deceit in History" of science and "Fraud and the Structure of Science", and list of frauds with published exposures).

398 A. Kohn*, *False Prophets* (1987).

399 Quinn*, *The Philosopher of Science as Expert Witness*, in Science and Reality: Recent Work in the Philosophy of Science 32, 48 (J. Cushing*, C. Delaney* & G. Gutting* eds. 1984).

400 Broad* and Wade* note:

> The great scientists of the past were *not all so honest* and they did not always obtain the experimental results they reported.
>
> • Claudius Ptolemy, known as "the greatest astronomer of antiquity," did most of his observing not at night on the coast of Egypt, but during the day, in the great library at Alexandria, where he *appropriated the work of a Greek astronomer* and proceeded to call it his own.
>
> • Galileo Galilei is often hailed as the founder of modern scientific method because of his insistence that experiment, not the works of Aristotle, should be the arbiter of truth. But colleagues of the seventeenth-century Italian physicist had *difficulty reproducing* his

results and doubted he did certain experiments.

• Isaac Newton, the boy genius who formulated the laws of gravitation, relied in his magnum opus on an unseemly *fudge factor* in order to make the predictive power of his work seem much greater than it was.

• John Dalton, the great nineteenth-century chemist who discovered the laws of chemical combination and proved the existence of different types of atoms, published elegant results that *no present-day chemist has been able to repeat.*

• Gregor Mendel, the Austrian monk who founded the science of genetics, published papers on his work with peas in which the *statistics are too good to be true.*

• The American physicist Robert Millikan won the Nobel prize for being the first to measure the electric charge of an electron. But Millikan extensively *misrepresented* his work in order to make his experimental results seem more convincing than was in fact the case.

W. Broad* & N. Wade*, *Betrayers of the Truth: Fraud and Deceit in the Halls of Science* 22-23 (1982) (italics added). *See also* R. Newton*, *The Crime of Ptolemy* (1977) (Ptolemy); Wade*, *Scandal in the Heavens: Renowned Astronomer Accused of Fraud*, 198 Science 707 (1977) (Ptolemy). Those are only a few of the scores of examples given, most from modern science.

[401] Lipson*, *A Physicist Looks at Evolution*, 31 Physics Bull. 138, 138 (1980).

[402] L. Eiseley*, *The Immense Journey* 18 (1957) ("At all events after it had passed under many eyes, interest waned, largely because the jaw was modern in appearance. . . . Since there was nothing about it that the anatomist would surely regard as primitive, interest quickly faded. Only time will tell how many other ancient human relics have been discarded simply because they did not fit a preconceived evolutionary scheme.").

[403] Romer*, *The Early Evolution of Fishes*, 2 Quarterly Rev. Biology 1, 35 (1946) ("There remained, however, a large number of Paleozoic fossils . . . which did not fit well into the general evolutionary picture nor into any familiar group. . . . A common solution was to ignore them. . . . They were in general treated rather as appendages to the recognized groups, as undesirable excrescences on an otherwise well-rounded evolutionary structure.").

[404] F. Weidenreich*, *Apes, Giants, and Men* 47 (1946) ("This is a striking example of the extent to which paleontological facts are disregarded and replaced with purely speculative constructions when the evolution of man was the topic and when facts did not agree with preconceived ideas."); *id.* at 6-7 ("But Huxley placed more emphasis on similarities in his illustration than dissimilarities, because he wanted to show that the organization of the human skeleton is, in principle, that of an anthropoid. Therefore he depicted the great apes in an 'erect' position but man in not a completely erect one.").

[405] 1 A. Keith*, *The Antiquity of Man* xi (1929) ("If human remains were found in one of the older Pleistocene deposits, and they proved to be modern in size and shape, they were rejected as spurious antiques, no matter what the state of their fossilization might be. On the other hand, if these remains

proved unmodern in character, then they were accepted as genuinely old, even if only imperfectly fossilized. It seemed to me then, as it does now, that, in this matter, the geologist's dice were so heavily loaded that it was scarcely possible for modern man to have a fair throw.").

406 *The Velikovsky Affair: Scientism vs. Science* 31-32 (A. de Grazia*, R. Juergens* & L. Stecchini* eds. 1966) (final italics added).

407 Hyman's* quotation was as follows:

> Every fool has greeted Darwin's theory, as earlier fools have greeted earlier evolutionary theories, with the statement that it would make a man a descendant of a baboon or chimpanzee. He [Darwin] writes: 'But we must not fall into the error of supposing that the early progenitor of the whole Simian stock, including man, was identical with, or even closely resembled, any existing monkey or ape.'

S. Hyman*, *Darwin for Today* 9 (1963). What Darwin* actually said in that passage was:

> But a naturalist would undoubtedly have ranked as an ape or monkey an ancient form which possessed many characters common to the Catarrhine and Platyrrhine monkeys, other characters in an intermediate condition, and some few, perhaps, distinct from those now found in either group. And as man from a genealogical point of view belongs to the Catarrhine or Old World stock, we must conclude, however much the conclusion may revolt our pride, that our early progenitors would have been thus designated.

Only after this context did Darwin* make the statement quoted out of context by Hyman*.

408 *The Velikovsky Affair: Scientism vs. Science* 27 (A. de Grazia*, R. Juergens* & L. Stecchini* eds. 1966) ("Neugebauer specified that Velikovsky had substituted the figure 3^0 14' for the correct value, 314', in a quotation from the work of another scholar. When Velikovsky protested in a letter to the late George Sarton, then editor of *Isis*, that the figure given in his book was correct and the 3^0 14' was in fact Neugebauer's own insertion, not his, Neugebauer dismissed the incident as a 'simple misprint of no concern.' . . .").

409 Galileo's colleagues "had difficulty reproducing his results and doubted he did certain experiments. . . . Dalton . . . published elegant results that no present-day chemist has been able to repeat. Gregor Mendel . . . published papers on his work with peas in which the statistics are too good to be true." W. Broad* & N. Wade*, *Betrayers of the Truth* 22-23 (1982). *See also* I. Cohen*, *Lives in Science* 14 (1957) (Galileo).

410 J. Partington*, *A Short History of Chemistry* 170 (1960) (Dalton); Nash*, *The Origin of Dalton's Chemical Atomic Model*, 47 Isis 101 (1956) (Dalton).

411 Fisher*, *Has Mendel's Work Been Rediscovered?*, 1 Ann. of Science 115 (1936) (Mendel*).

412 H. Lorentz*, A. Einstein*, H. Minkowski* & H. Weyl*, *The Principle of Relativity* 188 (W. Perrett* & G. Jeffery* trans. 1923).

413 "Often, if not normally, the proper scientific strategy is to continue

with the theory, and to try to work around the falsifying data—by showing the data not to be at all what it appears, by inventing ad hoc hypotheses to explain away the data, or if worse comes to worst, by ignoring the data and hoping that some day it will go away." Ruse*, *Falsification, Concilience and Systematics*, 28 Systematic Zoology 530, 531 (1979).

414 "Newton . . . relied in his magnum opus on an unseemly fudge factor in order to make the predictive power of his work seem much greater than it was. . . . Millikan extensively misrepresented his work in order to make his experimental results seem more convincing than was in fact the case." W. Broad* & N. Wade*, *Betrayers of the Truth* 22-23 (1982). *See also* Westfall*, *Newton and the Fudge Factor*, 179 Science 751 (1973) (Newton).

415 Horton*, *Subelectrons, Presuppositions, and the Millikan-Ehrenhaft Dispute*, 9 Historical Studies in the Physical Sciences 166 (1978) (Millikan*); Franklin*, *Millikan's Published and Unpublished Data on Oil Drops*, 11 Historical Studies in the Physical Sciences 185 (1981).

416 *E.g.*, Brush*, *Should the History of Science be Rated X?*, 183 Science 1164, 1168 (1974) (". . . In the first case, an apparently well-established theory of the nature of heat was rejected, not because of any new experimental evidence or theoretical calculations pertaining directly to heat, but because of new experimental and theoretical work in optics. In the second case, a theory of the nature of gases was clearly refuted by experimental tests (according to at least one proponent of the theory) but was accepted anyway. In the third case, a particular interatomic force law, derived by fitting experimental data, was abandoned in favor of another force law, which was in worse agreement with the data, primarily because of theoretical calculations. While these decisions were made in the first instance by individual scientists, their colleagues did not protest the irrationality of the decisions but simply followed the leader; hence these cases provide legitimate evidence for the behavior of the scientific community.").

417 *E.g.*, R. Levins* & R. Lewontin*, *The Dialectical Biologist* viii (1985) (Harvard U. Press) ("Indeed, it is a sign of the Marxist dialectic with which we align ourselves that scientific and political questions are inextricably interconnected—dialectically related."); Gould* & Eldredge*, *Punctuated equilibria: The tempo and mode of evolution reconsidered*, 3 Paleobiology 115, 146 (1977) ("one of us learned his Marxism, literally, at his daddy's knee"); *id.* at 115 ("Phyletic gradualism was an a priori assertion from the start . . .; it expressed the cultural and political biases of 19th century liberalism."); J. Haldane*, *Marxist Philosophy and the Sciences* (1939, repr. 1978); Section 13.5(b).

418 Klemke*, *Introduction*, in Introductory Readings in the Philosophy of Science 1, 16-17 (E. Klemke*, R. Hollinger* & A. Kline* eds. 1980).

419 N. Eldredge*, *The Monkey Business: A Scientist Looks at Creationism* 26 (1982).

420 Dolby*, *Science and Pseudo-Science: The Case of Creationism*, 22 Zygon 195, 203-04 (1987) (italics added).

421 *Id.* at 208.

CHAPTER 11

Theories of Evolution and Abrupt Appearance as Sole Scientific Alternatives

> *The existence of closely allied or representative species in any two areas, implies, on the theory of descent with modification, that the same parents formerly inhabited both areas. . . . It must be admitted that these facts receive no explanation on the theory of creation.*
>
> —Charles Darwin*,
> in *The Origin of Species*[1]

It is a widely held view that the sole alternative scientific explanations of the origin of the universe, life, and plants and animals are the theories of abrupt appearance or creation and the theory of evolution. That has been acknowledged by many evolutionist scientists and philosophers (Section 11.1), and is logically expected under the law of the excluded middle (Section 11.2). Yet a federal judge disagreed,[2] as have some others.

*Philosophers and scientists cited in this chapter, unless otherwise indicated, are not proponents of, and their quoted statements are not intended as endorsements of, either the theory of abrupt appearance or the theory of creation. However, their quoted statements are acknowledging the sole alternative status of the theories.

Figure 11.1
Sir JosephHooker: "the only other explanation"*

11.1 Evolutionist Acknowledgment of These Sole Alternatives

A typical evolutionist acknowledgment that the theories of abrupt appearance or of creation and the theory of evolution are the only possible scientific alternatives is made by Futuyma* (in a recent anticreationist book):

> Creation and evolution, between them, *exhaust the possible explanations* for the origin of living things. Organisms either appeared on the earth fully developed or they did not. If they did not, they must have developed from preexisting species by some process of modification.[3]

Another example is Wald*, a Nobel Prize recipient:

> The reasonable view was to believe in spontaneous generation; *the only alternative* to believe in a single, primary act of supernatural *creation. There is no third position.* . . . Most modern biologists, having reviewed with satisfaction the downfall of the spontaneous generation hypothesis, yet unwilling to accept the alternative belief in *special creation*, are left with nothing.[4]

A large number of other evolutionist scientists have reached the same conclusion, including the following (who are quoted in the footnotes):[5]

Lewontin*[6]
O'Grady*[7]
Thompson*[8]
Huxley* (who named the neo-Darwinian synthesis)[9]
Hoyle and Wickramasinghe[10]
Hunter* and Hunter*[11]
Heutschell* and Cook*[12]
Newman*[13]
Lyell*
Haeckel*
Oparin*
Watson*[14]
Jennings*[15]
Teller*[16]
Jastrow*[17]
Simon*[18]
Naylor*[19]

Many science educators and philosophers of science also agree, such as the following:

Alexander*[20]
Solomon*[21]
Klein*[22]
Smith*[23]
Leslie*[24]
Russell*[25]

That viewpoint of dual alternatives has a venerable history, because a century and a quarter ago it was assumed by Darwin* and was affirmed by both his scientific supporters (such as Haeckel*,[26] later Lyell*,[27] and Hooker*) and his creationist scientific opponents (such as Bron[28]). For example, Hooker* stated:

> Hitherto most have, as we have already observed, contented themselves with the hypothesis that they were independently created, and the minority have clung to the *only other explanation* hitherto conceived, that they have all been created by variation from a single first-created living organism, or a few such.[29]

The theory of creation has been criticized as dualistic and thus religious.[30] In fact, some of the most ardent anticreationists are the dualists in their perceptions of the sole alternatives that were cited above. Most of the anticreationists share an additional dualism, the two spheres or incommensurability approach (discussed in Section 13.3(b)), that posits that science and religion cannot conflict or concur because they involve nonoverlapping spheres. Miller* and Fowler* note the dualism inherent in that approach:

> Creation and evolution in some respects imply backgrounds about as different as one can imagine. In the sense that creation is an alternative to evolution for any specific question, *a case against creation is a case for evolution and vice versa.*[32]

Naylor* agrees: "Evidence in favor of one is necessarily against the other." [32A] The *McLean* court opinion disagreed,[33] and in doing so cast aside the implication of the score of authors cited earlier. Nevertheless, the question of the scientific nature of the theories of abrupt appearance and of evolution does not depend on that premise or on presentation of negative evidence against evolution, but instead is based on presenting affirmative evidence for abrupt appearance as described in Volume 1.[34]

Figure 11.2
Ernst Mayr: "It is impossible to believe simultaneously in two opposing theories explaining the same set of phenomena"*

11.2 Logical Recognition of These Sole Alternatives

The theories of abrupt appearance or creation and the theory of evolution or related theories are logical sole alternatives, under the law of the excluded middle. "It is impossible to believe simultaneously in two opposing theories explaining the same set of phenomena," as Mayr* points out in his introduction to an edition of *The Origin of Species* in reference to the theories of creation and evolution.[35] Each aspect of the theories poses the same logical choice between two scientific alternatives.

a. Biological Macroevolution and Biological Abrupt Appearance

In regard to the origin of plants and animals, either the various natural groups and higher categories appeared abruptly with discontinuous ancestry (biological abrupt appearance), or they emerged through common ancestry and ultimately progressive change (such as from simple organisms to fish to amphibians to reptiles to birds and lower mammals to primates to man—biological macroevolution), as Futuyma*,[36] Thompson*,[37] and Hunter*[38] maintain. That assumes that plants and animals have not existed forever in their current form, as assumed by all scientists of all viewpoints because of the finite age of the earth. Within each of these pairs of scientific alternatives, there are many subviews, such as the neoDarwinian synthesis, punctuated equilibria, macromutationism, and non-Darwinian evolution for the biological theory of evolution, and scientific concepts of abrupt appearance, the theory of discontinuity, the theory of creation, natural group systematics, the theory of vitalism, and the theory of directed panspermia for the biological theory of abrupt appearance.[39]

b. Biochemical Evolution and Biochemical Abrupt Appearance

With respect to the origin of the first life, either it appeared abruptly in complex form (biochemical abrupt appearance), or it emerged through ultimately progressive change from amino acids to polypeptides to nucleotides to biopolymers to protocells to the first life (biochemical evolution), as Wald*,[40] Jastrow*,[41] and Simon*[42] state. Again, there are many of the same subviews.

c. Cosmic Evolution and Cosmic Abrupt Appearance

In connection with the origin of the universe, either matter and energy came into being (cosmic abrupt appearance and some cosmic evolution views), or they have always existed (oscillating universe cosmic evolution views). Either most galaxy clusters and galaxies and stars appeared abruptly in substantially their present complex forms (cosmic abrupt appearance), or they reached their present complex forms through ultimately progressive change from a big bang or similar phenomenon (cosmic evolution).[43] Within these pairs of scientific alternatives, there are many subviews, such as an oscillating universe or closed universe, preexisting matter and energy, quantum and particle creation, or inflationary universe vacuum fluctuations among cosmic evolutionists.

Theistic evolutionists often have advocated a position that God began and perhaps directed the evolutionary process. That is not a third position, but instead combines a theory of cosmic creation, a theory of biological evolution, and some doctrines of religion. It is not a scientific explanation, because it usually involves an interpretation of Genesis and concepts of the human soul, although it certainly is one possible religious viewpoint. Theistic evolution is further described in Section 13.3.

Summary. Dozens of evolutionist scientists and educators have published the conclusion that the theories of abrupt appearance or creation and the theory of evolution are the sole alternatives. A typical statement is that Darwinian evolution "has long been perceived as the only legitimate theory of evolution, and thus the only alternative to creationism" (O'Grady*[44]). That was the view of Darwin's* contemporaries as well on both sides of the issue (Lyell*[45], Bron[46]). Logic also supports that duality, under the law of the excluded middle (Mayr*[47]). However, the theory of abrupt appearance does not depend on that assumption, because that theory is based on affirmative lines of scientific evidence.

Notes

[1] C. Darwin*, *The Origin of Species* 478 (1st ed. 1859, repr. 1964) (the final chapter, as well as much of the rest of the book, is a contrast between the two theories).

[2] That judge wrote:

> Creationists have adopted the view of Fundamentalists generally that there are only two positions with respect to the origins of the earth and life: belief in the inerrancy of the Genesis story of creation and of a worldwide flood as fact, or belief in what they call evolution.
>
> The two model approach of the creationists is simply a contrived dualism which has no scientific factual basis or legitimate educational purpose. It assumes only two explanations for the origins of life and existence of man, plants and animals. . . .

McLean v. Arkansas Bd. of Educ., 529 F. Supp. 1255, 1266 (E.D. Ark. 1982).

[3] D. Futuyma*, *Science on Trial* 198 (1983) (italics added).

4 Wald*, *The Origin of Life*, in Physics and Chemistry of Life 3, 5 (1955) (italics added). *See also* Wald*, *The Origin of Life*, Scientific Am., Aug. 1954, at 44, 46.

5 The author does not agree with the definition of the theory of creation or "creationism" given by Thompson*, Jastrow*, Simon*, and Hoagland*; and it is stressed that Futuyma*, Thompson*, Jastrow*, Hoagland*, and some others specifically argue that "creationism" is not scientific.

6 Lewontin*, *Introduction*, to Scientists Confront Creationism xxvi (L. Godfrey* ed. 1983) ("Yet . . . there is no escape from the fundamental contradiction between evolution and creationism. They are irreconcilable world views.").

7 O'Grady*, *Evolutionary Theory and Teleology*, 107 J. Theoretical Biology 563, 575 (1984) ("It [neo-Darwinism] has long been perceived as the only legitimate theory of evolution, and thus the only alternative to creationism.")

8 A. Thompson*, *Biology, Zoology, and Genetics* 1 (1983) ("There are *two doctrines* regarding biological change—the doctrine of evolution and the doctrine of special creation.").

9 J. Huxley*, *Evolution: The Modern Synthesis* 473 (1942) ("if we repudiate *creationism*, divine or vitalistic guidance, and the extremer forms of orthogenesis, as originators of adaptation, we must (unless we confess total ignorance and abandon for the time any attempts at explanation) invoke *natural selection*.").

10 F. Hoyle & N. Wickramasinghe, *Evolution from Space* 86-87 (1981) ("We can only explain the absence of intermediate insect forms in the fossil record either by supposing the different insect orders to be of *separate origin or* by arguing that the *divergencies from the common stock* indicated at the base of Figure 6.4 took place with extreme rapidity. Only the second of these possibilities is consistent with Darwinism, yet rapid expansion is just what Darwinism cannot achieve.") (italics added).

11 G. Hunter* & F. Hunter*, *College Zoology* 687 (1949) ("Either the present day forms began as such and have continued to exist in their original form, or life may have started in one common form from which all the others may have developed.").

12 C. Heutschell* & W. Cook*, *Zoology for Medical Students* 684 (1947) ("[T]wo theories have been propounded. The traditional idea was that of Special Creation, in which all organisms as we know them today were invented and made in the beginning of time with the same structure as we now find them. . . . The facts of biology, however, do not allow us to accept this view. The modern view is that of Organic Evolution.").

13 H. Newman*, *Evolution, Genetics, and Eugenics* 51 (1932) ("There is no rival hypothesis except the outworn and completely refuted idea of special creation, now retained only by the ignorant, the dogmatic, and the prejudiced.").

14 Watson*, *Adaptation*, 124 Nature 233 (1929) ("If so, it will present a

parallel to the theory of evolution itself, a theory universally accepted not because it can be proved by logically coherent evidence to be true but because the only alternative, special creation, is clearly incredible.").

[15] Jennings*, *Can We See Evolution Occurring?*, in Creation by Evolution 24, 32 (F. Mason* ed. 1928) ("Remember that there are two opposite doctrines. One holds that the constitution of organisms is permanent; that they were created as they are and do not change. The other, the doctrine of evolution, holds . . ..").

[16] J. Teller*, *Louis Agassiz, Scientist and Teacher* 263 (1947) ("The concept of development was accordingly untrue, and special creation remained the only valid interpretation.").

[17] *See* R. Jastrow*, *Until the Sun Dies* 51-52 (1977) ("Perhaps the appearance of life on the earth is a miracle. Scientists are reluctant to accept that view, but their choices are limited; either life was created on the earth by the will of a being outside the grasp of scientific understanding, or it evolved on our planet spontaneously, through chemical reactions occurring in a nonliving matter lying on the surface of the planet.").

[18] M. Simon*, *The Matter of Life* 162 (1971) ("If life was not created supernaturally, and if it did not simply develop from preexistent 'seeds' present from the creation of the universe (whenever that was), life must have come forth from nonliving matter.").

[19] Naylor*, *Vestigial Organs Are Evidence of Evolution*, 6 Evolutionary Theory 91, 94 (1982) ("Evidence *for* evolution is automatically evidence *against* special creation.") (italics in original).

[20] Alexander*, *Evolution, Creation, and Biology Teaching*, in Evolution versus Creationism 90, 91 (J. Zetterberg* ed. 1983) ("indeed, at this moment creation is the only alternative to evolution").

[21] P. Davis & E. Solomon*, *The World of Biology* 395 (1974) ("Such explanations tend to fall into one or the other of two broad categories: special creation or evolution. Various admixtures and modifications of these two concepts exist, but it seems impossible to imagine an explanation of origins that lies completely outside the two ideas.").

[22] Klein*, *Preface*, to L. Sunderland, Darwin's Enigma 5, 5 (1985) ("There remains only the trust that those with a vested interest in the theory of evolution as currently presented in textbooks will permit an equal opportunity for all students to be exposed to all scientific evidences and to the only competitive theory of origins. . . . But the theory that life abruptly appeared on Earth is no more a religious absolute than the theory of evolution, for they are both axioms and neither is subject to scientific proof.").

[23] Smith*, *Two Evolutions*, in On Nature 42, 46 (L. Rouner* ed. 1984) (italics added) ("These notions do not cohere, but they do fall into *two rather clearly demarcated camps*. On the one hand is the view backed by modern science, that the human self can be understood as an organism in an environment, endowed genetically like other organisms with needs and drives, who through *evolution*—natural selection working on chance

mutations—has developed strategies for learning and surviving by means of certain adaptive transactions with the environment. Over and against this is the Judeo-Christian view that the human being was *created* . . ..").

[24] Leslie*, *Cosmology, Probability, and the Need To Explain Life*, in Scientific Explanation and Understanding 53, 57 (N. Rescher* ed. 1983).

[25] Russell*, *Why I am not a Christian*, in The Basic Writings of Bertrand Russell 589 (R. Egner* & L. Dennon* eds. 1961).

[26] A. Oparin*, *The Origin of Life on the Earth* 34 (1957) (quoting Ernst Haeckel*).

[27] C. Lyell*, *Principles of Geology* 330 (11th ed. 1873) ("in truth there are only as yet two rival hypotheses, between which we have our choice in regard to the origin of species—namely, first, that of special creation—and, secondly, that of creation by variation and natural selection").

[28] Bron, *Book Review*, Neues Jahrbuch für Mineralogie 112-16 (1860), reprinted in D. Hull*, *Darwin and His Critics* 120, 122 (1973) ("But there are really only two possibilities. Either his [Darwin's] theory is false (and cannot be extended beyond the field of common varieties) or else it is true. If it is true, then variability is unlimited, which means that the organic world was not created, which means that the natural force through which the organic world originated has been found and the assumption of Creation is unnecessary. If there are 10, 5, 3 or even 2 different prototypes of plants and animals, then Creation is necessary.").

[29] [Hooker*], *Book Review*, Gardeners' Chronicle, Dec. 31, 1859, at 1051-52, reprinted in D. Hull*, *Darwin and His Critics* 81, 84 (1973).

[30] McLean v. Arkansas Bd. of Educ., 529 F. Supp. 1255, 1260 (E.D. Ark. 1982).

[31] Miller* & Fowler*, *What's Wrong with the Creation/Evolution Controversy?*, CTNS Bulletin, Autumn 1984, at 1, 1.

[32] Alexander*, *Evolution, Creation, and Biology Teaching*, in Evolution versus Creationism 90, 91 (J. Zetterberg* ed. 1983) (italics added).

[32A] Naylor*, *Vestigial Organs Are Evidence of Evolution*, 6 Evolutionary Theory 91, 94 (1982).

[33] McLean v. Arkansas Bd. of Educ., 529 F. Supp. 1260, 1266 (E.D. Ark. 1982).

[34] Chapters 2, 4 & 6.

[35] Mayr*, *Introduction*, to C. Darwin*, The Origin of Species vii, xii (1st ed. 1859, repr. 1964).

[36] D. Futuyma*, *Science on Trial* 197 (1983).

[37] A. Thompson*, *Biology, Zoology, and Genetics* 1 (1983).

[38] G. Hunter* & F. Hunter*, *College Zoology* 687 (1949).

[39] Several recent books on directed panspermia describe it as a theory related to creation. F. Hoyle & N. Wickramasinghe, *Evolution from Space: A Theory of Cosmic Creation* (1981); F. Hoyle, *The Intelligent Universe: A New View of Creation and Evolution* (1983); Section 13.1(f).

[40] Wald*, *The Origin of Life*, in Physics and Chemistry of Life 3, 5 (1955).

[41] R. Jastrow*, *Until the Sun Dies* 51-52 (1977).
[42] M. Simon*, *The Matter of Life* 162 (1971).
[43] Leslie*, *Cosmology, Probability, and the Need To Explain Life*, in Scientific Explanation and Understanding 53, 54 (N. Rescher* ed. 1984).
[44] Note 7.
[45] Note 27.
[46] Note 28.
[47] Note 35

PART VI

Whether the Theories of Abrupt Appearance and Evolution Are Non-Religious? The Definitions of Religion

The definition of religion is as elusive a holy grail as the definition of science. However, under most of the attempts to snare it, the theory of evolution and the theory of abrupt appearance are equally nonreligious.

The reason is that both theories consist of affirmative scientific arguments based on empirical data, and neither theory necessarily involves a concept of creation or of a creator. However, many scientific theories of evolution do incorporate concepts of creation, such as the big bang, inflationary universe, quantum and particle creation, and continuous creation theories about the origin of the universe, of panspermia theories about the origin of the first life, and of other theories of the origin of organisms. The history of modern science shows its basis in belief in creation. As Patterson* concludes, "evolution and creation seem to be sharing remarkable parallels that are increasingly hard to tell apart."[1]

Many scientists, both evolutionists and discontinuitists, hold firm beliefs about religion that are closely tied to their conclusions about origins. Maynard Smith* admits that about himself and Haldane*:

> Why did Haldane become an evolutionist and a biochemist? . . . I think

> that a clue to his interests may lie in a striking feature of his writing and conversation. This is the ubiquity of references to religion and of quotations from religious texts. These references are not only to Christianity, but to classical mythology and, after he settled in India, to Hindu and Buddhist writings. This is not an attempt to use religious arguments to support his case: Haldane was not a believer and, at least as far as Christianity was concerned, he rather enjoyed blasphemy. Neither was it, in any simple sense, an attempt to settle scores with a religion he had abandoned. I mention this possibility because such a motive has been important in my own case; having been raised in a rather literal version of Christianity, my interest in Darwin was first aroused because of the apparent contradiction between the theory of evolution and the Christian faith. Other evolutionary biologists have had a similar experience: E.O. Wilson is, I believe, an example, and I was amused to discover how many of my co-workers are lapsed Catholics. . . .[2]

Similary, Huxley* conceded that biologists "with very few exceptions" reject a theistic view of evolution:

> SHAPLEY: You're not an atheist, Julian; you're an agnostic.
>
> HUXLEY: I am an atheist, in the only correct sense, that I don't believe in the existence of a supernatural being who influences natural events. . . . I think we can dismiss entirely all idea of a supernatural overriding mind being responsible for the evolutionary process.
>
> DARWIN: I do, entirely.
>
> HUXLEY: And biologists do, with very few exceptions.[3]

Notes

[1] Address of Dr. Colin Patterson at Am. Museum of Natural History, tr. at 4 (Nov. 5, 1981).

[2] Maynard Smith*, *J.B.S. Haldane*, 4 Oxford Studies in Evolutionary Biology 1, 7 (1987).

[3] *At Random*, 3 Evolution after Darwin: Issues in Evolution 46 (S. Tax* & C. Callender* eds. 1960).

CHAPTER 12

Theories of Evolution and Abrupt Appearance and Prevailing Definitions of Religion

> *We shall look at doctrines which are believed to be scientific, but are not actually so, and whose persuasiveness seems to be due to their serving some of the functions of a religion, even though they are seen by their promoters as being hostile to 'religion' as such. . . . Marxism and evolutionism, the two great secular faiths of our day, display all of these religious-looking features. . . .*
>
> —Mary Midgley*, in
> *Evolution as a Religion*[1]

The definition of religion can be approached from a philosophical as well as a judicial standpoint (Sections 12.1 and 12.2). When either definition is applied, the theories of abrupt appearance and evolution are found to be comparably nonreligious (Section 12.3).

*Philosophers and scientists cited in this chapter, unless otherwise indicated, are not proponents of, and their quoted statements are not intended as endorsements of, either the theory of abrupt appearance or the theory of creation. However, their quoted statements are acknowledging concepts that support the non-religious nature of the theories of abrupt appearance and evolution.

Figure 12.1 Philosophical and theological definitions of religion: belief in a deity "neither singly nor in combination constitute[s] tight necessary and sufficient conditions for something being a religion" (Alston)*

12.1 Philosophical Definitions of Religion

The definitions of "religion" given by the field of philosophy of religion do *not* treat religion as most centrally involving God or a Supernatural Being, or as requiring those concepts at all, but as being centered in a variety of factors with few or none that are sine quibus non.

For example, the *Encyclopedia of Philosophy* article on religion states that not just one but many of nine characteristics are necessary for something to be religious:

> *Characteristic features of religion.* Despite the fact that none of the definitions specifies a set of characteristics which is present when and only when we have a religion, or gives us a unique essence, it does seem that they contribute to our understanding of the nature of religion. It appears that the presence of any of the features stressed by these definitions will help to make something a religion. We might call such features, listed below, religion-making characteristics.
>
> 1. Belief in supernatural beings (gods).
> 2. A distinction between sacred and profane objects.
> 3. Ritual acts focused on sacred objects.
> 4. A moral code believed to be sanctioned by the gods.
> 5. Characteristically religious feelings (awe, sense of mystery, sense of guilt, adoration), which tend to be aroused in the presence of sacred

objects and during the practice of ritual, and which are connected in idea with the gods.
6. Prayer and other forms of communication with gods.
7. A world view, or a general picture of the world as a whole and the place of the individual therein. This picture contains some specification of an over-all purpose or point of the world and an indication of how the individual fits into it.
8. A more or less total organization of one's life based on the world view.
9. A social group bound together by the above.[2]

That article emphasizes that no single factor, or minimum number of factors, are "tight necessary and sufficient conditions for something being a religion":

> *Definition in terms of characteristics.* If it is true that the religion-making characteristics *neither singly nor in combination constitute tight necessary and sufficient conditions for something being a religion*, and yet that each of them contributes to making something a religion, then it must be that they are related in some looser way to the application of the term. Perhaps the best way to put it is this. *When enough of these characteristics are present to a sufficient degree, we have a religion.* It seems that, given the actual use of the term "religion," this is *as precise as we can be.* If we tried to say something like "for a religion to exist, there must be the first two plus any three others," or "for a religion to exist, any four of these characteristics must be present," we would be introducing a degree of precision not to be found in the concept of religion actually in use.[3]

Alston* warns that there is real danger in selection for polemical purposes among the wide range of definitions of religion.[4]

The *Encyclopaedia Britannica* definition is similar. The *Micropaedia* article defines religion as follows:

> religion, man's relation to that which he regards as holy. The "holy" need not be thought of as supernatural, much less as personal; and if the word god be defined in personal or supernatural terms, it follows that *religion includes far more than the relation to God or a god.* Similarly, the phrase relation to the holy may be conceived of in a variety of forms. Worship is probably the most basic of these, but moral conduct, right belief, and participation in religious institutions are generally also constituent elements of the religious life as practiced by believers and worshippers and as commanded by religious sages and scriptures.[5]

The *Macropaedia* article on religion gives as the "essence or core of religion" a "moment of vision and disclosure," and lists as "subjective and objective aspects of religion" the characteristics of faith, prayer, ritual, mystery, public worship, sacralization, and often belief in salvation.[6]

The newer *Macropaedia* article points out that "there is dispute over the possibility of finding an essence of religion," and gives a multifaceted set of characters:

> *Attempts to arrive at a definition of religion*
>
> *The essence of religion and the context of religious beliefs, practices, and institutions.* An acceptable definition of religion itself is *difficult* to attain. Attempts have been made to find an essential ingredient in all religions (*e.g.*, the numinous, or spiritual, experience; the contrast between the sacred and the profane; belief in gods or in God), so that an "essence" of religion can be described. *But objections have been brought against such attempts*, either because the rich variety of men's religions makes it possible to find counterexamples or because the element cited as essential is in some religions peripheral. *The gods play a very subsidiary role for example, in most phases of Theravada ("Way of the Elders") Buddhism.* A more promising method would seem to be that of exhibiting aspects of religion that are *typical* of religions, though they may not be universal. The occurrence of the rituals of worship is typical, but there are cases, however, in which such rituals are not central. Thus, one of the tasks of a student of religion is to gather together an inventory of types of religious phenomena.
>
> The fact that *there is dispute over the possibility of finding an essence of religion* means that there is likewise a problem about speaking of the study of religion or of religions, for it is misleading to think of religion as something that "runs through" religions. This brings to light one of the major questions of method in the study of the subject. *In practice a religion is a particular system, or a set of systems, in which doctrines, myths, rituals, sentiments, institutions, and other similar elements are interconnected.*[7]

The one thing that is clear from those definitions is "that religion includes far more than the relation to God or a god"—"objections have been brought against such attempts" to "find an essential ingredient in all religions" of "belief in gods or God."

The *Oxford English Dictionary* similarly gives seven definitions, of which only the third and fifth involve a Supreme Being, and then only defines belief in a Supreme Being to be religious when accompanied by other characteristics.[8]

A representative and widely used definition of religion is the "ultimate concern" emphasis of Tillich*:

> Religion, in the largest and most basic sense of the word, is ultimate concern. . . . Religion is the substance, the ground, and the depth of man's spiritual life.[9]

That definition has been employed by the U.S. Supreme Court.[10] The disjunction between religion and deity is defended by Kurtz*, a philosopher:

> Religion means a commitment to values, an expression of human ideals. *It does not refer to any godhead* but to the heightened qualities of moral and aesthetic experience.[11]

The wide range of other philosophies and definitions of religion is indicated by the "vision of something which stands beyond, behind, and within, the passing flux of immediate things" of Whitehead*,[12] and the proposals of Jung*,[13] Geertz*,[14] and Richter*.[15]

Summary. Although there are many proposed definitions of religion, various factors such as belief in a deity "neither singly nor in combination constitute tight necessary and sufficient conditions for something being a religion" (Alston*[16]). None of the cited definitions, whether in encyclopedias (*Britannica*[17]) or by theologians (Tillich*[18]), says that belief in God or a Supreme Being necessarily constitutes religion, and each of those definitions finds belief in God nonessential to religion. "Beliefs in supernatural beings can be whittled away to nothing, as in certain forms of Unitarianism, or may never be present, as in certain forms of Buddhism" (Alston*[19]).

Figure 12.2
Legal definitions of religion: "anything 'arguably non-religious' should not be considered religious in applying the establishment clause" (Tribe)*

12.2 Judicial Definitions of Religion

The U. S. Supreme Court has defined "religion" as involving any "ultimate concern,"[20] citing Tillich*, and as *not* being centered in and *not* even requiring belief in God or a Supernatural Being. It added that "religion," in the conscientious objector exemption, protects "all sincere religious beliefs which are based upon a power or being, or upon a faith, to which all else is ultimately dependent."[21] That definition, according to some legal commentators, is the Supreme Court's "ultimate definition of religion for constitutional purposes."[22] The Court has used similar definitions both in cases construing the Establishment Clause of the First Amendment[23] and in cases involving statutory interpretation of the term "religion."[24] In contrast, the Supreme Court and lower courts have specifically found nonreligious the various references to a creator or God by public schools and other governmental bodies outside the context of public school prayers, as described in Section 20.2.

Legal commentators have generally followed the same approach. Choper* defines religion to involve "ultimate concerns," "extratemporal consequences," or "transcendent reality."[25] Tribe* favorably quotes the Tillich* definition of "ultimate concern,"[26] and suggests that "anything 'arguably non-religious' should not be considered religious in applying the establishment clause":

> For the establishment clause, an analogous dichotomy distinguishes all that is "arguably non-religious" from all that is clearly religious; anything "*arguably non-religious*" should not be considered religious in applying the establishment clause. Thus, when a government program has the effect of fostering, or encouraging—but not mandating—an activity, the fact that the activity is only *arguably* religious is not enough to make the government program a violation of the establishment clause; as long as the activity is arguably *not* religious, the establishment clause has not been violated by its facilitation. Since TM is arguably non-religious, it should not be considered a religion when an establishment question is raised; the teaching of TM as an elective course should therefore be deemed permissible. Similarly, since a moment of silence is arguably non-religious, even a statute *requiring* observance of a brief period of silence or meditation at the opening of the school day would not violate the establishment clause.[27]

Some commentators emphasize the institutional features of religion, requiring the three factors "whether the individual belongs to an organization, whether that organization provides its members with moral demands based upon some insight into the meaning of life and order in the universe, and whether the individual's membership entails conduct or practices based upon the organization's beliefs."[28] Other commentators give a wide range of definitions.[29]

Figure 12.3
Non-religious nature of the theories of evolution and of abrupt appearance (picture of Cologne Cathedral)

12.3 The Theories of Evolution and Abrupt Appearance and Religion

In a parallel manner, neither the theory of evolution nor the theory of abrupt appearance constitutes such an "ultimate concern" or religious belief system as required by those philosophical definitions or legal definitions. Each theory lacks most or all of the nine characteristics of the *Encyclopedia of Philosophy* definitions, lacks most or all of the aspects of the *Encyclopaedia Britannica* definitions, and does not substantially meet any of the prevailing philosophical definitions. The theory of abrupt appearance instead consists of empirical evidence and scientific interpretations, without any reference to or reliance on religious texts and doctrines.[30] Recognition of the scientific evidence supporting the theory of abrupt appearance can be and has been based entirely on nonreligious grounds, as several Agnostic scientists and philosophers demonstrate.[31] The concept of a God or creator is not a part of that scientific evidence, and thus is not a part of the theory when properly defined, as discussed later.[32]

Both the theory of evolution and the theory of abrupt appearance also differ from an "ultimate concern" or religious system under the legal definitions of religion. The Establishment Clause of the First

Amendment, while requiring a degree of separation between church and state, does not require a total wall of complete separation between those institutions.[33]

No court decisions have involved the scientific theory of abrupt appearance. Three lower court decisions discussed a theory of creation that was termed "creation-science," and have departed from the judicial mainstream in holding that the concept of creation is necessarily religious. These decisions were rendered by a three-judge panel of federal court of appeal judges (from among the nearly 200 such judges), and by two federal district court judges (from among the roughly 500 such judges). The appellate judges wrote that the phrase "creation-science" in a Louisiana law, which defined it as "scientific evidences,"[34] nevertheless "is a religious belief."[35] However, the full circuit of the U.S. Court of Appeals divided sharply on the issue, with eight judges deciding without a written opinion not to review the three-judge decision,[36] while seven judges concluded in a published opinion that the theory of creation is "scientific evidence" rather than "religious doctrine."[37] The U.S. Supreme Court found that that Louisiana law had a purpose on the part of the legislators to advance religion, but did *not* say that the theory of creation is inherently religious.[38] In a different case involving an Arkansas law, the *McLean* decision,[39] a federal district court judge wrote as follows:

> To the contrary, "creation out of nothing" is a concept unique to Western religions. In traditional Western religious thought, the conception of a creator of the world is a conception of God. Indeed, *creation* of the world "*out of nothing*" is the ultimate religious statement because God is the only actor. . . .
>
> . . ..
>
> . . .The idea of sudden creation from nothing, or creation ex nihilo, is an inherently religious concept. (Vawter, Gilkey, Geisler, Ayala, Blount, Hicks.)
>
> The argument advanced by defendants' witness, Dr. Norman Geisler, that teaching the existence of God is not religious unless the teaching seeks a *commitment* is contrary to common understanding and contradicts settled case law. . . .[40]

However, the theory of creation does not involve the concepts of "creation from nothing" or "creation by a creator."[41] Furthermore, neither of those concepts is necessarily religious (as indicated by the inflationary universe theory of "creation from nothing"[42] and the continuous creation and other theories of creation without a creator[43]). Also, the concept of God is not the hallmark of the religious, as shown by the above definitions of religion in Supreme Court decisions and philosophy of religion authorities, and as settled by the Supreme Court decisions upholding reference to God and to a creator.[44]

The *McLean* opinion also seems to say that a concept that is not scientific must be religious:

> Since creation-science is not science, the conclusion is inescapable that the *only* real effect of Act 590 is the advancement of religion.[45]

The incorrectness of this premise that nonscientific concepts are necessarily religious is universally recognized by philosophers, judges, and theologians. One philosopher writes:

> [T]hey lead Judge Overton ultimately to the claim, specious in its own right, that since Creationism is not "science," it must be religion.[46]

A different federal judge recently noted that "[m]erely because science cannot answer a question does not mean that that question is thrown into the realm of religion for purposes of the Establishment Clause, and this holds true even if theologians label the question religious."[47] Otherwise, philosophy and literature (which are not scientific) would be religious.

Summary. The theories of evolution and of abrupt appearance are not religious, under the prevailing definitions of religion offered by philosophers of religion, theologians, and judges. Even the theory of creation can be nonreligious under those standards, although it is a more difficult case to assess.

Notes

1 M. Midgley*, *Evolution as a Religion* 13, 15 (1985) (italics added).

2 Alston*, *Religion*, in 7 Encyclopedia of Philosophy 140, 141 (P. Edwards* ed. 1967) (italics were bold in original).

3 *Id.* at 141-42 (italics added except subheading was bold in original).

4 *Id.* at 142 ("Each party to the dispute will appeal to a definition suited to the position he is defending, and since none of these definitions is wholly adequate, there is an irreducible plurality of not wholly inadequate definitions to be used for this purpose. Person A, who claims that communism is a religion, will give, for instance, Caird's statement as his definition of religion, and person B, who denies this, will choose Martineau's. Obviously, the position of each is upheld by his chosen definition.").

5 *Religion*, 9 Encyclopaedia Britannica: Micropaedia 1016, 1016 (15th ed. 1985) (italics added).

[6] Ramsey*, *Religion, Philosophy of,* 15 Encyclopaedia Britannica: Macropaedia 592, 594 (15th ed. 1974) (the latter two characteristics come under "[e]ffects of religious beliefs and practices").

[7] Smart*, *Religions, The Study and Classification of,* 26 New Encyclopaedia Britannica: Macropaedia 548, 548 (15th ed. 1985) (italics added except headings).

[8] The full definitions (without etymology) are as follows:

Religion . . ..

1. A state of life bound by monastic vows; the condition of one who is a member of a religious order, esp. in the Roman Catholic Church.
2. A particular monastic or religious order or rule; a religious house. Now *rare.*
3. Action or conduct indicating a belief in, reverence for, and desire to please, a divine ruling power; the exercise or practice of rites or observances implying this. Also *pl.*, religious rites. Now *rare*, exc. as implied in 5.
4. A particular system of faith and worship. . . .
5. Recognition on the part of man of some higher unseen power as having control of his destiny, and as being entitled to obedience, reverence, and worship; the general mental and moral attitude resulting from this belief, with reference to its effect upon the individual or the community; a personal or general acceptance of this feeling as a standard of spiritual and practical life. . . .
6. *transf.* †a. Devotion to some principle; strict fidelity or faithfulness; conscientiousness; pious affection or attachment. *Obs.* . . ..
7. The religious sanction or obligation of an oath, etc. *Obs.*

Oxford English Dictionary 410 (1971) (italics in original).

[9] P. Tillich*, *Theology of Culture* 7 (1959) (Oxford U. Press).

[10] United States v. Seeger, 380 U.S. 163, 187 (1965); Torcaso v. Watkins, 367 U.S. 488, 495 & n.11 (1961).

[11] P. Kurtz*, *In Defense of Secular Humanism* 9-10 (1983) (italics added).

[12] A. Whitehead*, *Science and the Modern World* 191 (1925).

[13] C. Jung*, *Psychologie und Religion* 11 (1947) ("religion is one of the earliest and most general expressions of the human soul").

[14] Geertz*, *Religion as a Cultural System,* in 3 Anthropological Approaches to the Study of Religion 4 (M. Banton* ed. 1966) ("A religion is a system of symbols which acts to establish powerful, pervasive and long lasting modes of motivations in men by formulating conceptions of a general order of existence and clothing these conceptions with such an aura of factuality that the modes and motivations seem uniquely realistic"); Geertz*, Bellah* & Dittes*, *Religion,* in 13 International Encyclopedia of the Social Sciences 398, 411 (D. Sills* ed. 1977) (anthropological, epistemological, sociological, and psychological/phenomenological approaches) ("The concept of religion briefly sketched here—religion as the most general mechanism for integrating meaning and motivation in action systems applies to all types of action systems, not only to whole societies or groups of them".).

[15] Richter*, *Religion*, in Lexikon für Theologie und Kirche 1164, 1169 (M. Buchger* & H. Snäufele* eds. 1963) (Religion is defined "as an experimental meeting with holy reality and as an active response of the person thus confronted with the Holy. . . . The variety of the objects, ways and contents of the meeting with the Holy form along with the typical forms of active response the appearance and world of ideas of religion. The one thing with which all religion has to do is 'reality'." "Religion" can take many forms such as those of power, as Gods, as a God, as an impersonal "divine sense" and in various "typical structural forms".).

[16] Note 2.

[17] Note 5 & 7

[18] Note 9.

[19] Alston*, *Religion*, in 7 Encyclopedia of Philosophy 140, 142 (P. Edwards* ed. 1967).

[20] United States v. Seeger, 380 U.S. 163, 187 (1965) (construction of term "religion" in statute).

[21] *Id.* at 180-83.

[22] Giannella*, *Religious Liberty, Nonestablishment and Doctrinal Development: Part I*, 80 Harv. L. Rev. 1381, 1425 (1967).

[23] Torcaso v. Watkins, 367 U.S. 488, 495 & n.11 (1961) (nontheistic religions); Everson v. Board of Educ., 330 U.S. 1, 16 (1947) (protection of "Non-believers").

[24] Gillette v. United States, 401 U.S. 437, 443 (1971); Welsh v. United States, 398 U.S. 333, 340 (1970); United States v. Seeger, 380 U.S. 163, 166 (1965) (ethical creed with skepticism toward existence of God).

[25] Choper*, *Defining "Religion" in the First Amendment*, 1982 U. Ill. L. Rev. 579, 594-604.

[26] L. Tribe*, *American Constitutional Law* 827 n.8 (1978).

[27] *Id.* at 828-29 (italics in original). Tribe* takes quite a different view in his second edition (1988).

[28] Comment*, *Beyond* Seeger/Welsh: *Redefining Religion Under the Constitution*, 31 Emory L.J. 973, 998-99 (1982) (footnotes deleted).

[29] *E.g.*, Freeman*, *The Misguided Search for the Constitutional Definition of "Religion"*, 71 Geo. L.J. 1519 (1983); Note*, *The Sacred and the Profane: A First Amendment Definition of Religion*, 61 Tex. L. Rev. 139 (1982).

[30] Chapters 2, 4 & 6.

[31] Sections 2.1, 6.1, 17.3.

[32] Section 13.2.

[33] Chapter 20.

[34] La. Rev. Stat. §286.3(2) (1986) (enacted in July 1981).

[35] Aguillard v. Edwards, 765 F.2d 1251, 1253 (5th Cir. 1985).

[36] Aguillard v. Edwards, 778 F.2d 225 (5th Cir. 1985) (en banc).

[37] *Id.* at 226.

[38] Edwards v. Aguillard, 482 U.S. . . . , 96 L. Ed. 2d 510 (1987).

[39] McLean v. Arkansas Bd. of Educ., 529 F. Supp. 1255 (E.D. Ark. 1982).

40 *Id.* at 1265-66 (italics added).

41 Sections 1.1(b) & 13.2.

42 Section 13.1(c).

43 Section 13.1(d)-(e).

44 Sections 12.1-12.2 & 20.2.

45 McLean v. Arkansas Bd. of Educ., 529 F.Supp. 1255, 1272 (E.D. Ark. 1982). The reasoning of the *McLean* opinion is criticized in Section 20.2(e).

46 Laudan*, *Commentary: Science at the Bar—Causes for Concern*, Science, Technology & Human Values, Fall 1982, at 16, 16.

47 Womens Services, P.C. v. Thone, 483 F. Supp. 1022, 1036 (D. Neb. 1979), *aff'd*, 626 F.2d 206 (8th Cir. 1980)(expressly affirming the Establishment Clause issue), *vacated on other grounds*, 452 U.S. 398 (1981); *see* Harris v. McRae, 448 U.S. 297, 319 (1980).

CHAPTER 13

Theories of Evolution and Abrupt Appearance and Concepts of Abrupt Appearance, Creation, and a Creator

> *Authors of the highest eminence seem to be fully satisfied with the view that each species has been independently created. To my mind it accords better with what we know of the laws impressed on matter by the Creator, that the production and extinction of the past and present inhabitants of the world should have been due to secondary causes, like those determining the birth and death of the individual.*
>
> —Charles Darwin*, in *The Origin of Species*[1]

The theory of abrupt appearance does not incorporate or refer to a concept of creation or a concept of a creator, and the theory of evolution need not do so. However, both theories are modified by some scientists, theologians, and others to include a concept of

*Philosophers and scientists cited in this chapter, unless otherwise indicated, are not proponents of, and their quoted statements are not intended as endorsements of, either the theory of abrupt appearance or the theory of creation. However, their quoted statements are acknowledging concepts that support the non-religious nature of the theories of abrupt appearance and evolution.

creation (the scientific theory of creation and the evolutionary theories of the big bang, inflationary universe, creation fields, etc.), and sometimes to include a concept of a creator (religious doctrines of creation and religious doctrines of evolution such as theistic evolution). In either case, the modifications made by some discontinuitists and evolutionists do not alter the scientific nature of the theories of abrupt appearance and of evolution.

Thus, concepts of creation are not more prominent in the theory of abrupt appearance than in the theory of evolution, and in fact are potentially scientific concepts (Section 13.1). By contrast, the concept of a creator is not a necessary part of either the theory of abrupt appearance or of the theory of evolution because, while empirical scientific evidence can point to an abrupt appearance or evolutionary development of the universe, life, and organisms, that evidence does not give direct information about the source or cause of either sequence. Hence, the concept of a creator is not central to either theory, but instead is an inference made by some proponents of modified theories that reaches outside the realm of science into philosophy, metaphysics, or theology (Section 13.2). A teacher, in presenting the theories of abrupt appearance and evolution, would not need to refer to a creator in the classroom in either case (and certainly need not discuss characteristics of a creator). Yet such a nonscientific inference of the existence of a creator is not necessarily religious, but instead may be philosophical or metaphysical and in fact has been in the history of thought (Section 13.3). The concepts of creation and of a creator play a parallel nonreligious role in the theories of evolution and of abrupt appearance (absent) and in various modified theories (present), with many evolutionists interpreting their view to disprove the existence of God and other evolutionists interpreting development to be the process used by God (Section 13.4). Important world views are consistent with evolution (materialism, naturalism, and positivism) as well as with abrupt appearance (theism, deism, and metaphysical dualism), and the evolutionist world views are often overlooked and sometimes surprising (Section 13.5).

Figure 13.1
Non-religious concepts of abrupt appearance, such as Plato's "Demiurge, or Craftsman, who... arranges existing material and does not create" (Bambrough), and "abrupt appearances" within punctuated equilibria (Gould*)*

13.1 Non-Religious Nature of Scientific Evidence Supporting the Theories of Abrupt Appearance and Evolution

The concept of abrupt appearance is anything but religious, and is instead a scientific theory organizing empirical evidence. Examples of that empirical evidence are the abrupt appearance of complex life in the fossil record, the abrupt appearance of complex information in plants and animals, the abrupt appearance of the first life, and the abrupt appearance of the universe because of the first and second laws of thermodynamics (Sections 2.1, 2.4, 4.1, 6.1, and 6.6), according to proponents of the theory of abrupt appearance. The concept of abrupt appearance prominently figures in many evolutionist theories, in fact, such as the punctuated equilibria (Sections 2.1 and 3.2(c)) and big bang theories (Section 13.1(b)).

The concept of creation as well is not inherently religious, but can be instead a proper scientific theory arising from empirical evidence (Section 1.1(b)). The concept of creation can mean "nothing more than the simple fact of appearing," and is so used "in all current cosmological contexts," according to North*:

> Dingle was perfectly well aware of the distinction between the senses of 'created' according to which it may be used either to indicate *nothing more than the simple fact of appearing*, or to make the positive assertion that something may come to exist out of nothing. Likewise Samuel had earlier quoted Hoyle as saying, not that material comes from nothing, but that 'it does not come from anywhere'. . . . We have no wish to deny that *cosmologists do occasionally use the less happy alternative*, but in doing so they are certainly not erecting it as profound metaphysical principle.
>
> . . ..
>
> In conclusion, *we may defend the concepts of age, First Event, and creation as they are encountered in all current cosmological contexts*; but in all cases with important reservations. . . . Several theories may lead one to suppose the occurrence of a First Event. . . .[2]

The non-religious and scientific meaning of "creation" is noted by Tax*:

> Here, there is ambiguity as to the meaning of the term creation. That this could imply *for some people a natural process* and *for others a Creator is evident*.
>
> . . ..
>
> . . .Both a believing *theist* and a believing *atheist can give their respective meanings* to the word creation and accept it as occurring so early in time that everything else that exists in the universe has had ample time to develop "naturally."[3]

Lipson* argues that creation is supported by "the experimental evidence" and thus is "the only acceptable explanation."[4] Gillespie* uses "the word 'create' occasionally in the more general sense of 'originate'."[5] North* says that, "[g]enerally speaking, by 'act of creation' we mean an act whereby some or other material is 'transformed', 'form' being the only new thing."[6]

Historically, the "conventional practice" was "using the term creation as a synonym for 'appear' or 'originate'."[7] The "term had four distinct meanings," one of which was "simply a conventional term meaning the origin of species, the world, matter, or whatever, and had no theological referent," Gillespie* notes.[8] Examples from Darwin*, Hooker*, Lyell*, and others were given in Section 1.1(b).

The nonreligious concepts of creation appear in a number of scientific hypotheses and other fields, as follows:

- a. Nonreligious use of "creation" in philosophy and history
- b. Scientific use of "creation" in the big bang theory
- c. Scientific use of "creation" in the inflationary universe theory
- d. Scientific use of "creation" in quantum creation, particle creation, and creation field theories
- e. Scientific use of "creation" in continuous creation and steady state theories
- f. Scientific use of "creation" in the panspermia theory
- g. Scientific use of "creation" in other biological theories
- h. Scientific use of "creation" as a biological term.

It is important to reiterate that the theory of creation is different from the theory of abrupt appearance. Clarifying the potential scientific and nonreligious nature of the former, however, helps remove any question about the totally scientific and nonreligious nature of the latter.

a. Non-Religious Use of "Creation" in Philosophy and History

The concept of creation itself is not inherently religious, such as the conclusion that an arrowhead, Stonehenge, or "creative art" was created. Foster* summarizes some usages in the arts:

> This may be most easily seen in the contrast of fine or *creative art* with the activity of a Demiurge or artificer. It is notorious that the creative artist, *e.g.*, the painter, has no clear knowledge of what he is going to achieve before he has achieved it; and the critic on his side, when confronted with a work of creative art, is indeed aware that there is 'something more' in it than the sensible material—a great painting is more than a certain complexity of coloured surfaces—but this 'something more' (we may call it loosely 'the meaning') is *not* capable of being conceived in distinction from the sensible material in which it is expressed. . . .[9]

The nonreligious use of "creation" is also evident and in fact "indispensable" in moral and aesthetic philosophy:

> "Creation," "creativity," and related concepts are *indispensable in any adequate moral and aesthetic philosophy*. In those contexts they are logically connected with the ideas of human freedom, moral vision, moral criticism, ideas of inventiveness, originality, and the life of imagination. Indeed, a significant part of the metaphysical and theological discussion of creation can be translated or *"demythologized" into moral and aesthetic terms*, and it has been indirectly relevant to the development of moral philosophy and aesthetic theory.[10]

For example, Plato posited a "Demiurge, or Craftsman, [who] is represented as ordering and arranging the physical world," and who "arranges existing materials and does not create them."[11] That Demiurge acted nonnaturalistically but lacked the supernatural characteristics of the omnipotent God of Genesis, and is an important part of the history of philosophy.[12] Leslie* and some other modern philosophers argue for the "creative ethical requiredness" of the universe "independent of Theistic religion":

> (a) Belief in the *universe's creative ethical requiredness* can exist *independently of any centuries-old association with Christianity*. So it need not share what you or I may think of as Christianity's *implausibility*, conflict with scientific findings, moral defects, etc.
>
> (b) . . . Above all *no recourse* need be had to any inexplicably existing *Divine Person* endowed with a desire to produce good.[13]

While the concept of creation (except nomothetic creation) concededly has a nonnaturalistic aspect (as evolution does), it is not necessarily supernatural, as these examples show, because empirical scientific evidence pointing to creation cannot indicate whether the source of creation was a nonnaturalistic force or process or a supernatural deity (as discussed later[14]).

b. Scientific Use of "Creation" in the Big Bang Theory

The scientific and nonreligious nature of the concept of creation can be seen in the frequent use of that term to mean "abrupt appearance" by scientists other than discontinuitist and creationist scientists. Tipler* notes that "the standard big bang theory has the Universe coming into existence out of nothing, and cosmologists use the phrase 'creation of the universe' to describe this phenomenon!"[15] The following standard scientific books about the big bang theory have used the term "creation" in a totally scientific sense:

- George Gamow*, *The Creation of the Universe* (1955)
- John D. Barrow* and Joseph Silk*, *The Left Hand of Creation: The Origin and Evolution of the Expanding Universe* (1983)
- James S. Trefil*, *The Moment of Creation: Big Bang Physics Before the First Millisecond to the Present Universe* (1983)
- Albert C. Choate*, *The Core of Creation: An Investigation into the Fundamentals of Reality and the Foundations of Existence* (1982)
- Joseph Silk*, *The Big Bang: The Creation and Evolution of the Universe* (1980)
- H. Fritzsch*, *The Creation of Matter: The Universe from Beginning to End* (1984)

There are many other examples.[16]

That is as true of the history of the big bang theory as of its current presentation. North* points out the "creation terminology" and the "creation idea" there:

> Friedmann used the creation-terminology in his first contribution to cosmology. Lemaitre was cautious and spoke of the 'initial state', but the creation idea was soon to be very frequently and quite casually applied to the appropriate discontinuity. The notion of a transmuted material was always absent: if anything this was thought to be creation *ex nihilo*, although later there came McCrea's indication of a source of the created material. . . .[17]

Although the concepts of "creation" and "first event" are different from much of physics, "there is nothing contradictory or absurd in separating the idea of a cause from that of a beginning of existence."[18] Thus, Gamow*, who formulated the modern revision of the big bang theory, described it as "the creation of the universe."[19] Einstein*, who formulated the theory of relativity, also "felt the necessity for a 'beginning'."[20] Proponents of the big bang theory, including Sagan*,[21] continue to describe it as a "creation."[22] That evinces the scientific nature of the term.

c. Scientific Use of "Creation" in the Inflationary Universe Theory

The term "creation *ex nihilo*" (creation from nothing) is used to describe the recent inflationary universe theory, as Guth* of Massachusetts Institute of Technology writes:

> Recently there has been some serious speculation that the actual *creation* of the universe is describable by physical laws. In this view the universe would originate as a quantum fluctuation, starting *from absolutely nothing*. The idea was first proposed by Edward P. Tryon of Hunter College of the City University of New York in 1973, and it was put forward again in the context of the inflationary model by Alexander Vilenkin of Tufts University in 1982.[23]

Tryon* uses the same terminology:

> In 1973, I proposed that our Universe had been *created* spontaneously from nothing (*ex nihilo*), as a result of established principles of physics. This proposal variously struck people as preposterous, enchanting, or both.
>
> The novelty of a *scientific theory of creation ex nihilo* is readily apparent, for science has long taught us that one cannot make something from nothing. . . .
>
> . . . .
>
> Thus, the proposal of *creation ex nihilo*, originally motivated by a simple Newtonian estimate for gravitational energy and by the princi-

ples of quantum field theory, remains speculative, but appears viable in rather striking detail.[24]

Pagels*, another proponent of the inflationary universe theory, further describes the theory, and notes that "[n]o law of physics prevents a creation *ex nihilo*":

> The alternative idea that the universe began as "nothing," a *creation ex nihilo*, satisfies the criterion that it leave no unanswered questions about a preexistent state of the universe. But what is "nothing"?
>
> . . ..
>
> Tryon in his 1973 article "Is the Universe a Vacuum Fluctuation?" points out that the sum of all conserved charges, such as electric charge, for the whole universe is consistent with being zero and therefore the universe can be *created* out of the vacuum. *No law of physics prevents a creation ex nihilo.*
>
> Tryon also suggests that the universe originates as a quantum fluctuation of the vacuum —a tiny fluctuation that turned into the big bang. Just as quantum particles can be spontaneously created out of a vacuum, so too the universe might have been *created* out of a vacuum. . . .[25]

The inflationary view of "creation *ex nihilo*" as a scientific alternative is also summarized by Davies*,[26] and set forth by Pollock*[27] and Linde*.[28] That theory, like the big bang theory, underscores the nonreligious nature of the term "creation" and even of "creation *ex nihilo*."

d. Scientific Use of "Creation" in Quantum Creation, Particle Creation, and Creation Field Theories

Quantum creation theory, based on applying quantum mechanics to the origin of space and time, is related to the inflationary universe theory. "The best known model of quantum creation *ex nihilo* is due to Hartle and Hawking."[29] The model is summarized by Pagels*:

> [T]he Hawking-Hartle analysis suggests that the origin of the universe can be treated like other quantum events. Theirs is an unfamiliar application of quantum theory because it involves the *creation of space and time* rather than the creation of a few quantum particles as in the decay of a nucleus. But there is in principle no reason that the origin of the universe cannot be subjected to rational analysis and computation in the quantum theory.
>
> . . ..
>
> Our growing familiarity with these new ideas should not distract us from realizing how strange they were just a few years ago. When historians of science look back on the 1970s and '80s they will report that for the first time scientists constructed rational mathematical models based on the laws of physics which described the *creation of the universe out of*

> *nothing*. And that will mark the beginning of a new outlook on the creation of existence.[30]

Similar quantum creation models are proposed by Goncharov* and Bytsenko*[31] and Alvarez*.[32]

Particle creation theory is a "natural hypothesis connecting the particle creation rate with the macroscopic expansion of the universe," which Parker* outlines.[33] It is discussed by such other authors as Grib* and Mamaev,*[34] Audretch*,[35] and Selak*.[36]

A creation field theory, based on alternative solutions of Einstein's* equations, is offered as "a natural way for creating the matter" and as "a viable alternative to the standard big-bang model," by Narlikar* and Padmanabhan*.[37] That, and the other theories summarized here, involves a scientific use of the term and concept of creation.

e. Scientific Use of "Creation" in Continuous Creation and Steady State Theories

The continuous creation theory, or steady state theory, was formulated by Bondi*, Hoyle*, and Gold*, and was the major challenge to the big bang theory from the late 1940's until the late 1960's. It was defined to include "creation . . . out of nothing" by Bondi* (of University of London):

> There is only one way in which a constant density can be compatible with a motion of expansion, and that is by the continual creation of matter. Only if the diminution of density due to the drift to infinity is counteracted by a constant replenishment of newly created matter can an expanding universe preserve an unchanging aspect.
>
> There is little doubt that the continual *creation* of matter necessary in this theory is the most revolutionary change proposed by it. There is, however, no observational evidence whatever contradicting continual *creation* at the rate demanded by the perfect cosmological principle.
>
> . . ..
>
> It should be clearly understood that the *creation* here discussed is the formation of matter not out of radiation but out of *nothing*.[38]

North*, in his history of cosmological theories, summarized Bondi's* position that particle creation "is brought within the scope of physical inquiry . . . instead of . . . being handed over to metaphysics," such as allowing discussion of "the rate at which matter appears for the first time and its distribution at the time of its appearance," as well as discussing "the kind of matter (for example its chemical or electrical nature) and its initial motion."[39]

A similar view was expressed by Hoyle* (then of Cambridge), who was then an evolutionist and is an Atheist:[40]

> For I find myself forced to assume that the nature of the Universe requires continuous *creation*—the perpetual bringing into being of new background material.[41]

That theory was based on "mathematical equations, whose consequences can be . . . compared with observations":

> Some people have argued that continuous creation introduces a new assumption into science—and a very startling assumption at that. Now I do not agree that continuous creation is an additional assumption. It is certainly a new hypothesis, but it only replaces a hypothesis that lies concealed in the *older theories*, which assume, as I have said before, that the whole of the matter in the *Universe was created in one big bang* at a particular time in the remote past. On scientific grounds this big bang assumption is much the less palatable of the two. For it is an irrational process that cannot be described in scientific terms. *Continuous creation*, on the other hand, *can be represented by mathematical equations whose consequences can be worked out and compared with observation*.[42]

The continuous creation theory involved a "creation" in which "theistic implications are again eliminated."[43]

A different model, the two-centered static universe of Ellis*, Maartens*, and Nel*, involved the concept that "creation is a continuously proceeding process . . .."[44] There are several recent continuous creation theories as well.[45]

f. Scientific Use of "Creation" in the Panspermia Theory

The panspermia theory is a major alternative to biochemical evolution. One model is advocated by Sir Francis Crick, a Nobel Prize laureate, who was the co-discoverer of DNA structure.[46] Its proponents have similarly used the term "creation" in a scientific and nonreligious sense in describing the hypothesis of directed panspermia (life originating from outer space), such as in the following books:

> Sir Fred Hoyle and N. Chandra Wickramasinghe, *Evolution from Space: A Theory of Cosmic Creationism* (1984)
>
> Sir Fred Hoyle, *The Intelligent Universe: A New View of Creation and Evolution* (1983)

For example, Hoyle, the eminent British astronomer, describes his scientific conclusion that "creation" occurred by a nonpersonal and nonJudeo-Christian "creator":

> This it seems to me explains why another intelligence, an intelligence which preceded us, was led to put together, as a *deliberate act of creation*, a structure for carbon-based life.

. . ..

The intelligence responsible for the *creation* of carbon-based life in the cosmic theory is firmly *within the Universe* and is subservient to it. Because the creator of carbon-based life was *not all-powerful*, there is consequently no paradox in the fact that terrestrial life is far from ideal.[47]

That theory is also advocated by N. Chandra Wickramasinghe (a Hindu and a Nontheist), who is chairman of applied mathematics and astronomy at University College in Cardiff.[48]

g. Scientific Conclusions of "Creation" in Other Theories

Other scientists have been forced by scientific evidence to mention and even accept creation, in the sense of a sudden origination of the first life or of organisms. A recent example is Ambrose*, emeritus professor of cell biology at University of London, who finds that information content and probability considerations compel the conclusion of "creative intelligence":

We conclude therefore that recent hypotheses about the origin of species fall to the ground, unless it is accepted that an intensive input of new information is introduced at the time of isolation of the new breeding pair. This can be explained in terms of the operation of *creative intelligence.*

. . ..

It looks as though the advances in molecular, cellular, and developmental biology, which have been made in recent years and are summarised in this book, have brought us to the stage where a *creative view of the origin of life and species* no longer needs to be defended *against evolutionary arguments.*[49]

Lipson*, although an Agnostic and still an evolutionist, is forced by the "experimental evidence" to conclude "that the only acceptable explanation is creation."[50] Bergson*, a Nobel Prize recipient, proposed the model of "creative evolution."[51] Smith* recently proposed the "Great Origins Thesis" to account for the inception of matter and energy by an unknown force.[52]

Similar conclusions can be found in the "secular creationism" of Heribert-Nilsson[53] (who firmly rejected the Genesis account of creation), a professor of botany and former director of the Botanical Institute at Lund, Sweden.[54] Creationist conclusions were also reached by Agassiz of Harvard, "America's leading biologist" at the time of Darwin,*[55] who was a Unitarian and rejected the Genesis account of creation.[56] Pitman "started as devil's advocate for the creationist view and came . . . to prefer it."[57] All of these scientists were driven to the conclusion of creation by scientific data totally independent of religious considerations (and in fact they rejected Genesis).

h. Scientific Use of "Creation" as a Biological Term

The term "creation" is used widely by evolutionists in a scientific sense "whereby some or other material is 'transformed'," as North* said earlier, or "as a synonym for 'appear' or 'originate'," as Gillespie* recounted.[58] Darwin* used the 'term of creation, by which I really meant 'appeared' by some wholly unknown process,"[59] and many great scientists gave the same scientific meaning that was discussed in Section 1.1(b). As part of biochemical evolution, Fox* proposes that molecular selection "was a 'creative' process,"[60] Ponnamperuma* speaks of the process as "the process of creation,"[61] and Ayala* and Valentine* speak of the "creation and concentration of active molecules . . .."[62] In connection with biological evolution, Dobzhansky* said that "[c]reation is not an event that happened in 4004 B.C.; it is a process that began some 10 billion years ago and is still under way."[63] Gould* writes that "[s]election must superintend the process of creation . . .," and "is the creative force of evolutionary change."[64] Schopf* described "[m]utation in the broad sense of the creation of new hereditary types,"[65] while O'Grady* proposes that "the hierarchy itself was created by a basic evolutionary instability of the organisms involved."[66]

The term "creation" is widely used for the physical or biological world. For example, Dobzhansky*, Ayala*, Stebbins*, and Valentine* write of man as " 'lord of creation',"[67] and Monod*, a Nobel Prize winner, says that "chance alone is at the source of every innovation, of all creation in the biosphere."[68] The term "creatures" is widely used for organisms. For instance, Gould* refers to "creatures in the oceanic plankton,"[69] and Stanley* writes of "fossil assemblages consisting of the imprints of softbodied creatures,"[70] while Darwin* frequently referred to "creatures."[71] To call the term or concept of "creation" inherently religious would be to disqualify much of the modern scientific literature.

Summary. Thus, the term "abrupt appearance" is pristinely scientific, and means in a discontinuous sense what is meant in a continuous sense by the "abrupt appearance" of complex life in punctuated equilibria (Sections 2.1 and 3.2(c)), the "abrupt appearance" of vast information content in information theory (Sections 2.4 and 4.1), the "abrupt appearance" of the earth because of polonium halos without uranium decay (Section 6.6), and the "abrupt appearance" of the universe because of the first two laws of thermodynamics (Section 6.1) and of the structure of the universe in the big bang theory (Section 13.1(b)).

Even the term "creation," although different, is nonreligious and can be scientific in meaning " 'appeared' by some wholly unknown process" (Darwin*[72]), "an act whereby some or other material is 'transformed' " (North*[73]), or coming into existence as "cosmologists use the phrase 'creation of the universe' " (Tipler*[74]). It so appears in the writings of leading proponents of the big bang, inflationary universe, quantum and particle creation, and continuous creation theories about the origin of the universe; in the writings of directed panspermia advocates and some biochemical evolutionists about the origin of the first life; and in the writings of others about the origin of organisms.

In philosophy and history, "creation" is used in the nonreligious sense of "creative art with the activity of a Demiurge or artificer" (Foster*[75]), and is "indispensable in any adequate moral and aesthetic philosophy" (Hepburn*[76]).

In cosmic evolution, "cosmologists use the phrase 'creation of the universe' to describe this phenomenon" (Tipler*[77]). Among big bang theorists, "the creation idea was soon to be frequently and quite casually applied to the appropriate discontinuity" (North*[78]). The inflationary universe theory proposes "a creation *ex nihilo*," and "[n]o law of physics prevents a creation *ex nihilo*" (Pagels*[79]). Quantum creation theory involves "models based on the laws of physics which described the creation of the universe out of nothing" (Pagels*[80]), while particle creation theory involves "creation of matter" (Grib* and Mamaev*[81]), and creation field theory is a "natural way for creating the matter" of the universe (Narlikar* and Padmanabhan*[82]). The continuous creation (or steady state) theory involved "creation out of nothing" described by physical laws (Bondi*[83]).

In biological and biochemical evolution, panspermia is "a theory of cosmic creationism" (Hoyle and Wickramasinghe[84]). Various nonreligious theories propose that exceedingly high information content is only explained by "creative intelligence" (Ambrose*[85]), that an unknown force requires the "Great Origins Thesis" (Smith*[86]), and that mechanistic evolution must be replaced by "creative evolution" (Bergson*[87]). The "process of creation" is a widely used synonym for evolution (Gould*[88]).

Figure 13.2
Non-religious concepts of a creator, such as Aristotle's "Unmoved Mover," Ambrose's "Creative Intelligence," and Hoyle's non-omnipotent "intelligence"*

13.2 Non-Centrality of a Creator to the Theories of Abrupt Appearance and Evolution when Properly Defined

The concept of a creator is not an inherent part of presenting either the theory of evolution or the theory of abrupt appearance, and is certainly not central to either theory. However, the concept of a creator is not necessarily religious.

a. Non-Centrality of a Creator to the Theories of Evolution and Abrupt Appearance

The theories of abrupt appearance and of evolution consist of scientific evidence (Volume 1), and do not offer ultimate causes for events of origin (Section 10.2). Neither theory necessarily refers to or posits a creator. However, some advocates of each theory (advocates of a religious theory of creation and of a theory of theistic evolution) do add premises about a creator. Those premises are not necessarily parts of either evolution or abrupt appearance.

The concept of a creator is not an inherent part of presenting even the theory of creation, simply because that theory consists of empirical evidence and scientific interpretations that point to creation.

Neither the theory of creation nor any other scientific theory must provide a full causal theory (as discussed in Section 10.2(b)): "there is nothing contradictory or absurd in separating the idea of a cause from that of a beginning of existence," North* points out,[89] and all theories of origin confront singularities and thus contain incomplete causation (as discussed in Section 10.2(a)). Further inferences about the source or cause of creation (such as a creator, a force, or a process) move outside of the realm of science into the realm of philosophy, metaphysics, or theology. That distinction is made by Etkin, former professor of biology at Columbia, Chicago, City University of New York, and Yeshiva Universities:

> Of course in invoking *creation, science does not distinguish* as to whether the creation is the act of a *purposeful creator* or a mere *random accident*. It merely asserts that the study of mechanisms has run into a dead end in which the non-mechanistic notion of creation must be invoked. Science by its nature cannot study the character of a creation. For the business of natural science is the interpretation of evidence in terms of mechanistic cause and effect. *Where the evidence leads to the concept of creation science may follow. But where the evidence stops it must stop....* Science can accept the concept of creation, as evidenced by the fact that it does so accept it today. Whatever scientific theory may become dominant in the future is not important. What is important is that scientific theory has been unfrozen. It is not committed in advance to complete determinism. It can use both the concept of mechanism and also that of creation.[90]

The detachment of the concept of creation from the concept of a creator is also evident in the scientists who have concluded from scientific evidence that an event or events of creation occurred but that a creator does not exist, such as Jastrow* (an Agnostic),[91] Lipson* (also an Agnostic),[92] Bondi*, Gold*, and Hoyle* in the recent continuous creation theory,[93] and the other theorists described in Section 13.1.

Further, the concept of a creator is not central to the theory of creation in any event, because the empirical evidence involves an occurrence or occurrences of creation and not the source or cause of those occurrences. Just as evolution often cannot resolve the question of who or what originated matter and energy in the cosmos and what mechanism brought about macroevolution,[94] the theory of creation need not and, if scientific, cannot address the question of the source or cause of creation. The chain of causal reasoning eventually reaches a dead end for every group of scientific theories at some point—that is not unique to the theories under discussion—as Gale* points out:

> [Wheeler] maintains that the logic consists in reducing a phenomenon to a more fundamental one. Thus the concept of valence in chemistry was reduced to the electrical properties of atoms and the temperature of a gas was reduced to the movement of atoms and molecules. It seems the logic of reduction can have only two possible outcomes, both of which Wheeler finds untenable. Physical theory could terminate in some fundamental, indivisible object or field; alternatively reduction could reveal layer on layer of structure ad infinitum.[95]

The non-centrality of a creator to the theory of creation is evident in the absence of a creator from definitions of "creation" given by several public school textbooks produced by secular national publishers, such as the following definition:

> Besides theories of change, some people believe that the many different kinds of organisms are a result of a special creation. These people believe that each organism was created separately. The organisms did not change in form. Instead, they were created as they appear now.[96]

Some older textbooks give similar definitions.[97]

Mention of "creation" does not require discussion about a creator any more than mention of "evolution" does: either can generate questions about ultimate origins and religious implications, but so can the theory of relativity, the history of Rome under Augustus and Nero, the absolute or relative nature of truth and values, and virtually any other nonreligious subject. But even if the theories of creation and evolution inherently involved a creator, that concept would not necessarily be religious.

b. Non-Religious Nature of Some Concepts of a Creator

(1) Nonsupernatural Concepts of a Creator. Many individuals in the history of philosophy have made a nonreligious inference of the existence of a creator from secular observations or thoughts. Plato described a Demiurge who intervened in nature and exercised creative powers over existing matter and forms, yet who was not supernatural in the sense of Genesis.[98] Foster* and most people refer to "creation" of an art work by an artist—the term does not imply or require a divine creator.[99]

The modern day advocates of the panspermia hypothesis, exemplified by Hoyle, similarly make a scientific inference of the existence of a nonpersonal creator ("intelligence") of information content who is very different from the creator of Genesis:

> It is far less difficult to grapple with the issues in a future-to-past sense, because then we approach the ultimate cause instead of receding from it, the ultimate cause being a *source of information*, an *intelligence* if you like, placed in the remote future.[100]

Ambrose* concludes that the vast information content in living organisms could only arise from "creative intelligence," which is also a nonpersonal nonbiblical creator:

> Having our *factor X as input of new information* into a biological system, which is essential at each level of increased complexity in the biological world, we are in a position to examine in more detail how this new information could arise. . . . I now suggest that our factor X, being an input of new information, requires the operation of *Creative Intelligence*, and I hope to show that the operation of creative intelligence leads to a minimum number of universals to explain both the origin and basic nature of living organisms.[101]

Morowitz* finds evidence in nature for a "plan or cosmic intelligence."[101A] Many Agnostics recognize the possibility of an unorthodox "watchmaker" for the universe as a nonreligious matter of causal reasoning, such as Macbeth* (a "skeptic").[102] Similarly, Wickramasinghe was compelled by information content considerations to reject his " 'philosophical preference' . . . to have life form in the cosmos by random shuffling," and to acknowledge the possible existence of a nonpersonal "creator," while rejecting Genesis and " 'inerrancy of the Bible.' "[103] Even Gould* says that "[n]atural selection is a creator; it builds adaptation step by step."[104]

(2) Academic Secular Discussion about a Creator. The nonreligious nature of the concept of a creator is evident in the detached academic discussion of the creator within general philosophy and metaphysics, within history, and within literature.

Philosophic considerations about a creator include the nonreligious arguments of William James and other philosophers about the logical existence of a creator, as well as the argument for a "creative force" by Leslie* that "does not always indicate belief in a Designer" and "can be defended independently of any religion."[105] Similarly, Aristotle used secular causal reasoning to derive the existence of a "First Unmoved Mover" who was not "an object of worship" (and did not actually exercise creative powers).[106]

Historical discussions of the creator include recorded beliefs of historical leaders such as George Washington, Abraham Lincoln, and Stonewall Jackson, who had and expressed very strong religious convictions; and historical documents such as the Mayflower Compact and the Declaration of Independence. The Declaration of Independence refers to "the Creator" in four places such as the following:

> When in the Course of human events, it becomes necessary for one people to dissolve the political bands which have connected them with another,

> and to assume among the powers of the earth, the separate and equal station to which the *Laws of Nature and of Nature's God* entitle them, a decent respect to the opinions of mankind requires that they should declare the causes which impel them to the separation. We hold these truths to be self-evident, that all men are *created* equal, that they are endowed by their *Creator* with certain unalienable Rights, that among these are Life, Liberty and the pursuit of Happiness. . . . [107]

Literary consideration of a creator includes study of "the Bible . . . for its literary and historical qualities," as well as of "comparative religion or the history of religion," as permitted by the Supreme Court's decision on public school Bible reading.[108] Other literary study includes the divine judgment themes of Dante's *Divine Comedy*, the light and dark themes of Melville's *Billy Budd*, and the similar imagery and content of many other literary works. All of these secular discussions about a creator are nonreligious.

Moreover, reference to a creator is not religious in violation of separation of church and state, if the reference occurs in a nonworship and nonprayer context, under many court decisions.[109]

Summary. The theories of evolution and of abrupt appearance do not involve any necessary reference to or concept of a creator. The theory of abrupt appearance, like the theory of evolution, instead consists of scientific evidence such as the abrupt appearance of complex life in the fossil record, of vast information content, and of the matter and energy of the universe (Chapters 2, 4, and 6). That is evident in advocacy of some of those empirical data and scientific interpretations by Agnostics (Lipson*[110] and for the thermodynamics argument Jastrow*[111]) and by Atheists (Hoyle and Wickramasinghe[112]). On the other hand, some advocates of each theory add a theistic gloss (religious creationism and theistic evolution).

Even for the theory of creation, that gloss is not a necessary element, as is evident in some textbook presentations (Webster* *et al.*[113]). Neither the theory of creation nor any theory of origins must address questions of ultimate origins or can provide a complete mechanism. Many scientists who draw a conclusion of "creation" do not believe in a creator and do not think that creation requires a creator, and their reference to creation does not necessitate reference to a creator, as in the case of the big bang, inflationary universe, quantum creation, particle creation, and continuous creation (steady state) theories (Sections 13.1(b)-(e)). The many references in evolutionist writings do not unavoidably evoke discussion of a creator (Section 13.1).

Nevertheless, the concept of a creator is not inherently religious. The history of philosophy and of art underscores that point, as do the skeptical scientists who see creation without a creator.

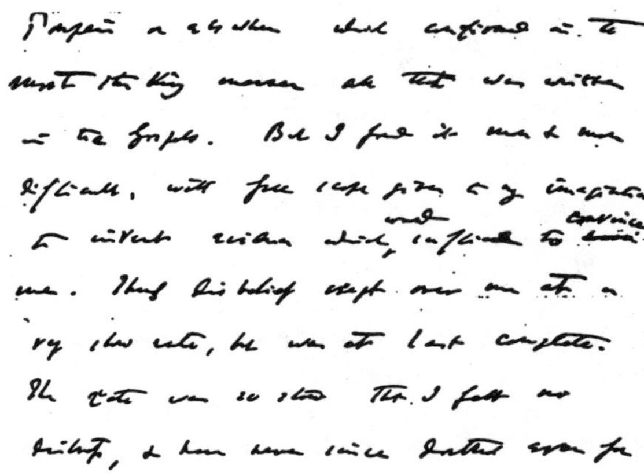

Figure 13.3
Darwin's manuscript in which he wrote, "Thus disbelief crept over me at a very slow rate, but was at last complete"*

13.3 Non-Religious Parallel Relation to a Creator and Creation of the Theories of Evolution and Abrupt Appearance

The theory of evolution and the theory of abrupt appearance are exactly parallel in their implications about a creator. This can be seen in several areas:

- a. Evolutionist inferences about the existence of a creator
- b. Evolutionist allegations of no scientific implication for religion
- c. Evolutionist references in science publications to a creator.

a. Evolutionist Inferences about the Existence of a Creator

A large number of evolutionist scientists, if not all, make inferences about the existence or nonexistence of a creator from the scientific data on origins. The nostrum that evolution does not have any implications about a creator[114] is belied by the world of evolutionists, and in fact is based on a theological assumption that itself is open to question.[115]

(1) Atheistic and Agnostic Inferences. In fact, evolutionists do make inferences about a creator, and at least a sizable minority of evolutionist scientists infer that "[t]here are no gods" and that science and religion are not "compatible", as Provine*, a biologist and historian of science at Cornell, points out:

> *Evolutionists* still disagree about the precise mechanisms of evolution in nature, but they have nevertheless given overwhelming support to Darwin's belief that design in nature results from purely mechanistic causes. . . .
>
> Here are the implications of this mechanistic view of life as I see them. First, except for purely mechanistic ones, no organizing or purposive principles exist in the world. *There are no gods* and no designing forces. *The frequently made assertion that modern biology and the assumptions of the Judeo-Christian tradition are fully compatible is false. . . .*[116]

The "great majority of modern evolutionary biologists now are atheists or something very close to that."[117] Similar conclusions about the effect of Darwinism have been published by Mayr*[118] and Dawkins*[119]. Many evolutionist philosophers and historians have also noted that evolution had the effect that "a Deity or Providence . . . was ruled out," in the words of Barzun*,[120] such as Nelkin*,[121] Ghiselin*,[122] Grene*,[123] Cauthen*,[124] and Roszak*.[125]

Darwin* himself moved to "agnosticism tending at times toward atheism," in the words of historian Moore* and others:

> [F]rom an early orthodoxy Darwin passed in middle life into a liberal form of theism, and thence, in his last decades, into an *agnosticism* tending at times towards atheism.
>
> . . ..
>
> . . .All he could believe in was 'my deity, "Natural Selection" '.[126]

In fact, Darwin* wrote that "disbelief crept over me at a very slow rate, but was at last complete."[127] He also wrote the following:

> The mystery of the beginning of all things is insoluble by us; and I for one must be content to remain an Agnostic.
>
> . . ..
>
> Nothing is more remarkable than the spread of scepticism or rationalism during the latter half of my life.[128]

And Darwin* recorded "that the theory of evolution 'would make a man a predestinarian of a new kind, because he would tend to be an atheist'."[129]

"It is no coincidence that almost all the early proponents of Darwinism were atheistic materialists—or their near relatives," according to philosopher Hull*.[130] T.H. Huxley*, "Darwin's bulldog"[131] and leading advocate, was an Agnostic[132] and actually coined that term.[133] Haeckel*, the formulator of the "biogenetic law" of embryological recapitulation and a leading Darwinian, was an Atheist who argued "no miracle, no Creation, no Creator,"[134] who found "the deity anulled,"[135] and had "hatred" for Christianity.[136] By early in this century, a clear majority of American scientists disbelieved or doubted in the existence of God, according to studies in 1914[137] and 1922.[138]

Modern leading evolutionists who are Atheists include Simpson*[139] and Asimov*,[140] astronomers Abell*, Pecker*,[141] Shapley*,[142] and Tipler*,[143] and anthropologists Birx*, Thomashevich*, and Firth.*[144] Julian Huxley*, who devised the name of and co-formulated the neo-Darwinian "evolutionary synthesis," was also "an Atheist" and argued that in "the evolutionary pattern of thought there is no longer either need or room for the supernatural."[145]

The evolutionist expert witnesses in the recent national test case on the theories of "creation-science" and evolution, in the fields of science and philosophy and history, provide similar examples. Atheists include geologist Dalrymple*,[146] historian McLoughlin*,[147] and sociologist Nelkin*,[148] while Agnostics include astronomer Sagan*,[149] paleontologist Gould*,[150] philosopher Ruse*,[151] and historian Numbers*.[152]

(2) Theistic Evolutionist Inferences. On the other hand, a significant minority of evolutionist scientists draw the specific inference of the existence of a creator as part of a theistic evolutionary viewpoint. For example, "Einstein use[d] his concept of God more often than a Catholic priest,"[153] and held to an "idea of God,"[154] while Milne* concluded his treatise on relativity by saying: "As to the first cause of the Universe, in the context of expansion, that is left for the reader to insert, but our picture is incomplete without Him."[155] Historically, Owen*, Argyll*, Mivart*,[156] Asa Gray*,[157] and Alfred Russel Wallace*,[158] as well as many Theological Liberals (dicussed later),[159] were theistic evolutionists.

If the theory of evolution is not made religious by these evolutionist inferences about the nonexistence or existence of a creator, the theory of abrupt appearance is similarly not made religious by some proponents' inferences about the existence of a creator. In either case, the inference is not part of the scientific explanation, but is an implication outside of the realm of science. Unfortunately, however, a double standard seems to be applied, as Shallis* at Oxford remarks:

> It is no more heretical to say the Universe displays purpose, as Hoyle has done, than to say that it is pointless, as Steven Weinberg has done. Both statements are metaphysical and outside science. Yet it seems that

> scientists are permitted by their own colleagues to say metaphysical things about lack of purpose and not the reverse. This suggests to me that science, in allowing this metaphysical notion, sees itself as religion and presumably as an atheistic religion (if you can have such a thing).[160]

The theories of abrupt appearance and evolution are parallel in inferences about a creator drawn by some of their proponents.

b. Evolutionist Allegations of No Scientific Implication for Religion

Some evolutionists try to deny the evolutionist implications about a creator by statements such as that "[r]eligion and science are separate and mutually exclusive realms of human thought . . .," as a committee of the National Academy of Sciences wrote.[161] Examples are Mayer*[162] and Moyer*.[163]

(1) Criticisms of the Incommensurability Thesis. That approach is repudiated by many leading evolutionists such as Nelkin* and Provine* and others:

> The recurrence of textbook disputes suggests that the truce between science and religion, based on the *assumption that they deal with separate domains*, may be a convenient but *unrealistic myth*. Religion as well as science purports to be a picture of reality, a means through which people render their lives and the world around them intelligible.[164]

> [M]odern evolutionary biology instead of being fully compatible with Christianity . . . is actually deeply incompatible with fundamental assumptions not only of Christianity but also of most other religions of the world.[165]

Instead, Provine* adds that "religion is compatible with modern evolutionary biology . . . if the religion is effectively indistinguishable from atheism" (his own faith), and that "the great majority of modern evolutionary biologists" find a compatibility precisely because they "are atheists or something very close to that":

> Called Deism in the seventeenth and eighteenth centuries and considered equivalent to atheism then, it is no different now. A God or purposive force that merely starts the universe or works through the laws of nature has nothing to do with human morals, answers no prayers, gives no life everlasting, in fact does nothing whatsoever that is detectable. In other words, religion is compatible with modern evolutionary biology (and indeed all of modern science) if the religion is effectively indistinguishable from atheism.
>
> My observation is that the great majority of modern evolutionary biologists now are atheists or something very close to that. Yet prominent atheistic or agnostic scientists publicly deny that there is any

conflict between science and religion. Rather than simple intellectual dishonesty, this position is pragmatic. . . .[166]

As for Darwin* and the early Darwinians, "[t]here was never any doubt in Darwin's mind as to a conflict between science and religion," Gillespie* notes;[167] and Darwinism and evolution were "immediately taken to be in prima facie opposition to a number of theological doctrines, especially the following: the uniqueness of man as God's supreme creation; the importance of natural theology; and the dominant theory, in Protestant circles, that the Bible is an authoritative source of beliefs about the natural world."[168] Draper* agreed in his influential book,[169] as many scientists do today[170] such as Smith*[171] and Strike*.[172]

The incommensurability or " 'two spheres' model for understanding the science/religion relationship is inadequate for five reasons," which are "[h]istorical, epistemological, theological, moral, and existential,"[173] according to Miller* and Fowler*. Their analysis is as follows:

> [1] In the first place it is inadequate *historically*. Although there has been an historiographic tradition which has described the relationship between science and religion as essentially a hostile one, recent studies in the history of science indicate both that the Western Judeo-Christian tradition provided a cultural medium which nourished the investigation of nature and also that findings in the process of such investigations have been formative in Western theological development. While the relationship between scientific investigation and the religious milieu is not simplistically a hostile one, neither is it simply one of mutual constructive support. Still, it does appear that the relationship is highly interactive, contrary to the expectations of the "two spheres" model.
>
> [2] One reason for this interaction is *epistemological*. The distinctions between faith and reason or revelation and discovery which have appeared to be absolute and substantive in the past, today appear less and less epistemologically sound. One of the characteristics of the emerging post-modern and post-critical perspective is the dissolution of the modern and criticial distinction between the subjective and the objective and a collateral challenge to the view that facts of any sort, natural or religious, are simply out there to be gathered up like so many nuggets of truth. Instead, human knowing on all its occasions is seen to involve value commitments, imaginative construction, and social relations.
>
> [3] *Theologically*, the bifurcation of existence into two isolated domains runs counter to two main themes within the Judeo-Christian religious tradition itself. . . .
>
> [4] Fourth, within the *moral* context, by separating empirical nature from human values the "two spheres" model provides no ground for

> addressing the central pragmatic questions which we face in these last decades of the 20th century. . . .
>
> Evolutionary biology provides a very dynamic understanding of living things. On the other hand it does not of itself provide any criteria for making choices about how to shape or control the dynamic process. . . .[174]

The fifth point, that the two spheres approach "promotes an existential dualism," is discussed below.[175] The authors conclude that "science and religion are necessarily interacting ways of knowing reality."[176]

Philosophers, as well as theologians, have excoriated the incommensurability approach. Adler*, the editor of the *Great Books of the Western World* (published by *Encyclopaedia Britannica*), is scornful:

> I can now explain what I mean by the unity of truth. It is merely an extension, but nonetheless a very important extension, of the principle of noncontradiction. To affirm the unity of truth is to deny that there can be two separate and irreconcilable truths which, while contradicting one another and thought to be irreconcilably contradictory, avoid the principle of noncontradiction by claiming to be logic-tight compartments. Thus, for example, one approach to the conflict between religion and philosophy, or between science and either philosophy or religion, is to claim that these are such separate spheres of thought or inquiry, employing such different methods or having such different means of access to the truth, that the principle of noncontradiction does not apply. . . . As we have already seen, there cannot be irreconcilable contradictions between one segment of the whole truth and another. What is regarded as true in philosophy and religion must not conflict with what is regarded as true in science.[177]

Watkins*,[178] Pearson*[179] and Smart*[180] (in the article on "Religion and Science" in the *Encyclopedia of Philosophy*) similarly have rejected the "incommensurate domain" approach. "The view that science is quasi-independent of such disciplines is itself a research tradition, one of relatively recent origin," and not shared by most philosophers of science, Laudan* writes.[181]

(2) Theological Basis of the Incommensurability Approach. Indeed, that view of exclusive realms is primarily the product of one particular theological view: Neo-Orthodoxy and Existentialism. That relationship is described by Schoch* and Prins*:

> Contemporary theology of the *Neo-Orthodox* movement, in line with most religious thinkers through the ages, stresses the specificity of Biblical language. Immanent meaning resides in the Word, which is both the occasion and content of Truth expressed. The Word is historical, directional, self-contained and self-referential. . . . Thus, religion and science use two coexistent, *nonoverlapping* language meaning structures, even when the words sound and are applied the same. Religion and science

> *need not contradict* one another, but *can coexist without intruding on each other's realms.*[182]

Modern Neo-Orthodox theologians such Gilkey*,[183] Vawter*,[184] and others*[185] champion the incommensurability approach. That approach "promotes an existential dualism" that radically separates body and soul or spirit, Miller* and Fowler* add,[186] and it "is integral to the position of theistic evolutionists."[187] Before the rise of Neo-Orthodoxy, the incommensurability approach arose "[m]ainly as a result of the creative and courageous efforts of the liberal theologians" of Protestant[188] and Catholic[189] faiths. Thus the argument that evolution cannot have implications about a creator, and that they are "mutually exclusive realms," is at best a minority theological-philosophical position and at worst incorrect.

c. *Evolutionist References in Science Publications to a Creator*

Further, many evolutionist science publications actually do refer to a creator or to God. For example, Darwin's* *Origin of Species* contains many references to a creator, and ends with a reference in the last paragraph to "the Creator."[190] That "book had a surprising amount of positive theological content," Gillespie* observes.[191]

Many other evolutionist books on science refer to God or the Bible. For example, Eldredge* quotes all of Genesis 1;[192] Weisskopf* finds "the Judeo-Christian tradition" and the Bible "surprisingly similar" to modern science;[193] and the treatise by Dobzhansky*, Ayala*, Stebbins*, and Valentine* says that "in Christianity the doctrine of original sin coexists with the doctrine of divine grace."[194] Ponnamperuma* notes "several Biblical incidents";[195] Dobzhansky* quotes the theistic evolutionary views of Teilhard de Chardin* and states that "Christianity was the cornerstone of his world view";[196] Hardy* writes of "the biology of God";[197] and Polkinghorne* writes a rhapsody to evolution and "the worship of God and the knowledge of his grace in Jesus Christ."[198]

Evolutionary textbooks are no exception. One of the leading biology textbooks for high schools quotes Darwin's* reference to "the Creator," and quotes another scientist's reference to " 'the Supreme and Omnipotent Creator' " and to " 'kinds of plants and animals.' "[199] Another of the leading evolutionary textbooks refers to "the flood recorded in Genesis of the Hebrew Bible."[200] Other widely used texts encourage teachers to discuss the "Biblical account of special creation" and to refer to God, and endorse theistic evolution:[201]

> This question could lead to a discussion of other theories of the origin of

> life and species. Several students might mention the Biblical account of special creation. Other students might mention other beliefs.[202]

> Many theologians view evolution as 'God's plan' for the development of a new species.[203]

The biology textbook by Weinberg* similarly discusses theistic evolution.[204] A college evolution text by Moody* states that "the first chapters of Genesis are great religion. Why worry about the fact that they are not valid science?"[205] Many others, such as the texts by Stansfield*,[206] Van Wylen*,[207] and Kluge*,[208] refer to God and theistic evolution.

Many evolutionist scientists have written books discussing Genesis, theistic evolution, a "religion of Evolutionary Humanism," etc., as described later.[209] While such statements are not appropriate for either evolutionist or nonevolutionist textbooks in public schools, it is significant to note that evolutionist books extensively refer to a creator, to God, and to the Bible, just as some nonscientific nonevolutionist publications do.

Summary. Advocates of the theory of evolution and of the theory of abrupt appearance to the same extent make inferences about and references to a creator. Among evolutionists, the "great majority of modern evolutionary biologists are now atheists or something very close to that" (Provine*[210]), just as "almost all the early proponents of Darwinism were atheistic materialists—or their near relatives" (Hull*[211]). Darwin* himself moved "into an agnosticism tending at times toward atheism" (Moore*[212]), as do many leading proponents of his theory (Sagan*, Gould*, Ruse*, Simpson*, etc.). On the other hand, a minority of evolutionist scientists add a creator to their viewpoint; that does not make the theory of evolution inherently religious any more than a parallel addition by many discontinuitists makes the theory of abrupt appearance inherently religious.

Just as Darwin's *The Origin of Species* "had a surprising amount of positive theological content" (Gillespie*[213]), and many Darwinians through the years have written heavily religious books (Section 15.1), evolutionist textbooks often take the theistic evolutionist position that "evolution is 'God's plan' " (Heimler*[214]). Evolutionist books and articles frequently refer to religion (Eldredge*[215]).

In view of such widespread inferences by evolutionists, "the truce between science and religion, based on the assumption that they deal with separate domains, may be a convenient but unrealistic myth" (Nelkin*[216]), as many scientists and philosophers concede. That "two spheres" approach has serious historical, epistemological, theological, and moral difficulties and is simply wrong (Miller* and Fowler*[217]), and may be "intellectual dishonesty" (Provine*[218]). In fact, the two spheres approach is based on the theological assumption of Neo-Orthodoyy and Existentialism (Schoch*[219]).

Figure 13.4
For founders of scientific disciplines such as Sir Isaac Newton, "belief in a divine creation was a major presupposition in the emergence of natural science" (Klaaren)*

13.4 Non-Religious Role in Scientific History of a Creator and Creation

Modern science "owes its very birth and life" to the once nearly universal belief in a creator, according to Jaki*, the eminent Seton Hall University physicist and theologian (with doctorates in both fields) who recently won the Templeton Prize:

> Its thesis can easily be summed up. Great cultures, where the scientific enterprise came to a standstill, invariably failed to formulate the notion of physical law, or the law of nature. Theirs was a theology with *no belief* in a personal, rational, absolutely transcendent Lawgiver, or *Creator*. Their cosmology reflected a pantheistic and animistic view of nature caught in the treadmill of perennial, inexorable returns. *The scientific quest found fertile soil only when this faith in a personal, rational Creator had truly permeated a whole culture*, beginning with the centuries of the High Middle Ages. It was that faith which provided, in sufficient measure, confidence in the rationality of the universe, trust in progress,

and appreciation of the quantitative method, all indispensable ingredients of the scientific quest.

. . ..

. . .To this belief, science owes its very birth and life.[220]

Gilkey* of University of Chicago agrees that the

idea of a transcendent Creator actually made possible rather than hindered the progress of the scientific understanding of the natural order. In a real sense the modern conviction that existence is good because it is intelligible to scientific inquiry finds some of its most significant roots in the Christian belief that God created the world.[221]

Other philosophers of science and scientists who have published similar conclusions include Whitehead*,[222] Oppenheimer*,[223] Foster*,[224] Klaaren*,[225] Calvin*,[226] Hooykaas*,[227] Eiseley*,[228] Weizsacker*,[229] Hodgson*,[230] Glover*,[231] Oakley*,[231A] and Mach*.[231B] As Eiseley* says, "It is surely one of the curious paradoxes of history that science, which professionally has little to do with faith, owes its origins to an act of faith that the universe can be rationally interpreted, and that science today is sustained by the assumption."[232]

Most of the individual founders of modern science believed in the existence of a creator, as well as in the creator's intervention in nature contrary to natural law, and in fact were creationists. Sir Francis Bacon, the "father of modern science," was a creationist who wrote:

To conclude, let no one weakly imagine that man can search too far, or be too well studied in the book of God's word and works, divinity or philosophy; but rather let him endeavor an endless progression in both, only applying all to charity and not to pride.[233]

Sir Isaac Newton, the father of physics, discoverer of the laws of gravity, and inventor of calculus, was a creationist[234] who for his famous *Principia* and other scientific work "had an eye upon such Principles as might work w[i]th considering men for the beleife of a Deity & nothing can rejoyce me more than to find it usefull for that purpose."[235]

Newton's widely circulated condemnation of hypothesizing about creation by natural law and his insistence on the necessity of divine intervention left the distinct impression that 'Newtonianism and cosmogony were absolutely incompatible.'[236]

Robert Boyle, the father of chemistry, was a strong creationist,[237] as were most of the early members of the Royal Society in England, Trevelyan* states:

Robert Boyle, Isaac Newton, and the early members of the Royal Society were religious men, who repudiated the sceptical doctrines of Hobbes.

> But they familiarised the minds of their countrymen with the idea of law in the Universe and with scientific methods of enquiry to discover truth. It was believed that these methods would never lead to any conclusions inconsistent with Biblical history and miraculous religion; Newton lived and died in that faith.[238]

Other creationist scientists included "Descartes, Kepler, Galileo, Newton, and Leibnitz," Lakatos* states.[239] René Descartes[240] "[f]ounded analytical geometry;"[241] Johannes Kepler "laid the foundations of modern astronomy";[242] Galileo Galilei made major astronomical contributions; Gottfried Wilhelm Liebnitz "invented the calculus (. . . independently, it appears, of Newton)."[243] Numbered among creationist founders of branches of science were also Blaise Pascal, who developed analytic geometry; John Ray,[244] the "founder of systematic biology and natural history in Britain";[245] Nicholas Steno, who "pioneered in geology, paleontology, crystallography";[246] William Harvey, who was the "founder of modern physiology";[247] and John Woodward,[248] who was a "founder of exp[erimental] plant physiology."[249]

Creationists in the eighteenth century included Carolus Linnaeus,[250] the "father of modern systematic botany";[251] and Edmund Halley,[252] a noted astronomer. Mid-nineteenth century creationists included paleontologist Louis Agassiz, geologists Benjamin Silliman and Adam Sedgwick, physicists Lord Kelvin and Michael Faraday and James Clerk Maxwell, bacteriologist Louis Pasteur, and others, as discussed later.[253]

Summary. Many historians of science have made the point "that religion was conducive to the advent of modern science, specifically that belief in divine creation was a major presupposition in the emergence of natural science in seventeenth century England" (Klaaren*[254]). Thus, "Robert Boyle, Isaac Newton, and the early members of the Royal Society were religious men" who were creationists (Trevelyan*[255]). The other founders of most branches of modern science—such as "Descartes, Kepler, Galileo, Newton, and Leibnitz"—were also creationist scientists (Lakatos*[256]). Although their beliefs differ from the theory of abrupt appearance, they show that even a theory of creation can be nonreligious in nature and consistent with scientific inquiry.

Figure 13.5
"Biological arguments for racism . . . increased by orders of magnitude following the acceptance of evolutionary theory" (Gould), as in this textbook used by Scopes**

The Races of Man. — At the present time there exist upon the earth five races or varieties of man, each very different from the other in instincts, social customs, and, to an extent, in structure. These are the Ethiopian or negro type, originating in Africa; the Malay or brown race, from the islands of the Pacific; the American Indian; the Mongolian or yellow race, including the natives of China, Japan, and the Eskimos; and finally, the highest type of all, the Caucasians, represented by the civilized white inhabitants of Europe and America.

13.5 Non-Religious Parallel Relation to World Views of the Theories of Evolution and Abrupt Appearance

There are world views that are consistent with the theories of evolution and of abrupt appearance, although those theories are not necessarily tied to those world views. (a) The primary world views consistent with the theory of evolution are materialism and naturalism, and neo-positivism, and in the thought of some proponents theism and deism; and the primary world views consistent with (but different from) the theory of abrupt appearance are theism, deism, and metaphysical dualism. Any view of science necessarily presupposes and implies something about God and a creator,[257] and the world views of materialism, naturalism, and positivism logically rule out any deity or creator, while the world views of theism, deism, and metaphysical dualism logically imply a God or Supreme Being. (b) Evolution has also been an integral part of several controversial and harmful political views.

Science is not value-free, but "drips" with values; and the view that science is value-free is "pathetically naive," Ruse* states while discussing biology:

> First, anyone who thinks there are no values, no ideology, in biology—past or present—is pathetically naive. Biology drips with as many wishes/wants/desires/urges, as many exhortations towards right actions, as a sermon by Luther or Wesley . . ..
>
> Second, let me try in a tentative manner to unpack the way or *ways in which values enter* into science. To begin, there is the simple act of choosing a problem as worthy of study . . .. Yet another point is the way in which the theory is presented or laid out; the *structure*, if you like. Lewontin's way of discussing the various hypotheses about genetic variation shows and supports his commitment of the Marxist dialectic.

> Next, I think we get values in the whole *manner in which the ideas and concepts of a theory are presented*. . . .
>
> Continuing my list of ways in which values enter into science, I argue that the very statements of science itself reflect and endorse values. . . .
>
> But, these value claims apart, what I would argue is that *many of the claims of biology are supporting of particular value positions*, and that without the scientific factual claims the positions would be unsupported. . . .
>
> The final place where I see values entering into biology is in what I like to follow the Kantians in calling "*regulative principles*" (Ruse 1980). By these I mean the standards and criteria to which theories must conform, if they are to be judged "good" science, or indeed if they are to be judged "science" at all . . ..[258]

What is true of science generally[259] is at least as true of "the Darwinian theory of evolution": "It is just as much a reflector and propagator of values, as anything to be named in the 'softer sciences,' or in the humanities for that matter."[260]

Darwinism is closely related to a "world-view," which is described by Grinnell*, a historian of science at McMaster University:

> I have done a great deal of work on Darwin and can say with some assurance that Darwin also did not derive his theory from nature but rather superimposed a certain philosophical world-view on nature and then spent 20 years trying to gather the facts to make it stick.[261]

He is joined in that conclusion by Gillespie*, who frames the contrast as between the two world views of "positivism" (including evolution) and "creationism,"[262] Lewontin*, who calls them "irreconcilable world views,"[263] Muller*,[264] Hofstadter*,[265] and Ruse*:

> With a growing number of distinguished evolutionists—including Ernst Mayr, Edward O. Wilson, and Francisco J. Ayala—I believe that Darwinism is more than just a scientific theory. *It is the basis for a full-world view*, a *Weltanschauung*. It is not itself a religion, but it offers hope for a naturalistic alternative to religion. . . .[266]

a. Evolution and World Views of Materialism, Naturalism, and Positivism

Philosopher Greene* acknowledges and describes the "evolutionary world view" as combining materialism and positivism, in the following words:

> Thus, by the middle of the nineteenth century all of the materials that were to be forged into a distinctive kind of *evolutionary world view* lay at hand—the *law-bound system of matter* in motion, *evolutionary deism verging toward agnosticism* under the influence of *positivistic empiricism*, the idea of *organic evolution*, the idea of a social science of histori-

> cal development, faith in the beneficent effects of competitive struggle—all these ideas lay waiting for the architect who could combine them into a single all-embracing synthesis.[267]

Darwin* was the architect who combined materialism, naturalism, and positivism in that world view, as Gillespie* states:

> Darwin's materialism, it would seem, was nothing more than positivism. It committed him, not to a metaphysics of matter in motion as the ultimate reality, but only to a system of naturalistic and lawful science.[268]

Marsden* similarly acknowledges the critical role of evolution in a world view:

> Evolution is sometimes the key mythological element in a philosophy that functions as a *virtual religion*.[269]

That world view can be seen to involve materialism, naturalism, and neo-positivism. As noted in Section 9.4(b), "evolutionary positivism" is one of "two fundamental kinds of positivism," and a "materialistic . . . metaphysics is often associated with evolutionary positivism."[270]

(1) Materialism. Materialism "asserts that the real world consists of material things, varying in their states and relations, and nothing else."[271] The consistency of materialism with early evolutionary theory is described by Hull*:

> Darwin did not formulate evolutionary theory for the express purpose of helping to foster *atheistic materialism*, but that was one of its more significant *consequences*. It is no coincidence that almost all the early proponents of Darwinism were *atheistic materialists*—or their near relatives.[272]

Darwin* himself espoused "philosophical materialism," Gould* states,[273] and Barzun* describes Darwin's*, Marx's*, and Wagner's* "contributions as forming a single stream of influence which I have called mechanical materialism."[274] T.H. Huxley* embraced "the purer faith of Evolution,"[275] and "Huxley and Darwin might legitimately be called materialists," Hull* adds.[276] Haeckel*, a leading evolutionist, actively advocated materialism,[277] as did Bückner*.[278] The evolutionist "majority of men of science held unconsciously a naive materialism" at the beginning of the twentieth century, Dampier-Whetham* concludes.[279]

"[M]aterialism is still a principal belief of the scientists," and it "is simply a religious belief, not even a religious belief; it is a superstition based on no evidence worth considering at all," Eccles*, a Nobel Prize recipient, observes.[280] Materialism is "outspokenly religious" particularly in that it "denies God," Collingwood* added.[280A]

Whitehead* agreed,[281] and Dobzhansky* found a "materialist philosophy explicitly or implicitly shared" by most leading biologists:

> Monod has accomplished more than a delineation of his own world view. He has stated with admirable clarity, and eloquence often verging on pathos, *the mechanistic materialist philosophy explicity or implicitly shared by most of the present 'establishment' in the biological sciences.* But while many see this philosophy through a glass darkly, Monod makes it crystal clear.[282]

There is a veritable "war" waged by the materialists, Bethell* remarks,[283] and evolutionists have "given overwhelming support to Darwin's belief that design in nature results from purely mechanistic causes," Provine* adds.[284] For example, Oparin* agrees with a "materialistic philosophy,"[285] Jastrow* holds to "scientific materialism,"[286] and Simpson* sees the origin of complex processes as "materialistic."[287] Greene* finds Darwinism a "mechanical view of nature,"[288] Elders* sees it as "a materialistic and atheistic monism,"[289] Gould* exposes "the materialistic character of Darwin's theory,"[290] and Denton* says "[w]hat was once a deduction from materialism has today become its foundation."[291] Edward O. Wilson of Harvard* speaks favorably of the "scientific materialism" of evolution:

> Make no mistake about the power of scientific materialism. It presents the human mind with an alternative mythology that until now has always, point for point in zones of conflict, defeated traditional religion. Its narrative form is the epic, the evolution of the universe from the big bang.[292]

(2) Naturalism. "Naturalism, in recent usage, is a species of philosophical monism according to which whatever exists or happens is natural," thus "repudiating the view that there exists or could exist any entities or events which lie, in principle, beyond the scope of scientific explanation," Danto* writes.[293] It is "compatible with the various forms of materialism,"[294] and as *Encyclopaedia Britannica* puts it, a "modified form of Materialism is perhaps better described as naturalism."[295] The propinquity between naturalism and evolution is described by Oldroyd*:

> Naturalism was a major premise of Darwin's thinking and the success of his theory gave strong sanction to the validity of naturalism, showing that the supernatural account of the world's seeming design was a superfluity. And the belief in the evolutionary origin of man's body and mind draws enormous strength from the Darwinian theory. . . .
>
> So a metaphysical system, although naturalistic and secular, has been built up by modern humanists around the nucleus of biological evolutionism. . . .[296]

"The theory of evolution that Darwin gave to the world was 'naturalistic,'" Gillespie* adds,[297] and in fact, Grene* states, Darwinism "appears as the very keystone of the naturalistic universe."[298]

(3) Positivism. Positivism and neo-positivism, as defined by Gillespie*, "typically used mechanistic or materialistic models of causality, rejected supernatural, teleological, or other factors, which were in principle beyond scientific examination as legitimate aspects of scientific inquiry, and—whatever the desires or beliefs of individual practitioners, many of whom were theists or even good Christians—embraced and promoted those far-reaching cultural tendencies conventionally known as secularism and naturalism . . .."[299] Positivism and then neo-positivism came to "general acceptance . . . as a world view":

> Darwin's progress toward positivism in science must have been duplicated in other scientists and scientifically inspired laymen: a dialectical movement through particular scientific work to a general acceptance of positivism as a tool for such work and as a world view. . . .[300]

The close relationship between neo-positivism and evolution is evident in Greene's* description of the "evolutionary world view"[301] that was quoted above, and is manifest in Darwin's* own thought according to Gillespie*:

> What, then, were the reigning principles of Darwin's view of science when he wrote the *Origin*? He assumed, like most positivists, a system of natural causes operating according to uniform laws of nature. . . . The *Origin* was, in effect, a manifesto for positivist science. . . .[302]

Astronomer Carl Sagan* provides a good example of materialism, naturalism, and positivism and their close relation to evolution in his opening paragraph to *Cosmos*, with parallel wording to biblical verses:

> THE COSMOS IS ALL THAT IS OR EVER WAS OR EVER WILL BE. . . .[303]

He gave a similar invocation in his popular television program:

> It is the Universe that made us, and we are creatures of the Cosmos.[304]

Sir Julian Huxley*,[305] Dobzhansky* and Teilhard de Chardin*,[306] and other leading evolutionists have often reflected that same viewpoint.

b. Evolution and Controversial Political Views

Evolution has also been interpreted by some historical figures to be consistent with and integral to several highly controversial and harmful political views. Those include Social Darwinism, Marxism, racism, and Naziism. Needless to say, most evolutionists do not embrace those political faiths. Evolutionists who do not hold those views nevertheless generally concede, as did Dobzhansky*, "that the implications of biological evolution reach much beyond biology into philosophy, sociology, and even socio-political issues."[307]

(1) *Social Darwinism*. "The social thought of the later nineteenth century drew so heavily from the theories of evolution that its major ideas became known as social Darwinism," and "provided the United States with its justification for the . . . competition that we associate with the Robber Barons."[308] In the definitive book by Hofstadter*, James J. Hill* is quoted as saying that "the fortunes of railroad companies are determined by the law of the survival of the fittest"; John D. Rockefeller* as contending that the "growth of a large business is merely a survival of the fittest" and "the working out of a law of nature"; and Andrew Carnegie as testifying that "light came as in a flood and all was clear. Not only had I got rid of theology and the supernatural, but I had found the truth of evolution."[309] Although some argue that social Darwinism was not a logical extension, Young* argues that "the extrapolations from Darwinism to either humanity or society are not separable from Darwin's own views, nor are they chronologically subsequent. They are integral."[310] Hsü* adds that "Darwin has made mistakes, and his mistakes have brought misery to humanity."[311]

(2) Marxism. "Marxism . . . has a good deal in common with the evolutionist faith," Midgley* observes.[312] Marxism quickly adopted evolution, as Gould* notes:

> The most ardent *materialists* of the nineteenth century, Marx and Engels, were quick to recognize what Darwin had accomplished and to exploit its radical content. In 1869, Marx wrote to Engels about Darwin's *Origin*:
>
> > Although it is developed in the crude English style, this is the book which contains the *basis in natural history for our view*.
>
> Marx later offered to dedicate volume 2 of *Das Kapital* to Darwin, but Darwin gently declined, stating that he did not want to imply approval of a work he had not read.[313]

Marx* thereafter wrote to Engels* that "Darwin's book is very important and serves me as a basis in natural selection for the class struggle in history . . . not only is it a death blow dealt here for the first time to 'Teleology' in the natural sciences but their rational meaning is emphatically explained."[314] Marx* emphasized the role of evolution in his ideology:

> But nowadays, in our evolutionary conception of the universe, there is absolutely no room for either a Creator or a ruler . . ..[315]

Stalin* was also greatly influenced: "He began to read Darwin and became an atheist."[316]

There are many "biologists who are avowed Marxists, and who are quite candid about wanting to produce a Marxian-inspired evolutionary biology," Ruse* states, listing Gould*, Lewontin*, and Oparin*.[317] Oparin*[318] "was quite open in his subscription to a Marxist-Leninist philosophy of nature, and consciously applied it to his work on the appearance of new life."[319] Haldane*[320] and Bernal*[321] were also Marxists. Gould* "is a Marxist," according to Ruse*,[322] and writes that he "learned his Marxism, literally, at his daddy's knee."[323] He frequently compares punctuated equilibria to Marxism.[324]

(3) Racism. Racism also was heavily supported by evolutionists as a logical outgrowth of their Darwinism, Gould* states:

> *Biological arguments* based on innate inferiority spread rapidly after *evolutionary theory* permitted a literal equation of modern 'lower' races with ancestral stages of higher forms. . . .
>
> . . ..
>
> Biological arguments for racism may have been common before 1859, but they increased by orders of magnitude following the acceptance of *evolutionary theory*. The litany is familiar: cold, dispassionate, objective, modern science shows us that races can be ranked on a scale of superiority.
>
> . . ..
>
> At this point, I hasten to add that I am not selecting the crackpot statements of a bygone age. I am quoting the major works of recognized leaders.[325]

Darwin* predicted that "an endless number of the lower races will have been eliminated by the higher civilized races" through survival of the fittest,[326] and made the following racist comments about "the savage races" in *The Descent of Man*:[327]

> At some future period, not very distant as measured by centuries, the civilized races of man will almost certainly exterminate, and replace, the savage races throughout the world. At the same time the anthropomorphous apes, as Professor Schaaffhausen has remarked, will no doubt be exterminated. The break between man and his nearest allies will then be wider, for it will intervene between man in a more civilised state, as we may hope, even than the Caucasian, and some ape as low as a baboon, instead of as now between the negro or Australian and the gorilla.[328]

Many prominent Darwinians held racist views based on evolutionary survival of the fittest, as Haller*[329] and Brace* recount.[330] For example, Osborn* of Columbia, "the dean of American evolutionists" and president of the American Museum of Natural History,[331] stated that blacks were of a different genus or species, and that the "intelligence of the average adult Negro is similar to that of the eleven-year old youth of the species *Homo sapiens*."[332] Conklin* of Princeton said that "the negroid races more closely resemble the original stock than the white or yellow races," and that "should lead those who believe in the superiority of the white race to strive to preserve its purity and to establish and maintain the segregation of the races . . .."[333] The equally racist and evolutionist writings of Topinard*, Ripley*, Ammon*, Vacher de Lapouge*, and others are described by Oldroyd*.[334]

(4) Naziism. Naziism based its genocidal beliefs on evolution, as Gasman* states:

> [Hitler] stressed and singled out the idea of *biological evolution* as the most forceful weapon against traditional religion and he repeatedly condemned Christianity for its opposition to the teachings of evolution. . . . For Hitler, evolution was the hallmark of modern science and culture, and he defended its veracity as tenaciously as Haeckel.[335]

For instance, Hitler* in *Mein Kampf* said that "permanent struggle is the law of life," and struggle between "a superior race" and "an inferior one" brings "an evolutionary higher stage."[336] He also wrote:

> No more than Nature desires the mating of weaker with stronger individuals, even less does she desire the blending of a higher with a lower race, since, if she did, her whole work of higher breeding, over perhaps hundreds of thousands of years, might be ruined with one blow.
>
> Historical evidence offers countless proofs of this. It shows with terrifying clarity that in every mingling of Aryan blood with that of lower peoples the result was the end of the cultured people. North America, whose population consists in by far the largest part of Germanic elements who mixed but little with the lower colored peoples, shows a different humanity and culture . . ..
>
> All great cultures of the past perished only because the originally creative race died out from blood poisoning.
>
> . . . This preservation is bound up with the rigid law of necessity and the right to victory of the best and stronger in this world.
>
> Those who want to live, let them fight, and those who do not want to fight in this world of eternal struggle do not deserve to live.
>
> . . ..
>
> The man who misjudges and disregards the racial laws actually forfeits the happiness that seems destined to be his. He thwarts the triumphal march of the best race . . ..[337]

Keith* acknowledged that "[t]he leader of Germany is an evolutionist," and "has consciously sought to make the practice of Germany conform to the theory of evolution."[338]

Haeckel*, the leading German proponent of Darwinism, "developed what he called the 'monist' philosophy from Darwin's evolutionary naturalism," and the resultant Monist League "provided the chief intellectual basis of Hitler's National Socialism. Evolutionary humanism did not always lead in directions that one would wish to commend," Oldroyd* comments.[339] It led to Naziism.[339A]

c. *The Theory of Abrupt Appearance and the World Views of Theism, Deism, and Metaphysical Dualism*

The theory of abrupt appearance is consistent with (although not part of) the world views of theism, deism, and metaphysical dualism, to the same extent that the theory of evolution is consistent with the world views of materialism, naturalism, and neo-positivism. As described earlier, modern science actually arose from a world view of belief in creation, which most of the founders of various scientific fields held, so that there is no inconsistency between those views and scientific progress.[340]

Summary. Science "drips" with values (Ruse*[341]), and evolution "is just as much a reflector and propagator of values, as anything to be named in the 'softer sciences', or in the humanities" (Ruse*[342]). Those values often take the form of an "evolutionary world view" (Greene*[343]), which is often materialistic, naturalistic, or neo-positivistic. Evolution has "help[ed] to foster atheistic materialism" (Hull*[344]), and there is a "materialist philosophy explicitly or implicitly shared by most of the present 'establisment' in the biological sciences" (Dobzhansky*[345]). Darwinism "appears as the very keystone of the naturalistic universe" (Grene*[346]), and "Naturalism was a major premise of Darwin's thinking" (Oldroyd*[347]). Darwin* moved "to a general acceptance of positivism as a tool for such work and as a world view" (Gillespie*[348]), and the scientific world generally followed to a positivistic episteme.

Evolutionary values have also borne fruit in controversial political views, and "the extrapolations from Darwinism to either humanity or society are not separable from Darwin's own views, nor are they chronologically subsequent. They are integral" (Young*[349]). Social Darwinism arose as an economic "survival of the fittest" (Hofstadter*[350]). "Marxism . . . has a good deal in common with the evolutionist faith" (Midgley*[351]), as Marx* recognized in saying that *The Origin of Species* "contains the basis in natural history for our view," and in offering "to dedicate volume 2 of *Das Kapital* to Darwin" (Gould*[352]). "Biological arguments for racism . . . increased by orders of magnitude following the acceptance of evolutionary theory" (Gould*[353]), as Darwin* categorized "the negro" as among "the savage races" (Darwin*[354]). Naziism defended genocide as an evolutionary survival of the fittest races (Gasman*[355]), and Hitler* "consciously sought to make the practice of Germany conform to the theory of evolution" (Keith*[356]).

The theories of evolution and of abrupt appearance are parallel in their consistency with but distinctiveness from various world views. If it is at all relevant that the theory of abrupt appearance is consistent with some religious faiths (although different from them), it logically must be equally relevant that the theory of evolution is consistent with Marxism, racism, and Naziism, as well as with a comparable number of other religious faiths. The world views with which the theory of abrupt appearance is consistent are not peculiar or narrow, but are the world views from which modern science arose and that most great scientists held before the late nineteenth century. The materialistic, naturalistic, and neo-positivistic world view with which evolution is consistent has much to say about religious things, because it rules out the existence of God or of a creator and bars any actual miracle, as the philosophers and historians cited above have argued.

* * *

The theories of evolution and of abrupt appearance are parallel in their relation to various concepts of creation and of a creator, and such concepts are not part of or central to either. The scientific concepts of abrupt appearance and even creation are not religious, and in fact are a vital part of some scientific viewpoints such as the inflationary universe, quantum creation, particle creation, directed panspermia, and continuous creation theories, all of which firmly reject Genesis. The theories of evolution and of abrupt appearance are parallel in their relation to various world views, as well as in their relation to various religions, as the next chapter discusses.

Notes

1 C. Darwin*, *The Origin of Species* 488 (1st ed. 1859, repr. 1964).

2 J. North*, *The Measure of the Universe* 403, 405 (1965) (italics added, footnotes omitted).

[3] Tax*, *Reconciling Evolution and Creation*, Free Inquiry, Jan.-Feb. 1983, at 37 (italics added).

[4] Lipson*, *A Physicist Looks at Evolution*, 31 Physics Bulletin 138, 138 (1980).

[5] N. Gillespie*, *Charles Darwin and the Problem of Creation* 158 n. 10 (1979).

[6] J. North*, *The Measure of the Universe* 399 (1965).

[7] N. Gillespie*, *Charles Darwin and the Problem of Creation* 32 (1979).

[8] *Id.* at 22, 24.

[9] Foster*, *The Christian Doctrine of Creation and the Rise of Modern Natural Science*, 43 Mind 446, 462 (1934) (italics added).

[10] Hepburn*, *Creation, Religious Doctrine of: Creation in the Context of Scientific Cosmological Theories*, 2 Encyclopedia of Philosophy 255, 256 (P. Edwards* ed. 1967) (italics added).

[11] Bambrough*, *Demiurge*, in 1 Encyclopedia of Philosophy 337, 337 (P. Edwards* ed. 1967).

[12] Plato, *Timaeus*, in The Collected Dialogues of Plato 1161-1211 (E. Hamilton* & H. Cairns* eds. 1961).

[13] Leslie*, *Cosmology, Probability, and the Need To Explain Life*, in Scientific Explanation and Understanding 53, 56 (N. Rescher* ed. 1983) (italics added).

[14] Section 13.2.

[15] Tipler*, *How to Construct a Falsifiable Theory in Which the Universe Came Into Being Several Thousand Years Ago*, 2 Philosophy of Science Association 873, 894 (1984).

[16] *E.g.*, Wilczek*, *The Cosmic Asymmetry between Matter and Antimatter*, Scientific Am., Dec. 1980, at 82, 83 ("creation"); Wynn-Williams*, *The Newest Stars in Orion*, Scientific Am., Aug. 1981, at 46, 65 ("creation"); Trefil*, *Closing in on Creation*, Smithsonian, May 1983, at 33 ("creation"); Trefil*, *Matter vs. Antimatter*, Science 81, Sept. 1981, at 66, 66-67 ("creation"); Sandage*, *Time Scale of Creation*, in Galaxies and the Universe 75 (L. Woltjer* ed. 1968) ("creation").

[17] J. North*, *The Measure of the Universe* 401 (1965) (italics in original).

[18] *Id.* at 398.

[19] G. Gamow*, *The Creation of the Universe* 20 *passim* (1955).

[20] Douglas*, *Forty Minutes with Einstein*, 50 J. Royal Astronomical Society of Canada 99, 100 (1956).

[21] C. Sagan*, *Cosmos* 259 (1980) ("In one, the universe is *created*, somehow, ten or twenty billion years ago and expands forever, the galaxies mutually receding until the last one disappears over our cosmic horizon.... In the other, the oscillating universe, the Cosmos has no beginning and no end, and we are in the midst of an infinite cycle . . ..").

[22] J. Silk*, *The Big Bang* 144 (1979) ("the singularity, when *creation* of matter possibly occurred"); Trefil*, *Matter vs. Antimatter*, Science 81, Sept. 1981, at 66, 66-67 ("One argument is that more matter than antimatter was

created during the Big Bang, the cataclysmic explosion that marked the beginning of the universe."); P. Davies*, *Superforce: The Search for a Grand Unified Theory of Nature* 16 (1984) ("creation event"); Davies*, *Chance or choice: is the Universe an accident?*, 80 New Scientist 506, 507 (1978) ("Modern cosmology also has a *version of the creation*—a hot big bang, which occurred about 15 billion years ago."); Waldrop*, *Before the Beginning*, Science 84, Jan.-Feb. 1984, at 45, 46, 47 ("Except for a few educated guesses, no one has the slightest idea what went on in that first instant of *creation*.").

[23] Guth* & Steinhardt*, *The Inflationary Universe*, Scientific Am., May 1984, at 116, 128 (italics added).

[24] Tryon*, *What Made the World?*, New Scientist, Mar. 8, 1984, at 14, 16 (italics added).

[25] H. Pagels*, *Perfect Symmetry: The Search for the Beginning of Time* 338-40 (1985) (italics added).

[26] P. Davies*, *Superforce: The Search for a Grand Unified Theory of Nature* 199 (1984).

[27] Pollock*, *On the Creation of an Inflationary Universe from "Nothing"* . . ., 167B Physics Letters 301, 301 (1986).

[28] Linde*, *Quantum creation of an inflationary Universe*, 60 Soviet Physics JETP 211, 211 (1984).

[29] J. Barrow* & F. Tipler*, *The Anthropic Cosmological Principle* 443 (1986).

[30] H. Pagels*, *Perfect Symmetry: The Search for the Beginning of Time* 347, 349 (1985) (italics added).

[31] Goncharov* & Bytsenko*, *The Supersymmetric Casimir Effect and Quantum Creation of the Universe with Nontrivial Topology*, 106B Physics Letters 385, 385 (1985) ("quantum creation of the universe" "from literally nothing").

[32] Alvarez*, *Quantum Creation of Multidimensional Universes*, 30 Zeitschrift fur Physik: Particles & Fields 157, 157 (1986).

[33] Parker*, *Quantized Fields and Particle Creation in Expanding Universe [I]*, 183 Physical Rev. 1057, 1057 (1969).

[34] Grib* & Mamaev*, *Creation of Matter in the Friedmann Model of the Universe*, 14 Soviet J. Nuclear Physics 450, 450 (1972).

[35] Audretsch*, *Quantum-Mechanical Analogue of Particle Creation Caused by the Expansion of the Universe*, 17B Nuovo Cimento 284 (1973).

[36] Selak*, *A Model of Expanding Universe with Continuous Mass-Creation*, 60 Astrophysics & Space Science 465 (1979).

[37] Narlikar* & Padmanabhan*, *Creation-field cosmology: A possible solution to singularity, horizon, and flatness problems*, 32 Physical Rev. D 1928, 1929, 1928 (1985).

[38] H. Bondi*, *Cosmology* 143-44 (1968).

[39] J. North, *The Measure of the Universe* 400 (1965) (italics added).

[40] F. Hoyle, *The Intelligent Universe: A New View of Creation and Evolution* 171 (1983) ("In 1948 I was criticised for proposing a theory in which

matter could be created, but it is interesting to note that today many physicists find the notion quite acceptable.").

41 F. Hoyle*, *The Nature of the Universe* 122-23 (1950) (italics added).

42 *Id.* at 124 (italics added).

43 Hepburn*, *Creation, Religious Doctrine of: Creation in the Context of Scientific Cosmological Theories*, 2 Encyclopedia of Philosophy 255, 256 (P. Edwards* ed. 1967).

44 Ellis*, *Alternative to the Big Bang*, 22 Ann. Rev. Astronomy & Astrophysics 157, 180 (1984).

45 Pimentel*, *Exact Self-Creation Cosmological Solutions*, 116 Astrophysics & Space Science 395, 395 (1985) ("In an attempt to produce a continuous creation theory Barber (1982) has proposed two theories. The first is a modified Brans-Dicke theory that is unsatisfactory since the equivalence principle is violated. The second is an adaptation of general relativity to include continuous creation and is within the limits of the observations. In this work we have been able to reduce the cosmological equations of the second self-creation theory to quadratures, under the assumption of a power law between the expansion factor of the Universe and the scalar field of the theory.").

46 F. Crick*, *Life Itself: Its Origin and Nature* (1981).

47 F. Hoyle, *The Intelligent Universe: A New View of Creation and Evolution* 226, 236 (1983) (italics added).

48 Wickramasinghe is described as follows:

> Raised a Hindu in Ceylon (now Sri Lanka), he says he doesn't even share the basic premise of the Christian faith, much less the Christian fundamentalists' trust in the general 'inerrancy of the Bible in its original autographs.' And the book of Genesis couldn't be farther . . .. 'Some 2,000 or so enzymes are known to be crucial [for] life—ranging from simple microorganisms all the way up to man. . . . [T]he probability of discovering this set by random shuffling is one in $10^{40,000}$,' a number that 'exceeds by many powers of 10 the number of all atoms in the entire observable universe.'
>
> . . ..
>
> . . .'But the general concept of *creation*, that could be separated from the theological arguments, was one that I felt some intellectual sympathy for.'

Raloff*, *They Call It Creation Science*, Science News, Jan. 16, 1982, at 44, 46.

49 E. Ambrose*, *The Nature and Origin of the Biological World* 143 (1982) (italics added). Another example is Weisskopf*, who remarks that the universe "looks as if 'somebody' has arranged it so that the density is the same all over." Weisskopf*, *The Origin of the Universe*, 71 Am. Scientist 473, 478 (1983).

50 Lipson*, *A Physicist Looks at Evolution*, 31 Physics Bulletin 138, 138 (1980).

51 H. Bergson*, *L'Evolution Créatrice* (1907).

[52] Smith*, *Two Evolutions*, in On Nature 42, 47 (L. Rouner* ed. 1984).

[53] Gray*, *Alternative in Science: The Secular Creationism of Heribert-Nilsson*, Kronos, Summer 1982, at 8, 8, 13-14.

[54] Heribert-Nilsson wrote about "suddenly appearing . . . higher and lower forms":

> Instead they consist in each period of *well distinguished groups* of biota, *suddenly appearing* at a given time, always including *higher and lower forms*, always with a complete variability. At a certain time the whole of such a group of biota is destroyed. There are *no bridges* between these groups of biota following one upon the other.

D. Heribert-Nilsson, *Synthetische Artbildung* 1211 (1953).

[55] Gould*, *Catastrophes and Steady State Earth*, Natural History, Feb. 1975, at 15, 15-16.

[56] J. Moore*, *The Post-Darwinian Controversies* 207, 208-09 (1979). Agassiz's biographer wrote:

> [T]he scientific study of nature . . . supplied the materials for an idealistic world view that *transcended mere recorded assumptions about the powers of the Deity*. The essence of the Creative Power was to be discovered in the book of nature itself, *not in the Bible*.

E. Lurie*, *Louis Agassiz: A Life in Science* 100 (1960) (italics added). *See also* J. Teller*, *Louis Agassiz: Scientist and Teacher* 262 (1947).

[57] M. Pitman, *Adam and Evolution* 254 (1984).

[58] Notes 5 & 6.

[59] 2 *The Life and Letters of Charles Darwin* 202-03 (F. Darwin* ed. 1903); D. Hull*, *Darwin and His Critics* 53 (1973) (U. of Chicago Press).

[60] Fox*, *Molecular Selection and Natural Selection*, 61 Q. Rev. of Biology 375, 379 (1986).

[61] C. Ponnamperuma*, *The Origins of Life* 197 (1972).

[62] F. Ayala* & J. Valentine*, *Evolving: The Theory and Processes of Organic Evolution* 340 (1979).

[63] Dobzhansky*, *Nothing in Biology Makes Sense Except in the Light of Evolution*, 35 Am. Biology Teacher 125, 127 (1973).

[64] Gould*, *The Return of Hopeful Monsters*, Natural History, June-July 1977, at 28.

[65] Schopf*, *Punctuated equilibrium and evolutionary stasis*, 7 Paleobiology 156, 163 (1981).

[66] O'Grady*, *Evolutionary Theory and Teleology*, 107 J. Theoretical Biology 563, 574 (1984).

[67] T. Dobzhansky*, F. Ayala*, G. Stebbins* & J. Valentine*, *Evolution* 452 (1977).

[68] J. Monod*, *Chance and Necessity* 110 (A. Wainhouse* trans. 1971).

[69] Gould*, *The Five Kingdoms*, Natural History, June-July 1976, at 30, 30.

[70] S. Stanley*, *Macroevolution: Pattern and Process* 69 (1979).

[71] C. Darwin*, *The Origin of Species* 488 *passim* (1st ed. 1859, repr. 1964).

[72] Note 59.

[73] Note 6.

[74] Note 15.
[75] Note 9.
[76] Note 10.
[77] Note 15.
[78] Note 17.
[79] Note 25.
[80] Note 30.
[81] Note 34.
[82] Note 37.
[83] Note 38.
[84] F. Hoyle & N. Wickramasinghe, *Evolution from Space: A Theory of Cosmic Creationism* (1984).
[85] Note 49.
[86] Note 52.
[87] Note 51.
[88] Note 64.
[89] J. North*, *The Measure of the Universe* 398 (1965).
[90] Etkin, *Science and Creation*, in Challenge: Torah Views on Science and Its Problems 241, 250-51 (rev. ed. 1978) (italics added) (creationist scientist).
[91] R. Jastrow*, *God and the Astronomers* 11-12 (1978).
[92] Lipson*, *A Physicist Looks at Evolution*, 31 Physics Bulletin 138, 138 (1980).
[93] Section 13.1(e).
[94] Section 10.2(a).
[95] Gale*, *The Anthropic Principle*, Scientific Am., Dec. 1981, at 154, 168, 171.
[96] V. Webster* *et al.*, *Life Science* 41-42 (1980).
[97] R. Hegner* & K. Stiles*, *College Zoology* 790 (6th ed. 1959) ("The doctrine of special creation, that is that each species of animal was specially created, is sufficiently refuted to the satisfaction of most biologists by the facts of organic evolution."); G. Moment*, *General Biology* 563 (1950) ("One of the oldest ideas and, until recently, the most widely accepted, is the theory of special creation. Certainly very few, perhaps no, biologists now believe that each species was separately created and has existed since the beginning of the world."); P. Weatherwax*, *Plant Biology* 356 (1942) ("According to the various theories of special creation, every species of plant or animal was specially created long ago, when life was first placed on earth, and each species has continued unchanged to the present time."); Jennings*, *Can We See Evolution Occurring?*, in Creation by Evolution 24, 32 (F. Mason* ed. 1928) ("One holds that the constitution of organisms is permanent; that they were created as they are and do not change. . . . The facts observed are what the doctrine of evolution demands, not what the opposite theory demands.").
[98] Plato, *Timaeus*, in The Collected Dialogues of Plato 1161-1211 (E.

Hamilton* & H. Cairns* eds. 1961).

[99] Foster*, *The Christian Doctrine of Creation and the Rise of Modern Natural Science*, 43 Mind 446, 462 (1934).

[100] F. Hoyle, *The Intelligent Universe: A New View of Creation and Evolution* 189, 214 (1983) (italics added). *See also* F. Hoyle & N. Wickramasinghe, *Evolution from Space* 150 (1981) (italics added):

> From the beginning of this book we have emphasized the *enormous information content* of even the simplest living systems. The information cannot in our view be generated by what are often called 'natural' processes, as for instance through meteorological and chemical processes occurring at the surface of a lifeless planet. As well as a suitable physical and chemical environment, a large initial store of information was also needed. We have argued that the requisite information came from an '*intelligence*', the beckoning spectre.
>
> To be sure, the books in the library contain information. Yet we do not think of a book as an 'intelligence'. A further quality is needed to define intelligence, namely the ability to act on information which a book alone cannot do. As well as providing information, our spectre is required also to act on it, which is why we refer to the thing as an 'intelligence'.

[101] E. Ambrose*, *The Nature and Origin of the Biological World* 140-44, 164 (1982) (italics added).

[101A] H. Morowitz*, *Musings of a Mystic Scientist* (1987).

[102] N. Macbeth*, *Darwin Retried* 6, 94 (1971).

[103] Raloff*, *They Call It Creation Science*, Science News, Jan. 16, 1982, at 44, 46.

[104] Gould*, *Darwinism and the Expansion of Evolutionary Theory*, 216 Science 380, 381 (1982).

[105] Leslie*, *Anthropic Principle, World Ensemble, Design,* 19 Am. Philosophical Q. 141, 141 (1982).

[106] F. Copleston*, *A History of Philosophy* 317 (1946). *See also* Aristotle, *Metaphysics* bk. lambda.

[107] *Declaration of Independence* (1776), 1 Stat. 1 (1789) (italics added).

[108] Abington School District v. Schempp, 374 U.S. 203, 225 (1963). *See also* Epperson v. Arkansas, 393 U.S. 97, 106 (1968).

[109] Section 20.2.

[110] Note 92.

[111] Note 91.

[112] F. Hoyle & N. Wickramasinghe, *Evolution from Space: A Theory of Cosmic Creationism* (1984) (panspermia advocates).

[113] Note 96.

[114] "Evolution does not presuppose the absence of a creator or God and the plain inference conveyed by Section 4 is erroneous." McLean v. Arkansas Bd. of Educ., 519 F. Supp. 1255, 1266 (E.D. Ark. 1982).

[115] Section 13.3(b).

116 Provine*, *Implications of Darwin's Ideas on the Study of Evolution*, 32 BioScience 501, 506 (1982) (co-author of *The Evolutionary Synthesis*) (italics added).

117 Provine*, *Book Review of Trial and Error: The American Controversy over Creation and Evolution*, Academe, Jan.-Feb. 1987, at 50, 52.

118 Mayr*, *The Nature of the Darwinian Revolution*, 176 Science 981, 988 (1972) ("The natural causes postulated by the evolutionists *completely separated God from his creation*, for all practical purposes. The new explanatory model replaced planned teleology by the haphazard process of natural selection.") (italics added); Mayr*, *Foreword*, to M. Ruse*, *Darwinism Defended* at xi-xii (1982) ("This theory [natural selection] is so important for the Darwinian because it permits the explanation of adaptation, the 'design' of the natural theologian, by natural means, *instead of divine intervention*.") (italics added).

119 Dawkins*, *Universal Darwinism*, in Evolution from Molecules to Men 403, 417 (D. Bendall* ed. 1983) (" 'The greatest concession they could make to Darwin was that the Designer operated by tinkering with the generation of diversity, designing the variation'. *Darwin's* response was: 'If I were convinced that I required such additions to the theory of natural selection, I would reject it as rubbish. . . . I *would give nothing for the theory of Natural Selection, if it requires miraculous additions at any one stage of descent*.' ") (italics added).

120 J. Barzun*, *Darwin, Marx, Wagner* 10-11 (2d ed. 1958) ("The entire phrase and not merely the words Natural Selection is important, for the denial of purpose in the universe is carried in the second half of the formula—accidental variation. This denial of purpose is Darwin's distinctive contention. . . . In this way the notion of a *Deity or Providence* or Life Force having a tendency of its own, or even of a single individual having a purpose other than survival or reproduction, was *ruled out*.") (italics added).

121 D. Nelkin*, *Science Textbook Controversies and the Politics of Equal Time* 11 (1977) ("Beyond its impact on traditional science, Darwinism was devastating to conventional theology.").

122 Ghiselin*, *Darwin and Evolutionary Psychology*, 179 Science 964, 967 (1973) ("The Darwinian solution was to view evolution as a change in developmental mechanisms, with natural selection (and other mechanisms of adaptation) disposing of any need to invoke supernatural agencies.").

123 Grene*, *The Faith of Darwinism*, Encounter, Nov. 1959, at 48, 48 (" '. . . Darwin has demonstrated this force, this process of Nature; he has opened the door by which a happier coming race will *cast out miracles*, never to return. Everyone who knows what miracles imply will praise him, in consequence, as one of the greatest benefactors of the human race.' Thus wrote the Biblical critic David Strauss in *The Old Faith and the New*, published in English translation in 1873 . . ..") (italics added).

124 K. Cauthen*, *The Impact of American Religious Liberalism* 22 (1962) ("Darwin in 1859 propounded the theory of organic evolution with reference

to the biological world. These theories completely *ruled out the traditional notion that God had created* the world and its inhabitants in their present form by divine fiat at definite moments of time.") (italics added).

[125] T. Roszak*, *Unfinished Animal* 102 (1975) ("The irony is devastating. The *main purpose of Darwinism* was to *drive every last trace of an incredible God* from biology. But the theory replaced the old God with an even more incredible deity—omnipotent chance.") (italics added); *see also* Goldman*, *A Critical Review of Evolution*, in Challenge: Torah Views on Science and Its Problems 216, 218 (rev. ed. 1978) ("God is irrelevant in the Darwinian evolutionary scheme, and that is what is wrong with it for a Jew.").

[126] J. Moore*, *The Post-Darwinian Controversies* 314-15, 344 (1979) (italics added). *See also id.* at 109; Grene*, *The Faith of Darwinism*, Encounter, Nov. 1959, at 48, 48 (Darwin wrote in his autobiography: "I can indeed hardly see how anyone ought to wish Christianity to be true . . ..").

[127] C. Darwin*, Recollection of the Development of My Mind and Character 64 (unpub. ms. n.d.); G. Himmelfarb*, *Darwin and the Darwinian Revolution* 81 (1962).

[128] C. Darwin*, Recollection of the Development of My Mind and Character 73, 73b (unpub. ms. n.d.).

[129] C. Darwin*, Notebook M 74 (unpub. doc. at Cambridge U. n.d.), quoted in Ghiselin*, *Darwin and Evolutionary Psychology*, 179 Science 964, 967 (1973).

[130] Hull*, *Darwinism and Historiography*, in The Comparative Reception of Darwinism 388, 391 (T. Glick* ed. 1974).

[131] Goudge*, *Darwin, Charles Robert*, 2 Encyclopedia of Philosophy 294, 295 (P. Edwards* ed. 1967).

[132] T. Huxley*, *Agnosticism and Christianity* (1889).

[133] J. Barzun*, *Darwin, Marx, Wagner* 66, 67 (1958) ("I must again refer to *Huxley*, whose remark about 'the Hegira of Science from the idolatries of special creation' and the 'purer faith of Evolution' was made, not in the enthusiasm of 1859, but after fifteen years' reflection. Huxley could truthfully call himself an *agnostic* and a religious man at the same time, for he was completely devout about the new faith.") (italics added); Hepburn*, *Agnosticism*, 1 Encyclopedia of Philosophy 56, 56-67 (P. Edwards* ed. 1967).

[134] Levinton*, *Charles Darwin and Darwinism*, 32 BioScience 495, 495 (1982).

[135] E. Haeckel* , *The Riddle of the Universe* 337 (1899) ("With this single argument the mystery of the universe is explained, the *deity annulled*, and a new era of infinite knowledge ushered in."); *id.* at . . . . ("the *untenable myth* of a 'wise Providence' and of an 'All-loving Father in heaven.' ").

[136] E. Nordenskiold*, *The History of Biology* 506 (1935) ("with the hatred Haeckel felt for Christianity in later years").

[137] J. Leuba*, *The Belief in God and Immortality: A Psychological, Anthropological and Statistical Study* 230-59, 270-80 (1916).

[138] Leuba*, *Religious Beliefs of American Scientists*, 169 Harper's Magazine 291 (1934).
[139] G. Simpson*, *This View of Life* viii, 4, 12 (1964) ("the higher superstitions celebrated weekly in every hamlet of the United States").
[140] *Humanist Manifestos I & II* at 13, 16 (P. Kurtz* ed. 1973) ("We find insufficient evidence for belief in the existence of a supernatural.").
[141] Kurtz*, *A Secular Humanist Declaration*, Free Inquiry, Winter 1980-81, at 3, 7.
[142] Shapley*, *On the Evolution of Atoms, Stars and Galaxies*, in Adventures in Earth History 77, 78-79 (P. Cloud* ed. 1970).
[143] Tipler*, *How to Construct a Falsifiable Theory in Which the Universe Came Into Being Several Thousand Years Ago*, 2 Philosophy of Science Association 873, 895 (1984).
[144] Kurtz*, *A Secular Humanist Declaration*, Free Inquiry, Winter 1980-81, at 3, 7.
[145] Huxley*, *The Evolutionary Vision*, in 3 Evolution after Darwin at 249, 252 (S. Tax* & C. Callender* eds. 1960). *See also* J. Huxley*, *Religion without Revelation* 58 (rev. ed. 1957) ("astronomy had no need for the god hypothesis: Darwin and Pasteur between them did the same for biology").
[146] Deposition of G. Brent Dalrymple*, Keith v. Louisiana Dep't of Educ., 553 F. Supp. 295 (M.D. La. 1982).
[147] Deposition of William McLoughlin*, *id.*
[148] Trial tr., vol. 2, McLean v. Arkansas Bd. of Educ., 519 F. Supp. 1255 (E.D. Ark. 1982).
[149] Deposition of Carl Sagan*, Keith v. Louisiana Dep't of Educ., 553 F. Supp. 295 (M.D. La.).
[150] Tierney*, *Stephen Jay Gould: The Rolling Stone Interview*, Rolling Stone, Jan. 15, 1987, at 38, 58.
[151] Deposition of Michael Ruse*, Keith v. Louisiana Dep't of Educ., 553 F. Supp. 295 (M.D. La. 1982).
[152] Deposition of Ronald Numbers*, *id.*
[153] Ferris*, *The Other Einstein*, Science 83, Oct. 1983, at 35, 38.
[154] L. Barnett*, *The Universe and Dr. Einstein* 101 (1962).
[155] R. Jastrow*, *God and the Astronomers* 112 (1978).
[156] N. Gillespie*, *Charles Darwin and the Problem of Creation* 109 (1979).
[157] A. Gray*, *Natural Science and Religion* (1880); Gray*, *Natural Selection and Natural Theology*, 27 Nature 291, 527 (1882, 1883).
[158] J. Moore*, *The Post-Darwinian Controversies* 185-87 (1979).
[159] Section 15.1(b).
[160] Shallis*, *In the eye of a storm*, New Scientist, Jan. 19, 1984, at 42, 43.
[161] Committee on Science and Creationism*, *Science and Creationism* 6 (1984).
[162] Mayer*, *The 19th Century Revisited*, Biological Sciences Curriculum Study Newsletter, Nov. 1972, at 8.
[163] Moyer*, *Arguments for Maintaining the Integrity of Science Educa-*

tion, 43 Am. Biology Teacher 391 (1981).

[164] D. Nelkin*, *Science Textbook Controversies and the Politics of Equal Time* 11 (1977) (italics added).

[165] Address of Dr. William Provine* entitled "Theories of Creationism and Evolution from a Historical Perspective" before Sigma Xi Chapter at Corning, N.Y. (Nov. 17, 1981) (italics added).

[166] Provine*, *Book Review of Trial and Error: The American Controversy over Creation and Evolution*, Academe, Jan.-Feb. 1987, at 50, 51-52 (italics added).

[167] N. Gillespie*, *Charles Darwin and the Problem of Creation* 144 (1979).

[168] Beckner*, *Darwinism*, 2 Encyclopedia of Philosophy 296, 303 (P. Edwards* ed. 1979).

[169] J. Draper*, *History of the Conflict between Religion and Science* (1896).

[170] Gilkey*, *The Creationist and Controversy: The Interrelation of Inquiry and Belief*, in Creationism and the Law 129, 135 (M. LaFollette* ed. 1983).

[171] Smith*, *Two Evolutions*, in On Nature 42, 43 (L. Rouner* ed. 1984) ("Not only do these views not mesh; they are in head-on opposition, for according to science we are the more who have derived from the less, whereas our religions teach that we are the less who have derived from the more. In thus contradicting each other, our two views—one taught by our schools, the other by our churches and synagogues—cancel each other out, leaving us without a clear self-image or identity. It is impossible for both views to be true, yet simply by having been born into today's West, all of us believe parts of both of them.").

[172] Strike*, *The Status of Creation-Science: A Comment on Siegel and Hahn*, 63 Phi Delta Kappan 555, 556 (1982).

[173] Miller* & Fowler*, *What's Wrong with the Creation/Evolution Controversy?*, CTNS Bulletin, Autumn 1984, at 1, 7.

[174] *Id.* at 8-9 (italics added, footnotes deleted).

[175] *Id.* at 9.

[176] *Id.*

[177] Adler*, *World Peace in Truth*, Center Magazine, Mar.-Apr. 1978, at 56, 59, 61.

[178] Watkins*, *Against 'Normal Science'*, in Criticism and the Growth of Knowledge 36 (I. Lakatos* & A. Musgrave* eds. 1970) ("If someone holds that, say, Biblical myths and scientific theories are incommensurable, belong to different universes of discourse, he presumably implies that the Genesis account of the Creation should *not* be regarded as logically incompatible with geology, Darwinism, etc.; they *are* compatible and can peacefully co-exist just because they are incommensurable. But if the Ptolemaic system is logically incompatible with the Copernican system, or Newtonian theory with Relativity Theory, peaceful coexistence is not possible: they were *rival* alternatives; and it was possible to make a rational choice between them partly because it was possible to devise crucial experiments between them (stellar parallax, starshift, etc.).").

179 K. Pearson*, *Grammar of Science* 14, 24 (1911) ("The goal of science is clear—it is nothing short of the complete interpretation of the universe. Science does much more than demand that it shall be left in undisturbed possession of what the theologian and metaphysician please to call its 'legitimate field.' It claims that the *whole range of phenomena*, mental as well as physical—the entire universe—*is its field.* It asserts that the scientific method is the sole gateway to the whole region of knowledge.").

A Roman Catholic theologian concurs:

> That Revelation should be a "religious doctrine" does not mean it contains no information touching the subject matter of science, unless it is assumed science alone can comprehend and convey understanding of the visible world. That, however, is precisely the point at issue, which cannot be decided primarily on scientific grounds, but on other: the Catholic on one set of beliefs, the secular humanist on another. The Church does not maintain Revelation is a scientific textbook such as to provide exact parallels for every scientific question. *At certain points, however, science and Revelation meet*, and at those points (e.g., the question of origins) Revelation undoubtedly has something to say basic to scientific understanding and science.

P. Fehlner, *In the Beginning* 35 (1987) (italics added).

180 He writes:

> Separation of religion and science. If the foregoing arguments are correct, it would appear that *there are important areas in which science and religion impinge on each other.* Some of the battlefields are indeed now deserted, and many of the polemics of nineteenth-century writers are no longer of interest. Nevertheless, it has been suggested in this article that *in fundamental ways science does impinge on theology* and that some of the conflicts between them are even sharper than they were a hundred years ago.

Smart*, *Religion and Science*, 7 Encyclopedia of Philosophy 158, 162 (P. Edwards* ed. 1967) (italics added).

181 L. Laudan*, *Progress and Its Problems* 131 (1977) (italics deleted).

182 Schoch* & Prins*, *Letter*, Geotimes, May 1984, at 7 (italics added).

183 L. Gilkey*, *Maker of Heaven and Earth: A Study of the Christian Doctrine of Creation* 34 (1959).

184 B. Vawter*, *Biblical Inspiration* 150 (1972) ("The truth of the Bible has nothing to do one way or the other, pro or contra, with either scientific fact or scientific history.").

185 *E.g.*, C. Hyers*, *The Meaning of Creation: Genesis and Modern Science* (1984).

186 Miller* & Fowler*, *What's Wrong with the Creation/Evolution Controversy?*, CTNS Bulletin, Autumn 1984, at 1, 9.

187 *Id.* at 6.

188 L. Gilkey*, *Maker of Heaven and Earth: A Study of the Christian Doctrine of Creation* 34 (1959) ("Mainly as a result of the creative and

courageous efforts of the liberal theologians, the "prescientific science" of the biblical account of creation has at last been separated out from the profound religious affirmation contained in that account. The inquiries of the physical sciences and those of theology are now seen to be asking fundamentally different kinds of questions, in totally different areas of thought and experience. Consequently the answers to these questions, the hypotheses of science, and the affirmations or doctrines of theology, cannot and do not conflict.").

189 R. Cross*, *The Emergence of Liberal Catholicism in America* 152-53 (1958) ("Some of the liberals hoped to avoid the difficulties of 'concordism' altogether by arguing that the Bible did not teach any scientific or historical truth 'as such.' ").

190 C. Darwin*, *The Origin of Species: A Variorum Text* 759 (M. Peckham* ed. 1959). *See also id.* at 343, 753, 757-58 *passim.*

191 N. Gillespie*, *Charles Darwin and the Problem of Creation* xi (1979).

192 N. Eldredge*, *The Monkey Business* 7-9 (1982).

193 Weisskopf*, *The Origin of the Universe*, 71 American Scientist 473, 480 (1983) (comparing "the Judeo-Christian tradition" and "the Bible" to modern science as "surprisingly similar").

194 T. Dobzhansky*, F. Ayala*, G. Stebbins* & J. Valentine*, *Evolution* 455 (1977).

195 C. Ponnamperuma*, *The Origins of Life* 196 (1972).

196 Dobzhansky*, *Nothing in Biology Makes Sense Except in the Light of Evolution*, 35 Am. Biology Teacher 125, 129 (1973).

197 A. Hardy*, *The Biology of God* (1975).

198 J. Polkinghorne*, *The Particle Play* 125 (1979).

199 Biological Sciences Curriculum Study*, *Biological Science: Molecules to Man* 100, 111 (3d ed. 1973 & 1976).

200 Biological Sciences Curriculum Study*, *Biological Science: An Ecological Approach* 310 (3d ed. 1973 & 1976).

201 R. Oram*, *Biology: Living Systems* 74T (3d ed. Teacher's Ed. 1979) (italics added):

> Many biologists, as well as theologians, believe in *God*, and many of them believe that *He* created the world. But they also believe that *He* gave living creatures the ability to adapt to changing environments—and that, because of this ability, living creatures have evolved and developed into today's species.... In other words, there is no necessary conflict between those who believe that *God* created all living things and those who believe that living things have evolved over time. One can believe in evolution (or not believe in it) regardless of one's *religious* beliefs.
>
> There is nothing in the theory of evolution that is contrary to the religious beliefs of millions of people; and there is nothing in their religious beliefs that is *necessarily* contrary to the theory of evolution. . . .

Some may say that the theory of evolution is in conflict with the biblical account of the creation of humans. Strictly speaking, this is not so. If one takes every statement in the Bible as being *literally* true, there will indeed be conflict. But one can accept the *spirit* of the biblical account, recognizing God as the Creator of humans, and still regard them as the product of eons of evolutionary development. In this view, the evolutionary development which ended in humans was set in motion by God Himself.

202 *Id.* at 265.

203 C. Heimler*, *Focus on Life Science* 431 (Teacher's Ed. 1981).

204 S. Weinberg*, *Biology: An Inquiry into the Nature of Life* 415 (4th ed. 1977) ("The hand of God is just as evident in evolution extending over billions of years as in creation occurring in an instant or a few days.").

205 P. Moody*, *Introduction to Evolution* 513 (2d ed. 1962).

206 W. Stansfield*, *The Science of Evolution* 578 (1977) ("Deity . . . create[d] gradually through an evolutionary process").

207 G. Van Wylen* & R. Sonntag*, *Fundamentals of Classical Thermodynamics* 243 (2d ed. 1970) ("the prior and continuing work of a creator, who also holds the answer to the future destiny of man and the universe").

208 A. Kluge*, *Chordate Structure and Function* 7 (2d ed. 1977).

209 Section 14.1(g).

210 Note 117.

211 Note 130.

212 Note 126.

213 Note 191.

214 Note 203.

215 Note 192.

216 Note 164.

217 Note 174.

218 Note 166.

219 Note 182.

220 S. Jaki*, *Science and Creation* viii (1974) (italics added).

221 L. Gilkey*, *Maker of Heaven and Earth* 34 (1959).

222 A. Whitehead*, *Science and the Modern World* 12-13 (1925) ("It must come from the medieval insistence on the rationality of God, conceived as with the personal energy of Jehovah and with the rationality of a Greek philosopher. . . . My explanation is that the faith in the possibility of science, generated antecedently to the development of modern scientific theory, is an unconscious derivative from medieval theology.").

223 Oppenheimer*, *On Science and Culture*, Encounter, Oct. 1962, at 62.

224 Foster*, *The Christian Doctrine of Creation and the Rise of Modern Natural Science*, 43 Mind 448, 453, 465 (1934):

> The modern investigators of nature were the first to take seriously in their science the Christian doctrine that nature is *created*, and the main differences between the methods of ancient and the methods of modern natural science may be reduced to this; that these are and those are not

methods proper to the investigation of a created nature.

. . ..

. . .The reliance upon the senses for evidence, not merely for illustration, is what constitutes the empirical character peculiar to modern natural science; and the conclusion follows that only a *created* nature is proper object of an empirical science.

225 E. Klaaren*, *Religious Origins of Modern Science* v, vii, 1 (1977) ("The chief purpose of this essay is to show that religion was conducive to the advent of modern science, specifically that belief in divine creation was a major presupposition in the emergence of natural science in seventeenth-century England.").

226 M. Calvin*, *Chemical Evolution* 258 (1969).

227 R. Hooykaas*, *Religion and the Rise of Modern Science* (1972).

228 L. Eiseley*, *Darwin's Century: Evolution and the Men Who Discovered It* 62 (1961).

229 C. von Weizsacker*, *The Relevance of Physics* 163 (1964) (Modern science is a "legacy, I might even have said, a child of Christianity.").

230 Hodgson*, *Book Review of Jaki's Science and Creation*, 251 Nature 747 (1974) ("Although we seldom recognize it, scientific research requires certain basic beliefs about the order and rationality of matter, and its accessibility to the human mind. . . . They came to us in their full force through the Judeo-Christian belief in an omnipotent God, creator and sustainer of all things.").

231 W. Glover*, *Biblical Origins of Modern Secular Culture* (1984).

231A F. Oakley*, *Natural Law, Conciliarism and Consent in the Late Middle Ages* 452 (1984).

231B E. Mach*, *Science of Mechanics* 551-52 (T. McCormack* trans. 1942).

232 L. Eiseley*, *Darwin's Century: Evolution and the Men Who Discovered It* 62 (1961).

233 F. Bacon, *Advancement of Learning* 5 (1900).

234 I. Newton, *Mathematical Principles* 544-45 (A. Motte* trans., F. Cajori* ed., 1946).

235 Quoted in G. Christianson*, *In the Presence of the Creator: Isaac Newton and His Times* 352 (1984) (spelling in original).

236 R. Numbers*, *Creation by Natural Law* 5 (1977).

237 Boyle, *Some Motives and Incentives to the Love of God*, in I Works of Robert Boyle 167 (1744).

238 G. Trevelyan*, *English Social History* 257 (1942).

239 1 I. Lakatos*, *The Methodology of Scientific Research Programmes* 195 (J. Worrall* & G. Currie* eds. 1978).

240 R. Descartes, *Le Monde* (1664).

241 *World Who's Who in Science* 448 (A. Debus* ed. 1968).

242 *Id.* at 924.

243 *Id.* at 1020.

244 J. Ray, *The Wisdom of God Manifested in the Works of Creation* (1691).

245 *World Who's Who in Science* 1399 (A. Debus* ed. 1968).

[246] *Id.* at 1604.
[247] *Id.* at 764.
[248] J. Woodward, *An Essay Toward a Natural History of the Earth* (1695).
[249] *World Who's Who in Science* 1823 (A. Debus* ed. 1968).
[250] C. Linnaeus, *Systema Naturae* (1735); Patterson*, *Cladistics and classification*, 94 New Scientist 303, 303 (1982).
[251] *World Who's Who in Science* 1050 (A. Debus* ed. 1968).
[252] C. Sagan* & A. Druyan*, *Comet* 54 (1985) ("He never doubted that the Earth had been formed, or even created . . ..").
[253] Section 15.2(a)
[254] Note 225.
[255] Note 238.
[256] Note 239.
[257] Section 13.3.
[258] Ruse*, *The Ideology of Darwinism*, in Darwin Today 233, 247-49 (E. Geisler* & W. Scheler* eds. 1983) (italics added, capitalized names deleted).
[259] J. Habermas*, *Toward a Rational Society* 94-95 (1970) ("central world view" that tends to legitimate and support a particular conception of science).
[260] Ruse*, *The Ideology of Darwinism*, in Darwin Today 233, 234 (E. Geisler* & W. Scheler* eds. 1983).
[261] *Reexamination of the Foundations*, Pensée, May 1972, at 43, 44.
[262] N. Gillespie*, *Charles Darwin and the Problem of Creation* 3, 224 (1979).
[263] Lewontin*, *Introduction*, to Scientists Confront Creationism xxiii, xxvi (L. Godfrey* ed. 1983) ("Yet, whatever our understanding of the social struggle that gives rise to creationism, whatever the desire to reconcile science and religion may be, there is no escape from the fundamental contradiction between *evolution and creationism*. They are *irreconcilable world views*.") (italics added).
[264] Muller*, *One Hundred Years Without Darwinism Are Enough*, 49 School Science & Mathematics 305, 306 (1958) ("the wonderful world view opened up by Darwin and other western biologists").
[265] R. Hofstadter*, *Social Darwinism in American Thought* 3 (1955).
[266] Ruse*, *Darwin as Hollywood Epic*, 61 Q. Rev. Biology 509, 513 (1986) (first italics added).
[267] J. Greene*, *Science, Ideology and World View* 133 (1981) (italics added). *See also Reexamination of the Foundations*, Pensée, May 1972, at 43, 44 (interview with George Grinnell*) ("Darwin also did not derive his theory from nature but rather superimposed a certain *philosophical world-view* on nature and then spent 20 years trying to gather the facts to make it stick.") (italics added).
[268] N. Gillespie*, *Charles Darwin and the Problem of Creation* 139-40 (1979).
[269] Marsden*, *Creation versus evolution: no middle way*, 305 Nature 571, 574 (1983) (italics added).

[270] Abbagnano*, *Positivism*, 6 Encyclopedia of Philosophy 414, 415 (P. Edwards* ed. 1967); *see* Feigl*, *Positivism and Logical Empiricism*, 14 Encyclopaedia Britannica: Macropaedia 877, 877 (15th ed. 1974).
[271] Campbell*, *Materialism*, 5 Encyclopedia of Philosophy 179, 179 (P. Edwards* ed. 1967).
[272] Hull*, *Darwinism and Historiography*, in The Comparative Reception of Darwinism 388, 391 (T. Glick* ed. 1974) (italics added).
[273] S. Gould*, *Ever Since Darwin* 24 (1977).
[274] J. Barzun*, *Darwin, Marx, Wagner* 7 (2d ed. 1958).
[275] *Id.* at 66-67 ("Lest it be thought that I am exaggerating the *religious aspects of Darwinism* I must again refer to Huxley, whose remark about 'the Hegira of Science from the idolatries of special creation, and '*the purer faith of Evolution*' was made, not in the enthusiasm of 1859, but after fifteen years' reflection. Huxley could truthfully call himself an agnostic and a religious man at the same time, for he was *completely devout about the new faith*.") (italics added).
[276] D. Hull*, *Darwin and His Critics* 67 (1973).
[277] E. Haeckel*, *The Riddle of the Universe at the Close of the 19th Century* (1899).
[278] L. Büchner*, *Force and Matter* 18, 75, 77, 81 (P. Eckler* trans. 1891) ("*Matter must have been eternal* . . . [T]he universe must be uncreated . . . . [*N*]*atural laws* are immutable . . . . The experience of more than a thousand years has pressed on observers the conviction of the immutability of natural laws . . . with such absolute certainty, that not the least doubt can remain . . . . With the most absolute truth and with the greatest scientific certainty can we say this day: There is nothing miraculous in the world . . . . Belief in God is therefore almost confined at the present time to those so-called learned men who know scarcely anything about natural processes . . . . Whatever theological interest or narrow-minded pedantry can urge in opposition to this, is controverted by the strength of the facts, which in this respect leave no room for any doubt.") (italics added).
[279] W. Dampier-Whetham*, *A History of Science* 445 (1951).
[280] Eccles*, *Modern Biology and the Turn to Belief in God*, in The Intellectuals Speak Out About God 47, 50 (R. Varghese* ed. 1984).
[280A] R. Collingwood*, *The Idea of Nature* 104 (1945) (Oxford U. Press).
[281] A. Whitehead*, *Science and the Modern World* 17 (1925) ("There persists, however, throughout the whole period the fixed scientific cosmology which presupposes the ultimate fact of an irreducible brute matter, or material, spread throughout space in a flux of configurations. In itself such a material is senseless, valueless, purposeless. It just does what it does do, following a fixed routine imposed by external relations which do not spring from the nature of its being. It is this assumption that I call '*scientific materialism*.' Also it is an assumption which I shall challenge as being entirely unsuited to the scientific situation at which we have now arrived. It is not wrong, if properly construed. If we confine ourselves to certain types of facts, abstracted from the complete circumstances in which they occur,

the materialistic assumption expresses these facts to perfection. But when we pass beyond the abstraction, either by more subtle employment of our senses, or by the request for meanings and for coherence of thoughts, the scheme *breaks down* at once.") (italics added).

[282] Dobzhansky*, *A Biologist's World View*, 175 Science 49, 49 (1972) (italics added). *See also* T. Dobzhansky*, *The Uniqueness of Man* 43 (1969) ("Reductionism is now the semi-official creed of biological establishment.").

[283] Bethell*, *A Challenge to Materialism*, New Republic, Aug. 1, 1983, at 34, 34, 36 ("[T]he materialists have been waging war on the scientific pluralists. (How much better, after all, to officiate at the high altar than to sit in the pews.) It is not generally recognized, for example, that the current evolution/creation debate is an engagement in this war.").

[284] Provine* of Cornell writes:

> *Evolutionists* still disagree about the precise mechanisms of evolution in nature, but they have nevertheless given *overwhelming support* to Darwin's belief that design in nature results from *purely mechanistic causes*.... Here are the implications of this mechanistic view of life as I see them. First, except for purely mechanistic ones, no organizing or purposive principles exist in the world. There are no gods and no designing forces.

Provine*, *Implications of Darwin's Ideas on the Study of Evolution*, 32 BioScience 501, 506 (1982).

[285] A. Oparin*, *The Origin of Life* 33 (1953).

[286] Jastrow*, *The Astronomer and God*; in the Intellectuals Speak Out About God 15, 19 (R. Varghese* ed. 1984).

[287] G. Simpson*, *The Meaning of Evolution* 15 (1950) ("Nor is it necessary to suppose that the origin of the new processes of reproduction and mutation was anything but materialistic.").

[288] J. Greene*, *Science, Ideology and World View* 130 (1981) ("The oldest and most general component of the world view that came to be known as Darwinism was the idea of nature as a law-bound system of matter in motion, the mechanical view of nature (with its corollary of primary and secondary qualities) elaborated in the seventeenth century by Galileo, Descartes, Boyle, Newton, and others. To speculative thinkers like Descartes this mechanistic cosmology opened up the exhilarating prospect of deriving the present structures of nature—stars, solar systems, and others—from a previous, more homogeneous state of the universal system of matter in motion by the operation of the laws of nature. 'Give me extension and movement and I will remake the world,' said Descartes.").

[289] Elders*, *The Philosophical and Religious Background of Charles Darwin's Theory of Evolution*, 37 Doctor Communis 32, 35 (1984) (Address to Royal Spanish Academy of Sciences) ("Summing up, we can say that Darwinism is not metaphysically neutral, but holds a materialistic and atheistic monism, which also rejects the spirituality of the human mind. It demands strict uniformity in natural process and excludes God's special intervention as well as general Providence.").

[290] S. Gould*, *Hen's Teeth and Horse's Toes* 122 (1983).
[291] M. Denton*, *Evolution: A Theory in Crisis* 357-78 (1985).
[292] E. Wilson*, *On Human Nature* 196 (1978) (Harvard U. Press).
[293] Danto*, *Naturalism*, 5 Encyclopedia of Philosophy 448, 448 (P. Edwards* ed. 1967).
[294] *Id.*
[295] Wilshire* & Walsh*, *Metaphysics*, 12 Encyclopaedia Britannica: Macropaedia 10, 26 (15th ed. 1974).
[296] D. Oldroyd*, *Darwinian Impacts* 254 (1980).
[297] N. Gillespie*, *Charles Darwin and the Problem of Creation* xii (1979).
[298] Grene*, *The Faith of Darwinism*, Encounter, Nov. 1959, at 48, 48-49. *See also id.* at 48 ("under the benevolent banner of purely naturalistic nature"); I. Barbour*, *Science Ponders Religion* 200 (1960) ("To be sure, naturalism is still a live option, but it is clear that it must be defended as a philosophical viewpoint and not a conclusion of science.").
[299] N. Gillespie*, *Charles Darwin and the Problem of Creation* 8-9 (1979)
[300] *Id.* at 155-56.
[301] J. Greene*, *Science, Ideology and World View* 148-49 (1981) ("From the tradition of British empiricism and the *positivistic currents* of the nineteenth century they imbibed a sturdy faith in the methods of natural science as man's sole and sufficient means of acquiring knowledge of reality.").
[302] N. Gillespie*, *Charles Darwin and the Problem of Creation* 54, 61 (1979).
[303] C. Sagan*, *Cosmos* 4 (1980) (capitalization in original).
[304] C. Sagan*, *Cosmos*, tr. of television program (1981).
[305] Huxley*, *The Evolutionary Vision*, 3 Evolution After Darwin 249, 252 (S. Tax* & C. Callender* eds. 1960) ("[I]t is evolution, in the broad sense, that links inorganic nature with life, and the stars with the earth, and matter with mind, and animals with man. Human history is a continuation of biological evolution in a different form"); Section 14.1(g).
[306] Ayala*, *"Nothing in biology makes sense except in the light of evolution": Theodosius Dobzhansky*, 68 J. Heredity 3, 3 (1977) ("The place of biological evolution in human thought was, according to Dobzhansky, best expressed in a passage that he often quoted from Pierre Teilhard de Chardin, '[Evolution] is a general postulate to which all theories, all hypotheses, all systems must hence forward bow and which they must satisfy in order to be thinkable and true. Evolution is a light which illuminates all facts, a trajectory which all lines of thought must follow—this is what evolution is.' ") (bracket in original).
[307] *Id.*
[308] Beckner*, *Darwinism*, 2 Encyclopedia of Philosophy 296, 304 (P. Edwards* ed. 1967).
[309] R. Hofstadter*, *Social Darwinism in American Thought* 31, 45 (1955).
[310] Young*, *Darwinism* Is *Social*, in The Darwinian Heritage 609 (D. Kohn* ed. 1985).
[311] Hsü*, *Reply*, 15 Geology 177, 178 (1987).

[312] M. Midgley*, *Evolution as a Religion* 112 (1985).

[313] S. Gould*, *Ever Since Darwin* 26 (1977) (italics added).

[314] C. Zirkle*, *Evolution, Marxian Biology, and the Social Scene* 86 (1959).

[315] K. Marx*, *Marx and Engels on Religion* 295 (1964). *See also* J. Barzun*, *Darwin, Marx, Wagner* 8 (2d ed. 1958) ("Some of the biographical connections are of course well known. It is a commonplace that Marx felt his own work to be the exact parallel of Darwin's. He even wished to dedicate a portion of *Das Kapital* to the author of *The Origin of Species*."); Elders*, *The Philosophical and Religious Background of Charles Darwin's Theory of Evolution*, 37 Doctor Communis 1, 29 (1984) ("Darwinism became an important driving force in favour of materialism. . . . In a similar vein Friedrich Engels wrote to Marx: In one field teleology has not yet been destroyed. Darwin had now done this.").

[316] E. Yaroslavsky*, *Landmarks in the Life of Stalin* 8 (1940) (Moscow: Foreign Languages Publishing House).

[317] Ruse*, *Biology and Values: A Fresh Look*, in Logic, Methodology and Philosophy of Science 453, 455, 456 (B. Marcus* *et al.* eds. 1986).

[318] A. Oparin*, *The Origin of Life* 33 (1953).

[319] Ruse*, *Biology and Values: A Fresh Look*, in Logic, Methodology and Philosophy of Science 953, 456 (B. Marcus* *et al.* eds. 1986).

[320] R. Clark*, *The Life and Work of J.B.S. Haldane* 144, 283 (1968).

[321] M. Midgley*, *Evolution as a Religion* 35 (1985).

[322] Ruse*, *The New Dualism: "Res Philosophica" and "Res Historica"*, in Nature Animated 3, 18 (M. Ruse* ed. 1983).

[323] Gould* & Eldredge*, *Punctuated equilibria: The tempo and mode of evolution reconsidered*, 3 Paleobiology 115, 146 (1977) ("In the light of this official philosophy, it is not at all surprising that a punctuational view of speciation, much like our own, but devoid (so far as we can tell) of references to synthetic evolutionary theory and the allopatric model, has long been favored by many Russian paleontologists. It may also not be irrelevent to our personal preferences that one of us [Gould] learned *his Marxism*, literally, at his daddy's knee.").

[324] *Id.*; Gould*, *Evolution's Erratic Pace*, Natural History, May 1977, at 13, 16 ("In the Soviet Union, for example, scientists are trained with a very different philosophy of change—the so-called dialectical laws, reformulated by Engels from Hegel's philosophy. . . . Eldredge and I were fascinated to learn that most Russian paleontologists support a model very similar to our punctuated equilibria. The connection cannot be accidental.").

[325] S. Gould*, *Ontogeny and Phylogeny* 126-27, 130 (1977) (italics added). *See also* 2 T. Wallbank* & A. Taylor*, *Civilization Past and Present* 361 (4th ed. 1961) ("The pseudo-scientific application of biological theory to politics . . . constituted possibly the most perverted form of social Darwinism. . . . It led to racism and antisemitism and was used to show that only 'superior' nationalities and races were fit to survive.").

[326] 1 *The Life and Letters of Charles Darwin* 316 (F. Darwin* ed. 1888).
[327] Elders*, *The Philosophical and Religious Background of Charles Darwin's Theory of Evolution*, 37 Doctor Communis 1, 31 (1984) ("To a certain extent Darwin may be held responsible for this racism: in his *The Descent of Man* he repeatedly suggests that the black or primitive races stand between the animals and man. He compares the (bad) conduct of certain Indian tribes and of the Fijians with that of animals."); J. Greene*, *Science, Ideology, and World View* 150 (1981).
[328] C. Darwin*, *The Descent of Man* 241-42 (1901).
[329] J. Haller, Jr.*, *Outcasts from Evolution* 280 (1971).
[330] Brace*, *The Roots of the Race Concept in American Physical Anthropology*, in A History of American Physical Anthropology 496 (F. Spencer* ed. 1982).
[331] Provine*, *Book Review of Trial and Error: The American Controversy over Creation and Evolution*, Academe, Jan.-Feb. 1987, at 50, 51.
[332] Osborn*, *The Evolution of Human Races*, 89 Natural History, April 1980, at 129 ("This is the recognition that the genus *Homo* is subdivided into three absolutely distinct stocks, which in zoology would be given the rank of species, if not of genera, stocks popularly known as the Caucasian, the Mongolian, and the Negroid.... The standard of intelligence of the average adult Negro is similar to that of the eleven-year old youth of the species *Homo sapiens*.").
[333] E. Conklin*, *The Directions of Human Evolution* 34, 53 (1921).
[334] D. Oldroyd*, *Darwinian Impacts* 306 (1980).
[335] D. Gasman*, *The Scientific Origins of National Socialism: Social Darwinism in Ernst Haeckel and the German Monist League* xvi (1971) (italics added).
[336] Hitler*, *Mein Kampf* 239-40, 242 (4th ed. 1939).
[337] *Id.* at 286, 289 (1943).
[338] A. Keith*, *Evolution and Ethics* 10, 230 (1947).
[339] D. Oldroyd*, *Darwinian Impacts* 255 (1980).
[339A] Stein*, *Biological Science and the Roots of Naziism*, 76 Am. Scientist 50, 52 (1988).
[340] Section 13.4.
[341] Note 258.
[342] Note 260.
[343] Note 267.
[344] Note 272.
[345] Note 282.
[346] Note 298.
[347] Note 296.
[348] Note 299.
[349] Note 310.
[350] Note 309.

351 Note 312.
352 Note 313.
353 Note 325.
354 Note 328.
355 Note 335.
356 Note 338.

CHAPTER 14

Theories of Evolution and Abrupt Appearance and Consistency with Religion

> *Darwin. . .advanced falsifiable theories that have been falsified long ago . . . . And since falsified theories belong to the realm of metaphysics, we may infer that what were once 'empirical theories' have become religions.*
>
> —Soren Løvtrup* in *Darwinism*[1]

Another aspect of the non-religious nature of the theories of evolution and of abrupt appearance involves their acknowledged consistency with various religious faiths and their other areas of contact with religion. Just as the theory of abrupt appearance is consistent with (but different from) numerous religious faiths spanning the theological spectrum, the theory of evolution is equally consistent with many religious faiths that also encompass the full spectrum (Section 14.1 and 14.2):

*Theologians and others cited in Sections 14.1 and 14.3, unless otherwise indicated, are not proponents of, and their quoted statements are not intended as endorsements of, either the theory of abrupt appearance or the theory of creation. However, their quoted statements are acknowledging concepts that support the non-religious nature of the theories of abrupt appearance and evolution.

Theological Category	*Creationist Religions*	*Evolutionist Religions*
a. Protestant:	Conservative Evangelicalism and Fundamentalism, Church of Christ and Seventh-day Adventism	Religious Humanism and Unitarianism, Theological Liberalism and Neo-Orthodoxy
b. Catholic:	Much Orthodox Roman Catholicism and Eastern Orthodoxy	Neo-Modernist Roman Catholicism
c. Jewish:	Orthodox Judaism	Reform Judaism and Humanistic Judaism
d. Non-Judeo-Christian:	Islam (Muslims) and some Hinduism.	Buddhism and most Hinduism, Secular Humanism and other Humanist faiths, Nontheistic religions, and Atheism.

It is simply not accurate to say that the theory of abrupt appearance is primarily advocated by Fundamentalists while the theory of evolution is primarily advocated by scientists. Moreover, just as the theory of abrupt appearance is endorsed by some scientific writers with strong personal religious beliefs and publications, the theory of evolution has scientific proponents with strong religious beliefs and publications (Section 14.3).

The general parallels between the theory of evolution and the theory of creation recently were noted by Patterson*:

> So in general I am trying to suggest two themes. The first is that *evolutionism and creationism seem to have become very hard to distinguish*, particulary lately. I have just been showing how Gillespie's bitterest characterization of creationism seems to be, as I think, applicable to evolutionism—a sign that the two are very similar.
>
> . . ..
>
> So that is my first theme: that *evolution and creation seem to be sharing remarkable parallels* that are increasingly hard to tell apart.[2]

"Religious devotion . . . is probably the reason why severe methodological criticism employed in other departments of biology has not yet been brought to bear on evolutionary speculation," Conklin* of Princeton wrote[3] and Smith* of Syracuse University reiterates.[4]

Such harmony between scientific explanation and religious belief does not violate separation of church and state. As the United States Supreme Court said in *McGowan v. Maryland*,[5] "the 'Establishment' Clause does not ban federal or state regulation whose reason or effect merely happens to coincide or harmonize with the tenets of some or all religions."[6] The Court in *McGowan* sustained a Sunday closing law despite its consistency with many religions, and noted that "the fact that [the illegality of murder] agrees with the dictates of the Judaeo-Christian religions while it may disagree with others does not invalidate the regulation . . .. The same could be said of theft, fraud, etc., because those offenses were also proscribed in the Decalogue."[7] In *Harris v. McRae*,[8] the Supreme Court upheld a restriction on governmental funding of abortions despite consistency with Roman Catholicism and other religious belief.[9] For example, many people believe that Caesar Augustus was Emperor of Rome and that Nebuchadnezzar was King of Babylon on the basis of biblical references, yet those facts are also established by secular historical data. The mere mention of those facts in the Bible and the mere consistency of those facts with some religious views does not render either fact religious or make teaching either fact inappropriate in state institutions. The mere harmony or consistency of the theory of abrupt appearance and the theory of evolution with many religions and their doctrines logically should have the same consequence—it does not render either theory religious.

Figure 14.1
Asa Gray, the leading theistic evolutionist of the nineteenth century, whose theology included evolutionary doctrines; other "religions . . . have evolution as a central tenet" (Scheid*)*

14.1 Non-Religious Nature of the Consistency of the Theory of Evolution with Various Religions

Many religious faiths have evolutionist religious doctrines, and evolutionist religions span the entire religious spectrum to include Protestant, Catholic, Jewish, and non-Judeo-Christian faiths. A philosophy professor with a law degree, Scheid*, describes the evolutionist religions from his anticreationist vantage point:

> Most people would characterize one or more of the following as religions: Secular Humanism, Theological Liberalism and Buddhism. *Evolution is an important doctrine of each of these religions.* Arguably, Secular Humanism and Buddhism were recognized as "religions" within the meaning of the establishment clause in *Torcaso v. Watkins*.... The Court added a footnote: "Among religions in this country which do not teach what would be considered a belief in the existence of God are Buddhism, Taoism, Ethical Culture, Secular Humanism and others."
>
> ... It can hardly be doubted that the *teaching of evolution might lend some support to religions that have evolution as a central tenet.* This is so even if the tenet of evolution is logically separable from the other tenets that make up the body of doctrine of a given religion.[10]

The theory of evolution is, in fact, harmonious or consistent with as many religions and to the same extent that the theory of abrupt appearance is. Examples of evolutionist religions are:

Protestant:	a. Religious Humanism and Unitarianism
	b. Theological Liberalism
	c. Neo-Orthodoxy
Catholic:	d. Neo-Modernist Roman Catholicism
Jewish:	e. Reform Judaism and Humanistic Judaism
Non-Judeo-Christian:	f. Buddhism and most Hinduism
	g. Secular Humanism and other Humanist faiths
	h. Nontheistic religions
	i. Atheism.

Those evolutionist religions are evident in the recent theological book entitled *Is God a Creationist? The Religious Case Against Creation-Science*,[11] and in the one-sided article entitled "*Religious Leaders' Views on the Theory of Evolution*."[12] The point here is not that evolution is religious, but that the theories of evolution and abrupt appearance are non-religiously parallel in that evolutionist religious doctrines are held by the many religions that are described in the following paragraphs.

a. Evolutionary Consistency with Religious Humanism and Unitarianism

There are a number of varieties of Humanism, such as "religious-humanism, ethical-humanism, scientific-humanism, evolutionary-humanism, and secular-humanism."[13] Most Humanist organizations state explicitly that they are religious in their organizational documents and in their publications. Courts have generally agreed that Humanism is a religion, as Section 14.1(g) discusses. The long-standing self-descriptions of Humanist organizations should be accepted at face value, despite their newly-found and convenient positions that Humanism does not exist or does not speak seriously when claiming to be religious.

Those contrived positions place Humanism in the unique position of being the only ideology to deny its own existence and influence! However, both features are acknowledged in a highly academic book written by Ehrenfeld* of Rutgers and published recently by Oxford University Press, *The Arrogance of Humanism*:

> *Humanism is one of the vital religions*, perhaps no longer growing but very much alive. *It is the dominant religion of our time*, a part of the lives of nearly everyone in the "developed" world and of all others who want to participate in a similar development. There is very little ritual in humanism, and *most of its devout followers do not seem to be aware that they are humanists*. Ask them for the name of their religion and they will deny having one, or more commonly, name one of the traditional faiths. On the other hand, people who consider themselves humanists usually are—frequently, however, for reasons other than the ones they know and admit.[14]

Humanism is "an ideology that is unquestioningly adopted" by modern man, philosopher Ellul* adds.[15]

(1) Religious Nature of Many Forms of Humanism. Philosopher Paul Kurtz* knows as much about Humanism as anyone, as author of *In Defense of Secular Humanism*, editor of *Free Inquiry*, former editor of *The Humanist* (publication of the American Humanist Association), and compiler of the *Secular Humanist Declaration*. He candidly acknowledges that all but one of the Humanist organizations are concededly religious:

> But is secular humanism a religion? The lawyers in this [Alabama] case insist that it is and they subpoenaed the *bylaws and other documents of the major U.S. humanist organizations* to prove it. The organized humanist movement in America is put in a quandary; for the Fellowship of Religious Humanists (300 members), the American Ethical Union (3,000 members), and the Society for Humanistic Judaism (4,000 members) *consider themselves to be religious*. Even the American

> Humanist Association (3,500 members), which has both religious and nonreligious members and is often considered to be a 'naturalistic humanist' association, has a *religious tax exemption.* (I should point out that I and others have repeatedly urged the AHA to abandon its religious exemption, but to no avail.) *Regrettably there are no humanist membership organizations that are nonreligious in legal status.* The *only* exception is the Council for Democratic and Secular Humanism (publisher of FREE INQUIRY magazine), which has a nonprofit *educational* exemption, but as yet has not been a membership organization.[16]

Contrary to the implication that Humanism is a numerically insignificant viewpoint, Kurtz* might have included the Unitarian-Universalist Church (131,844 members[17]), as described below, and might have credited Humanistic Judaism with "30,000 followers."[18] Before he began to try to make Humanism an invisible religion, Kurtz* argued that "humanism is the *dominant moral and religious point of view* in this scientific age among our intellectual and educated classes, though some may not be aware that they are humanists."[19]

Religious Humanism is represented by the first *Humanist Manifesto*,[20] which was signed primarily by theologians.[21] It characterized its position as describing the "religion" of the "[r]eligious humanists,"[22] and its communicants agreed.[23] John Dewey*, the "most influential" modern educator, signed and substantially drafted that *Humanist Manifesto*,[24] and saw Humanism as "a religious faith."[25]

One current group that advocates Religious Humanism is the Fellowship of Religious Humanists, which is concededly religious,[26] as is evident in articles in *Religious Humanism* magazine by Mason*,[27] Hemstreet*,[28] Farmer*,[29] Beattie*,[30] and Haydon*.[31] It is "affiliated with the American Ethical Union, the American Humanist Association, the Unitarian-Universalist Association, and the International Humanist and Ethical Union," as well as the "Society for Humanistic Judaism."[32]

The American Humanist Association was organized by "a group composed primarily of liberal ministers and professors who were predominantly Unitarians and considered themselves religious humanists," according to a former president[33] (although it currently inclines toward Secular Humanism and other varieties of Humanism). It regularly publishes articles advocating a religious variety of Humanism, such as by Wilson*,[34] Arisian*,[35] Larue*,[36] Samson*,[37] and Skolimowski.*[38] There are many other Religious Humanists.[39] *The Churchman* is an "independent journal of religious humanism."[40]

"Unitarianism has created more humanists than any other movement in America" and is "closest to a distinctively humanist religion," according to Beattie*, a president of the Fellowship of Religious Humanists and co-editor of *Religious Humanism*.[41] Morain*, former president of the American Humanist Association, agrees.[42] "[O]ne hundred seventy Unitarian Universalist ministers" signed *Humanist Manifesto II*.[43]

Religious Humanism is not merely an armchair religion, but one that seeks to provide "proselytizers of a new faith" and to "utiliz[e] a classroom instead of a pulpit to convey humanist values in whatever subject they teach," according to Dunphy* in the periodical *The Humanist*:

> I am convinced that the battle for humankind's future must be waged and won in the *public school classroom* by *teachers* who correctly perceive their role as the *proselytizers of a new faith*: a *religion* of humanity that recognizes and respects the spark of what theologians call divinity in every human being. These teachers must embody the same selfless dedication as the most rabid fundamentalist preachers, for they will be *ministers* of another sort, utilizing a classroom instead of a pulpit to *convey humanist values* in *whatever subject they teach*, regardless of the educational level—preschool day care or large state university. The classroom must and will become an arena of conflict between the old and the new—the rotting corpse of Christianity, together with all its adjacent evils and misery, and the *new faith of humanism* . . ..
>
> . . . It will undoubtedly be a long, arduous, painful struggle replete with much sorrow and many tears, but humanism will emerge triumphant. It must if the family of humankind is to survive.[44]

Similarly, the co-founder and leader of the Society for Humanistic Judaism calls for an effort to proselytize and to share eagerly that faith:

> Many liberals who think it perfectly appropriate to *proselytize* actively for nuclear freezes and abortion freedom resent the same enthusiasm when it is applied to religion. This attitude prevents us from being effective. If we, as humanists and Humanistic Jews, have something important to say about the path to self-esteem, *we should be eager to share it*. . . .[45]

Other Humanists seek to "recruit" the unaffiliated[46] and are "promoting" their faith and "organizing groups."[47]

(2) Evolutionary Doctrines of Humanism. Evolution is an important point of Religious Humanist doctrine. Four of the fifteen points of *Humanist Manifesto I* explicitly affirm evolution; point 1 states that "Religious Humanists regard the universe as self-existing and not created," while point 2 affirms the evolution of man.[48] In the

early part of this century, other Religious Humanists affirmed evolution, such as Potter*,[49] Dietrich*, and Reese*.[50] Evolution is central to that faith, according to Morain*, a former president of the American Humanist Association:

> There are, however, certain specific ideas which have gone into the making of *modern humanism*. Seven of these, although at some points shading into one another, seem to us to stand out.
>
> . . ..
>
> *Things Evolve*
>
> . . ..
>
> In the first shock of this discovery most felt that a common ancestry with animals lowered the human race to a level with them. There were others, however, who sensed that in the idea of *evolution* there lay cause for special encouragement. . . . The idea that men can turn the process of evolution to their own advantage to further their own highest good, and to recreate the world and themselves, is at the *very center* of present-day humanism.[51]

Modern Religious Humanists still stress belief in evolution, as Wine*, the co-founder of the Society for Humanistic Judaism, states:

> Humanists not only do not believe in Biblical creation; *they do believe in evolution*. They not only do not believe in the efficacy of prayer; they do believe in the power of human effort and responsibility. They not only do not believe in the reality of the supernatural; they do believe in the natural origin of all experiences.[52]

"[B]eing religious as a liberal humanist involves seeking to further the process of cosmic evolution," Hemstreet* adds.[53] Humanist belief in evolution is evident in the publication *Religious Humanism*,[54] and in articles by Sellars*[55] and Levine*.[56]

b. Evolutionary Consistency with Theological Liberalism

Theological Liberalism also encompasses a doctrinal belief in evolution. Theological Liberalism arose through the primary "formative factor" of evolution, Cauthen*[57] and *Encyclopaedia Britannica*[58] point out. Its leading theologians have almost all incorporated evolution into their theology.

(1) *Late Nineteenth Century*. The leading Darwinists in the late nineteenth century are discussed in a recent scholarly book by Moore* entitled *The Post-Darwinian Controversies* (published by Cambridge University Press), and their evolutionary theology is described as follows:

> The Darwinists, in contrast, were overwhelmingly committed to theological reconstruction. There were neologians, striving to assimilate

faith to scientific speculation and religious experience, discarding traditional views whenever expedient and rendering the residue in a form acceptable to their contemporaries. St. George Mivart's autonomous rationalism earned him the epithet '*modernist*' and brought about his *expulsion from the Roman Catholic Church.* Frederick Temple fared somewhat differently in the Church of England, becoming archbishop of Canterbury, but this despite his consistent latitudinarianism, from his contribution to *Essays and Reviews* onwards. John Bascom rejected the 'perverse theory' of Calvinism on which he had been reared and elaborated a philosophy which 'belonged to the most *liberal form of Christian apologetics*'. Joseph Le Conte was—to use his own words—at 'first orthodox of the orthodox; later as thought germinated and grew apace, I adopted a liberal interpretation of orthodoxy; then, gradually I became unorthodox; then, in deep sympathy with the most *liberal movement* of Christian thought; and finally, to some extent, a leader in that movement'. Thomas Howard MacQueary's evolutionary and iconoclastic approach to Christian doctrines cost him his clerical career in the first outcome of a *heresy trial* in the history of the Protestant Episcopal Church. Lyman Abbott, believing the New Theology to be an advance over the New School Calvinism he had formerly accepted, was America's leading representative of evangelical *liberalism.* Francis Howe Johnson, perhaps the weightiest of the 'Andover *liberals*,' also moved far from his Calvinist heritage in assimilating Christian doctrine to a personalist philosophy. George Matheson, a 'conspicuous representative of *liberal theology*,' retained the doctrinal forms of conventional Calvinist orthodoxy but invested them with a new Hegelio-Spencerian meaning. 'I am as broad as can be,' he said, 'but it is a broad positive.' Henry Ward Beecher was *similarly expansive*, though with neither the philosophical sophistication nor the consistently positive approach. 'I am an evolutionist,' he declared, 'and that strikes at the root of all medieval and orthodox modern theology.' Minot Judson Savage and John Fiske, like Beecher, jettisoned Calvinism for the theological liberties of the *Synthetic Philosophy* but both became *Unitarians* in the process. Henry Drummond was twice subjected to *charges of heresy*, in 1892 and 1895, and on the latter occasion no less than twelve overtures were made to the General Assembly of the Free Church of Scotland regarding his *Ascent of Man.*[59]

The evolutionary element in early Theological Liberalism is evident in the writings of each of Moore's Darwinists, and the religious support for evolution is evident in the clerical profession of nearly every leading Darwinist (as quoted in the footnotes):

Rev. Frederick Temple* (Anglican, Archbishop of Canterbury)[60]
Rev. Henry Ward Beecher* (Congregational minister)[61]
Rev. George Henslow* (Anglican minister and botanist)[62]

Hon. George Douglas Campbell*, Duke of Argyll (politician)[63]
Dr. St. George Mivart* (Roman Catholic lay theologian and biologist)[64]
Rev. John Bascom* (Congregational minister and professor)[65]
Rev. Henry Drummond* (Free Church minister)[66]
Rev. Thomas Howard MacQueary* (Episcopal minister)[67]
Rev. Lyman Abbott* (Congregational minister)[68]
Rev. Francis Howe Johnson* (Congregational minister)[69]
Rev. George Matheson* (Church of Scotland minister)[70]
Rev. Minot Judson Savage* (Church of the Unity minister)[71]
Rev. John Fiske* (Congregational then Unitarian philosopher)[72]
Rev. Joseph S. Van Dyke* (Presbyterian minister)[73]
Rev. James Iverach* (Free Church minister)[74]
Rev. Aubrey Lackinton Moore* (Anglican minister).[75]

The central role of evolution in their theology is reflected in such titles of their books as Beecher's* *Evolution and Religion*, Henslow's* *Genesis and Geology*, MacQueary's* *The Evolution of Man and Christianity*, Abbott's* *The Theology of an Evolutionist*, and Savage's* *Evolution and Religion from the Standpoint of One Who Believes in Both.*

Ahlstrom*, the dean of American religious historians, describes the "evolutionary theophanies" of the Theological Liberals:

> When men outside the church could speak in this manner of Darwinism, it goes without saying that many other liberal Christian thinkers would sing evolutionary theophanies as well. . . . Abbott (1835-1922), a bolder exponent, in *The Evolution of Christianity* (1892) sought to show that "in the spiritual, as in the physical, God is the secret and source of light." Accordingly, Abbott spoke of the evolution of the Bible, the Church, Christian Society, and the Soul.[76]

The table of contents of Abbott's* later book, *The Theology of an Evolutionist*, shows that Alstrom* does not exaggerate:

I. Some Definitions
II. Creation by Evolution
III. The Genesis of Sin
IV. The Evolution of Revelation
V. The Place of Christ in Evolution
VI. Redemption by Evolution
VII. Evolution and Sacrifice
VIII. Evolution and Propitiation
IX. Evolution and Miracles
X. Evolution and Miracles (continued)
XI. Evolution and Immortality
XII. A Summary of Conclusions[77]

He simply claimed that "[t]he doctrine of evolution, in its radical form, is the doctrine that all God's processes are processes of growth,—not processes of manufacture."[78] Beecher* similarly wrote:

> In every view of it, I think we are to expect great practical fruit from the application of the truths that flow now from the application of *Evolution*. . . . Old men may be charitably permitted to die in peace, but young men and men in their prime are by God's providence laid under the most solemn obligations to thus discern the signs of the times, and to make themselves acquainted with the knowledge which science is laying before them.[79]

The leading evolutionists were primarily theologians during the late nineteenth century, while the leading antievolutionists and creationists were generally scientists.[80]

(2) *Early Twentieth Century*. The foremost Theological Liberals in the early twentieth century discarded the religious doctrine of creation for a religious doctrine of theistic evolution, and popularized the incommensurability approach, Gilkey* states:

> Mainly as a result of the creative and courageous efforts of the *liberal theologians*, the "prescientific science" of the biblical account of creation has at last been separated out from the profound religious affirmation contained in that account. The inquiries of the physical sciences and those of theology are now seen to be asking fundamentally different kinds of questions, in *totally different areas* of thought and experience. Consequently the answers to these questions, the hypotheses of science, and the affirmations or doctrines of theology, cannot and do not conflict. *Religious myth* has finally become that for which it was most aptly fitted: a symbolic story expressing the religious answer to man's ultimate questions. . . .[81]

The leading Theological Liberals readily can be identified from *Encyclopaedia Britannica*,[82] and evolutionary doctrines easily can be found throughout their theology:

Rev. Edward Scribner Ames*[83]
Rev. William Newton Clarke*[84]
Rev. George A. Coe*[85]
Rev. Harry Emerson Fosdick*[86]
Rev. Shailer Mathews*[87]
Rev. Walter Rauschenbusch*[88]
Rev. Ernst Troeltsch*.[89]

For example, Fosdick*, whom Ahlstrom* calls "the nation's most influential Protestant preacher"[90] and the pastor of the nation's largest congregation, wrote that "[w]e hold a worldview whose structural bases were not laid down by Moses in the thirteenth century B.C.," but by "the evolutionary hypothesis."[91] Rauschenbusch*, who named the social gospel, was as explicit:

> Translate the evolutionary theories into religious faith, and you have the

> doctrine of Kingdom of God. This combination with scientific evolutionary thought has freed the kingdom ideal of its catastrophic setting and its background of demonism, and so applied it to the climate of the modern world.[92]

Many other examples exist such as Aveling*,[93] Lyon*,[94] Macintosh*,[95] and Millikan*.[96]

The Theological Liberal faction in the mainline Protestant denominations similarly affirmed evolution, as is discussed in Section 15.1(b).

(3) Late Twentieth Century. Theological Liberalism at present still holds to a religious belief in evolution, as Miller*[97] and Stiernotte*[98] state. Liberal theology typically embraces theistic evolution, Miller* and Fowler* indicate,[99] and the innumerable examples include Anderson* in *The Interpreter's Dictionary of the Bible*[100] and Speisor* in the *Anchor Bible* commentary on Genesis.[101] The National Council of Churches, in a liturgy for a national meeting, recited from Teilhard de Chardin* that, "Whosoever has discovered . . . the secret of serving the evolving Universe . . ., Blessing and honor, glory and power be unto him. Amen."[102]

Theological Liberalism is a viewpoint held by a large number of churches, as shown by a Roper survey of seminary professors[103] and a sociologist's survey of ministers nationally[104]:

Religion	*Ministers*	*Seminary Professors*
United Methodists	33.8%	69%
Episcopals	25.7%	78%
American Baptists	17.9%	54%
United Presbyterian Church	18.4%	63%
American Lutheran Church/Lutheran	12.9%	52%
United Church of Christ	—	53%

c. *Evolutionary Consistency with Neo-Orthodoxy*

Neo-Orthodoxy also generally incorporates evolution. Its leading exponents have been Karl Barth*, Reinhold Niebuhr*, Emil Brunner*, Rudolf Bultmann*, and Paul Tillich*, according to *Encyclopaedia Britannica.*[105] While Barth* "has specialized in ambiguity on the whole matter,"[106] evolution has an important place in the theological writings of the other spokesman. Niebuhr* viewed creation as a "myth,"[107] and Brunner* devoted a chapter to "The Growth of Man and the Doctrine of Evolution,"[108] and elsewhere celebrated "the victory of the scientific view" of evolution.[109]

Tillich* adhered to evolution and decried "the misguided attacks on it on the part of traditional religion."[110]

Tillich* stated the following as part of his *Systematic Theology*:

> The dynamics of nature create the new by producing individuality in the smallest parts as well as in the largest composites of nature and also by producing *new species* in the *evolutionary process* and *new constellations of matter* in the extensions and contractions of the *universe*. . . .
>
> . . ..
>
> . . . If this were true, there would be no prehistorical man, and historical man would be a "*creation out of nothing*." But all empirical evidence stands *against* such an assumption. Prehistorical man is that organic being which is predisposed to actualize the dimensions of spirit and history and which in his development drives toward their actualization. There is *no identifiable moment when animal self-awareness becomes human spirit* and when human spirit enters the historical dimension. . . . If *evolution* proceeded only by leaps, one could identify the result of each leap. If *evolution* proceded only by a slow transformation, no radical change could be noticed at all. But *evolutionary processes* combine both the leap and the slow change, and therefore, although one can distinguish the results, one cannot fix the moments in which they appear. The darkness which veils prehistorical mankind is not a matter of preliminary scholarly failure but rather of the indefiniteness of all *evolutionary processes* with respect to the appearance of the new. . . .[111]

Neo-Orthodoxy and evolution are joined in such other theologians as Gilkey*[112] and Hyers*, who also gives a theological criticism of a scientific theory of creation.[113] Neo-Orthodoxy is embraced by large elements within several major Protestant denominations as well as within Roman Catholicism.[114]

d. Evolutionary Consistency with Neo-Modernist Roman Catholicism

Neo-Modernist Roman Catholicism generally holds evolution as part of its theology (just as Orthodox Roman Catholicism often or generally accepts creation). A book on Neo-Modernist Catholicism (published by Harvard) observes that divergence:

> *Conservatives* stubbornly defended the belief that God created man directly, constituting him a species immutably distinct from all other animals. . . . The *liberals* followed Asa Gray and John Fiske in believing *evolution* perfectly compatible with theism. . . . Zahm agreed with Fiske that this view was more devout than one which confined God's creativity to the first days of the world; it enabled the 'unbiased and reverent' to see 'in nature the evidence of a Power which is originative, directive, immanent.' *Liberal Catholics* agreed with the age that with God thus taking an

active part in the world's progress, it was easy to believe in indefinite *evolution* 'onward and upward.' Some of the liberals flatly asserted that man's body, like other physical forms, had *evolved* from lower animals.[115]

In the nineteenth century after Darwin*, the censure of Zahm* for Modernist evolutionary views is recounted by Ahlstrom*:

> Modernism is the usual Roman Catholic term for the movement condemned by Pope Pius X in the encyclical *Pascenti Gregis* of 1907. . . . Far more publicized was the case of Father John A. Zahm, a professor at Notre Dame University. During the very years when the Americanism agitation was at its height, the Holy Office ruled that his pro-Darwinian *Evolution and Dogma* (1896) could not be translated into other languages, and for a time threatened to put it on the Index. Zahm was, in effect, silenced. . . .[116]

Mivart*, whose evolutionary theology was mentioned earlier, had evolutionary articles "placed on the Vatican's index of forbidden readings, and further controversial articles led to Mivart's excommunication . . ..''[117]

In the first half of the twentieth century, the evolutionary doctrines of Neo-Modernist Catholicism were exemplified in the theological publications of Pierre Teilhard de Chardin*, who wrote:

> C. A NEW MYSTICAL ORIENTATION:
> THE LOVE OF *EVOLUTION*
>
> II. Reduced to the initial and still crude form in which it is now emerging in the modern world, the *new religious spirit* appears, as we have said (cf. I), as the impassioned vision and anticipation of some super-mankind. . . . To believe and to serve was not enough: we now find that it is becoming not only possible but imperative literally to *love evolution.*
>
> 12. Analyzed from the Christian point of view, as spontaneously and necessarily born from contact between faith in Christ and faith in the world, *love of evolution* is not a mere extension of love of God to one further object. It corresponds to a radical reinterpretation (one might almost say it emerges from a recasting of the notion of charity).[118]

He wrote many such works,[119] and his evolutionary theology is described by Jaki*,[120] Birx*,[121] and Delfgaauw*.[122] Teilhard de Chardin* was forbidden to publish or teach on philosophical subjects, suffered the banning of one book and the refusal to publish others, and was the subject of a "monitum, or simple warning, against uncritical acceptance of his ideas" issued by the Holy Office under Pope John XXIII in 1962.[123]

More recently, the leading Neo-Modernists have incorporated evolution in their theology. Schillebeeckx*, "arguably the most influential Catholic Continental theologian on the church as a whole,"[124] combined evolution with theology.[125] Rahner*, "the most renowned contemporary Catholic theologian,"[126] did the same, saying that "Creation can be understood as an evolutionary movement intended by God to reach its finality in Christ,"[127] and using such titles as "Evolution and Original Sin."[128] Küng*, who "might be a rival" for the claim of greatest influence,[129] fuses evolution with theology, and "was the object of a previously unheard of Vatican document, a Declaration that he 'can no longer be considered a Catholic theologian or function as such in a teaching role.' "[130] Brown*, a prolific and influential American Catholic, similarly combines Neo-Modernism with evolution.[131] Neo-Modernism, while accepted by only a minority of the Roman Catholic laity and clergy, is advocated by a majority of its theological faculty in America.[132]

e. Evolutionary Consistency with Reform Judaism and Humanistic Judaism

Reform Judaism generally includes doctrinal belief in evolution (just as Orthodox Judaism embraces belief in creation).[133] That is evident in the new Reform Jewish commentary on the Torah, which calls the creation accounts in Genesis "antiquated myths" and instead prefers "evolution."[134]

Humanistic Judaism is the viewpoint of the Society for Humanistic Judaism, its periodical *Humanistic Judaism*,[135] and the International Federation of Secular Humanist Judaism.[136] Its advocates describe it as religious, such as Rabbi Wine*,[137] Friedman*,[138] and Borowitz*.[139]

f. Evolutionary Consistency with Buddhism and Most Hinduism

Buddhism holds to an evolutionary doctrine, in viewing the universe as always existing with developmental cycles while denying a divine creator.[140] Most Hinduism also embraces evolution.[141]

g. Evolutionary Consistency with Secular Humanism and Other Humanist Faiths

Secular Humanism does indeed exist. It is true that there are many varieties of Humanism,[142] including Secular Humanism,[143] Naturalistic Humanism,[144] Scientific Humanism,[145] Atheistic Humanism,[146] Evolutionary Humanism,[147] and Religious Humanism (discussed earlier). Secular Humanism is defined in *A Secular Humanist Declaration*, which many people signed,[148] in the book *In*

Defense of Secular Humanism,[149] and by Fletcher*,[150] Kurtz*,[151] and DeFord*.[152] Thus, Secular Humanism "is not simply the practice of being humane," and "does not mean 'the pursuit of the humanities'," Ehrenfeld*[153] and Giustiniani*[154] note. Not only does Secular Humanism exist, but in fact "American secular humanism is manifesting its potency in altering long-held doctrine and practice . . .," Pfeffer* writes.[155]

(1) Religious Nature of Humanism. Secular Humanism and other Humanist faiths are regarded as religions by most proponents. Kurtz* concedes that many Humanists see their views as a religion:[156]

> [H]umanistic values *function religiously. Humanistic religion*, as distinct from humanistic philosophy, thus involves: (1) expressive elements; that is, it appeals to the whole man, including his attitudes and emotions, and not simply his reason; (2) social organization, shared experiences, ways and methods of acting out and performing moral principles; and (3) commitments to ideal ends. . . .[157]

The American Humanist Association "acknowledges that many of its' [*sic*] members regard their Humanism as a religion."[158] Many Humanists also admit the religious nature of Secular Humanism, such as Haydon*[159] and Beattie*,[160] and some sourcebooks on religion agree, such as the article in *Encyclopaedia Britannica*[161] and Rosten's* guide to religions.[162]

Humanist ministers perform normal clerical functions, as the American Humanist Association states:

> As the legal equivalent of ministers, priests, or rabbis, Humanist Counselors, AHA, certified by the American Humanist Association, solemnize marriages and officiate at memorials, namings, and other rights of passage. Counselors also may act as chaplains on campuses and in prisons, hospitals, and other institutions where the presence of a nontraditional or nontheistic minister is often a need.
>
> Just as ministers are authorized to counsel those who come to them in personal difficulty, so are Humanist Counselors, AHA.[163]

As a religion, Humanism seeks to influence others through many means including through public schools:

> *Public Education*
>
> Education has always been the cardinal activity and the main hope of a humanist movement. . . .[164]

Humanistic Judaism includes Secular Humanist elements, as exemplified by Silberman*,[165] Weisman*,[166] Bain*,[167] Chuman*,[168] Levinrew*,[169] Bauer*,[170] Jerris*,[171] and Mirsky*.[172] Organizations holding a Secular Humanist faith include the Congress of Secular and Humanistic Jews,[173] the International Federation of Secular

Humanist Jews,[174] and the loose movement of "Secularistic Judaism."[175]

Courts generally have treated Secular Humanism as a religion. The United States Supreme Court has recognized the religious nature of "a 'religion of secularism'," [176] as have commentators such as Harvey Cox* of Harvard:

> Secularism . . . is the name for an ideology, a new closed world view which functions very much like a new religion. . . . [I]t must therefore be watched carefully to prevent its becoming the ideology of a new establishment. It must be especially checked where it pretends not to be a world view but nonetheless seeks to impose its ideology through the organs of the state.[177]

The U.S. Supreme Court also has recognized (in a unanimous decision) that "[a]mong religions in this country . . . are . . . Secular Humanism and others," in *Torcaso v. Watkins*.[178] Other courts have treated that language as a holding that "recognized Secular Humanism as a religion," in the words of the Eighth Circuit of the U.S. Court of Appeals.[179] An earlier decision of the Ninth Circuit similarly treated "Comte's humanism" as a "religion,"[180] and the District of Columbia Circuit referred to "creeds like Humanism."[181] In a concurring opinion of the Supreme Court, Justice Brennan* referred to impermissible discrimination between theistic faiths and "nonorthodox humanistic faiths."[182] A number of other federal court[183] and state court[184] decisions, as well as some conscientious objector statutory decisions,[185] have treated Humanism as a religion.

Numerous commentators have reached the same conclusion,[186] such as Dencer in the *Yale Law Journal*:

> In its most common forms, Secular Humanism assumes the irrelevance of supernatural phenomena, regards man as a natural object, asserts man's innate goodness and potential to achieve self-realization through reason, and views man as the sole and ultimate judge of his own morality. By many definitions, *Secular Humanism is a religion*, and the courts have in fact, at least for certain purposes, characterized it as a religion.[187]

Ehrenfeld* of Rutgers concurs:

> Is *humanism a religion?* This is a more difficult question, and the entire book will have to serve as a complete answer. But I am not being hasty when I point out that *if humanism is not a religion it certainly does act like one.* Its adherents eat, sleep, work, and play according to its central doctrine, they recite the rosary of humanism as they make their most important plans, and they receive the last rites of humanism as they try to avoid dying. . . . In some details humanism is not like other religions. There are no buildings labeled "Church of Humanism" in your neighborhood, and humanist missionaries will not knock at your door. There is

> no organized humanist priesthood, although the unofficial priests of humanism are in high and low stations everywhere. But in its most significant respects *humanism now is a religion*, even if it is not a religion of the ordinary kind.[188]

And Congress has agreed in forbidding certain funding for the "religion of secular humanism."[189]

(2) Evolutionary Doctrine of Humanism. Most Humanist faiths include a doctrinal belief in evolution, as DeFord*,[190] Lamont*,[191] Saladin*,[192] Harneck*,[193] and the following examples show. Secular Humanism and other Humanist faiths are represented by two principal statements. *Humanist Manifesto II* emphasizes evolution in such passages as that "science affirms that the human species is an emergence from natural evolutionary forces."[194] That *Manifesto* was signed by "one hundred seventy Unitarian Universalist ministers,"[195] as well as twenty-nine American Ethical Union ministers and many other Humanist clergy.[196] *A Secular Humanist Declaration* similarly lists evolution as one of ten points, and states that "the evolution of the species is supported so strongly by the weight of evidence that it is difficult to reject it . . .."[197]

The link between evolution and Humanism is described by Oldroyd* as follows:

> But in some quarters there was a much more positive response, with new *quasi-religious systems* of a curious secular character being *built on the foundation provided by the new evolutionism.*
>
> . . . Much more widespread, and of far greater significance, was the general philosophical movement known as *humanism*; and this—also *a kind of secular religion—drew very considerably on evolutionism* in general and the Darwin/Wallace theory in particular.
>
> Humanism is not a new philosophical movement, but it has only come into wide esteem and prominence in the twentieth century. . . . Corliss Lamont has listed ten of the major *tenets* of the humanist movement as:
> [1] naturalism;
> [2] the idea that man is an *evolutionary* product of nature;
> . . ..
>
> The first two items on the list of Lamont's articles of faith are *intimately related to the Darwinian Revolution. . . .*
>
> . . ..
>
> So a metaphysical system, although naturalistic and secular, has been built up by *modern humanists around the nucleus of biological evolutionism. . . .*[198]

Similarly, Lamont* writes that "humanism, drawing especially upon the laws and facts of science, believes that man is an evolutionary product of the Nature of which he is part,"[199] and Larue* says that "[w]e see the human as the end product of the more than 17 billion years of evolution of the cosmos . . .."[200] It should be no surprise that the "Humanist of the Year" award has been conferred by the American Humanist Association on such leading evolutionist scientists as Carl Sagan (1981) and Isaac Asimov (1984) (who thereafter became its president).

"Evolutionary Humanism as a Developed Religion" is the concluding chapter of a book of Sir Julian Huxley*, a prominent evolutionist,[201] who described that religion in many publications[202] as follows:

> On the basis of our present understanding, all reality is in a perfectly valid sense one universal process of *evolution*. The single process occurs in three phases. . . .
>
> . . ..
>
> The new framework of ideas on which any new dominant *religion* will be based is *at once evolutionary and humanist*. For evolutionary humanism, gods are creations of man, not vice versa. . . .
>
> *Evolutionary Humanism*
>
> The beliefs of this *religion of evolutionary humanism* are not based on revelation in the supernatural sense, but on the revelations that science and learning have given us about man and the universe.[203]

Oldroyd* points out "the existence of evolutionary humanism as a philosophical system and its affinities with religious modes of thinking."[204] Evolutionary Humanism, like Secular Humanism and other Humanist faiths, obviously incorporates and stresses evolution as a doctrine.[205]

h. Evolutionary Consistency with Nontheistic Religions

Other Nontheistic religions similarly include evolutionist doctrines. Scientology rejoices that its primary sacrament serves "to vindicate the theory of evolution proposed by Darwin . . .."[206] Theosophists "see in it [evolution] the only universal and eternal reality."[207] Anthroposophy also is an evolutionist faith.[208]

i. Evolutionary Consistency with Atheism

Atheism generally holds to a doctrinal belief in evolution, as Brown*,[209] Bock*,[210] Gurley*,[211] and Bozarth*[212] manifest in the *American Atheist*. Many leading evolutionists who were Atheists have been mentioned earlier.[213] Although many Atheists do not regard their viewpoint as religious, it has been treated as religious along with any other secularistic world view for purposes of the Establishment Clause of the Constitution.[214]

Summary. Both the theory of evolution and the theory of abrupt appearance are different from religion, but are comparably consistent with various theistic evolutionist and creationist religions. "Most people would characterize one or more of the following as religions: Secular Humanism, Theological Liberalism and Buddhism. Evolution is an important doctrine of each of these religions" (Scheid*[215]). In its many varieties, "Humanism is one of the vital religions, perhaps no longer growing but very much alive. It is the dominant religion of our time" (Ehrenfeld*[216]). Humanism is religious in organization (Kurtz*[217]), profession (*Humanist Manifestos I and II*,[218] *Secular Humanist Declaration*[219]), and publications (Kurtz*[220]). It is a pervasively evolutionist faith (*Humanist Manifesto I*,[221] *Humanist Manifesto II*,[222] *Secular Humanist Declaration*[223]), and one sect is the "religion of evolutionary humanism" (Huxley*[224]). Theological Liberalism also embodies evolutionist doctrines: "Liberal religious leaders and theologians . . . proclaim the compatibility of religion and evolution" (Provine*[225]), and by "the liberal theologians, the 'prescientific science' of the biblical account of creation has at last been separated out . . ." (Gilkey*[226]). Neo-Modernist Catholics generally came to "believe in indefinite evolution 'onward and upward' " (Cross*[227]). Reform Jews generally follow evolution (Plaut*[228]), as does Humanistic Judaism (Wine*[229]). The same is true of other faiths such as Buddhism, Scientology, Theosophy, Anthroposophy, and Atheism.

14.2 Non-Religious Nature of the Parallel Consistency of the Theory of Abrupt Appearance with Various Religions

The theory of abrupt appearance, like the theory of evolution, is consistent with but different from some religious beliefs. Creationist religions, like evolutionist religions, span the entire religious spectrum to include Protestant, Catholic, Jewish, and nonJudeo-Christian faiths. Creationist religions are not by any means limited to Fundamentalism, and the great majority of creationists are not Fundamentalists. Examples of creationist religions, which parallel the evolutionist religions listed in Section 14.1, are as follows:

Figure 14.2
"Increasingly . . . people without strong religious commitment. . . are expressing some acceptance of the arguments made by . . . creationists" (Raup) and other discontinuitists*

Protestant:	a. Conservative Evangelical denominations Fundamentalism Other groups such as the Church of Christ, Seventh-day Adventists, Jehovah's Witnesses, most Mormons, etc.
Catholic:	b. Much Orthodox Roman Catholicism and Eastern Orthodoxy
Jewish:	c. Orthodox Judaism
Non-Judeo-Christian:	d. Islam (Muslims) and some Hinduism.

The American public splits almost evenly between religious faiths that are creationist and that are evolutionist.

This is not an argument that either the theory of abrupt appearance or the theory of creation is primarily supported by creationist religions, however, because the teaching of one or the other theory is instead supported by eighty-six percent of the general public as indicated by scientific surveys,[230] and by many people for non-religious reasons as recognized by Raup*:

> Increasingly, however, people without strong religious commitment are being drawn into and are expressing some acceptance of the arguments

> made by the scientific creationists. Therefore, control by an ideology may represent an argument in some quarters but certainly not in all. Furthermore, I think it can be argued that whether a body of reasoning is scientific or not should be decided independently of the question of whether the adherents are committed to one ideology or another.[231]

Furthermore, the theory of abrupt appearance itself is built on scientific evidence, as is the theory of evolution.

a. Consistency with Some Protestant Religions

Creationists among Protestants are not restricted to Fundamentalists—and in fact the great majority of creationists are not Fundamentalists—but include Conservative Evangelicals such as many denominational groups of Presbyterians, Baptists, Methodists, Lutherans, Episcopalians, Pentecostals, and Bible churches, as well as many members within other denominational groups. Creationists also include the Churches of Christ and Seventh-day Adventists, and other groups such as Jehovah's Witnesses and most Mormons.[232]

b. Consistency with Orthodox Roman Catholicism and Eastern Orthodoxy

In contrast to the Neo-Modernist wing of Roman Catholicism, its Orthodox wing is generally or significantly creationist. Fehlner, the editor of *Miles Immaculatae* in Rome, where he earned his doctorate in sacred theology at the Seraphicum (Pontifical Theological Faculty of St. Bonaventure), has summarized Orthodox Roman Catholic doctrine on creation as follows:

> *Creation*
>
> The teaching of the Church on origins from her foundation embraces a body of doctrine consistent and unvarying, not only as regards its general content and tenor, but the explicit formulation of its details as well.
>
> . . . .
>
> While the Church does not hold that God has revealed all that can be known about His creation, or . . . that the precise sense has in every instance been definitively explained by the Church in the most explicit manner possible, certain points concerning the origin of the world and of the species within it have been so revealed and definitively explained by the Church, either solemnly or in her ordinary Magisterium, in such ways that they may not be questioned or subjected to modification to accommodate human theorizing.
>
> 1. The whole *world was created* by God *ex nihilo* in the beginning of time.
>
> . . . .

3. The nature of the *first man and first woman* was made directly by God, by forming the male body out of pre-existing matter, the female body out of the body of the first man, by creating out of nothing a soul for each and then uniting soul to body as its form. . . .
4. God made only one man and one woman in this fashion. All others find their origin in *descent from these two*, human procreation through conception accounting for the origin of the body . . ..[233]

He has similarly summarized Catholic doctrine on evolution:

> *Evolution*
>
> In the matter of origins the Church permits the proposal of theories of evolution as scientific explanations of the origin of the species (*never of the world*) in *only a very restricted way*, and on conditions reflecting what she otherwise knows to be the truth, in such ways that any such hypothesis only doubtfully merits the designation evolutionary. . . . Nor can the difficulty be avoided by a facile distinction claiming for science the task of solving the "how" of origins and for religion the "Who." It is precisely because the *Catholic faith claims to explain not only Who did it, but how He did it (by creation)*, that we are able to distinguish the world as created from God as uncreated and infinite . . ..[234]

St. Maximillian agreed that "evolution is not a true fact, but . . . a religious-philosophical creed contrary to that of the Church."[235] Arthadeva, editor in Rome of *Christ to the World*, recently published an endorsement of creation over evolution.[236] Similar stances are taken by Sennott,[237] Johnson,[238] O'Connell,[239] Long,[240] and Haigh.[241]

Thomas Aquinas in his *Summa Theologica* taught a form of creation,[242] as did the Fourth Lateran Council, a magisterial statement by Pope Innocent III, the Council of Vienna, the Fifth Lateran Council, the Council of Trent, and Vatican I.[243]

The encyclical *Humani Generis* of Pope Pius XII, while allowing for belief in creation or some forms of theistic evolution, warned against "fictitious tenets of evolution" and exclusion of divine intervention in natural laws:

> 5. . . . Some *imprudently and indiscreetly* hold that *evolution*, which has not been fully proved even in the domain of natural sciences, explains the origin of all things, and *audaciously* support the monistic and pantheistic opinion that the world is in *continual evolution*. . . .
>
> 6. Such *fictitious tenets of evolution* which repudiate all that is absolute, firm and immutable, have paved the way for the new erroneous philosophy . . ..
>
> . . ..
>
> 36. For these reasons the Teaching Authority of the Church does *not forbid* that, in conformity with the present state of human sciences and sacred theology, *research and discussions* on the part of men experienced in both fields, take place with regard to the doctrine of evolution, in as far

> as it inquires into the origin of the human body as coming from pre-existent and living matter—for the Catholic faith obliges us to hold that souls are immediately created by God. However this must be done in such a way that the reasons for *both opinions*, that is, those favorable and those unfavorable to evolution, be weighed and judged with the necessary seriousness, moderation and measure, and provided that all are prepared to *submit to the judgment of the Church* to whom Christ has given the mission of interpreting authentically the Sacred Scriptures and of defending the dogmas of faith. *Some however rashly transgress* this liberty of discussion, when they act as if the origin of the human body from pre-existing and living matter were already *completely certain and proved* by the facts which have been discovered up to now....[244]

Pope Paul VI, in *Credo of the People of God*, similarly warned against views of human evolution that exclude divine intervention and creation of the soul.[245] The remarks of Pope John Paul II are consistent with those of his predecessors.[246] Several leading creationist scientists have been Roman Catholics.[247] Although it is certainly true that many Roman Catholics hold an evolutionist belief,[248] it would be wrong to overlook the many Catholics who are creationists and the statements of various Catholic leaders endorsing creation or warning against unrestricted evolution.

The following summary has been given regarding Orthodox Catholic opinion on uncensored instruction in various scientific views:

> *Evolution Exclusively Presented*
>
> . . . But in the context of what is defined and proclaimed as a "neutral" school, the *exclusive presentation of evolution* as the only plausible explanation of cosmic and of human origins, or worse as a "fact" beyond doubt, belies the religious neutrality of the school. Such a presentation does *conflict directly with the teachings of the Church at many points*, and is tantamount to indoctrination of a religious kind, one judged by the Church to be false. Presentation of arguments for an evolutionary theory and against it and set forth in a truly scientific manner . . ., for a creationistic theory and against it, is in principle fair, provided both can be presented merely as scientific hypotheses and appreciated as such by public and parochial students.[249]

c. *Consistency with Orthodox Judaism*

Orthodox Judaism is generally creationist. The Association of Orthodox Jewish Scientists published two books in which writers defend creation and criticize evolution, such as Perlman,[250] Etkin,[251] Radkowsky,[252] Schneersohn,[253] and Goldman.[254] Orthodox Jews in Israel recently convened a Conference on Inquiries into Evolution and the Origin of Life.[255] A recent survey of the Torah and science describes the Orthodox Jewish position as creationist as follows:

> Creation as described in the Torah, both written and oral, is not ruled out by the available facts, and moreover in some instances the evidence makes a better case for creation than it does for evolution.[256]

The Rabbinical Alliance of America joined the plaintiffs in defending balanced treatment of the theory of creation in one case,[257] and joined in a supportive brief before the U.S. Supreme Court.

d. Consistency with Some NonJudeo-Christian Faiths

Islam, one of the world's largest religions, is also creationist, as *Encyclopaedia Britannica*,[258] Khalifa,[259] and Nasr[260] indicate. The Koran contains a creation account.[261] Some sects of Hinduism are creationist as well.

Summary. The theories of evolution and of abrupt appearance are parallel in their consistency with but difference from various religions. In fact, the religious faiths in the United States divide almost evenly between theistic evolutionist and creationist ones, and that division internally splits Protestant, Catholic, Jewish, and nonJudeo-Christian faiths. That consistency does not make either the theory of abrupt appearance or of evolution religious.

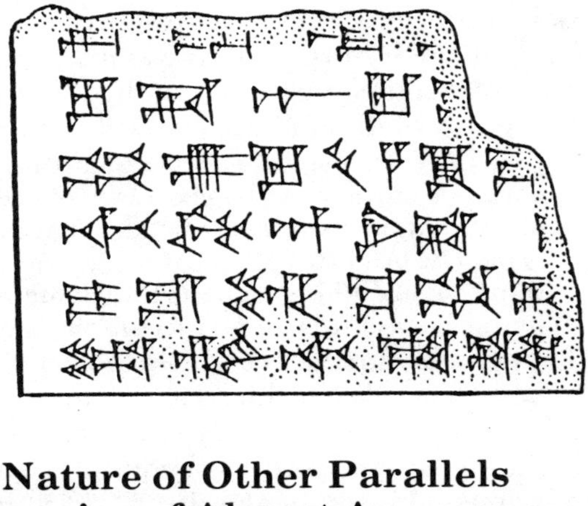

Figure 14.3
Other parallels between the theories: Evolution first was articulated in the "Babylonian Genesis" (Spence), and "evolution and creation seem to be sharing remarkable parallels" (Patterson*)*

14.3 Non-Religious Nature of Other Parallels between the Theories of Abrupt Appearance and Evolution

The spate of anticreationist books[262] have stressed several features of the theory of creation, besides its consistency with some religions, that are assumed to make it religious. Those include the following characteristics:

- a. Original presentation in religious texts
- b. Some scientific proponents with strong religious beliefs or motivations
- c. Some scientific writers with other religious publications or activities
- d. Faith
- e. Teleological aspects.

The same standard should be applied to the theory of evolution, and in most cases the characteristics are equally true of it. Several of the following points do not apply at all to the theory of abrupt appearance, and the others do not apply directly because the theory of abrupt appearance is different from the theory of creation in significant areas.

a. Original Presentation in Religious Texts

Both concepts, creation and evolution, were first articulated in religious writings, and at roughly the same time. Just as creationist concepts were first set forth in the Pentateuch and the Koran, evolutionist concepts were first presented in the "Babylonian Genesis" or Enuma Elish in roughly the same time period, as well as in other ancient religious writings. In the Babylonian Genesis, the universe existed eternally and life evolved from water, as Spence* states:

> Like the cosmological efforts of most primitive or barbarian peoples it does not partake of the character of a creation myth so much as an account of an *evolution* from chaos and the establishment of physical laws. The primitive mind cannot grasp the idea of the creation of something out of nothing, and the Babylonians and Akkadians did not differ in this respect from other races in the same stage of development. . . .[263]

That can be further seen in Jacobsen*[264] and Heidl*.[265]

Both general concepts, creation and evolution, were first stated by religious leaders. Just as creation was first mentioned by Moses and Mohammed and others, evolution was first articulated in the religious-philosophical writings of the ancient Greeks, as Osborn* noted:

> When I began the search for anticipations of the evolutionary theory, . . . I was led back to the Greek natural philosophers and I was astonished to find how many of the pronounced and basic features of the Darwinian theory were anticipated even as far back as the seventh century B.C.[266]

Examples are the religious and philosophical writings of Thales*, Anaximander*,[267] Anaximenes*, Xenophanes*, Heraclitus*,[268] the Milesian school*,[269] Empedocles*, who "may justly be called the father of the evolution idea,"[270] the Roman Lucretius*,[271] and the ancient Chinese,[272] as well as in the earlier religious writing of the priestly Babylonian author of the Enuma Elish. In particular, Empedocles* "described a true Darwinian evolution," according to Fuller*,[273] Stansfield*,[274] Lull*,[275] Zeller*,[276] and Peck*.[277]

Because those ancient religious concepts are merely consistent with the theories of evolution and creation, that common historical background does not make either religious. It certainly does not make the theory of abrupt appearance religious.

b. Scientific Proponents with Strong Religious Beliefs or Motivations

Philosophers have long treated the source or inspiration of a concept as irrelevant to its objective merit, as Reichenbach* argued,[278] and as Ruse*,[279] Laudan*,[280] Gillespie*,[281] and most philosophers of science recognize (Section 9.6(b)). Raup*, dean of the Field Museum of Natural History, has acknowledged the corollary that "whether a body of reasoning is scientific or not should be decided independently of the question of whether the adherents are committed to one ideology or another."[282] Both the theory of evolution and the theories of abrupt appearance and of creation are supported by some scientists who hold strong religious convictions and who sometimes are motivated or inspired by those religious beliefs (Section 13.3), but that does not make either theory religious.

(1) Strong Religious Beliefs. Strong personal religious beliefs—which many diverse people have—do not necessarily make everything that the individual does or thinks to be religiously motivated and biased. To give literary examples, Nathaniel Hawthorne and Lewis Wallace were Christians who were inspired by strong religious beliefs and reflected them in their literary works, but that does not render *The Scarlet Letter* or *Ben Hur* inherently religious or exclude them from the literature classroom.[283]

Charles Darwin* himself was professionally trained as a theologian rather than as a scientist, and ultimately held an "agnosticism tending at times toward atheism," Moore* states.[284] Gillespie* describes the spiritual odyssey of Darwin*:

> Darwin's religious disillusionment, as recorded in the *Autobiography*, is familiar. He remembered that he had been conventionally orthodox

> during the *Beagle* voyage but had come to *doubt the full truth of the Old Testament* containing as it did a "false history of the world, with the Tower of Babel, the rainbow as a sign, etc. etc." Far worse than any of this was the depiction of God as "a revengeful tyrant." These doubts led Darwin to *question the validity of Christianity* as a revelation. His growing interest in science led him to *think miracles impossible*. The contradictions in the Gospels and their not being convincing as eyewitness accounts, coupled with the evident superstitions of the age which they reflected, led him to *give up on Christianity as revealed*.... Thus he wrote, "disbelief crept over me at a very slow rate, but was at last complete." He had no doubts or regrets about his loss of faith and was glad enough to get rid of the "damnable doctrine" of the unjust condemnation of unbelievers to hell. . . .[285]

That does not render Darwin's books inherently religious or exclude his scientific discoveries from the classroom.

Stansfield* and some other evolutionists hold a theistic evolutionary position, that God "create[d] gradually through an evolutionary process,"[286] but that religious belief does not make his textbook and other scientific writings religious or inappropriate for the public school classroom. The mere consistency of the personal religious convictions of either evolutionist or discontinuitist authors with their textbooks and technical works obviously does not render the books inherently religious, and the religious motive in writing one book obviously does not necessarily carry over into every other book or conclusion.

(2) Religious Inspiration or Source. The inspiration or source of a scientific discovery or explanation is similarly irrelevant to the objective merit and scientific validity of that scientific discovery or explanation.

Some aspects of science have had mystical origins. Medicine arose from occultism[287] and chemistry arose from mystical alchemy.[288] Kepler, "in searching for his laws of planetary motion, was motivated by Pythagorean mysticism."[289] Kepler's mystical motivation is an example of how permissibly "the scientist may give free reign to his imagination, and the course of his creative thinking may be influenced even by scientifically questionable notions," Hempel* states.[290] Mendeleev*, in formulating the periodic system of the elements, had a "pantheistic mystical longing to see a Chain of Being ramify through the chemical facts" as his inspiration.[291] Kekulé* was inspired by a vision of a snake biting its tail,[292] which Hempel* describes:

> Kekulé [1829-1896], for example, tells us that he had long been trying

> unsuccessfully to devise a structural formula for the benzene molecule when, one evening in 1865, he found a solution to his problem while he was dozing in front of his fireplace. Gazing into the flames, he seemed to see atoms dancing in snakelike arrays. Suddenly, one of the snakes formed a ring by seizing hold of its own tail and then whirled mockingly before him. Kekulé awoke in a flash: he had hit upon the now famous and familiar idea of representing the molecular structure of benzene by a hexagonal ring. . . .[293]

A vision on reading a pantheistic poet was the inspiration for Tesla's* discovery of the alternating current motor.[294] Three dreams were the inspiration for René Descartes's philosophy of rationalism.[295]

Some modern biologists are strongly influenced by their Marxism: "Gould admits to his Marxism, and lauds the way in which his science is informed by his beliefs, and how conversely his beliefs are bolstered by his science," Ruse* states.[296] Lewontin* and Levins* "have tried to let their theorizing be influenced by their Marxism," acknowledging that " 'we have been attempting with some success to guide our research by a conscious application of Marxist philosophy'," [297] and that their newest book is "written largely from a Marxist perspective."[298] The merit of an idea in any discipline is independent of its source.

Some creationist scientists are members of the Creation Research Society, which requires its members to sign a religious statement of faith. That does not make all adherents of the theory of creation religiously motivated, any more than the signature by some leading scientists of *Humanist Manifesto II* makes all evolutionists religiously motivated. Instead, as Caudill states:

> Finally, to deny any criticism of evolutionary theory on the basis that the critics are religiously motivated is the equivalent of "religious" dogmatism in science. . . .
>
> . . . Likewise, scientific theories offering alternatives to evolution cannot be rejected simply because the proponent is a religious person. A particular scientist may be a Hindu, a dogmatic atheist, a witch, or even a fundamentalist Christian, but such a religious belief should not be identified as an inability to be scientific. Any personal attack on the proponent of a scientific theory is irrelevant to the scientific merit of the theory.[299]

The widespread attacks on the theory of creation, in the form of attacks on supportive scientists for their religious beliefs, by Kitcher*,[300] Crawford*,[301] Ruse*,[302] and others, are ad hominem attacks on an irrelevant issue.

(3) Religious Motive or Purpose. The motive or purpose of a scientist is also irrelevant to the objective validity of the scientist's conclusions.

Sir Francis Bacon, the father of the scientific method, had as his purpose in scientific studies to "subdue the world" according to the command in Genesis, and urged others to "[s]tudy the Heaven and the Earth" to see the creator's handiwork.[303] Sir Isaac Newton was motivated to study science by a biblical prophecy in the book of Daniel,[304] and by a purpose to promote "Belief of a Deity":[305]

> WHEN I wrote my Treatise about our System, I had an Eye upon such Principles as might work with considering Men, for the Belief of a Deity, and nothing can rejoice me more than to find it useful for that Purpose.[306]

Kepler sought for God to be "glorified in astronomy":

> I strive to publish them *in God's honor* who wishes to be recognized from the book of nature. But the more others continue in these endeavors, the more I shall rejoice; I am not envious of anybody. This I pledged to God, this is my decision. I had the intention of becoming a theologian. For a long time I was restless: but now see how *God is, by my endeavors, also glorified in astronomy*.[307]

Robert Boyle was inspired to study nature by his perception of God's works.[308] In fact, modern science[309] arose from a theistic and creationist basis.[310] On the other side, T. H. Huxley*, Ernst Haeckel*, and many other Darwinian spokesmen were Agnostics or Atheists motivated by an antipathy toward Christianity and a desire to disprove the Bible.[311]

In an analogous field, the eminent archaeologists Albright (of Johns Hopkins) and Glueck (of Hebrew Union College) were motivated in their archaeological work by a desire to confirm the Bible, and have used the Bible as their primary guide to possible sites for excavations:

> They [our methods] had been perfected in modern times especially by William F. Albright. The first task was to assemble and examine the literary evidence. *The chief source of information was the Bible itself.* Its historical memories and descriptions and sometimes exact references to particular places are of inestimable value to the scholar.[312]

The religious motivation of those and countless other archaeologists, as with a scientist's motivation, is irrelevant to the validity of their archaeological conclusions.

c. *Scientific Writers with Other Religious Publications or Activities*

Both the theory of evolution and the theories of abrupt appearance and of creation are advocated by scientific authors who have written theological treatises. Theological writings, like religious beliefs, do not disqualify a scholar from being scientific in other publications.

Sir Julian Huxley* and many other evolutionists have authored religious treatises[313] as well as scientific books,[314] but this does not make their scientific works inherently religious or impermissible for public school use. Isaac Asimov* has written both religious[315] and scientific books,[316] but his scientific ones are proper for the classroom. The religious publications of either evolutionist or discontinuitist scientists do not deprive the authors of their status as scientists and do not deprive their scientific works of their scientific character. It is just as intellectually dishonest to select a creationist scientist who has written religious books, to quote from such a book that does not purport to describe a scientific theory of creation, and to claim that that religious content is the sum of the theory of creation, as to do the same with an evolutionist author.

The history of science is replete with instances of religious writings by undisputed scientists. Kepler closed one book with a "hymn in praise to the glory of God."[317] Newton wrote books on biblical chronology (defending Ussher's dates) and on interpreting prophecy.[318] Boyle "took a special interest in promoting the Christian religion abroad," and "developed his theological views in *The Christian Virtuoso*."[319] Pascal began an apologetic work.[320]

d. Faith of Evolutionist and Creationist Scientists

Both the theory of evolution and the theories of abrupt appearance and of creation are supported by some scientists who manifest faith in some ways.[321] Patterson* of the British Museum refers to evolution as based on "faith", because of the lack of evidence for it:

> I think many people in this room would acknowledge that during the last few years, if you had thought about it at all, you have experienced a shift from evolution as knowledge to evolution as *faith*.[322]

Good*, formerly of the University of Hull, finds that macroevolution is "a fundamental article of biological faith"—a faith that his book casts doubt on while not denying:

> For nearly a century now a belief that the many thousands of different kinds of plants and animals at present inhabiting the earth have come into being by descent from fewer and earlier kinds through a process of continuing gradual change, that is to say by what is commonly described as a process of organic evolution, has been a fundamental article of biological faith. . . .[323]

Macroevolution must be accepted as "an act of faith" because it is "not a scientifically ascertained fact," in Scott's* view;[324] and is "a matter of personal faith" and an "article of faith," in Rifkin's* estimation.[325]

Also within the field of biological evolution, Ehrlich* and Holm* question whether "faith" in Darwinism someday will be regarded as simplistic and inaccurate like Euclidean geometry:

> Current *faith* in the theory [of evolution] is reminiscent of many other ideas which at one time were thought to be self-evidently true and supported by all available data—the flat earth, the geocentric universe, the sum of all the angles of a triangle equaling 180 degrees. It is conceivable, even likely, that what might facetiously be called a non-Euclidian theory of evolution will be developed. Perpetuation of today's theory as dogma will not encourage progress toward more satisfactory explanations of observed phenomena . . ..[326]

Matthews* finds Darwinism a "faith," although a satisfactory one;[327] and Bateson* found it to require "extraordinary acts of faith. . . ."[328] Midgley* concludes that the "*belief* in future events does seem to be religious," with reference to "the escalator view of evolution" of "steady, careful progress."[329] Darwinism "has virtually become a religion itself" in Leith's* view, and many examples of its "religion in reverse" are cited by Macbeth* and others.[329A]

Within the field of biochemical evolution, Yockey* concludes that current theories are "based on faith" because of insuperable information content problems:

> It is concluded that belief in currently accepted scenarios of spontaneous biogenesis is based on *faith*, contrary to conventional wisdom.[330]

Kerkut* also finds that biochemical evolution is "a matter of faith":

> There is, however, little evidence in favour of [a]biogenesis and as yet we have no indication that it can be performed. There are many schemes by which [a]biogenesis could have occurred but these are still suggestive schemes and nothing more. They may indicate experiments that can be performed, but they tell us nothing about what actually happened some 1,000 million years ago. It is therefore a *matter of faith* on the part of the biologist that [a]biogenesis did occur and he can choose whatever method of [a]biogenesis happens to suit him personally; the evidence for what did happen is not available.[331]

Others write that "faith in science" can be a religion,[332] and that to many scientists, in fact, "pure science has become the new religion."[333] The prevalent intellectual attitude of science "is continuous with a typically religious view of the physical world."[334]

e. Teleological Aspects of the Theories of Evolution and of Creation

Both the theory of evolution and the theory of creation have teleological (or design) aspects. Just as the theory of creation mentions the complex order in nature as evidence of creation, the theory of evolution often involves teleology in many forms.[335] Teleology is not an inherently religious concept, philosophers Leslie*[336] and Feuer*[337] argue. In fact, "[t]eleological principles are essential to the functioning of sciences," Feuer* states,[338] and "teleological explanations in biology are not only acceptable but indeed indispensable," Ayala* adds.[339] "Teleology had been part of the conceptual framework of Western science from ancient Greece until the time of Darwin," according to Hull*,[340] and thereafter "teleology has on occasion led to significant scientific advances."[341] The "scientific method does not allow us to exclude data which lead to the conclusion that the universe, life and man are based on design," as von Braun observed.[342]

In connection with biological evolution, "adaptation, like its Victorian twin 'utility,' is itself a teleological concept; it is adjustment to something for some end," Grene* states.[343] "Purposefulness, or teleology, . . . is universal in the living world. . . . Living beings have an internal, or natural, teleology," Dobzhansky*, Ayala*, Stebbins*, and Valentine* point out.[344] In that sense, Darwin* "substituted a scientific teleology."[345] Paterson* was shocked to learn of the teleology introduced by Darwin*:

> I confess to experiencing a feeling of shock when I realized that Darwin's great achievement of freeing biology of teleology and the supernatural, had been surreptitiously supplanted by the old theological concept deceptively clad in new clothes.[346]

O'Grady* and other structuralists complain that neo-Darwinian functionalism "introduces an unnecessary degree of teleology which interferes with the theory's intentions of offering causal explanations."[347]

In the area of cosmic evolution, the anthropic cosmological principle proposes that "there really is a place for teleology and related concepts in today's science."[348] Philosophers of science have made arguments for design without a supernatural designer.[349] The search for extraterrestrial intelligence relies on teleology in order to recognize radio signals as a message from extraterrestrial life. It is not clear what the significant difference is, if any, between these evolutionary concepts of teleology and a creationist concept of teleology.

Summary. The theories of evolution and of abrupt appearance are parallel in several aspects besides consistency with various religions, although most of the following points only are relevant to the theory of abrupt appearance by virtue of its rough consistency with the theory of creation. Both the theory of evolution and the theory of creation were originally presented in religious texts: the Enuma Elish, or Babylonian Genesis, describes "an evolution from chaos" (Spence*[350]), and Empedocles* was "the father of evolution" (Lull*[351]). Both theories are championed by some people with strong religious beliefs and religious motivations: Darwin* himself rejected the Old Testament, miracles, Christianity as revealed, and finally God (Gillespie*[352]), and Marxist evolutionists today are "attempting with some success to guide our research by a conscious application of Marxist philosophy" (Lewontin* and Levins*[353]). The context of discovery is irrelevant to the context of justification, both in the case of Darwin* and Marxist evolutionists and in the case of discontinuitist and creationist scientists. Both the theory of evolution and the theory of creation are defended by scientists who have written religious works. Both theories involve elements of faith, and necessarily so because origins events are not subject to absolute proof: many scientists believe in "evolution as faith" (Patterson*[354]) and macroevolution as "a fundamental article of biological faith" (Good*[355]). Finally, both theories involve teleology: "teleological explanations in biology are not only acceptable but indeed indispensable" (Ayala*[356]). None of those parallels renders either theory religious.

Notes

1 S. Løvtrup*, *Darwinism: The Refutation of a Myth* 416 (1987).

2 Address of Dr. Colin Patterson at American Museum of Natural History, tr. at 3 & 4 (Nov. 5, 1981) (italics added) (speaking of theories of creation and evolution generally and not of consistency with religions specifically).

3 E. Conklin*, *Man Real and Ideal* 52 (1943).

4 Smith*, *Two Evolutions*, in On Nature 42, 53 (L. Rouner* ed. 1984).

5 366 U.S. 420 (1961).

6 *Id.* at 442. *See also* Lynch v. Donnelly, 465 U.S. 668, 682 (1984); Harris v. McRae, 448 U.S. 297, 319-20 (1980); Section 20.2.

7 336 U.S. at 442.

8 448 U.S. 297 (1980).

[9] *Id.* at 319-20. *See also* Lynch v. Donnelly, 465 U.S. at 682.

[10] Scheid*, *Evolution and Creationism in the Public Schools*, 9 J. Contemp. Law 51, 106-07 (1983) (italics added). *See also* Caudill, *Law and Worldview: Problems in the Creation-Science Controversy*, 3 J. Law & Religion 1, 18 (1985) ("for many evolutionists, evolutionary theory supports and justifies their religious beliefs.") (discontinuitist author).

[11] *Is God a Creationist? The Religious Case Against Creation-Science* (R. Frye* ed. 1983).

[12] *Religious Leaders' Views on the Theory of Evolution*, in A Compendium of Information on The Theory of Evolution and the Evolution-Creationism Controversy 55 (rev. ed. J. Lightner* ed. 1978).

[13] Beattie*, *Humanism: Secular or Religious?*, Free Inquiry, Winter 1980-81, at 11, 11.

[14] D. Ehrenfeld*, *The Arrogance of Humanism* 3 (1978) (emphasis added). *See also* P. Kurtz*, *In Defense of Secular Humanism* 135 (1983) ("Second, one may be speaking of the vast number of nominal humanists in the United States and throughout the world. Perhaps in this broad sense, humanism is the *dominant* moral and *religious* point of view in this scientific age among our intellectual and educated classes, though some may not be aware that they are humanists.") Even that last organization, however, was happy to publish in the first issue of its magazine an argument that Humanism is religious. Beattie*, *Humanism: Secular or Religious*, 1 Free Inquiry 11 (Winter 1980-81). (emphasis added).

[15] J. Ellul*, *The New Demons* 26-28 (1973).

[16] P. Kurtz*, *The New Inquisition in the Schools*, Free Inquiry, Winter 1986-87, at 4, 5 (emphasis added, original emphasis deleted).

[17] Reader's Digest, *1985 Almanac* 712 (1985). Beattie* calculates that "the Unitarians have about 67,000 humanists." Beattie*, *The Religion of Secular Humanism*, Free Inquiry, Winter 1985-86, at 12, 16.

[18] Roclofsma*, *Giving Judaism a Humanist Face*, Insight, May 4, 1987, at 56, 56 (quoting the co-founder of the Society for Humanistic Judaism).

[19] P. Kurtz*, *In Defense of Secular Humanism* 135 (1983) (emphasis added).

[20] *Humanist Manifesto I*, in Humanist Manifestos I and II (P. Kurtz* ed. 1973), reprinted from New Humanist, May-June 1933, at 1.

[21] Wilson*, *The Religious Element in Humanism Pervades Its Origin, Inspiration and Support*, 22 Humanist 173, 173 (1962) ("Of the 34 persons who signed the Humanist Manifesto in 1933, all but four can be readily identified as religious humanists who considered Humanism as the development of a better and truer religion . . ..").

[22] *Humanist Manifesto I*, in Humanist Manifestos I and II (P. Kurtz* ed. 1973).

[23] *E.g.*, C. Potter*, *Humanism: A New Religion* 114 (1930) ("Is Humanism a religion? It is both a religion and a philosophy of culture."); J. Auer*, *Humanism States Its Case* (1933).

[24] J. Hitchcock*, *What Is Secular Humanism?* 13 (1983).

[25] McNaughton*, *John Dewey and Religious Humanism*, Religious Humanism, Spring 1980, at 58, 67 (Dewey concluded his book, *A Common Faith*, with the following words: "Here are all the elements for a *religious faith* that shall not be confined to sect, class, or race. Such a faith has always been implicitly the common faith of mankind. It remains to make it explicit and militant.").

[26] *Humanism, A New Religion*, Religious Humanism, Spring 1968, at 96, 96.

[27] Mason*, *Religious Humanism: 19th and 20th Centuries*, Religious Humanism, Winter 1979, at 3, 13 ("That is indeed a religious humanism whose roots have supported strong branches and whose tree has borne fruit.").

[28] Hemstreet*, *On Being Religious, Humanistically*, Religious Humanism, Winter 1981, at 24, 40 ("I belong to and support as generously as possible with money and time those organizations that express and promote *humanistic* and liberal values—the Unitarian Universalist Church, the Fellowship of Religious Humanists, the American Humanist Association, Amnesty International, the American Civil Liberties Union, and the Democratic Socialist Organizing Committee.").

[29] Farmer*, *Must the Moral Majority Monopolize the "Good" Words?*, 41 Humanist 32 (May-June 1981).

[30] Beattie*, *Humanism: Secular or Religious*, 1 Free Inquiry 11 (Winter 1980-81).

[31] Haydon*, *Is Scientific Humanism Religious?*, 2 Religious Humanism 49 (1968).

[32] C. Lamont*, *The Philosophy of Humanism* 85 (1977).

[33] Wilson*, *The Religious Element in Humanism Pervades Its Origin, Inspiration and Support*, 22 Humanist 173, 173 (1962).

[34] *Id.* at 1131 ("So in that sense Humanism *is* a religion, albeit a secular one.").

[35] Arisian*, *A New Statement of Religious Humanism*, Humanist, Mar.-Apr. 1977, at 54, 54.

[36] Larue*, *The Way of Ethical Humanism*, Humanist, Sept.-Oct. 1984, at 20.

[37] Samson*, *Can Humanism Be Religious?*, Religious Humanism, Winter 1979, at 26.

[38] Skolimowski*, *True Humanism: More Than Secularism*, Religious Humanism, Winter 1978, at 33.

[39] *E.g.*, L. Morain* & M. Morain*, *Humanism as the Next Step* 4-5 (1954) (former president of American Humanist Association) ("Humanism, built squarely on the universal idea of brotherhood, upon the golden rule, shows promise of becoming a great *world faith.* Humanists are content with fixing their attention on this life and on this earth. Theirs is a *religion* without a God, divine revelation, or sacred scriptures. Yet theirs is a *faith* rich in

feeling and understanding.") (emphasis added).

[40] *Churchman*, Mar. 1983, at 3.

[41] Beattie*, *The Religion of Secular Humanism*, Free Inquiry, Winter 1985-86, at 12, 16.

[42] L. Morain* & M. Morain*, *Humanism as the Next Step* 5 (1954).

[43] Wilson*, *Pioneer of Evolutionary Humanism*, Humanist, May-June 1975, at 40, 40.

[44] Dunphy*, *A Religion for a New Age*, Humanist, Jan.-Feb. 1983, at 23, 26 (italics added).

[45] Wine*, *Believing Is Better than Non-Believing*, Humanistic Judaism, Spring 1986, at 7, 9 (co-founder of Society for Humanistic Judaism).

[46] Wine*, *Building Communities for the New American Jew*, Humanistic Judaism, Winter 1986-87, at 10, 11.

[47] Jerris*, *Will There Be a Second Generation of Humanistic Jews?*, Humanistic Judaism, Winter 1986-87, at 21, 22 (executive director of Society for Humanistic Judaism).

[48] *Humanist Manifesto I*, in Humanist Manifestos I and II, at 8 (P. Kurtz* ed. 1973).

[49] C. Potter*, *Humanism: A New Religion* 15 (1930)("Through his scientific study of the universe man has arrived at the theory of evolution. In this also, the Humanist finds himself at variance with many Theists.").

[50] Wine*, *Believing Is Better than Non-Believing*, Humanistic Judaism, Spring 1986, at 7, 8.

[51] L. Morain* & M. Morain*, *Humanism as the Next Step* 16, 22-23 (1954) (italics added except subtitle).

[52] Wine*, *Believing Is Better than Non-Believing*, Humanistic Judaism, Spring 1986, at 7, 8 (italics added).

[53] Hemstreet*, *On Being Religious, Humanistically*, Religious Humanism 24, 29-30 (Winter 1981)("To me, being *religious as a liberal humanist* involves the following attitudes and activities: 1. Revering life, especially human life, recognizing that it is probably necessary to deprive certain nonhuman species of life in order to protect, preserve, and enhance our human life. This reverence may extend to awe at the complexity and power of natural forces guiding the universe as a whole and a desire to understand those powers and cooperate with them to further the process of *cosmic evolution* as a whole. As a conscious, intelligent human being, I am a cooperating part of that *evolutionary process*. . . .") (italics added).

[54] Potter*, *Humanism, A New Religion*, Religious Humanism, Spring 1968, at 96, 96 ("The world and man evolved.").

[55] Sellars*, *Religious Humanism*, New Humanist, May-June 1933, at 7.

[56] Levine*, *The Mitzvah Speech: Adam and Eve*, Humanistic Judaism, Summer 1983, at 32.

[57] K. Cauthen*, *The Impact of American Religious Liberalism* 7 (1962). He points out the tie between evolution and Theological Liberalism:

It would be difficult to overemphasize the influence of the doctrine of

> evolution in all of its forms on theology. The combination of *evolution* and immanence goes a long way toward providing the basic context out of which liberalism came and in which it grew.

Id. at 22 (italics added).

> The *impact of modern science* in breaking down the orthodox scheme was decisive . . .. Mechanical causation appeared to be supreme, leaving little or no room for special divine activity. Thus, the gap between general and special revelation . . . was acutely called into question. . . .
>
> Moreover, the doctrine of *evolution* narrowed the gap between nature and man and, along with the developmental theories regarding the origin of the solar system and the earth, emphasized the fact that the whole natural world was characterized by a unity of process. . . .
>
> By virtue of these influences modern science had both a negative and a positive effect upon the development of theology. Its negative effect was to call into question the world view which had been believed for centuries upon the authority of the Scriptures . . .. It also called into question the possibility of miracles . . .. The positive effect of science was to prepare the way for a doctrine of God's immanence in which divine activity was found not in miraculous intervention into the normal sequences of cause and effect but in the law-abiding *evolutionary process* of nature itself.

Id. at 7 (italics added).

[58] Meland*, *Liberalism, Theological,* in 13 Encyclopaedia Britannica 1021, 1022 (W. Preece* ed. 1965) ("The decisive events" giving rise to religious Liberalism in the late nineteenth and early twentieth centuries were "the publication of Darwin's *Origin of Species* along with the industrial revolution.").

[59] J. Moore*, *The Post-Darwinian Controversies* 304-05 (1979) (italics added) [hereinafter cited as J. Moore].

[60] F. Temple*, *Relations between Religion and Science* 113-14, 167 (1885); *see generally* J. Moore* at 220.

[61] H. Beecher*, *Evolution and Religion* 113-15 (1885); *see generally* J. Moore* at 220-21.

[62] G. Henslow*, *Present-day Rationalism Critically Examined* (1904); G. Henslow*, *The Origin of Floral Structures* vi, xi, 335 (1888); G. Henslow*, *The Theory of Evolution of Living Things* (1873); G. Henslow*, *Genesis and Geology* (1871); *see generally* J. Moore* at 221, 232-34.

[63] G. Campbell*, *Organic Evolution Cross-Examined* 44, 64, 149, 155, 162 (1898); G. Campbell*, *Unity of Nature* 262 (1884); G. Campbell*, Primeval Man (1869); *see generally* J. Moore* at 221-22.

[64] G. Mivart*, *Lessons from Nature* 274-77 (1876); G. Mivart*, *Man and Apes* (1873); G. Mivart*, *On the Genesis of Species* 277, 314 (1871); *see generally* J. Moore* at 222-23.

[65] J. Bascom*, *Evolution and Religion* 10-11, 13, 16 (1897); J. Bascom*, *Natural Theology* 128, 144-45 (1880); J. Bascom*, *Science, Philosophy, and Religion* 228-29 (1871); *see generally* J. Moore* at 223-24.

[66] H. Drummond*, *Ascent of Man* 15-16, 44-45, 414, 418, 429, 435, 436 (1894); H. Drummond*, *Natural Law in the Spiritual World* (1883); *see generally* J. Moore* at 224.

[67] T. MacQueary*, *The Evolution of Man and Christianity* x, 16, 229-30 (rev. ed. 1891); T. MacQueary*, *Topics of the Times* (1891); *see generally* J. Moore* at 225-26.

[68] L. Abbott*, *The Theology of an Evolutionist* iii, 6-10, 19, 20, 176 (1897); L. Abbott*, *The Evolution of Christianity* 1, 3, 8-9, 246-47 (1892); *see generally* J. Moore* at 226-27.

[69] F. Johnson*, *What Is Reality*? 260-65, 272, 276, 282-83, 312, 493 (1891); *see generally* J. Moore* at 227-28.

[70] G. Matheson*, *Can the Old Faith Live with the New?* 79-80, 86-87, 91, 157-58 (1885); *see generally* J. Moore at 228-29.

[71] M. Savage*, *The Evolution of Christianity* (1892); M. Savage*, *The Irrepressible Conflict between Two World-Theories* 11, 26 (1892); M. Savage*, *Evolution and Religion from the Standpoint of One Who Believes in Both* 32-34 (1886); M. Savage*, *The Morals of Evolution* 166 (1880); M. Savage*, *The Religion of Evolution* 47, 59 (1876); *see generally* J. Moore* at 229-30.

[72] J. Fiske*, *Life Everlasting* (1901); J. Fiske*, *Through Nature to God* (1899); J. Fiske*, *The Idea of God as Affected by Modern Knowledge* 129-30, 150-51 (1885); J. Fiske*, *The Destiny of Man* (1884); J. Fiske*, *Darwinism and Other Essays* 2-3 (rev. ed. 1885); J. Fiske*, *Outlines of Cosmic Philosophy: Based on the Doctrine of Evolution* (1874); *see generally* J. Moore* at 230-31.

[73] J. Van Dyke*, *Theism and Evolution* xvii-xxi, 24-34, 41-47 (1886); *see generally* J. Moore* at 241-45.

[74] J. Iverach*, *Christianity and Evolution* (1894); J. Iverach*, *Theism in the Light of Present Science and Philosophy* (1899); J. Moore* at 253.

[75] A. Moore*, *Evolution and Christianity* (1889); Moore*, *Darwinism and the Christian Faith*, in A. Moore*, *Science and the Faith* 166, 167 (1889); J. Moore* at 259-62.

[76] S. Ahlstrom*, *A Religious History of the American People* 771 (1972) (Yale U. Press) (italics in original).

[77] L. Abbott*, *The Theology of an Evolutionist* i (1900).

[78] *Id.* at 17.

[79] Beecher*, *The Two Revelations*, in The Evolutionary Outlook, 1875-1900, at 43 (G. Ostrander* ed. 1971) (italics added).

[80] Sections 15.1-15.2.

[81] L. Gilkey*, *Maker of Heaven and Earth: A Study of the Christian Doctrine of Creation* 34 (1959) (italics added).

[82] Meland*, *Theological Liberalism*, 13 Encyclopaedia Britannica 1021,

1021-22 (13th ed. 1965) (also listing some others).

[83] Ames* wrote:

> Many of the problems long prominent in religion may find their answers through the discoveries of science. One of these is the problem of creation. By finding out how nature works . . . there may come knowledge of the nature of life itself. Already the astronomers tell of the beginnings . . . of heavenly bodies . . .. The rough outline of man's life on the earth has become clear to anthropologists . . ..

E. Ames*, *Religion* 84 (1929).

[84] Clarke* stated that, because "theology should remand the investigation of the time and manner of the origin of man to the science of anthropology with its kindred sciences, just as it now remands the time and manner of the earth to astronomy and geology, and should accept and use their discoveries on the subject," theology "will receive from them an evolutionary answer" and "special creation . . . may come to appear improbable." Thus "Genesis will be regarded . . . as the record of a human tradition or conception of beginnings, and not as a literal narrative of occurrence." W. Clarke*, *An Outline of Christian Theology* 223, 224, 225 (9th ed. 1894).

[85] Coe* believed that the essential truth of "the application of the theory of evolution to the whole of man's nature" and "belief in the immanence of God in nature and in man" "may be said to be already established." G. Coe*, *The Religion of a Mature Mind* 8 (1902).

[86] Fosdick* is quoted in note 91.

[87] Mathews* wrote that Modernism "trusts Him—the awful, mysterious God of abysmal space, of galaxies, of stars, of ether, of evolution, of human liberty—as Father." S. Mathews*, *The Faith of Modernism* 118 (1936). He further stated that "Modernists . . . accept the results of scientific research as data with which to think religiously," and so a Modernist "is frankly and hopefully an evolutionist because of facts furnished by experts." *Id.* at 29-30. *See also* Hutchinson*, *The Modernist Impulse in American Protestantism* 275 (1976) ("Shailer Mathews of the University of Chicago was the most prominent spokesman *during the twenties—rivaled only by Fosdick—* for both of these arguments. Fosdick's outspoken eloquence, and his involvement in a notorious public controversy, made him known to an especially wide circle of Americans. But Mathews, as dean of the divinity school that had become a sort of modernist headquarters, stood forth as *the leading statesman, politician, historian, and systematic spokesman for the movement.*") (italics added).

[88] Rauschenbusch* emphasized:

> According to orthodox theology, man's nature passed through a fatal debasement at the beginning of history. According to evolutionary science the [physical] impulses . . . run far back in the evolution of the race. . ., whereas the . . . spiritual impulses are of recent development and relatively weak. We can take our choice of the explanations, but there are defects in the doctrine of original sin.

Rauschenbusch*, *Sin: Its Reality and Power*, in A Gospel For The Social Awakening 77, 91-92 (B. Mays* ed. 1950).

[89] Troeltsch* wrote:

> In and of itself this concept ["of evolutionary development"] is one of the most reliable working tools there is, and it is one of the fundamental presuppositions of the scientific study of history. It has proved its worth beyond all shadow of doubt and corresponds to all knowable processes.

E. Troeltsch*, *The Absoluteness of Christianity And The History of Religions* 72-73 (D. Reid* trans. 1971).

[90] S. Ahlstrom*, *A Religious History of the American People* 911 (1972).

[91] H. Fosdick*, *The Modern Use of the Bible* 50-51 (1924). Fosdick* further stated:

> the more facts we know the better founded does the hypothesis appear. . . . We have not kept the forms of thought and categories of explanation in astronomy, geology, biology which the Bible contains. We have definitely and irrevocably gotten new ones diverse from and irreconcilable with the outlooks . . . the Bible in particular had.

[92] W. Rauschenbusch*, *Christianizing the Social Order* 90 (1914).

[93] E. Aveling*, *The Gospel of Evolution* (1884).

[94] E. Lyon*, *The Meaning and Truth of Religion* (1933).

[95] D. Macintosh*, *Theology as an Empirical Science* 253-54 (1919).

[96] R. Millikan*, *Evolution in Science and Religion* (1929).

[97] D. Miller*, *The Case for Liberal Christianity* (1981) (evolutionist and Humanist).

[98] Stiernotte*, *Liberal Religion and the Sciences*, in Together We Advance 79, 81-82 (S. Fritchman* ed. 1946).

[99] Miller* & Fowler*, *What's Wrong with the Creation/Evolution Controversy?*, CTNS Bulletin, Autumn 1984, at 1, 2.

[100] Anderson*, *Creation*, in 1 The Interpreter's Dictionary of the Bible 725 (G. Buttrick* ed. 1962).

[101] E. Speisor*, *Genesis* (1964).

[102] The following "Statement of Faith" was recited by 1000 ministers and delegates at a National Council of Churches convocation:

Leaders Reading	*People Reading*
Some thousands of millions of years ago	WE BELIEVE IN GOD:
a fragment of matter composed of par ticularly stable atoms	WHO CALLS
was detached from the surface of the sun	THE WORLDS
this fragment began to condense, to roll itself up, to take shape	INTO BEING,

The curve doubles back, the surface contracts, the solid disintegrates, the liquid boils, the *germ cell divides*, intuition suddenly bursts	CREATES US AND SETS BEFORE US
We are responsible for the quality of our future. We are *evolving* into an interdependent whole of which every person is called upon to become a vital part	THE WAYS OF LIFE
Every organization insensitive to our need for personal involvement in the well-being of our fellow humans is disintegrating	AND DEATH.
Shock troopers of *evolutionary change* are now attacking all separatist structures	WHO JUDGES PEOPLE AND NATIONS;
Whoever has discovered . . . the secret of serving the *evolving Universe* and identifying with it	TO BE CHRIST'S SERVANTS IN THE SERVICE OF HUMAN KIND.

BLESSING AND HONOR, GLORY AND POWER BE UNTO HIM. AMEN.

A Blending of Readings from Pierre Teilhard de Chardin: The Phenomenon of Man and the Divine Milieu; The Center Letter #1 and #5 and the Statement of Faith of the United Church of Christ.

National Council of Churches*, *A Statement of Faith*, Program of Convention (Nov. 6, 19) (capitalization in original, italics added).

103 Institute for Educational Affairs* & Roper Center*, *What Theologians Believe*, This World, Summer 1982, at 27, 72 (data on seminary professors).

104 J. Hadden*, *The Gathering Storm in the Churches* 39, 75 (1969) (data on ministers).

105 Nelson* & Chadwick*, *Protestantism*, 26 New Encyclopaedia Britannica: Macropaedia 205, 227 (15th ed. 1987).

106 Jewett*, *Neo-Orthodoxy*, Baker's Dictionary of Theology 375, 377 (E. Harrison* ed. 1960)(Barth* "has specialized in ambiguity on the whole matter of the relation of primal history [Genesis 1-11] to empirical fact.").

107 G. Wurth*, *Niebuhr* 26-27 (1960) ("What is true of creation, namely, that it is in essence a myth, is equally valid of the fall of man.").

108 E. Brunner*, *Man in Revolt* 390-408 (O. Wyon* trans. 1947).

[109] Brunner* wrote:

> This whole historic picture of 'the *first man*' has been finally and *absolutely destroyed* for us to-day. The conflict between the teaching of history, natural science and palaeontology, on the origins of the human race, and that of the ecclesiastical doctrine, waged on both sides with the passion of a fanatical concern for truth, has led, all along the line, to the *victory of the scientific view*, and to the gradual but inevitable decline of the ecclesiastical view.
>
> . . ..
>
> Far more important than this external reason for giving up the story of Adam and Eve is an inner one . . ..

E. Brunner*, *Man in Revolt* 85, 86, 88 (O. Wyon* trans. 1947) (italics added).

[110] P. Tillich*, *Systematic Theology* 20 (1951) ("The theological problem arising from the differences between the organic and the inorganic dimensions is connected with the theory of *evolution* and the misguided attacks on it on the part of traditional religion.").

[111] P. Tillich*, *Systematic Theology* 303, 307 (1951) (italics added).

[112] L. Gilkey*, *Maker of Heaven and Earth—The Christian Doctrine of Creation in the Light of Modern Knowledge* (1959); L. Gilkey*, *Religion and the Scientific Future: Reflections on Myth, Science and Theology* (1970).

[113] C. Hyers*, *The Meaning of Creation: Genesis and Modern Science* (1984).

[114] Neo-Orthodoxy is embraced by a large proportion of ministers and members in major denominations such as

	Ministers
United Methodists	31.8%
Episcopalians	30.1%
American Baptists	15.4%
United Presbyterian Church	41.2%
American Lutheran Church	23.5%

J. Hadden*, *The Gathering Storm in the Churches* 39, 75 (1969). *See also* Institute for Educational Affairs* & Roper Center*, *What Theologians Believe*, This World, Summer 1982, at 27, 72.

[115] R. Cross*, *The Emergence of Liberal Catholicism in America* 149 (1958) (italics added).

[116] S. Ahlstrom*, *A Religious History of the American People* 839-40 (1972).

[117] *Mivart, Saint George*, 8 Encyclopaedia Britannica: Micropaedia 202, 202 (15th ed. 1974).

[118] P. Teilhard de Chardin*, *Christianity and Evolution* 183-84 (R. Hague* trans. 1971) (italics added). *See also id.* at 85 ("Seen, however, on the panoramic screen of an *evolutive* world which we have just erected, the whole picture undergoes a most impressive change.") (italics added).

[119] P. Teilhard de Chardin*, *Science and Christ* (1968); P. Teilhard de Chardin*, *The Appearance of Man* (1965).
[120] S. Jaki*, *The Road of Science and the Ways to God* 303 (1978) ("If one adds to this Gabriel Marcel's consternation on hearing Teilhard de Chardin brush aside the extermination of millions in Soviet slave labor camps as a mere episode in a march toward a glorious future, one may grasp the extent to which evolutionism can act as an ethical blindfold.") (italics added).
[121] H. Birx*, *Pierre Teilhard de Chardin's Philosophy of Evolution* (1972).
[122] B. Delfgaauw*, *Evolution: The Theory of Teilhard de Chardin* (H. Hoskins* trans. 1969).
[123] *Teilhard de Chardin*, 11 New Encylopaedia Britannica: Micropaedia 605, 605 (15th ed..1974).
[124] Schreiter*, *Edward Schillebeeckx*, in A Handbook of Christian Theologians 625, 630 (M. Marty* & D. Peerman* eds. rev. ed. 1984).
[125] R. Schreiter*, *A Schillebeeckx Reader* (1984).
[126] Swidler*, *Hans Küng*, in A Handbook of Christian Theologians 710, 712 (M. Marty* & D. Peerman* eds. rev. ed. 1984).
[127] Carr*, *Karl Rahner*, in A Handbook of Christian Theologians 519, 526 (M. Marty* & D. Peerman* eds. rev. ed. 1984).
[128] Rahner*, *Evolution and Original Sin*, in The Evolving World and Theology (J. Metz* ed. 1967).
[129] Schreiter*, *Edward Schillebeeckx*, in A Handbook of Christian Theologians 625, 630 (M. Marty* & D. Peerman* eds. rev. ed. 1984).
[130] Swidler*, *Hans Küng*, in A Handbook of Christian Theologians 710, 720 (M. Marty* & D. Peerman* eds. rev. ed. 1984).
[131] R. Brown*, *The Critical Meaning of the Bible* (1981); 1 *Jerome Biblical Commentary* (R. Brown* ed. 1968).
[132] Institute for Education Affairs* & Roper Center*, *What Theologians Believe*, This World, Summer 1982, at 27, 72 (60% of Catholic theological faculty describe themselves as "liberal").
[133] *See* L. Barish* & R. Barish*, *Basic Jewish Beliefs* 108-11 (1961); Schulman*, *Statement of Principles for the Guidance of the Modern Jew*, in 48 Central Conference of American Rabbis 421 (I. Marcuson* ed. 1937).
[134] That commentary states:

> Ancient people considered the earth the center of the universe and *natural law not as unalterable* but as subservient to the will of God. This view is the basic principle underlying many stories, especially the opening chapters of the Book of Genesis which have become a formidable obstacle to the reading of the Bible. Why—it is asked—should we concern ourselves at all with stories of the six days of *creation*, with *Adam and Eve*, and the *Garden of Eden*? All these are *unscientific, antiquated myths*, and therefore appear to be irrelevant. . . ..
>
> The contemporary readers thus should restrain their inclination to do battle with or look for modern comparisons to ancient notions of *creation*.

. . ..

. . .The Book of Genesis does not appear to tell of human growth and development in a way palatable to moderns, schooled in the principles of *evolution*.

W. Plaut*, *The Torah: A Modern Commentary* 6, 16 (1974) (italics added).

135 S. Wine*, *Judaism Beyond God* (1985).

136 *Conference of Secular and Humanistic Jews*, Humanistic Judaism, Summer 1982, at 34.

137 Society for Humanistic Judaism*, Humanistic Judaism: What Is It? (n.d.) ("*There are two kinds of religion. Theistic religions* assert that the ultimate source of moral authority and of the power for the solution to human problems is to be found outside of people—in a supernatural realm. *Humanistic religions* affirm that moral authority lies within each person and that we have the power, the right and the responsibility to be the masters of our own lives. . . . *Humanistic religions, such as Humanistic Judaism*, declare that reason, rather than faith, is the source of truth and that human intelligence and experience are capable of guiding our destiny.") (emphasis added); Wine*, *What Does Humanistic Judaism Offer?*, Humanistic Judaism, Spring 1986, at 3, 3 ("We offer the possibility of a secular religion."); Wine*, *Is Humanistic Judaism A Religion?*, Humanistic Judaism, Spring 1986, at 17, 20 ("Thus, humanism is more than a *religion*. While there are certain areas of its discipline that provide the religious experience, there are many areas in which the religious temperament is either irrelevant or harmful.") (emphasis added); S. Wine*, *Judaism Beyond God* (1985); S. Wine*, *Humanistic Judaism* (1978).

138 Friedman*, *Some Popular Misunderstandings of Our Philosophy*, Humanistic Judaism, Spring 1986, at 23, 23 ("Humanistic Judaism is a non-doctrinal religion.").

139 Borowitz*, *Humanism and Religious Belief in Martin Buber*, 53 Thought 320 (1978).

140 *See* K. Nakamura*, *Buddhist Philosophy*, in 3 Encyclopaedia Britannica: Macropaedia 425, 425 (15th ed. 1975).

141 *See* Basham*, *Hinduism*, in 8 Encyclopaedia Britannica: Macropaedia 888, 889 (15th ed. 1975).

142 Beattie*, *Humanism: Secular or Religious*, Free Inquiry, Winter 1980-81, at 11, 11.

143 *A Secular Humanist Declaration*, Free Inquiry, Winter 1980-81, at 3.

144 Lamont*, *Naturalistic Humanism*, Humanist, Sept.-Oct. 1971, at 9.

145 Haydon*, *Is Scientific Humanism Religious?*, 2 Religious Humanism 49 (1968).

146 De Ford*, *Humanism and Atheism I*, Humanist, July-Aug. 1971, at 5.

147 Huxley*, *Evolutionary Humanism: Part I*, Humanist, Jan.-Feb. 1962, at 3.

148 *A Secular Humanist Declaration*, Free Inquiry, Winter 1980-81, at 3, 5 ("6. Religious Skepticism. As secular humanists, we are generally skeptical about supernatural claims. . . . However, we find that traditional views of

the existence of God either are meaningless, have not yet been demonstrated to be true, or are tyrannically exploitative. *Secular humanists may be agnostics, atheists, rationalists, or skeptics*, but they find insufficient evidence for the claim that some divine purpose exists for the universe.") (italics added).

[149] P. Kurtz*, *In Defense of Secular Humanism* (1983).

[150] He defines it in terms of its Atheism:

> This is because the quintessential description of humanism is negative. Its concern is with man, yes, of course, but *definitively it does not have any place for God* or the gods. The real significance of the aphorism of Protagoras of Abdera—that man is the measure of all things—is and always has been the universally understood implication: *Man, not God, is the measure of both reality and values.*
>
> . . ..
>
> Once these features are pointed out, however, we can see that *they could just as well be part of a religious world-view or a nonreligious one. What counts about humanism is the negative side*, what it does not include or accept. That is, it does *not accept the* superhuman and the *supernatural. . . .*

Fletcher*, *Secular Humanism: It's the Adjective that Counts,* Free Inquiry, 1984, at 17, 18 (italics added).

[151] Kurtz*, *Humanism and Religion: A Reply to the Critics of Humanist Manifesto II*, Humanist, Jan.-Feb. 1974, at 4, 5 ("Thus in answer to the question, can one *believe in God and still be a humanist*, we need to ask of the believer: What do you mean by 'God'? If it is still a transcendent divine being or reality who created man and influences and controls his destiny, then the answer is '*No,*' for there is insufficient evidence. If, on the other hand, by 'God' one refers to the depth of human longing for a better life, and if by 'God' you allow man a choice, then the answer may be, for many humanists, 'Yes.' ") (italics added).

[152] DeFord*, *Humanism and Atheism I*, Humanist, July-Aug. 1971, at 5, 5 ("humanism, in my viewpoint, must be *atheistic* or it is not humanism") (italics added).

[153] D. Ehrenfeld*, *The Arrogance of Humanism* 6-7 (1978) (Oxford U. Press).

[154] Giustiniani*, *Homo, Humanis, and the Meanings of "Humanism"*, 46 J. History of Ideas (1985).

[155] Pfeffer*, *Issues That Divide: The Triumph of Secular Humanism*, 19 J. Church & State 203, 216 (1977).

[156] *E.g.*, Kurtz*, *Humanism and Religion: A Reply to the Critics of Humanist Manifesto II*, Humanist, Jan.-Feb. 1974, at 4, 4 ("It is no secret that the issue of antitheism is a hotly contested one in the humanist movement. One point of view maintains that humanism is primarily a scientific, philosophical, or moral outlook and that it must decisively reject any religious trappings. Humanism should unabashedly defend atheism, agnosticism, or

skepticism on intellectual and moral grounds. . . . Others hold the contrasting viewpoint that religious values are important in human experience, that humanism, under one interpretation, is itself a *religion* and that it ought to appreciate and be sensitive to humanist values within the religions, even the most orthodox ones.") (italics added).

[157] P. Kurtz*, *In Defense of Secular Humanism* 135 (1983) (italics added).

[158] Br. of American Humanist Association* at 11, Smith v. Board of School Comm'rs, No. 87-7216 (5th Cir. 1987).

[159] Haydon*, *Is Scientific Humanism Religious?*, Religious Humanism, Spring 1968, at 49, 50-51 ("Others, more emancipated, will gladly salute Humanism as a religion, and they will be factually justified.").

[160] Beattie*, *The Religion of Secular Humanism*, Free Inquiry, Winter 1985-86, at 12, 17 ("My religion is the religion of secular humanism.").

[161] Ramsey*, *Religion, Philosophy of*, 15 Encyclopaedia Britannica: Macropaedia 592, 597-98 (15th ed. 1974) (discussing "secular religion").

[162] L. Rosten*, *Religions of America* 1975 (chapter on Humanism).

[163] *1980 Humanist Counselor Directory*, Humanist, Nov.-Dec. 1980, at 48.

[164] H. Blackham*, *Humanism* 182 (1968)(italics in original).

[165] Silberman*, *Some Contributions of Psychology to Humanistic Religion*, Humanistic Judaism, Summer 1982, at 42.

[166] Weisman*, *From Orthodox Judaism to Humanism*, Humanist, May-June 1979, at 32, 33 ("I dared to speak out against Fundamentalists and to acknowledge Humanism as the most reasonable theology.").

[167] Bain*, *Jewish Identity and Survival: A Challenge for Secular/Humanistic Jews*, Humanistic Judaism, Winter 1986-87, at 26 (Chairman of Congress of Secular Jewish Organizations).

[168] Chuman*, *Creating a Secular Humanist Alternative*, Humanistic Judaism, Winter 1986-87, at 30.

[169] Levinrew*, *How I Came to Secular Humanistic Judaism in Israel*, Humanistic Judaism, Winter 1985, at 35.

[170] Bauer*, *On Being Jewish, Humanistic, and Secular*, Humanistic Judaism, Summer 1985, at 18; Bauer*, *Being a Secular/Humanistic Jew in Israel*, Humanistic Judaism, Spring 1984, at 15.

[171] Jerris*, *Being Secular/Humanistic Jews: Secular and Humanistic Jews Unite*, Humanistic Judaism, Spring 1984, at 32.

[172] N. Mirsky*, *Unorthodox Judaism* 142-45 (1978).

[173] *Conference of Secular and Humanistic Jews*, Humanistic Judaism, Summer 1982, at 34.

[174] Roclofsma*, *Giving Judaism a Humanist Face*, Insight, May 4, 1987, at 56, 56.

[175] *E.g.*, Bauer*, *On Being Jewish, Humanistic, and Secular*, Humanistic Judaism, Spring 1986, at 15, 16 ("We invite those people to join us and become participants in the venture of Jewish secular humanism."); S. Goodman, *Faith of Secular Jews* (1976); Jerris, *Will There Be a Second Generation of Humanistic Jews?*, Humanistic Judaism, Winter 1986-87, at

21, 22, 25 (executive director of Society for Humanistic Judaism) ("Secular Jewish communities—which generally pre-dated the inception of Humanistic Judaism—banded together in 1970 to form the *Congress of Secular Jewish Organizations (CSJO)*. . . . The most exciting development for training future leaders for Humanistic Judaism comes from the newly formed *International Institute for Secular and Humanistic Judaism in Israel*.") (emphasis added); Goodman, *The Faith of Secular Jews*, Humanistic Judaism, Summer 1982, at 3; Gales, *Trends and Countertrends in Jewish Secularism*, Humanistic Judaism, Fall 1980, at 10.

176 Abington School District v. Schempp, 374 U.S. 203, 225 (1963).

177 H. Cox, *The Secular City* 18 (1965). *See also* B. Bakser*, *Judaism and Modern Man: Essays in Jewish Theology* 19 (1957) ("Secularism has here invaded the *sanctum sanctorum* of religion itself, and remade it in its own image.") (emphasis in original).

178 367 U.S. 488, 495 n.11 (1961). *See also* Welsh v. United States, 398 U.S. 333, 357 n.8 (1970) (Harlan, J., concurring).

179 In re Weitzman, 426 F.2d 439, 457, 460 (8th Cir. 1970). *See also*, *e.g.*, Van Schaick v. Church of Scientology, 535 F. Supp. 1125, 1143 (D. Mass. 1982); Womens Services, P.C. v. Thone, 483 F. Supp. 1022, 1034 (D. Neb. 1979), *aff'd*, 636 F.2d 206 (8th Cir. 1980), *vacated on other grounds*, 452 U.S. 398 (1981); Loney v. Scurr, 474 F. Supp. 1186, 1194 (S.D. Iowa 1979); In re Adoption of "E," 279 A.2d 785, 795 n.4 (N.J. 1971).

180 Berman v. United States, 156 F.2d 377, 384 (9th Cir. 1946). *See also id.* at 384 n.2 ("To attribute to such highly educated men as Hughes, Holmes, Brandeis and Stone an ignorance of Taoism or Comte's humanism, or their denial that either is a *religion* if the question had been presented to them, would be an unwarranted assertion of their ignorance of the history of religious beliefs.") (emphasis added).

181 Anderson v. Laird, 466 F.2d 283, 305 n.18 (D.C. Cir. 1972) ("Even *creeds* like Humanism or Rationalism, which profess no belief in a Supreme Being but represent a set of firmly held moral and ethical convictions, are an important part of the moral fabric of our pluralistic society.") (emphasis added).

182 McDaniel v. Paty, 435 U.S. 618, 632 n.4 (1978) (Brennan, J., concurring).

183 *E.g.*, In re Weitzman, 426 F.2d 439, 457 n.5 (8th Cir. 1970) ("Secular Humanism is acknowledged as a '*religion*' in Torcaso . . ..") (emphasis added); United States ex rel. Brooks v. Clifford, 409 F.2d 700, 703 (4th Cir. 1969) ("*religious* denomination of his parents as Humanistic") (emphasis added); United States v. Seeger, 326 F.2d 846, 852 (2nd Cir. 1964) (Secular Humanism is a "well-established *religious* sect[].") (emphasis added); Greater Houston Chapter of the A.C.L.U. v. Eckels, 589 F. Supp. 222, 227, 228, 230, 231, 239 n.20 (S.D. Tex. 1984) (3 witnesses testified "defin[ing] Humanism as a *religion*," while 1 opposing witness said that Humanism is not necessarily a religion but performs marriages, funerals, and counseling); Crockett v. Sorenson, 568 F. Supp. 1422, 1425 (W.D. Va. 1983) ("The

First Amendment was never intended to insulate our public institutions from any mention of God, the Bible or religion. When such insulation occurs, another *religion*, such as secular humanism, is effectively established.") (emphasis added); Van Schaick v. Church of Scientology, 535 F. Supp. 1125, 1143 (D. Mass. 1982) ("In *Torcaso v. Watkins*, the Court held that '*religion*' as used in the First Amendment applied to nontheistic faiths, too, and explicitly recognized as religions Buddhism, Taoism, Ethical Culture and Secular Humanism.") (emphasis added); Womens Services, P.C. v. Thone, 483 F. Supp. 1022, 1034 (D. Neb. 1979) (*Torcaso* "listed several nontheistic *religions*," including Secular Humanism) (emphasis added, case history omitted); Loney v. Scurr, 474 F. Supp. 1186, 1194 (S.D. Iowa 1979) (Supreme Court had categorized " '. . . Secular Humanism' as *religions*"); Reed v. Van Hoven, 237 F.Supp. 48, 53 (W.D. Mich. 1965) ("[I]t seems clear that, in light of decided cases, the public schools, as between theistic and humanistic *religions*, must carefully avoid any program of indoctrination in ultimate values.") (emphasis added).

184 *E.g.*, Schowgurow v. State, 213 A.2d 475, 478 n.1, 481 (Md. 1965) (Secular Humanism as a religion); In re Adoption of "E", 279 A.2d 785, 795 n.4 (N.J. 1971) ("Mr. Burke described himself as a humanist which is specifically mentioned as a '*religion*' by the Supreme Court in Torcaso.") (emphasis added); State v. Woodville Appliance, Inc., 171 N.E.2d 565, 569 (Ohio Co. Ct. 1960) ("*religious* theories" such as Humanism) (emphasis added); Salem College & Academy v. Employment Division, 659 P.2d 415, 422 n.5 (Or. App. 1983) ("humanistic *faiths*") (emphasis added); Welker v. Welker, 24 Wis. 2d 570, 575-76, 129 N.W. 2d 134 (Wis. 1964) ("nontheistic *creeds* as Buddhism, Taoism, Ethical Culture, and Secular Humanism") (emphasis added); Gould v. Gould, 342 N.W.2d, 426, 432 (Wis. 1984) (same); Fellowship of Humanity v. County of Alameda, 315 P.2d 394, 398 (Cal. App. 1957) ("humanists as a *religious* group") (emphasis added); Spillers v. State, 245 S.E.2d 54, 55 (Ga. App. 1978) ("the American Humanist Association, a non-theistic *religion*") (emphasis added).

185 United States v. Seeger, 380 U.S. 163 (1965) (same) (Humanism basis), *aff'g*, 326 F.2d 846, 852 (2d Cir. 1964) ("among other well-established *religious* sects, . . . Secular Humanism") (emphasis added); United States v. Vlasits, 422 F.2d 1267, 1268, 1269 (4th Cir. 1970) ("his humanistic philosophy and belief"); Czubaroff v. Schlesinger, 385 F.Supp. 728, 737, 738, 741, 742, 743, 753, 754 (E.D. Pa. 1974) (his "Humanistic *faith*").

186 *E.g.*, Note, *The Myth of Religious Neutrality by Separation in Education*, 71 Va.L.Rev. 127, 148 (1985) ("once Secular Humanism or Marxism is recognized as a religion for establishment clause purposes, the discrete theories may be better described as components of a broader religion").

187 Dencer, *The Establishment Clause, Secondary Religious Effects, and Humanistic Education*, 91 Yale L.J. 1196, 1209-10 (1982) (italics added, footnotes omitted) (discontinuitist author).

188 D. Ehrenfeld*, *The Arrogance of Humanism* 4 (1978)(italics added).

[189] Education for Economic Security Act, 20 U.S.C. §§3901-4074 (1985) (in public education funding); Amend. No. 263 to H.R. 12,851, 94th Cong., 1st Sess. (1976) (for education funding, the Conlan amendment was passed by the House but not included in the Senate version).

[190] DeFord*, *Humanism and Atheism I*, Humanist, July-Aug. 1971, at 5, 5 ("My own tentative general *definition of humanism* would be that it is a philosophical system based on the concept that the universe, life, and consequently mankind are the result of natural *evolutionary* processes alone, and hence that our view of them must be monistic.") (italics added).

[191] Lamont*, *Naturalistic Humanism*, Humanist, Sept.-Oct. 1971, at 9, 9 ("Humanism believes, first, that Nature or the universe makes up the totality of existence and is completely self-operating according to *natural law*, with no need for God or gods to keep it functioning. . . . Second, Humanism holds that the race of man is the present culmination of a time-defying *evolutionary* process on this planet that has lasted billions of years . . . .") (italics added).

[192] Saladin*, *Getting Ahead By Getting Together: Symbiosis and Evolution*, Humanist, Jan.-Feb. 1979, at 10, 11 ("Zillions of months ago, people were just little bits of amoebid ooze, crawling about on the ocean floor, eating up their equally primitive comrades in their lethargically barbaric way, leaving behind only their shoes and other indigestible remains.").

[193] Harneck*, *Carl Sagan: Cosmic Evolution v. the Creationist Myth*, 41 Humanist 5 (July-Aug. 1981).

[194] *Humanist Manifesto II*, in Humanist Manifestos I and II, at 13, 14 (P. Kurtz* ed. 1973), reprinted from *Humanist Manifesto II*, Humanist, Sept.-Oct. 1973, at 4.

[195] Wilson*, *Pioneer of Evolutionary Humanism*, Humanist, May-June 1975, at 40, 40.

[196] *Humanist Manifesto II*, in Humanist Manifestos I and II, at 13, 24-31 (P. Kurtz* ed. 1973).

[197] *A Secular Humanist Declaration*, Free Inquiry, Winter 1980-81, at 3, 6. Its original signers include the president of the Fellowship of Religious Humanists. *Id.*

[198] D. Oldroyd*, *Darwinian Impacts* 253-54 (1980)(italics added except "quasi" and "humanism").

[199] C. Lamont*, *The Philosophy of Humanism* 13 (1977).

[200] Larue*, *The Way of Ethical Humanism*, Humanist, Sept.-Oct. 1984, at 20, 21.

[201] J. Huxley*, *Religion without Revelation* 203 (rev. ed. 1957).

[202] Huxley* believed in a "religion of evolutionary humanism." Huxley*, *The Coming New Religion of Humanism*, Humanist, Jan.-Feb. 1962, at 3, 5. That religion "must be organized round the facts and ideas of evolution." J. Huxley*, *The Humanist Frame* 14 (1961). His religion was "not based on revelation in the supernatural sense, but on the revelations [of] science," *id.* at 5, that "all reality is in a perfectly valid sense one universal process of

evolution." *Id.* at 4. He believed that "any Humanist ideology or religion must itself be an evolutionary system . . . ." Huxley*, *Evolutionary Humanism: Part I*, Humanist, Sept.-Oct. 1952, at 201, 208.

203 Huxley*, *The Coming New Religion of Humanism*, Humanist, Jan.-Feb. 1962, at 3, 4, 5 (italics added).

204 D. Oldroyd*, *Darwinian Impacts* 255 (1980).

205 Huxley*, *Evolutionary Humanism: Part I*, 12 Humanist 201, 206 (1952) ("What are the main elements which must be taken into account today in formulating a *Humanist view* of man's destiny, in expressing man's relations with the facts and problems of existence in a religious way, yet one which does not do violence to reason and science or to our accumulated knowledge about the past? In the first place, I would put the facts and principles of *evolution*.") (italics added); Huxley*, *Evolutionary Humanism: Part II*, 12 Humanist 249, 256 (1952) ("One of the articles of any *Humanist creed* must be this: that knowledge can be increased and that increase of knowledge is indispensable for anything that deserves to be called advance, whether in practice or in thought. . . . The comprehensive fact is that of *evolution*.") (italics added).

206 L. Hubbard*, *Scientology: A History of Man* 22 (1965) ("The discovery of the GE makes it possible at last to vindicate the theory of evolution proposed by Darwin . . . ."); L. Hubbard*, *Dianetics* 50 (2d ed. 1974) ("The proposition on which dianetics was originally entered was evolution.")

207 H. Blavatsky*, *The Key to Theosophy* 65 (1889) ("No one creates [the universe]. Science would call the process evolution . . . ; we, Occultists and Theosophists, see in it the only universal and eternal reality . . . ."); *id.* ("In short, our Deity is the eternal, incessantly *evolving*, not *creating*, builder of the universe . . . .") (italics in original).

208 *Anthroposophy*, 8 Encyclopedia of Philosophy 13 (P. Edwards* ed. 1967).

209 Brown*, *Stellar Evolution*, Am. Atheist, Mar.1982, at 21.

210 Bock*, *Some Thoughts on Evolution*, Am. Atheist, Dec. 1981, at 4.

211 Gurley*, *Alternate Theories for Cosmology*, Am. Atheist, Oct. 1980, at 13.

212 Bozarth*, *The Meaning of Evolution*, Am. Atheist, Sept. 1978, at 19.

213 Section 13.3(a).

214 *E.g.*, Malnak v. Yogi, 440 F. Supp. 1284, 1326 n.29 (D.N.J. 1977), *aff'd per curiam*, 592 F.2d 197 (3d Cir. 1979)("Atheism may be a religion under the establishment clause in that the government cannot aid the propagation of a belief in the nonexistence of a supreme being. *See Abington School District v. Schempp*, [374 U.S. 203,] 225 [1963]; *Zorach v. Clauson*, 343 U.S. 306, 314 (1952).").

215 Note 10.

216 Note 14.

217 Note 16.

218 Note 20.

[219] Note 143.
[220] Note 157.
[221] Note 48.
[222] Note 194.
[223] Note 197.
[224] Note 202.
[225] Provine*, *Book Review of Trial and Error: The American Controversy Over Creation and Evolution*, Academe, Jan.-Feb. 1987, at 50, 52.
[226] Note 81.
[227] Note 115.
[228] Note 134.
[229] S. Wine*, *Humanistic Judaism* (1978).
[230] Introduction to Volume 1, notes 50-56; Section 15.3(a).
[231] Raup*, *The Geological and Paleontological Arguments of Creationism*, in Scientists Confront Creationism 147, 159 (L. Godfrey* ed. 1983).
[232] Those denominational organizations are the Presbyterian Church in America and Reformed Presbyterian Church; Free Will Baptist Church and most Southern Baptist churches; Southern Methodist Church and Free Methodist Church; Missouri Synod, Wisconsin Evangelical Synod, and Orthodox Lutherans; Anglican Orthodox Church, American Episcopal Church, and other smaller Episcopal denominations; numerous Pentecostal denominations; Brethren, Christian and Missionary Alliance, Bible churches, and other nondenominational churches; Christian Reformed Church; etc. [Bird*], *Freedom of Religion and Science Instruction in Public Schools*, 87 Yale L.J. 519-20 nn. 21-22 (citing sources).
[233] P. Fehlner, *In the Beginning* 37 (1987) (italics added except ex nihilo), reprinted in 33 Christ to the World—(1988).
[234] *Id.* at 38 (italics added).
[235] Fehlner, *Vertex Creationis: St. Maximillian and Evolution*, 21 Miles Immaculatae 236, 238 (1985).
[236] B. Arthadeva, *Scienza e Verità: Evoluzionismo, Biogenesi e Uomo Scimmia* (1987).
[237] T. Sennott, *The Six Days of Creation* (1984); Sennott, *The Immaculate Conception and Evolution*, 21 Miles Immaculatae 221 (1985).
[238] W. Johnson, *The Crumbling Theory of Evolution* 105-06 (1982) ("It is fundamental that we believe in Creation, out of nothing, of heaven and earth by one almighty personal God whose power now sustains His creation. (Fourth Lateran and First Vatican Councils). We may believe in evolution of the body (if convinced of it on the evidence) but not evolution of the soul; and, among the earthly race of man, polygenism is forbidden. (Humani Generis). Any idea of a god evolving with the universe was condemned by the First Vatican Council."); W. Johnson, *The Case Against Evolution* (1976).
[239] P. O'Connell, *The Origin and Early History of Man* 9, 10, 11 (1965).
[240] Long, *Evolutionism: A Fairy Tale for Adults*, Friar Magazine, Oct. 1978, at 35.

[241] P. Haigh, *What's Wrong with Evolution?* 4 (1975).
[242] Thomas Aquinas, 13 *Summa Theologica: Man Made To God's Image* 23 (E. Hill trans. 1964) ("REPLY: The original fashioning of the human body can only have been done directly by God, not by means of any created forces. . . . God, however, although he is wholly immaterial, is nonetheless the only being who in his might can bring forth matter by creating it."); Thomas Aquinas, 15 *Summa Theologica: World Order* 161 (M. Charlesworth trans. 1970) ("Hence: 1. God is said to have ceased from work on the seventh day—not from all work (since it is said in John, *My father works even until now*) but rather from the *creation of new genera and species* which would not have already existed in God's first works. . . . 2. Certain things can be added daily to the perfection of the universe as regards individual things but not as regards species."); Thomas Aquinas, 2 *Summa Theologica* q. XLV, at 221 (English Dominican Province trans. 1912) ("Therefore as the generation of a man is from the not-being which is not-man, so creation, which is the emanation of all being, is from the not-being which is nothing.").
[243] P. Fehlner, *In the Beginning* 13-27 (1987) reprinted in 33 Christ to the World—(1988).
[244] Pope Pius XII, *Humani Generis: Encyclical Letter of His Holiness Pope Pius XII* 4, 16-17 (1950) (italics added). It goes on to condemn polygenism. *Id.* at 17 ("When, however, there is question of another conjectural opinion, namely polygenism, the children of the Church by no means enjoy such liberty. For the faithful *cannot embrace* that opinion which maintains either that after Adam there existed on this earth true men who did not take their origin through natural generation from him as from the first parent of all, or that Adam represents a certain number of first parents."). *See also* Pope Pius XII, *Man*, in The Pope Speaks 17 (M. Chinigo ed. 1957) ("On the topmost rung of the ladder of the living, God placed man, endowed with a spiritual soul, to be the prince and sovereign of the animal kingdom. Manifold research in the fields of paleontology, biology, and morphology on various problems regarding the origin of man has not yet yielded anything positively clear and certain.").
[245] Pope Paul VI, *Original Sin and Modern Science*, in 11 The Pope Speaks (1966) ("*Evolution* The theory of evolution will not seem acceptable to you whenever it is not decisively in accord with the immediate creation of each and every human soul by God, and whenever it does not regard as decisively important for the fate of mankind the disobedience of Adam, the universal first parent.") (italics in original).
[246] P. Fehlner, *In the Beginning* 32-34 (1987).
[247] These include Louis Pasteur, the famous microbiologist, in the mid 1800's; Paul Lemoine, president of the Geological Society of France, director of the Natural History Museum in Paris in the early 1900's, and a major editor of the *Encyclopedie Francaise* (1937); and W.R. Thompson, director of the Institute of Biological Control of Canada, in the mid 1900's. Section 15.2; *e.g.*, Thompson, *Introduction*, to C. Darwin*, The Origin of Species at xxii-

xxiii (1956); G. Sermonti* & R. Fondi*, *Dopo Darwin: Critica all' Evoluzionismo* (1980). An antievolutionist, Giuseppe Sermonti*, professor of biology at University of Perugia and former director of the Institute of Genetics at University of Palermo, was one of twelve lecturers at the recent Vatican Symposium on Recent Advances in the Evolution of Primates sponsored by the Pontifical Academy of Sciences. Montalenti*, *Darwinism Today*, 77 Scientia 21, 27 (1983).

[248] Section 14.1(d).

[249] P. Fehlner, *In the Beginning* 38-39 (1987).

[250] *E.g.*, Perlman, *Science vs. Evolution?*, in A Science and Torah Reader 28, 28 (Y. Komreich ed. 1970) ("The 'theory' of evolution lacks most of the characteristics of a scientific theory, and, in fact, leads to serious conceptual difficulties. Rather than being a scientific theory, evolution is a doctrine or conviction of many who use it as a justification for an atheistic or agnostic world outlook or philosophy. In fact, many of these people have more 'faith' in evolution than would be required of them in a religion.").

[251] Etkin, *The Religious Meaning of Contemporary Science*, in A Science and Torah Reader 30, 31 (Y. Komreich ed. 1970) ("And though the religions still survive, all, even Judaism, have become deeply penetrated by the attitudes and ideas generated by evolution. Their foundations have been gnawed away and the faith of the believer is now overcast with doubt.").

[252] Radkowsky, *The Faith of an Orthodox Jewish Scientist Revisited*, in B' Or Ha' Torah 21, 28 (ed. 198) ("Our sages of old always indicated that the validity of Judaism depended first of all on the necessary existence of G-d to explain Creation, then on the direct involvement with and revelation of G-d to the Jewish people in the exodus from Egypt and the giving of the Torah on Sinai. . . . Fortunately we don't have to face the problem of trying to fit Evolution into Judaism because Evolution has no scientific basis whatever.").

[253] Schneersohn, *A letter on science and Judaism*, in Challenge: Torah Views on Science and Its Problems 142, 146-47 (2d ed. A. Carmell & C. Domb eds. 1978).

[254] Goldman, *A critical review of Evolution*, in Challenge: Torah Views on Science and Its Problems 216 (2d ed. A. Carmell & C. Domb eds. 1978).

[255] *Proceedings of the Conference on Inquiries into Evolution and the Origin of Life* (1981).

[256] L. Spetner, *Evolution: An Analysis from the Torah Premises* 1 (unpublished ms. 1986).

[257] Amended Complaint at 1, Keith v. Louisiana Dept. of Educ., 553 F. Supp. 295 (M.D. La. 1982).

[258] Rahman*, *Islam*, 9 Encyclopaedia Britannica: Macropaedia 911, 912 (15th ed. 1975).

[259] R. Khalifa, *Creation: Why We Must Teach It in Schools* (1982).

[260] Nasr, *Eternity and temporal order: A view of evolution from the Islamic perspective*, 77 Rivista di Biologia 211, 215-17 (1984).

261 *Koran* sura 16, v. 3-5 (E. Rhys* ed., J. Rodwell* trans. 1909); *id.* sura 35, v. 12-14.
262 Introduction to Volume 1, n. 44.
263 L. Spence*, *Myths and Legends of Babylonia and Assyria* 84 (1916).
264 *See* Jacobsen*, *Enuma Elish—"The Babylonian Genesis"*, in Theories of the Universe 9 (M. Munitz* ed. 1957).
265 A. Heidel*, *The Babylonian Genesis* 88 (2d ed. 1951).
266 H. Osborn*, *From the Greeks to Darwin* xi (2d ed. 1929).
267 Mayer*, *Evolution in the Twentieth Century*, in A Compendium of Information on The Theory of Evolution and the Evolution-Creationism Controversy 95, 96 (rev. ed. J. Lightner* ed. 1978) ("Anaximander (611-547 B.C.) had the concept of a gradual evolution from a formless or chaotic condition to one of organic coherence. He had an understanding of what today we would call adaptation, and an almost modern view of the transformation of aquatic species into terrestrial ones."); Guthrie*, *Anaximander*, in 1 Encyclopaedia Britannica 885, 885 (14th ed. 1960).
268 Dobzhansky*, *Evolution*, 10 Encyclopedia Americana 734 (1976).
269 Harrison*, *Universe, Origin and Evolution of*, in 18 Encyclopaedia Britannica: Macropaedia 1007, 1007 (15th ed. 1974) (Milesian & Pythagorean schools).
270 H. Osborn*, *From the Greeks to Darwin* 52 (2d ed. 1929).
271 Lucretius*, *The Nature of the Universe* 58 (R. Latham* trans. 1951).
272 Veith*, *Creation and Evolution in the Far East*, in 3 Issues in Evolution: Evolution after Darwin 1, 2, 7 (S. Tax* & C. Callender* eds. 1960).
273 B. Fuller*, *History of Greek Philosophy: Thales to Democritus* 195 (1923) (Empedocles described "a true Darwinian evolution, the direction of which is explained entirely by chance, by the struggle for life, and by the survival of the fittest").
274 W. Stansfield*, *The Science of Evolution* 26 (1977) ("Although most of his biological concepts were primitive, in at least one of them he approached very closely the modern view: (1) higher forms of life gradually evolve, (2) plants evolved before animals, and (3) better adapted forms tend to replace the less adapted ones.").
275 R. Lull*, *Organic Evolution* 6 (rev. ed. 1948) ("Empedocles may be called the father of evolution.").
276 E. Zeller*, *Outlines of the History of Greek Philosophy* 75 (13th ed. 1960).
277 Peck*, *Empedocles*, in 8 Encyclopaedia Britannica 400, 400 (14th ed. 1960).
278 H. Reichenbach*, *Experience and Prediction* 6-7, 382-84 (1938) (U. Chicago Press).
279 Ruse*, *A Philosopher at the Monkey Trial*, 93 New Scientist 317, 318 (1982).
280 Laudan*, *Commentary: Science at the Bar—Causes for Concern*, Science, Technology & Human Values, Fall 1982, at 16, 17.

281 N. Gillespie*, *Charles Darwin and the Problem of Creation* 6 (1979).

282 Raup*, *The Geological and Paleontological Arguments against Creationism*, in Scientists Confront Creationism 147, 159 (L. Godfrey* ed. 1983).

283 "Vonnegut's intent to give religious comments did not render assignment of *Slaughterhouse-Five* an establishment of religion." Todd v. Rochester Community Schools, 41 Mich. App. 320, 200 N.W.2d 90 (1972).

284 J. Moore*, *The Post-Darwinian Controversies* 315 (1979). Darwin* and other Agnostic and Atheistic evolutionists are discussed in Section 13.3(a).

285 N. Gillespie*, *Charles Darwin and the Problem of Creation* 136-37 (1979).

286 W. Stansfield*, *The Science of Evolution* 578 (1977) ("If there be any conflict between religion and science, it would seem to reside in the minds of those whose concept of their *Deity* is too limited to allow Him the power to *create gradually through an evolutionary process*. If *God* is God, then He can do as He wishes with His universe; He could have brought all living things into being instantaneously, or He could have unfolded His creativity through the geological ages according to 'natural laws.' And what is the source of these natural laws? To those who believe in a Deity, they are part of the way that He sustains His creation."). Other theistic evolutionists are described in Sections 13.3(a) & 14.1(b)-(c).

287 H. Haggard*, *Mystery, Magic, and Medicine* (1933).

288 A. Ihde*, *The Development of Modern Chemistry* 10-18 (1964).

289 Smart*, *Religion and Science*, 7 Encyclopedia of Philosophy 158, 159 (P. Edwards* ed. 1967). *See also* Rosen*, *Kepler*, 22 Encyclopaedia Britannica: Macropaedia 506, 506 (15th ed. 1974).

290 C. Hempel*, *Philosophy of Natural Science* 16 (1966).

291 Feuer*, *Teleological Principles in Science*, 21 Inquiry 377, 381 (1978).

292 *Kekule*, 7 Dictionary of Scientific Biography 281 (C. Gillispie* ed. 1973).

293 C. Hempel*, *Philosophy of Natural Science* 16 (1966).

294 J. O'Neill*, *Prodigal Genius: Life of Nikola Tesla* (1944).

295 J. Maritain*, *The Dream of Descartes* 14 (M. Anderson* trans. 1944).

296 Ruse*, *The Ideology of Darwinism*, in Darwin Today 233, 246 (E. Geissler* & W. Scheler* eds. 1983).

297 R. Levins* & R. Lewontin*, *The Dialectical Biologist* 267 (1985).

298 *Id.* at 241.

299 Caudill, *Law and Worldview: Problems in the Creation-Science Controversy*, 3 J. Law & Religion 1, 43, 18 (1985) (discontinuitist author).

300 *E.g.*, P. Kitcher*, *Abusing Science: The Case Against Creationism* (1982).

301 Crawford*, *Science as an Apologetic Tool for Biblical Literalists*, in Creationism, Science, and the Law: The Arkansas Case 104 (M. LaFollette* ed. 1983).

302 Ruse*, *Creation-Science Is Not Science*, in *id.* at 150; M. Ruse*, *Darwinism Defended* 285-302, 322-24 (1982).

[303] F. Bacon, 1 *Novum Organum* cxxix (1902); F. Bacon, *Refutation of Philosophies* (1608) ("[God] did not give you reliable and trustworthy sense in order that you might study the writings of a few men. Study the Heaven and the Earth, the works of God himself, and do so while celebrating His praises and singing hymns to your Creator.").

[304] I. Newton, *Observations upon the Prophecies of Daniel, and The Apocalypse of St. John* 248-49 (B. Smith ed. 1733)("[I]n the very end, the Prophecy [of Daniel and John] should be so far interpreted as to convince many. Then, saith Daniel, many shall run to and fro, and knowledge shall be increased. . . . 'Tis therefore a part of this Prophecy, that it should not be understood before the last age of the world; and therefore it makes for the credit of the Prophecy, that it is not yet understood. But if the last age, the age of opening these things, be now approaching, as by the great successes of late Interpreters it seems to be, we have more encouragement than ever to look into these things.").

[305] B. Stoddard*, *The Relationships between Natural Philosophy, Natural Theology and Revealed Religion in the Thought of Newton and Their Historiographic Relevance* 116-20 (Ph.D. diss., Northwestern U. 1976).

[306] *Isaac Newton's Papers and Letters on Natural Philosophy* 280 (2d ed. I. Cohen* ed. 1978) (Harvard U. Press) (capitalization in original).

[307] C. Baumgardt*, *Johannes Kepler: Life and Letters* 31 (1951) (italics added).

[308] Boyle, *Some Motives and Incentives to the Love of God*, in 1 Works of Robert Boyle 167 (1744).

[309] Another example is Maury, superintendent of the U.S. National Observatory. R. Numbers*, *Creation by Natural Law* 88 (1977) (Maury wrote: "[T]hat rule is never to forget who is the author of the great volume which nature spreads out before us, and always to remember that the same Being is also the author of the Book which Revelation holds up to us; and though the two worlds are entirely different their records are equally true, and when they bear upon the same point, as now and then they do, it is as impossible that they should contradict each other, as it is that either should contradict itself. If the two cannot be reconciled, the fault is ours, and because in our blindness and weakness we have not been able to interpret aright, either the one or the other or both.").

[310] Section 13.4.

[311] Section 13.3(a).

[312] N. Glueck, *Rivers in the Desert* 30 (1959) (italics added).

[313] J. Huxley*, *Evolution in Action* (1953).

[314] J. Huxley*, *Religion without Revelation* 203 (rev. ed. 1957); Section 14.1(g).

[315] I. Asimov*, *In the Beginning: Science Faces God in the Book of Genesis* 1-66 (1981); I. Asimov*, *Asimov's Guide to the Bible* 9-13, 15-32 (1968).

[316] I. Asimov*, *Asimov on Physics* (1976); I. Asimov*, *Asimov's Guide to Science* (rev. ed. 1972).

[317] M. Caspar*, *Kepler* 67 (C. Hellman* ed. 1958).
[318] I. Newton, *The Chronology of Ancient Kingdoms Amended* (1728); I. Newton, *Observations Upon the Prophecies of Daniel and the Apocalypse of St. John* (1733). Newton did not accept Ussher's late date for creation.
[319] *Boyle, Robert,* 2 Encyclopaedia Britannica: Micropaedia 447, 447 (15th ed. 1974).
[320] B. Pascal, *Pensees* (A. Krailsheimer* trans. 1966) (notes planned to be a work entitled Apologie de la Religion Chrétienne).
[321] Leith*, *Are the Reports of Darwin's Death Exaggerated?*, 166 The Listener 390, 392 (1981) ("Just as preDarwinian biology was carried out by people whose faith was in the Creator and His plan, post-Darwinian biology is being carried out by people whose *faith* is in, almost, the deity of Darwin.") (italics added).
[322] Address of Dr. Colin Patterson* at American Museum of Natural History, tr. at 4 (Nov. 5, 1981) (emphasis added).
[323] R. Good*, *Features of Evolution in the Flowering Plants* 1 (1974).
[324] Scott*, *Presidential Address*, 108 Nature 153 (1921) ("Is even then evolution not a scientifically ascertained fact? No! We must hold it as an act of *faith* because there is no alternative.") (italics added).
[325] J. Rifkin*, *Algeny* 119 (1983) ("[E]volution must be a matter of *personal faith*. About the best that can be said about the theory is that it represents a belief that many people share about how life developed, a belief that can be neither proved nor disproved. Of course, everyone is entitled to his own beliefs, speculations, and personal convictions, but evolution proponents profess that their theory represents much more than a simple *article of faith*. It is pure truth, they contend, even though unprovable, and in their zeal they are unwilling to brook any opposition to its central tenets.") (italics added).
[326] P. Ehrlich* & R. Holm*, *The Process of Evolution* 310 (1963) (italics added).
[327] Matthews*, *Introduction*, to C. Darwin*, The Origin of Species xii (1971).
[328] W. Bateson*, *The Limitations of Science* 200 (1933) ("We have the impression that it is only by extraordinary acts of *faith* that biologists can suppose that the actual progress of life can be explained in the terms they adopt.") (italics added).
[329] M. Midgley*, *Evolution as a Religion* 61 (1985).
[329A] B. Leith*, *The Descent of Darwin: A Handbook of Doubts about Darwinism* 10-11 (1982); N. Macbeth*, *Darwin Retried* 124-32 (1971); Section 10.5 (b) (2).
[330] Yockey*, *A Calculation of the Probability of Spontaneous Biogenesis by Information Theory*, 67 J. Theoretical Biology 377, 377 (1977) (italics added).
[331] G. Kerkut*, *Implications of Evolution* 150 (1960) (italics added).
[332] J. Greene*, *Science, Ideology, and World View* 177 (1981) ("In both

cases science was only a tool, a weapon, in defense of positions that were essentially religious and philosophical. *Faith* in science can be no less a religion than faith in God.") (italics added).

[333] Hammond*, *The Value System in the Scientific Subculture*, 32 Bull. Atomic Scientists 10, 36-40 (1976) ("To many scientists, *pure science has become the new religion*. We have developed our own mystique; we have dogma, ritual, a high priesthood, a system for training young priests of science and a reverence for science that rivals my grandmother's reverence for her personal deity. I have real fear that *blind belief in the majesty of established science* may reduce it to a role as ineffective as that of the churches that it has supplanted.") (italics added).

[334] M. Midgley, *Evolution as a Religion* 112 (1985).

[335] *E.g.*, J. Barrow* & F. Tipler*, *The Anthropic Cosmological Principle* (1986).

[336] Leslie*, *Anthropic Principle, World Ensemble, Design*, 19 Am. Philosophical Q. 141, 141 (1982) ("But let us first be clear that calling it evidence of Design (rather than of a World Ensemble) does not always indicate belief in a Designer. God might be not a Person but a creative force: our world of life may through its own nature have requiredness which is creatively effective. This can be defended independently of any religion.").

[337] Feuer*, *Teleological Principles in Science*, 21 Inquiry 377 (1978).

[338] *Id.* at 377.

[339] Ayala*, *Teleological Explanations in Evolutionary Biology*, Philosophy of Science, Mar. 1970, at 1, 1.

[340] D. Hull*, *Darwin and His Critics* 55 (1973).

[341] J. Barrow* & F. Tipler*, *The Anthropic Cosmological Principle* 11 (1986).

[342] Letter from Dr. Wernher von Braun to Dr. Vernon Grose (Sept. 14, 1972) (creationist scientist).

[343] Grene*, *Bohm's Metaphysics and Biology*, in Toward a Theoretical Biology 61, 66 (C. Waddington* ed. 1969).

[344] T. Dobzhansky*, F. Ayala*, G. Stebbins* & J. Valentine*, *Evolution* 95-96 (1977).

[345] Ayala*, *Teleological Explanations in Evolutionary Biology*, Philosophy of Science, Mar. 1970, at 1, 1-2.

[346] Paterson*, *Darwin and the Origin of Species*, 78 S. African J. Science 272, 274 (1982).

[347] O'Grady*, *Evolutionary Theory and Teleology*, 107 J. Theoretical Biology 563, 563, 565, 571 (1984).

[348] Press*, *A place for teleology?*, 320 Nature 315, 315 (1986).

[349] Leslie*, *Cosmology, Probability, and the Need To Explain Life*, in Scientific Explanation and Understanding 53, 54 (N. Rescher* ed. 1983).

[350] Note 263.

[351] Note 275.

[352] Note 285.

[353] Note 297.
[354] Note 322.
[355] Note 323.
[356] Note 339.

PART VII

Whether the Theories of Abrupt Appearance and Evolution Are Non-Religious? The History of the Creation-Evolution Controversy

The history of the creation-evolution controversy is instructive, although the theory of abrupt appearance differs from the theory of creation. This historical setting is much misunderstood, because it is not one of religion versus science, but of religious and scientific support for each explanation.

Religious support for the theory of evolution has been persistent. It was evident in the "theological arguments" in Darwin's* *Origin* that Gillespie* notes;[1] in the seventeen Theological Liberal evolutionists that Moore* exhaustively documents;[2] and in the "early proponents of Darwinism [who] were atheistic materialists—or their near relatives" that Hull* describes.[3] Religious support for evolution continued with the factions in the mainline denominations that argued for an evolutionary view;[4] the Modernist and Theological Liberal leaders who held evolutionary beliefs;[5] and the more recent religious support for evolution by most Humanists and Theological Liberals.[6]

Scientific support for the theory of creation historically has been equally widespread. It began with the "Goliaths" of science who challenged Darwin* such as Agassiz, Thomson, Harvey, and Brewster (listed by Moore*),[7] as well as Pasteur, Silliman, Maxwell, Faraday, and Hitchcock; and continued with Fleischman, Fabre, Strutt, Maunder, Fleming, von Braun, Hoyle, and others.[8] A *New Republic* article noted that the "leading participants on the creationist side—who are often portrayed as Bible-thumpers but have science Ph.D.s—are in fact scientists."[9] Although the theory of creation, like evolution, has had religious as well as scientific support, that is not primarily Fundamentalist but Conservative Evangelical, Orthodox Catholic, Orthodox Jewish, Muslim and often Hindu.[10] The support for teaching all scientific views of origins is much broader, encompassing eighty-six percent of the public, sixty-seven percent of school board members, fifty-six percent of lawyers (opposed by only twenty-six percent), and forty-two percent of teachers.[11]

Political activity has been greater among evolutionists than creationists. There is a "national network of anti-creationist citizen lobbies" with chapters in "forty-two [states] and still rising," according to Saladin*.[12] Eight other evolutionist organizations have nationally lobbied against the creationist menace.[13]

Notes

[1] N. Gillespie*, *Charles Darwin and the Problem of Creation* 124 (1979).

[2] J. Moore*, *The Post-Darwinian Controversies* 220-69 (1979).

[3] Hull*, *Darwinism and Historiography*, in The Comparative Reception of Darwinism 388, 391 (T. Glick* ed. 1974).

[4] K. Cauthen*, *The Impact of American Religious Liberalism* 7, 22 (1962).

[5] S. Ahlstrom*, *A Religious History of the American People* 771 (1972).

[6] Section 14.1 (b) & (g).

[7] N. Gillespie*, *Charles Darwin and the Problem of Creation* 26-27 (1979).

[8] Section 15.2(b)-(c).

[9] Bethell*, *A Challenge to Materialism*, New Republic, Aug. 1, 1983, at 34, 36.

[10] Section 14.2

[11] Introduction to Vol. 1, notes 50-56.

[12] Saladin*, *Opposing Creationism: Scientists Organize*, Humanist, Mar.-Apr. 1982, at 59, 59.

[13] Section 15.1(b).

CHAPTER 15

Theories of Evolution and Abrupt Appearance and the History of Religious Involvement

Darwinism did have an impact on religion. But it is a grave historiographical solecism to judge the participants in the evolutionary debate in terms of black and white—the evolutionists pure as driven snow; the theologians foolish bigots. . . .

—David R. Oldroyd*,
Professor of philosophy and history of science, University of New South Wales[1]

The histories of the theory of abrupt appearance, the theory of creation, and the theory of evolution are parallel in terms of the

*Historians and others cited in this chapter, unless otherwise indicated, are not proponents of, and their quoted statements are not intended as endorsements of, either the theory of abrupt appearance or the theory of creation. However, their quoted statements are acknowledging information that supports the nonreligious nature of the theories of abrupt appearance, creation, and evolution.

involvement of religious forces and leaders. It is simply not accurate—Oldroyd* calls it "a grave historiographical solecism"—to say that the theory of creation has been uniformly supported by religious zealots while the theory of evolution has been uniformly supported by scientists over the last century. Instead, there has been substantial religious involvement on the evolutionist side (Section 15.1), and there has been substantial scientific involvement on the creationist side of the controversy (Section 15.2). There has not been more than a parallel religious involvement with the creationist side (Section 15.3). This issue does not directly involve the theory of abrupt appearance, but shows that it is no more made religious by historical creationism than evolution is made religious by historical theistic evolutionary views.

Figure 15.1
Evolutionist theologians included Henry Ward Beecher, pastor of the nation's largest church; and today "Liberal religious leaders and theologians proclaim the compatibility of religion and evolution" (Provine*)*

15.1 Religious Involvement on the Evolutionist Side of the Creation-Evolution Controversy

The theory of abrupt appearance is no more inherently a tenet or product of religious Fundamentalism or other creationist religions than the theory of evolution is inherently a tenet or product of evolutionist religions such as Theological Liberalism, Neo-Orthodoxy, Religious Humanism, Neo-Modernist Roman Catholicism, Reform Judaism, or Evolutionary Humanism.[2] Religious groups and leaders have advocated and supported evolution to at least the same extent that religious groups and leaders have advocated and supported creation through the past century and a quarter.

a. Religious Support for Evolution in the Late Nineteenth Century

During the late nineteenth century, the leading exponents of evolution were primarily religious spokesmen from such evolutionist religions as Theological Liberal Protestantism, Unitarianism, Religious Humanism, Agnosticism, and Atheism.

Darwin* himself was formally trained as a theologian rather than a scientist, and made "frequent" theological arguments against creation and for evolution, according to Gillespie* in his thorough history published by University of Chicago Press:

> In the *Origin of Species*, and in the writings that culminated in it, Darwin frequently condemned special creation on theological grounds. . . . *The Origin*, in all of its editions, not only has numerous references to such a Creator, but theological arguments based on such a conception had some importance in its overall logic as that existed for Darwin.[3]

A recent and heavily documented book from Cambridge University Press by Moore*, a history professor at Open University in England, describes leading evolutionists of the late nineteenth century, and features the following seventeen Theological Liberals whose evolutionist theology was described in Section 14.1(a):

Rev. Frederick Temple* (Anglican, Archbishop of Canterbury)
Rev. Henry Ward Beecher* (Congregational minister)
Rev. George Henslow* (Anglican minister and botanist)
Hon. George Douglas Campbell*, Duke of Argyll (politician)
Dr. St. George Mivart* (Roman Catholic lay theologian and biologist)
Rev. John Bascom* (Congregational minister and professor)
Rev. Henry Drummond* (Free Church minister)
Rev. Thomas Howard MacQueary* (Episcopal minister)
Rev. Lyman Abbott* (Congregational minister)
Rev. Francis Howe Johnson* (Congregational minister)
Rev. George Matheson* (Church of Scotland minister)
Rev. Minot Judson Savage* (Church of the Unity minister)
Rev. John Fiske* (Congregational then Unitarian philosopher)
Rev. Joseph S. Van Dyke* (Presbyterian minister)
Rev. James McCosh* (Presbyterian minister)
Rev. James Iverach* (Free Church minister)
Rev. Aubrey Lackinton Moore* (Anglican minister).[4]

They published dozens of religious evolutionist books with titles such as Beecher's* *Evolution and Religion*, Henslow's* *Genesis and Geology*, MacQueary's* *The Evolution of Man and Christianity*, Abbott's* *The Theology of an Evolutionist*, and Savage's* *Evolution and Religion from the Standpoint of One Who Believes in Both*.[5]

Among evolutionist scientists, "almost all the early proponents of Darwinism were atheistic materialists—or their near relatives," according to historian Hull*.[6] As Greene* indicates,[7] examples are such Agnostics as Darwin* and Huxley*, and such Atheists as Spencer* and Haeckel*, as discussed earlier.[8]

Several religious denominations rapidly embraced evolution in large part, Numbers* states:

> But the available studies do indicate that the *religious bodies most sympathetic to organic evolution* were ones that attracted large numbers of educated persons: the Unitarians, Congregationalists, and, to a lesser degree, Presbyterians.[9]

"Unitarians in America were the most receptive [denomination] to evolution, [and] in interpreting and propagating it," Moore* adds.[10] Others followed suit in the early twentieth century.

b. Religious Support for Evolution in the Early Twentieth Century

During the early twentieth century, many leading exponents of evolution were still religious leaders from Theological Liberal, Neo-Orthodox, Unitarian, Modernist Roman Catholic, Religious Humanist, Agnostic or Atheist, and other faiths. As Provine* concludes, "many, probably most, evolutionists were religious":

> In the 1920s many, probably most, evolutionists were religious. The most outspoken critic of William Jennings Bryan from the scientific community was the dean of American evolutionists, Henry Fairfield Osborn, then president of the American Museum of Natural History. His 1925 book, *The Earth Speaks to Bryan*, eloquently argued that evolution and Christian religion were wonderfully compatible. . . .[11]

Most Theological Liberals, such as the following leaders, were strong advocates of evolution, as discussed previously:

Rev. Edward Scribner Ames*
Rev. William Newton Clarke*
Rev. George A. Coe*
Rev. Harry Emerson Fosdick*
Rev. Shailer Mathews*
Rev. Walter Rauschenbusch*
Rev. Ernst Troeltsch*.[12]

Divisions occurred within most mainline religious denominations between Modernists (or Theological Liberals) and Fundamentalists (or Conservatives), and the evolution-creation issue was one of the most fought issues.[13] The Modernists and Theological Liberals generally aligned with evolution to the same extent that the Fundamentalists and Conservatives generally aligned with creation,[14] as is shown by studies[15] of the Methodist,[16] Northern Lutheran,[17] Northern Baptist,[18] Northern Presbyterian,[19] and other denominations.[20]

Anti-evolution bills that were considered in several states in the 1920s were actively opposed by Modernists and Theological Liberals to the extent they were supported by Fundamentalists and Theological Conservatives, as described later.[21]

Neo-Orthodoxy arose after World War I, and most of its leading exponents, such as Niebuhr*, Brunner*, and Tillich*, held to religious views of evolution.[22] Religious Humanists, including many Unitarians, signed[23] the first *Humanist Manifesto* in 1933 to affirm that "religious humanism" adheres to evolution (in 4 of 15 points) and other doctrines.[24]

c. *Religious Support for Evolution in the Later Twentieth Century*

The evolutionist position still receives at least the same degree of religious support as the creationist position. The unlikely coalition of "atheistic evolutionists and liberal theologians" is described by Provine*:

> Liberal religious leaders and theologians, who also proclaim the compatibility of religion and evolution, achieve this unlikely position by two routes. First, they retreat from traditional interpretations of God's presence in the world, some to the extent of becoming effective atheists. Second, they simply refuse to understand modern evolutionary biology and continue to believe that evolution is a purposive process.
>
> We are now presented with the specter of atheistic evolutionists and liberal theologians, whose understanding of the evolutionary process is demonstrable nonsense, joining together with the ACLU and the highest courts in the land to lambast creationists, who are caught in an increasing bind. Evolutionary biology, as taught in public schools, shows no evidence of a purposive force of any kind. This is deeply disturbing to creationists. Yet in court, scientists proclaim that nothing in evolutionary biology is incompatible with any reasonable religion, a view also supported by liberal theologians and religious leaders of many persuasions. . . .[25]

For instance, a recent book is entitled *Is God a Creationist?: Religious Arguments Against Creation-Science.*[26]

A position paper opposing balanced treatment for the theory of creation along with the theory of evolution has been issued by the United Ministries in Education, a "ministry of agencies of eight denominations" including the Executive Council of the Episcopal Church and boards of the American Baptist and Presbyterian Churches and United Church of Christ,[27] just as opposite resolutions have been passed by the Southern Baptist Convention[28] and Lutheran Church-Missouri Synod.[29] Vitriolic religious articles opposing creation and supporting evolution appear regularly in *The Humanist* (American Humanist Association), *Religious Humanism* (Fellowship of Religious Humanists), *Christian Century* (Theological Liberal), *American Atheist*, and other religious publications.[30]

A number of clergy holding Theological Liberal and Neo-Orthodox viewpoints joined the American Civil Liberties Union side of the *McLean* case[31] and the recent *Aguillard* case as plaintiffs,[32] just as religious leaders of the Orthodox Roman Catholic, Orthodox Jewish, and Muslim faiths joined the balanced treatment side of the related *Keith* case as plaintiffs,[33] attempted to intervene on the balanced treatment side of the *McLean* case,[34] and filed briefs in the *Aguillard* case.[35]

Summary. Religious support has been at least as great for the evolutionist side as for the creationist side of the creation-evolution controversy over the last century. The point is not that this makes the scientific theories of evolution, abrupt appearance, or creation religious, but that the history of religious support for the theories of evolution and creation is essentially parallel. Darwin* himself in *The Origin of Species* "frequently condemned special creation on theological grounds" (Gillespie*[36]), and the first generation of Darwinists consisted heavily of clergymen who held evolutionary religious doctrines (Moore*[37]). In the ensuing split, some religious denominations became "sympathetic to organic evolution" (Numbers*[38]), as part of Theological Liberalism and Neo-Orthodoxy, and "[i]n the 1920s, many, probably most, evolutionists were religious" (Provine*[39]). Today, there is an unlikely combination "of atheistic evolutionists and liberal theologians, whose understanding of the evolutionary process is demonstrable nonsense, joining together with the ACLU" to defend evolutionary hegemony and to oppose creationist scientific claims (Provine*[40]).

Figure 15.2
The "pre-Darwinian creationists" were "true 'scientific creationists'," such as Louis Agassiz of Harvard, "America's leading biologist" (Gould)*

15.2 Scientific Involvement on the Creationist Side of the Creation-Evolution Controversy

The creationist side of the creation-evolution controversy has always been strongly advocated by some scientists, while its religious support has not been stronger than the religious support for the evolutionist side. Nearly all the leading scientists before the mid-nineteenth century were creationists, as Section 13.4 demonstrated. The creationist conclusions of those scientists amounted to true science, and were "very similar" to modern scientific theories of creation, according to Dolby*, a philosopher of science:

> The principles which scientific creationism develops have the interesting feature that they are very similar to some of the doctrines proclaimed in the name of science in the century after the scientific revolution, in particular in the early eighteenth century. . . .
>
> . . . I do not wish to say that those eminent natural philosophers of the seventeenth and eighteenth centuries who produced syntheses like those of modern creationism were doing pseudo-science. Further, if such an activity was describable as science then, there is a case for describing it as science now. So whatever may be wrong with creationism, I do not wish to say that *it* is pseudo-science, either. I am inclined to the view that it is archaic science functioning as a framework for criticism of science.[41]

In general, "it has always been the anti-evolutionists, not the evolutionists, in the scientific community who have stuck . . . to a more strictly empirical approach," Denton* observes:

> [T]he doctrine of continuity has always necessitated a retreat from pure empiricism, and contrary to what is widely assumed by evolutionary biologists today, it has always been the anti-evolutionists, not the evolutionists, in the scientific community who have stuck rigidly to the facts and adhered to a more strictly empirical approach.
>
> . . . It was, again, the actual facts that led Linnaeus, Cuvier and most of the professional biologists of the seventeenth, eighteenth and early nineteenth centuries to favour a discontinuous view of nature. . . .
>
> . . . When, half a century later, Agassiz referred to the notion of continuity in its new Darwinian guise as "a phantom" he was speaking as a true empiricist. It was Darwin the evolutionist who was retreating from the facts.[42]

Although this subject is ably treated in a creationist work, Morris's *History of Modern Creationism*,[43] the following discussion is based only on original sources or evolutionist authors.

a. Scientific Support for the Theory of Creation in the Late Nineteenth Century

When Darwin* published his *Origin of Species* in 1859, the leading creationists and antievolutionists were scientists, and in fact were some of the most renowned scientists in the world, according to Moore*:

> Goliaths loomed everywhere: Roderick Murchison, second only to Lyell among British geologists; David Brewster, the Scottish natural philosopher, principal of the University of Edinburgh and founder of the British Association; William Clark, professor of anatomy at Cambridge; William Henry Harvey, professor of botany in the University of Dublin; Louis Agassiz, the Harvard zoologist, whose massive intellect had been nurtured by Cuvier; Fredrich Max Muller, the leading philologist in Britain; William Whewell, the Cambridge historian and philosopher of science; William Thomson, professor of natural philosophy in the University of Glasgow ; and of course Sedgwick and Henslow. However, it was not cogency of argument, nor even his imposing reputation as a vertebrate anatomist and paleontologist, that made Richard Owen, superintendent of the natural history department of the British Museum, Darwin's most formidable opponent.[44]

(1) Creationist Scientists. Most of the creationist scientists did not hold a religious belief in "miraculous creation" but based their position on "empirical evidence," in the words of Gillespie*:

> Of all those mentioned by Darwin in 1859 as being foes of the mutability of species—Cuvier, Owen, Agassiz, Barrande, Falconer, Forbes, Lyell,

> Murchison, Sedgwick—apparently *not one*, with the exception of Agassiz, (Cuvier and Forbes were dead, of course) believed in *miraculous creation* in 1859. All of these men, however, were paleontologists or geologists, and special creation, whether miraculous or nomothetic, was commonly recognized by them to have strong *empirical evidence* in the fossil series which seemed to support the idea that species appeared full-blown suddenly, endured unchanged, and became extinct without leaving descendents.[45]

These "pre-Darwinian creationists" were "true 'scientific creationists'," in Gould's* estimation.[46] Most of the creationists were also catastrophists at the time of Darwin*, and they similarly were committed to "the uniformity of law," "were as 'scientific' as the uniformitarians," and "were the empirical literalists," he adds:

> This homily supposes that the catastrophists directly denied science by rejecting the first two uniformities in favor of an earth ruled directly by a god who capriciously changed his own laws.
>
> The catastrophists did no such thing. They held as staunchly as Lyell to the *uniformity of law*, for they matched him in their *commitment to science* (Rudwick, 1972). . . .
>
> The textbook tale of uniformitarian goodies versus catastrophist baddies is a bit of self-serving, historically inaccurate rhetoric (see Porter, 1976, on Lyell's creative use of history). Lyell . . . was not using the weapon of uniformitarianism specifically to uphold science against a group of aging theological apologists, who wished to retain the earth as a domain of miracles. *The catastrophists were as "scientific"* as the uniformitarians. Everyone upheld the two methodological uniformities as part of the definition of science. The two schools had major substantive disagreements about rates and direction. Moreover, in advocating paroxysmal change, the *catastrophists were not letting a reverence for God blind them to the facts* of earth history. If anything, as they saw it, *they were the empirical literalists*, who read their story directly, without interpolation. Local and regional geological sections usually record an episodic history with profound faunal and stratigraphic breaks. Lyell was the interpolationist, the non-literalist. To preserve his belief in gradualism, he argued that appearances are misleading and that gaps in the record can explain away nearly all supposed catastrophes—if a record preserves only one step in a thousand, then truly gradual changes will appear to be abrupt.[47]

"The catastrophists were the hardnosed empiricists of their day, not the blinded theological apologists," Gould* concludes elsewhere.[48]

Professor Louis Agassiz of Harvard was a leading creationist scientist in this period, was the world's leading ichthyologist and "America's leading biologist" according to Gould*,[49] and was "beyond question one of the ablest, wisest, and best informed of the biologists of his day" who was so influential that "every notable teacher of natural history in the U.S. for the second half of the 19th century was a pupil either of Agassiz or of one of his students" according to *Encyclopaedia Britannica*.[50] Agassiz strongly argued on scientific grounds for creation and against Darwinism, but not on the basis of the Genesis account of creation (which he did not believe to be literally true or inerrant) or of Fundamentalism (which he rejected as a Unitarian).[51] He wrote, for example:

> Until the facts of Nature are shown to have been mistaken by those who have collected them, and that they have a different meaning from that now generally assigned to them, I shall therefore consider the transmutation theory as a scientific mistake, untrue in its facts, unscientific in its method, and mischievous in its tendency.[52]

Louis Pasteur was the "[f]ounder of microbiological sciences, germ theory of disease, and science of immunity," "laid [the] foundations of stereochemistry when he discovered isomerism," and discovered the nature of fermentation and overthrew belief in spontaneous generation.[53] He was also a creationist.[54]

Adam Sedgwick was Darwin's* geology professor at Cambridge and was "one of the founders of the science of geology in England" according to Hull* of University of Chicago,[55] possibly "the best geologist who ever lived" in the estimation of Cannon* of University of California at Berkeley,[56] and "one of the foremost British geologists of our century" according to Gillespie*.[57] Sedgwick was a creationist whose "tool was science" in Gould's* words,[58] and whose conclusions were based on the "facts of geology":

> I think the foregoing heads give the substance of Darwin's theory; and I think that the great broad facts of geology are directly opposed to it.
>
> . . ..
>
> . . . But how, and by what causation? I say by *creation*. But, what do I mean by creation? I reply, the operation of a power quite beyond the powers of a pigeon-fancier, a cross-breeder, or hybridizer; a power I cannot imitate or comprehend; but in which I can believe, by a legitimate conclusion of sound reason drawn from the laws and harmonies of Nature. For I can see in all around me a design and purpose, and a mutual adaptation of part which I *can* comprehend, and which prove that there is exterior to, and above, the mere phenomena of Nature a great prescient and designing cause. . . .[59]

Sedgwick's scientific studies were "scientific work" and not theological, Cannon* adds:

> As it turned out, the belief in miracles did not bias the scientific findings of such excellent scientists as . . . Sedgwick, and was not basic to Sedgwick's essential belief that the evidence does show an increase in fossil

complexity as we approach modern times. It was unscientific books, such as the *Vestiges of the Natural History of Creation*, and not anti-miraculous books, against which Sedgwick and his fellow Catastrophists (along with young Tom Huxley) were prejudiced. It is interesting how often Lyell's and Darwin's scientific opponents are castigated as being credulous, prejudiced, or simply "unscientific" by modern critics who do not point out how excellent and lasting the scientific work of many of these men has proved to be. It would not be hard to construct a case, for example, to show that Sedgwick was the best geologist who has ever lived.[60]

James Clerk Maxwell was professor of experimental physics at Cambridge,[61] and "is regarded by most modern physicists as the scientist of the 19th century who had the greatest influence on 20th-century physics; he is ranked with Sir Isaac Newton and Albert Einstein for the fundamental nature of his contributions," *Encyclopaedia Britannica* states.[62] He too attacked evolution and found creation more credible.[63]

Other leading scientists were creationists as well. Benjamin Silliman was professor of natural history and geology at Yale, the first president of the Association of American Geologists, an original member of the National Academy of Sciences, and the founder and first editor of the *American Journal of Science*.[64] Edward Hitchcock was president and professor of natural history and geology at Amherst College, and wrote the leading textbook on geology of the time.[65] He was an outspoken creationist.[66] Michael Faraday was a physicist and professor of chemistry at the Royal Institute of Great Britain, and was the "discoverer of electromagnetic induction" and "one of [the] greatest experimentalists of all times . . .."[67] Sir David Brewster was a physicist and vice chancellor of University of Edinburgh, president of the Royal Society in Edinburgh, and a cofounder of the British Association for the Advancement of Science, who is "[n]oted for researches into polarization of light" and optics generally.[68] He too was a creationist.[69] James P. Joule also was a physicist and a Fellow of the Royal Society, who devised the formulas for generating heat by an electric current and measuring electrical current in units.[70] He was a creationist.[71] Sir William Thomson (Lord Kelvin) was professor of natural history and chancellor of University of Glasgow, was "perhaps the most eminent physicist of the nineteenth century,"[72] and was president of the Royal Society of London and of Edinburgh.[73] Sir John William Dawson was professor of geology and principal of McGill University, and was president of the American Association for the Advancement of Science and first president of the Royal Society of Canada.[74] He was a creationist.[75] H.G. Bronn "was a respected German zoologist, professor of geology and paleontology at Freiburg and later at Heidelberg."[76] "In 1859 he published a defense of Special Creationism entitled 'On the laws of evolution of the organic world during the formation of the crust of the earth' "—" 'evolution' had not taken on Darwinian connotations," Hull* states.[77]

Thomas Vernon Wollaston was an entomologist, who was a creationist[78] on the basis of "the great body of facts":

> [W]hilst the theories are in one direction (and made to dovetail into each other), the great body of facts is unquestionably on the opposite side. More especially will this apply to that gravest of all objections (as Mr. Darwin frankly admits), *the thorough and complete absence* (both in geological collections, imperfect though they be, and those, extensive and endless as they are, of the Recent Period) of that countless host of transitional links which, on the "natural selection" theory, must certainly have existed at one period or another of the world's history. . . . On whichever side we turn we find order and symmetry to be the law of creation, instead of confusion and disorder. . . .[79]

Pierre Flourens was professor of natural history at the College of France and permanent secretary of the French Academy of Science, who made many physiological discoveries.[80] He "concluded that the doctrine of evolution itself was therefore invalid" and held to creation.[81] "Four years later Ernest Faivre argued in the same terms" in France.[82] Philip H. Gosse was an ornithologist and Fellow of the Royal Society,[83] who was a creationist.[84] James Simpson was the royal physician for Scotland, who introduced chloroform as an anesthetic and was "a leading founder of gynecology"; his bust stands in Westminster Abbey.[85] Charles R. Bree was a noted physician who similarly endorsed creation over evolution.[86]

A "Declaration of Students of the Natural and Physical Sciences" was published in 1865 by 717 signatories as a questioning of the theory of evolution and an affirmation of a theory of creation. It was signed by 65 present and 21 future Fellows of the Royal Society.[87]

During the remainder of the nineteenth century, as Darwinism became widely accepted, the creationist position was primarily advocated by scientists on the basis of scientific and non-religious considerations, in contrast to the evolutionist position with its strong theological support. Moore* describes twenty-one anti-Darwinians, most of whom were creationists, and states that "Biblically related objections to evolution were the stock-in-trade of only two of the anti-Darwinians we have discussed (Townsend and Dawson) . . . ."[88] Denton* finds that their primary basis was "the absence of factual evidence" for evolution and "not religious prejudice":

One of the traditional escapes from this dilemma is to presume that these scientists' typological model of nature was derived not from the facts of nature but from religious and metaphysical preconceptions which were prevalent at that time. . . . It has persisted as one of the great myths of twentieth-century biology, with the unfortunate consequence that the views of the pre-evolutionary biologists are nowadays largely ignored or considered archaic and overly influenced by religious belief. . . ..

Anyone prepared to read the views of the leading opponents of evolution in the nineteenth century . . . will be forced to conclude that it was the absence of factual evidence which was the primary source of their scepticism and not religious prejudice. . . . [89]

Hull* agrees that, "[t]oo often, all the opponents of evolutionary theory are lumped together and their resistance to it explained away as religious bigotry."[90]

(2) Antievolutionist Scientists. Many other scientists, although not creationists, were antievolutionists. Sir Richard Owen* was "England's foremost comparative anatomist" according to Gillespie*[91] and Hull*,[92] and was the director of the Natural History Department of the British Museum.[93] He simply found the "facts of actual organic nature" to oppose Darwinian evolution:

But do the facts of actual organic nature square with the Darwinian hypothesis? Are all the recognised organic forms of the present date, so differentiated, so complex, so superior to conceivable primordial simplicity of form and structure, as to testify to the effects of Natural Selection continuously operating through untold time? Unquestionably not. . . . [94]

He eschewed any theory of creation with any miraculous element, but proposed a theory of "creative power," as Gillespie* describes:

He denounced the "miracle theory of creation" as a "theological notion" and even censured Darwin for supposedly invoking a miracle to originate life. . . . So far, Owen might seem to be on his way to a positive theory of evolution. But this interpretation would be a mistake. "Derivation," as he called his theory, relied on a "creative power" which possessed a "grandeur . . . which is manifested daily, hourly, in calling into life many forms by conversion of physical and chemical into vital modes of force, under as many diversified conditions of the requisite elements to be so combined." . . . [95]

Gregor Mendel*, the Austrian biologist and monk who discovered the principles of heredity,[96] also was an antievolutionist or at least an antiDarwinian.[97]

Other noted scientists took an antiDarwinian stance. E.D. Cope*, a paleontologist and professor of comparative zoology and botany at Haverford College and University of Pennsylvania, and president of the American Association for the Advancement of Science,[98] argued that natural selection "could only preserve favorable traits that must arise in some other manner, unknown to Darwin."[99] Rudolph Virchow*, professor of pathological anatomy at University of Berlin, and the "founder of modern pathology,"[100] rejected Darwinian evolution.[101] N. Danilevsky* led a Russian "attack on Darwinism," and "believed that he had proven both empirically and logically that natural selection was not an operative factor in the evolutionary process."[102] William North Rice*, the "recipient of Yale's first doctorate in geology, examined Darwin's theory and found it scientifically untenable."[103] In fact, "at the time of Darwin's death in 1882 those who advocated natural selection as the primary mechanism of evolution were outnumbered by those who believed in alternative mechanisms of evolution by more than two to one," Provine* concludes.[104]

Opposition to Darwinism was not limited to Protestants, but included such Roman Catholics as Pasteur and Mendel, and Orestes A. Brownson, "the most outspoken American Catholic critic of evolution."[105] "The immediate Catholic reaction to evolution varied from bitter hostility to friendly tolerance, but it rarely included outright acceptance," as Morrison*[106] and Numbers* conclude.[107] The Vatican censured St. George Mivart*, a lay theologian and biologist, for embracing Darwinism.[108]

b. Scientific Support for the Theory of Creation in the Early Twentieth Century

In the early twentieth century, although the number of creationist scientists declined with the enthusiastic acceptance of Darwinism in many quarters, the leading creationists were still generally scientists rather than theologians.

(1) Creationist Scientists. Creationist scientists included Albert Fleischmann, professor of zoology at Erlangen University,[109] whom Mayr* describes as a "competent zoologist" who denied common descent and called macroevolution "a beautiful myth not substantiated by any factual foundation,"[110] in two technical books.[111] Jean Henri Casimir Fabre was an eminent French biologist who taught at Avignon and Orange, was a member of the French Academy of Sciences and the Royal Academy of Sweden,[112] and was a creationist. Along with other "leading French scientists," he "insist[ed] that there was no proof for transformism and that Darwin had not offered an adequate explanation,"[113] Stebbins* states:

> Fabre published an incredible number of books, dealing with many different sciences. Seventeen columns in *Bibliothèque Nationale Catalogue* are devoted to Fabre's works. Many of Fabre's books were textbooks which were widely used in French schools. Fabre corresponded with Darwin, but he never accepted Darwin's theories. He remained interested only in empirical work and minute descriptions, and he never mentioned evolutionary theories as even a possible explanation for the oddities of nature that he loved to note. . . .[114]

Oswald Spengler, the German social philosopher, found a "refutation of Darwinism . . . by palaeontology," and instead saw that "perfectly stable and unaltered forms persever[e] through long ages" and "appear suddenly and at once in their definitive shape. . . ."[115]

Other creationist scientists included John W. Strutt, a Nobel Prize winning physicist, professor and chancellor at Cambridge, and co-discoverer of argon and the rare gases;[116] Edward W. Maunder, an astronomer, superintendent of the solar department of the Royal Observatory at Greenwich, president of the British Astronomical Association, and vice president of the Royal Astronomical Society;[117] George Washington Carver, the world authority on peanuts and sweet potatoes and their uses, and professor at the Tuskegee Institute;[118] Sir John Ambrose Fleming, a pioneer in electronics, and professor of physics at University College at Nottingham and then of electrical technology at University of London;[119] Sir William Mitchell Ramsay, an archaeologist and professor at Oxford and Aberdeen;[120] Alexander MacAlister, professor of anatomy at Cambridge;[121] and A. H. Sayce, professor of philology at Oxford.[122] Other creationist scientists, all with earned doctorates in sciences, were D. N. Heribert-Nilsson, professor of botany at Lund University and director of the Swedish Botanical Institute;[123] W. R. Thompson, director of the Commonwealth Institute of Biological Control of Canada;[124] L. Allen Higley, a geologist; William J. Tinkle, a geneticist[125] and author of a college zoology textbook;[126] George Barry O'Toole, biology professor at Seton Hall College;[127] and Frank L. Marsh, a biologist.[128] Around the time of the *Scopes* trial in 1925, it is important to note that there were many creationist scientists with significant influence.

During this period, more of the Protestant denominations split over the creation-evolution issue,[129] with the Modernists or Theological Liberals generally embracing evolution to the same extent that the Fundamentalists supported creation. Examples were given in Section 14.1(b).

As earlier, creationists included not just many Protestants but, according to a 1935 study, "as a whole, Catholic opinion leads away rather than toward evolutionism."[130] Roman Catholic creationists included scientists Fabre, O'Toole, Thompson, and Alfred Watterson McCann,[131] and lawyer Arnold Lunn, as well as widespread French sentiment.[132]

(2) Anti-Evolutionist and Anti-Darwinian Scientists. Anti-evolutionists who were not creationists during this period included physicist Louis T. More*,[133] zoologist Louis Vialleton* at Montpellier University,[134] who spoke of "transformism as an illusion,"[135] geologist Paul Lemoine* (president of the Geological Society of France and director of the Natural History Museum in Paris),[136] paleontologist Austin H. Clark* (curator of paleontology at the Smithsonian Institution and vice chairman of the American Geophysical Union[137]),[138] zoologist D. Carazzi* at University of Padua, and physiologist Giulio Fano* at University of Rome.[139]

Some prominent scientists were antiDarwinians, although not antievolutionists, in the early twentieth century. De Beer* writes that "the leading geneticists, de Vries, Bateson, and, in his earlier work, T.H. Morgan, would have nothing to do with natural selection at any price";[140] and he could have added "Wilhelm Johannsen, the inventor of the word gene," Dawkins* states.[141] They were joined by authors of leading textbooks, Dobzhansky* and others point out:

> Far from lending strength to Darwin's theory of natural selection, the first decades of Mendelian genetics were largely responsible for a temporary decline in Darwin's reputation among biologists. Anti-selectionist works, such as A.F. Shull's textbook on evolution (1936) and *The Variations of Animals in Nature* by G.C. Robson and O. W. Richards (1936), became standard reading for many undergraduate and graduate students in biology, and many professors told their students that "Darwinism is dead," by which they meant that natural selection could not be regarded as a major agent of evolutionary change. . . . A common belief among biologists of this period was that some as yet unknown processes would have to be discovered before evolution could be fully understood.[142]

A leading biologist, "Osborn, using 'facts' of paleontology, firmly rejected the three major evolutionary theories of his day (Darwinism, Lamarckism, and de Vriesian mutation)," Gould* states.[143] In Europe, antiDarwinism was even more predominant:

> His [Darwin's] theory of natural selection has experienced a much different, and checkered, history. It attracted some notable followers during his lifetime (Wallace in England, Weismann in Germany), but never enjoyed majority support. It became an orthodoxy among English-speaking evolutionists (but never, to this day, in France or Germany) during the 1930s, and received little cogent criticism until the 1970s. . . .[144]

c. Scientific Support for the Theory of Creation in the Recent Twentieth Century

In recent years, the leading creationists have still been trained scientists rather than theologians, as a *New Republic* article notes:

> The leading participants on the creationist side—who are often portrayed as Bible-thumpers but have science Ph.D.s—are in fact *scientists*. The evolutionists are defending not so much science as the hegemony of science.[145]

The identity of the leading creationists as scientists is conceded by Gilkey*, an outspoken opponent:

> I say "surprising" because the persons who have formulated, elaborated, and defended creation science are not "preachers" ignorant of modern science and its implications—as most of the media and certainly the established academic and scientific communities have assumed. Rather, these are "scientists" by any normal, useful, or descriptive definition of that word. That is, most of them have gone through a scientific training of the highest order, and numbers of them have been, or are at present, functioning as professors or instructors of science in recognized universities.
>
> . . . *Creation science is as much an example of the warfare of scientists with American religion as of the opposition of American religion to science. . . .*[146]

(1) Creationist Scientists. There are probably several thousand creationist scientists across the world,[147] many of whom belong to the Creation Research Society and/or the American Scientific Affiliation. The Creation Research Society includes over 600 creationist individuals with doctorate or masters degrees in the natural sciences.[148] The American Scientific Affiliation includes about the same number of individuals with such scientific credentials, a significant proportion of whom identify themselves as creationists.[149] A large number of scientists not affiliated with either organization are also creationists.[150] Notable creationist scientists in recent years have included Dr. Wernher von Braun,[151] a rocket physicist and director of NASA's Space Flight Center;[152] Dr. J. J. Duyvene De Wit, former professor of zoology at University of Orange Free State;[153] in a different sense Sir Fred Hoyle, former professor of astronomy at Cambridge University and Fellow of the Royal Society and the Royal Astronomical Society;[154] and Dr. Dean H. Kenyon, professor of biology at San Francisco State University and co-author (in his evolutionist days) of *Biochemical Predestination* on origin of life research. The Institute for Creation Research includes on its staff seven full-time scientists and science educators with earned doc-

torate degrees from institutions including Harvard and University of California at Berkeley.[155]

The corporate purposes of some of the creationist organizations are "religious and educational." Those do not purport to be exclusively devoted to a scientific theory of creation, and do not regard many of the publications that they disseminate as constituting science. Some creationists have written religious books, but only to the same extent that some evolutionist scientists have.[156] The inspiration or motivation of some proponents is irrelevant to the merit and scientific validity of a concept, as described earlier.[157] The existence of religious writings on both sides of the creation-evolution controversy should not block from view the existence of scientists and scientific assessment.

(2) Antievolutionist Scientists. Antievolutionist and anti-Darwinian ideas are still significant among scientists, as summarized in Sections 3.2(e)-(f). For example, only twenty years ago did the scientific "institutional summit" in France first get a Darwinian occupant:

> The top of the system, the Paris Faculty of Science, until the 1960s was quite aloof from evolutionary developments. Its major chair devoted to evolutionary biology, created for Giard in 1887, shows a striking pattern of continuity: Giard was succeeded by his student Caullery in 1908, who was himself succeeded by Grassé until his retirement in 1965. Only then with Bocquet, the first Darwinian ever to occupy the chair, did the second wind of evolutionary thinking, first heralded in France by Teissier and L'Héritier, reach the institutional summit.[158]

Granting grudging respect to the creationists for being vigilant "in spotting places where Darwinism rides on faith rather than fact," Smith* (of Syracuse University and formerly of Massachusetts Institute of Technology) concludes that "[a]n important chapter in the sociology of knowledge is being written: one in which establishment forces as represented by the university, the American Civil Liberties Union, and mainline churches will not, in the eyes of history, emerge as heroes."[159]

Summary. "[C]ontrary to what is widely assumed by evolutionary biologists today, it has always been the anti-evolutionists, not the evolutionists, in the scientific community who have stuck rigidly to the facts and adhered to a more strictly empirical approach" (Denton*[160]). The "pre-Darwinian creationists" were "true 'scientific creationists'" (Gould*[161]), who accepted a theory of creation because it "was commonly recognized by them to have strong empirical evidence in the fossil series" (Gillespie*[162]). At and just after the publication of *The Origin of Species*, many of the most eminent scientists were creationists such as Agassiz, Pasteur, Sedgwick, Maxwell, Silliman, Hitchcock, Faraday, Brewster, Joule, Kelvin, Dawson, etc. (Moore*[163]); and many other leading scientists were antievolutionists such as Owen*, Mendel*, Cope*, Virchow*, etc. Their arguments were scientific rather than religious (Moore*[164]); "it was the absence of factual evidence which was the primary source of their scepticism and not religious prejudice" (Denton*[165]). In the early twentieth century, the same was true on a smaller scale with distinguished creationist scientists including Fleischmann, Fabre, Strutt (a Nobel Prize recipient), Maunder, Carver, Fleming, Heribert-Nilsson, Thompson, etc.; and antievolutionist scientists such as More*, Vialleton*, and Lemoine*. In recent years, "the persons who have formulated, elaborated, and defended creation science are not 'preachers' . . .—as most of the media and certainly the established academic and scientific communities have assumed"—but "these are 'scientists' by any normal, useful, or descriptive definition of that word" (Gilkey*[166]). Examples are von Braun, De Wit, Hoyle, and Kenyon, as well as a large number of antievolutionists (Sections 3.2(e)-(f)). It is simply not historically accurate to say that the theory of evolution is exclusively propounded by scientists while the theory of creation is exclusively or even primarily advocated by theologians.

15.3 Parallel Religious Involvement on the Creationist Side of the Creation-Evolution Controversy

The frequent charge that the theory of creation and balanced treatment requirements are the results of Fundamentalist influence is simply not accurate. (a) Most supporters of the theory of creation are nonFundamentalists, and (b) many opponents of public school instruction in the theory of creation are Fundamentalists. (c) Many advocates of the theory of creation hold to the conventional views of the age of the universe and earth, and of the geologic column and epochs. The significant scientific involvement on the creationist side of the creation-evolution controversy has been discussed in the preceding section.

a. Primary Support by NonFundamentalists

Most of the religious faiths with which the theory of creation is consistent (just as the theory of evolution is consistent with other

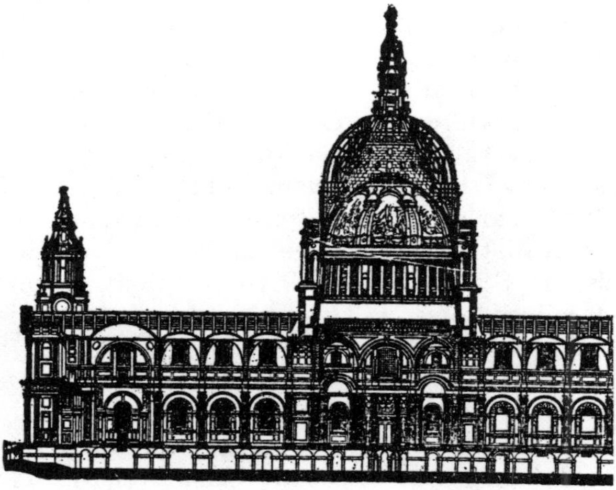

Figure 15.3
NonFundamentalist beliefs of many historical creationists (drawing of St. Paul's in London)

religious faiths) are actually nonFundamentalist. Those nonFundamentalist but creationist religions include Conservative Evangelicals and many other Protestants, Orthodox Roman Catholics, Orthodox Jews, and Muslims and many Hindus, thereby spanning the religious spectrum from Protestants to Catholics to Jews to nonJudeo-Christians, as discussed earlier.[167]

Most of the support for balancing the theories of creation and evolution is nonFundamentalist, because there is overwhelming public support for public school instruction in the theory of creation (86%), according to an Associated Press and NBC News professional survey[168] and other surveys.[169] The nonFundamentalist nature of the call for balanced treatment is also evident in the equal and overwhelming Protestant and Catholic support for creation instruction, and in the overwhelming nonFundamentalist and nonEvangelical support for creation instruction, which are noted in recent scientific surveys.[170] That overwhelming public support shows that the theory of creation simply does not have a Fundamentalist core, or even a religious core, of support. It is interesting that lawyers by more than a two-to-one margin support creation science instruction in public schools (56% to 26%);[171] nearly half of even biology teachers in public high schools support creation science instruction (42.3% to 53.7%);[172] and a heavy majority of school board members concur (67%).[173]

"Fundamentalism" is a term that many critics define as whatever they oppose. The term properly is defined to include belief not only in the deity of Christ and the inerrancy of scripture but also normally in ecclesiastical separatism, personal moral separatism, premillennialism, pretribulationism, dispensationalism, strong evangelism, opposition to the charismatic movement, opposition to Neo-Evangelicalism, opposition to public education, support of private Christian education, and conservative political views.[174] Belief in a literal interpretation and inerrancy of the Bible is not equivalent to Fundamentalism—many Orthodox Roman Catholics, Orthodox Jews, Muslims, and Evangelical Protestants share those views.[175] Even if Fundamentalism is much more broadly defined, most creationists are not Fundamentalists.

b. Significant Opposition or Nonsupport by Fundamentalists

In contrast, a significant number of Fundamentalists have actually opposed balanced treatment of the theories of creation and evolution in public schools, such as Crowley[176] and Hall and Robbins,[177] while a majority of Fundamentalists have generally ignored and remained uninvolved in the issue because of their opposition to public education and support of private religious schools.[178] As pointed out in the next section, most of the leading creationist scientists and national creationist organizations oppose legislation as the means for bringing balanced treatment of the theories of creation and evolution (although the general public itself strongly supports balanced treatment and does not oppose legislation). The single organization that encourages balanced treatment legislation is an unincorporated association, Citizens for Fairness in Education, directed by a Roman Catholic, Paul Ellwanger, who is not a Fundamentalist and who has been "opposed by several . . . fundamentalist . . . groups."[179]

Thus, there is no Fundamentalist core to the theory of creation, and it is more accurate to characterize the general Fundamentalist attitude as apathy and in many cases even opposition. That is underscored by the creationist split over the age of the universe and earth and over the role of a worldwide flood in the formation of the geologic column.

c. Creationist Division over Issues of Age and a Flood

The nonFundamentalist nature of most support for the theory of creation is evident in the creationist split on the issues of the age for the universe and earth and of flood geology. As pointed out in

Section 1.1(b), those issues are not elements of the theory of abrupt appearance, because they are not essential to the origin of the universe, first life, and plants and animals.

(1) Division between Old Age and Young Age Creationists. Creationists split over the question of the age of the universe and earth. The old age position is taken by many scientists who describe themselves as creationists such as Davis A. Young,[180] Walter L. Bradley,[181] Dan Wonderly,[182] Robert Newman,[183] Russell Mixter,[184] and John Wiester;[185] as well as many theologians who describe themselves as creationists such as Arthur Custance,[186] Francis Schaeffer,[187] W.H. Griffith Thomas,[188] William H. Green,[189] B.B. Warfield,[190] Gleason Archer,[191] Byron Nelson,[192] and Bernard Ramm.[193]

The same is true of such past creationist scientists as Agassiz,[194] Sedgwick,[195] Hitchcock,[196] and James D. Dana[197] in the eighteenth century; and Sir Isaac Newton[198] and Gottfried Wilhelm Leibnitz[199] in the seventeenth. Creationist scientists who took an old age viewpoint earlier in this century included Arthur I. Brown, Carl Theodore Schwarze, L. Allen Higley, Robert E. D. Clarke, A. Rendle Short, and non-scientists Harry Rimmer, Douglas Dewar, and George McCready Price in the early nineteenth century.[200]

By contrast, those who advocate a young age position today rely on scientific considerations, some of which are summarized by Stansfield* without any endorsement. He lists the "rate of sedimentation," "water in the oceans" in comparison with "volcanic outgassings," "[u]ranium salts . . . accumulating in the oceans at about one hundred times the rate of their loss" that at present rates would have reached present levels in "less than one million years," the "rate of accumulation of helium" that at present rates for four billion years would leave "thirty times as much helium in our atmosphere as is presently there," "the amount of meteoric dust settling to earth" that at constant rates for five billion years would produce "over fifty feet of meteorite dust . . . over all the surface of the earth," "that just four volcanoes spewing lava at the rate observed for Paricutin . . . for five billion years could almost account for the volume of the continental crusts," and "the great pressures found in some oil wells" that arguably could not be "retained over millions of years."[201] Stansfield* also summarizes the scientific arguments made by young earth proponents about the weakness of Carbon 14 and radiometric dating techniques.[202]

It is interesting to note the young age position taken by creationist scientists, in contrast to those cited above, such as Sir Edmund Halley[203] and René Descartes[204] in the seventeenth century, and Lord Kelvin[205] and Philip H. Gosse[206] in the eighteenth, along with many other prominent scientists.[207] Forty-four percent of the American public also agrees with a young age position, a Gallup Poll reveals,[208] so that it is hardly a narrow Fundamentalist viewpoint.

(2) Division between Uniformitarian and Catastrophist Creationists. Further, individuals who advocate creation of the universe, life, and man frequently split over the issue of a worldwide flood. That is evident in the denials of a worldwide flood by many scientists who describe themselves as creationists such as Young,[209] Wonderly,[210] Zimmerman,[211] Van de Fliert,[212] and Cuffey;[212A] as well as by many theologians such as Custance,[213] Ramm,[214] Griffith Thomas,[215] Jamieson,[216] and Montgomery.[217] The same was the position of many creationists of the past generation such as Robert E. D. Clarke, Douglas Dewar, and Harry Rimmer.

A split also occurred among prominent creationists of the nineteenth century. "Sedgwick likewise rejected scriptural geology as scientifically ignorant," Gillespie* states; and the antievolutionist "Owen, in his 1858 presidential address to the British Association, found it still worth his while to oppose the vestiges of a belief in the Mosaic flood . . .."[218] On the other hand, many eminent geologists held to catastrophism,[219] and it was often of the very nonbiblical type exemplified by Murchison, a president of the Geological Society and director of the Royal School of Mines:[220]

> Roderick Murchison, for example, argued that only two known forces could have produced the geology of the plains of Germany: glacial action or water action. Glaciers were clearly impossible. Water must have been the agent. But modern water action, he claimed, was incapable of producing the observed effect—the movement of boulders over great distances. Murchison therefore invoked "waves of translation" caused by sudden elevations of the land to account for the erratic drift. This uplift was not slight or gradual—such as Lyell could sanction—but "successive sudden upcasts which threw off great devastating and erosive waves." Murchison's wave of translation was a hypothetical creation admittedly lacking modern empirical verification. It was *based on experiments and mathematical calculations* which showed that only a solid wall of water moving at a speed of twenty-five to thirty miles per hour could have done the work. In this Murchison, unlike some other catastrophists, *clearly had no Mosaic axe to grind despite the "flood" motif*. His reasoning was *purely scientific* and not unlike Darwin's in his use of analogy . . ..[221]

Gillespie* concludes that "catastrophism was perfectly capable of positive practice," by which he means totally scientific practice;[222] and Gould* has been quoted above on the catastrophists being "the empirical literalists."

(3) Distinction between Age and Flood Views and Fundamentalism. Furthermore, belief in a short age or worldwide flood is not equivalent to Fundamentalism, because many nonFundamentalists hold those beliefs and many Fundamentalists have rejected one or both points.

The young age position is embraced by forty-four percent of the American public, according to a Gallup poll, and that near-majority is obviously not mostly Fundamentalist.[223] It has been held by nonFundamentalists such as Thomas Aquinas and many Orthodox Roman Catholics,[224] most Orthodox Jews (who use a calendar from creation of several thousand years) such as Rabbi Menahem Schneersohn, the leader of the Lubavitch Hassidim,[225] and most Muslims among nonJudeo-Christians.[226] It has been rejected by the *Scofield Reference Bible*,[227] "the single most influential publication in Fundamentalism's history,"[228] and by such leading Fundamentalist theologians as Griffith Thomas and Warfield who were cited earlier.

The worldwide flood viewpoint is similarly held by such nonFundamentalists as many Orthodox Roman Catholics,[229] almost all Orthodox Jews,[230] and almost all Muslims.[231]

Summary. The theory of creation is not a Fundamentalist phenomenon, just as it is not a religious phenomenon in comparison with the theory of evolution and its substantial religious support. Instead, most support for the theory of creation is manifestly nonreligious because eighty-six percent of the American public supports its teaching (NBC News—Associated Press*[232]), and even its religious support is comparable among Protestants and Catholics and is primarily nonFundamentalist (Stacey* and Shupe*, Public Policy Resources Laboratory*[233]). Advocates of the theory of creation are not unified on issues of the age for the universe and earth and of a worldwide flood and flood geology. Neither were they in the past century, when an old age was championed by Agassiz, Sedgwick, Hitchcock, and Dana while a young age was defended by Kelvin and Gosse, and catastrophism was propounded by Agassiz and Murchison while flood geology was vigorously opposed by Sedgwick and Owen. Nor are those Fundamentalist issues, because the advocates of a young age rely on empirical analysis (Stansfield*[234]) as proponents of catastrophism do (Austin[235]) and did (Gould*[236]), and some

Fundamentalists reject those positions while many nonFundamentalist religions embrace them (many Orthodox Roman Catholics, Orthodox Jews, and Muslims). Mere consistency with religion is different from identity with religion, and the context of discovery is irrelevant to the context of justification, as discussed in earlier sections. In any event, all of these issues differ from the theory of abrupt appearance, which has neither a religious dimension nor an age or geological column dimension.

* * *

In considering the history of the creation-evolution controversy, religious involvement has been no greater on the creationist side than on the evolutionist side, and in fact scientists have generally led the creationist side of the issue. The creationist side has not been essentially Fundamentalist, as some have argued, and in fact Fundamentalists often have opposed or ignored a scientific theory of creation. As Oldroyd* said at the beginning of this chapter, it is historically inaccurate to assume that the evolutionists were scientifically "pure as driven snow" while the creationists were theological "foolish bigots." And, of course, the scientific theory of creation is very different from the scientific theory of abrupt appearance, particularly in the area of religious overtones.

Notes

1 D. Oldroyd*, *Darwinian Impacts* 244 (1980) (italics added).

2 Section 14.1.

3 N. Gillespie*, *Charles Darwin and the Problem of Creation* 124 (1979) (italics in original). *See also id.* at xi ("the book had a surprising amount of positive theological content").

4 J. Moore*, *The Post-Darwinian Controversies* 220-69 (1979) (Moore* classifies the final two as "Christian Darwinists"); Section 14.1(b)(1).

5 Section 14.1(b) (1) (citing sources).

6 Hull*, *Darwinism and Historiography*, in The Comparative Reception of Darwinism 388, 391 (T. Glick* ed. 1974).

7 J. Greene*, *Science, Ideology, and World View* 177 (1981) ("*One group of scientists* approached nature as *agnostics or atheists*, the *other as Christians*; each found what it expected to find. Each had a moral commitment, the first to vindicate the values they held dear and discredit beliefs they regarded as inimical to the further progress of science, the second to con-

found skeptics and corroborate religious doctrines that made human duty and destiny intelligible to them. *In both cases science was only a tool*, a weapon, in defense of positions that were essentially religious and philosophical.") (italics added).

[8] Section 13.3 (a).

[9] R. Numbers*, *Creation by Natural Law* 119-20 (1977) (italics added).

[10] J. Moore*, *The Post-Darwinian Controversies* 11 (1979).

[11] Provine*, *Book Review of Trial and Error: The American Legal Controversy over Creation and Evolution*, Academe, Jan.-Feb. 1987, at 50, 51 (italics in original).

[12] Section 14.1(b)(2) (citing sources).

[13] *Id.* These Modernist-Fundamentalist divisions are summarized by Ahlstrom*:

> It was, in fact, a struggle for ecclesiastical control whose intensity varied in direct proportion to the strength of theological liberalism in a given denomination, unless (as in the cases of Congregationalism and Northern Methodism) the liberals were unassailably strong. . . . It was disputed with greatest fury among the Northern Presbyterians and the Northern Baptists, with the Disciples of Christ perhaps the next most agitated.

S. Ahlstrom*, *A Religious History of the American People* 910-11 (1972). *See also id.* at 775.

[14] K. Cauthen*, *The Impact of American Religious Liberalism* 7, 22 (1962); Meland*, *Liberalism, Theological*, in 13 Encylopaedia Britannica 1021, 1022 (14th ed. 1965); Section 14.1(b) (citing sources).

[15] W. Roberts*, The Reaction of the American Protestant Churches to the Darwinian Philosophy (1936) (unpublished Ph.D. dissertation at University of Chicago) (churches in America generally); *see* F. Szasz*, *The Divided Mind of Protestant America, 1880-1930* (1983).

[16] A. Ellegard*, *Darwin and the General Reader: The Reception of Darwin's Theory of Evolution in the British Periodical Press* (1958) (Methodists in England); Holifield*, *The English Methodist Response to Darwin*, 10 Methodist History 14 (1972) (Methodists in England).

[17] R. Dietz*, Eastern Lutheranism . . . Darwinism—Biblical Criticism—The Social Gospel (1958) (unpublished Ph.D. dissertation at University of Pennsylvania) (Lutherans).

[18] N. Furniss*, *The Fundamentalist Controversy, 1918-1931* (1954) (Northern Baptists); Reist*, *Augustus Hopkins Strong and William Newton Clarke: A Study in Nineteenth-Century Evolutionary and Eschatological Immanentism*, 18 Foundations 5 (1975).

[19] Street*, *The Evolutionary Controversy in the Southern Presbyterian Church . . .*, 37 J. Presbyterian Historical Society 232 (1959) (Southern Presbyterians); H. Smith*, *Evolution and Presbyterianism* (1922) (Free Church of Scotland).

[20] T. Simonsson*, *Logical and Semantic Structures in Christian Discourses* (A. George* trans. 1971) (Jews); Bezirgan*, *The Islamic World*, in The Comparative Reception of Darwinism 375 (T. Glick* ed. 1974) (Muslims).

[21] Section 16.1(a).

[22] Section 14.1(c) (citing sources).

[23] Wilson*, *The Religious Element in Humanism Pervades Its Origin, Inspiration and Support*, 22 Humanist 173, 173 (1962) ("Of the 34 persons who signed the Humanist Manifesto in 1933, all but four can be readily identified as religious humanists who considered Humanism as the development of a better and truer religion . . ..").

[24] *Humanist Manifesto I*, in Humanist Manifestos I and II (P. Kurtz* ed. 1973), reprinted from New Humanist, May-June 1933, at 1.

[25] Provine*, *Book Review of Trial and Error: The American Legal Controversy over Creation and Evolution*, Academe, Jan.-Feb. 1987, at 50, 52.

[26] *Is God a Creationist? Religious Arguments Against Creation-Science* (R. Frye* ed. 1983).

[27] V. Barker*, *Creationism, the Church, and the Public School* 18 (1983).

[28] Resolution 14 of Southern Baptist Convention (New Orleans, June 1982).

[29] Resolution 9-O2A, *Convention Proceedings of 53rd Regular Convention of Lutheran Church—Missouri Synod* (July 1979).

[30] Sections 14.1(a), 14.1(g) & 14.1(i) (citing sources).

[31] Those "individual plaintiffs include the resident Arkansas Bishops of the United Methodist, Episcopal, Roman Catholic and African Methodist Episcopal Churches, the principal official of the Presbyterian Churches in Arkansas, other United Methodist, Southern Baptist and Presbyterian clergy"; and among the "organizational plaintiffs are the American Jewish Congress, the Union of American Hebrew Congregations, the American Jewish Committee. . .." McLean v. Arkansas Bd. of Educ., 529 F. Supp. 1255, 1257 (E.D. Ark. 1982).

[32] Those include: Rev. Phillip Allen (Southern Baptist minister), Rabbi Murray Blackman (Reform Jewish), Rev. William W. Hatcher (Presbyterian minister), Fr. George Lundy (Roman Catholic priest), Rev. James H. Monroe (Presbyterian minister), Rabbinical Council of New Orleans (Reform Jewish organization), Rev. F. T. Schumacher (United Church of Christ minister), Bishop Kenneth Shamblin (United Methodist bishop), Rev. Lonnie M. Sibley (United Methodist minister), and Rev. James L. Stovall (minister and executive director of Louisiana Interchurch Conference). Amended Complaint at 1, 3-8, Aguillard v. Edwards, No. 81-4787 (E.D. La. Jan. 10, 1985).

[33] Those included Fr. Sam Jacobs (Roman Catholic priest), Rabbinical Alliance of America (national organization of Orthodox Jewish rabbis), Rabbi Jonah Gewirtz (Orthodox Jewish rabbi), Dr. Asadollah Hayatdavoudi (Muslim, chairman of department of petroleum engineering at University of Southwestern Louisiana), Dr. W. Scot Morrow* (Agnostic, profes-

sor of chemistry at Wofford College). Second Amended Complaint at 16-17, Keith v. Louisiana Dep't of Educ., 553 F. Supp. 295 (M.D. La. 1982).

[34] Those included John Mulloy (Roman Catholic writer), Rabbinical Alliance of America (national organization of Orthodox Jewish rabbis), Dr. Asadollah Hayatdavoudi (Muslim), and Dr. W. Scot Morrow* (Agnostic). Motion To Intervene at 1, McLean v. Arkansas Bd. of Educ., 529 F. Supp. 1255 (E.D. Ark. 1982).

[35] Those included the Catholic League for Religious and Civil Liberties and the Rabbinical Alliance of America.

[36] Note 3.

[37] Note 4.

[38] Note 9.

[39] Note 11.

[40] Note 25.

[41] Dolby*, *Science and Pseudo-Science: The Case of Creationism*, 22 Zygon 195, 206-07 (1987) (italics in original).

[42] M. Denton*, *Evolution: A Theory in Crisis* 353-54 (1985).

[43] H. Morris, *A History of Modern Creationism* (1984) (creationist author).

[44] J. Moore*, *The Post-Darwinian Controversies* 87 (1979) (a couple of these later embraced evolution). *See also* W. Stansfield*, *The Science of Evolution* 28-29 (1977) (Cuvier "has been called the 'father of modern comparative zoology,' " and "was violently opposed to the idea of evolution").

[45] N. Gillespie*, *Charles Darwin and the Problem of Creation* 26-27 (1979) (italics added).

[46] Gould*, *Evolution, Theology, and the Victorian Scientist*, 285 Nature 343, 343 (1980).

[47] Gould*, *Toward the Vindication of Punctuational Change*, in Catastrophes and Earth History: The New Uniformitarianism 9, 13-14 (W. Berggren* & J. Van Couvering* eds. 1984) (italics added).

[48] Gould*, *Catastrophes and Steady State Earth*, Natural History, Feb. 1975, at 15, 16-17, 18.

[49] *Id.* at 15-16.

[50] D. J.*, *Agassiz, (Jean) Louis*, 1 Encyclopaedia Britannica: Micropaedia 141, 142 (15th ed. 1974).

[51] J. Moore*, *The Post-Darwinian Controversies* 207-09 (1979); J. Teller*, *Louis Agassiz, Scientist and Teacher* 263 (1947); E. Lurie*, *Louis Agassiz: A Life in Science* 100 (1960); *see* D. Hull*, *Darwin and His Critics* 428-49 (1973).

[52] *Professor Agassiz on the Origin of Species*, 30 Am. J. of Science 142, 154 (1860).

[53] *World Who's Who in Science* 1313 (A. Debus* ed. 1968).

[54] L. Pasteur*, 2 *Oeuvres de Pasteur* 328 (P. Vallery-Radot* ed. 1922-39) (1864 address).

[55] D. Hull*, *Darwin and His Critics* 166 (1973) (U. of Chicago Press).

[56] Cannon*, *The Bases of Darwin's Achievement: A Revaluation*, 9 Victorian Studies 109, 132 (1961).

[57] N. Gillespie*, *Charles Darwin and the Problem of Creation* 15 (1979).
[58] Gould*, *Evolution, Theology, and the Victorian Scientist*, 285 Nature 343, 343 (1980).
[59] Sedgwick, *Objections to Mr. Darwin's Theory of the Origin of Species*, 32 The Spectator 334-35 (1860), reprinted in D. Hull*, *Darwin and His Critics* 159, 160-61 (1973).
[60] Cannon*, *The Bases of Darwin's Achievement: A Revaluation*, 5 Victorian Studies 109, 132 (1961).
[61] *World Who's Who in Science* 1133 (A. Debus* ed. 1968).
[62] Domb*, *Maxwell*, 23 Encyclopaedia Britannica: Macropaedia 725, 725 (15th ed. 1974).
[63] Maxwell, *Address to Section A*, 38 British Assn. Advancement of Science Report 1-6 (Trans. Sect. 1868); *see* Maxwell, *Atom*, 1 Encyclopaedia Britannica (9th ed. 1875).
[64] *World Who's Who in Science* 1547 (A. Debus* ed. 1968).
[65] *Id.* at 809.
[66] J. Moore*, *The Post-Darwinian Controversies* 197 (1979).
[67] *World Who's Who in Science* 545 (A. Debus* ed. 1968).
[68] *Id.* at 239.
[69] Brock* & Macleod*, *The Scientists' Declaration*, 9 British J. for History of Science 39, 53 (1976).
[70] *World Who's Who in Science* 896 (A. Debus* ed. 1968).
[71] Brock* & Macleod*, *The Scientists' Declaration*, 9 British J. for History of Science 39, 53 (1976).
[72] W. Stansfield*, *The Science of Evolution* 37-38 (1977).
[73] *World Who's Who in Science* 920 (A. Debus* ed. 1968).
[74] *Id.* at 422.
[75] J. Dawson, *The Story of the Earth and Man* (6th ed. 1880).
[76] D. Hull*, *Darwin and His Critics* 124 (1973).
[77] *Id.*
[78] *Id.* at 140.
[79] Wollaston, *Review of the Origin of Species*, 5 Annals & Magazine of Natural History 132-43 (1860) (italics in original), reprinted in D. Hull*, *Darwin and His Critics* 127, 136 (1973).
[80] *World Who's Who in Science* 581 (A. Debus* ed. 1968).
[81] Farley*, *The Social, Political, and Religious Background to the Work of Louis Pasteur*, 32 Ann. Rev. Microbiology 143, 150 (1978). *See also* P. Flourens, *Examen du Livre de M. Darwin sur L'Origine des Espéces* (1864).
[82] Farley*, *The Social, Political, and Religious Background to the Work of Louis Pasteur*, 32 Ann. Rev. Microbiology 143, 150 (1978). *See also* E. Faibre, *La Variabilité des Espéces et Ses Limits* 182 (1868).
[83] *World Who's Who in Science* 683 (A. Debus* ed. 1968).
[84] Brock* & Macleod*, *The Scientists' Declaration*, 9 British J. for History of Science 39, 53 (1976).
[85] *World Who's Who in Science* 1550-51 (A. Debus* ed. 1968).
[86] J. Moore*, *The Post-Darwinian Controversies* 199-200 (1979); C. Bree,

Species Not Transmutable nor the Result of Secondary Causes: Being a Critical Examination of Mr. Darwin's Work Entitled 'Origin and Variation of Species' (1860); C. Bree, *An Exposition of Fallacies in the Hypothesis of Mr. Darwin* (1872).

87 Brock* & Macleod*, *The Scientists' Declaration*, 9 British J. for History of Science 39, 41, 51, 54 (1976).

88 J. Moore*, *The Post-Darwinian Controversies* 218-19 (1979).

89 M. Denton*, *Evolution: A Theory in Crisis* 100, 104 (1985).

90 D. Hull*, *Darwin and His Critics* 450-51 (1973).

91 N. Gillespie*, *Charles Darwin and the Problem of Creation* 29 (1979).

92 D. Hull*, *Darwin and His Critics* 6 (1973).

93 *Id.* at 213.

94 Owen*, *Book Review*, 11 Edinburgh Rev. 487-532 (1860), reprinted in D. Hull*, *Darwin and His Critics* 175, 193 (1973).

95 N. Gillespie*, *Charles Darwin and the Problem of Creation* 91 (1979).

96 *World Who's Who in Science* 1160 (A. Debus* ed. 1968).

97 Caullery*, *The Present State of the Problem of Evolution*, Smithsonian Institute Report 321, 334 (1916) (head of Department of Evolution of Living Organisms, Faculty of Sciences at Paris) ("And it comes to pass that some of the biologists of greatest authority in the study of Mendelian heredity are led, *with regard to evolution*, either to more or less complete *agnosticism*, or to the expression of ideas quite opposed to those of the preceding generation; ideas which would almost take us back to creationism."); W. Bateson*, *Mendel's Principles of Heredity* 47 (1909) (Mendel* was antiDarwinian).

98 *World Who's Who in Science* 370 (A. Debus* ed. 1968).

99 Gould*, *Not Necessarily A Wing*, Natural History, Oct. 1985, at 12, 12. *See also* E. Cope*, *The Origin of the Fittest* (1887).

100 *World Who's Who in Science* 1724 (A. Debus* ed. 1968).

101 Ivanhoe*, *Was Virchow Right about Neandert[h]al?*, 227 Nature 577, 577 (1970).

102 Rogers*, *Russia: Social Sciences*, in The Comparative Reception of Darwinism 267 (T. Glick* ed. 1974). *See also* N. Danilevsky*, 1 *Darvinizm: Kriticheskoe Izsledoranie* 496 (1885-89).

103 R. Numbers*, *Creation by Natural Law* 111 (1977) ("In his dissertation on 'The Darwinian Theory of the Origin of Species' William North Rice, the twenty-one-year-old recipient of Yale's first doctorate in geology, examined Darwin's theory and found it scientifically untenable. Yet the young Methodist scholar did not find it theologically objectionable."); W. Rice*, The Darwinian Theory of the Origin of Species (1867) (unpublished Ph.D. dissertation at Yale University). Rice* apparently later changed his position.

104 Provine*, *Implications of Darwin's Ideas on the Study of Evolution*, 32 BioScience 501, 503 (1982).

105 R. Numbers*, *Creation by Natural Law* 122 (1977).

106 J. Morrison*, A History of American Catholic Opinion on the Theory of

Evolution, 1859-1950 (1951) (unpublished Ph.D. dissertation at University of Missouri).

[107] R. Numbers*, *Creation by Natural Law* 122-23 (1977).

[108] Section 14.1(d).

[109] *World Who's Who in Science* 577 (A. Debus* ed. 1968).

[110] E. Mayr*, *The Growth of Biological Thought* 218 (1982).

[111] A. Fleischmann, *Die Descendentheorie* (1901); A. Fleischmann, *Die Darwinsche Theorie* (1903).

[112] *World Who's Who in Science* 540 (A. Debus* ed. 1968).

[113] Stebbins*, *France*, in The Comparative Reception of Darwinism 162 (T. Glick* ed. 1974).

[114] Stebbins*, *France: Bibliographical Essay*, in The Comparative Reception of Darwinism 167 (T. Glick* ed. 1974).

[115] 2 O. Spengler*, *The Decline of the West* 32 (1914).

[116] *World Who's Who in Science* 1626 (A. Debus* ed. 1968).

[117] *Id.* at 1130.

[118] *Id.* at 1307.

[119] *Id.* at 578.

[120] *Id.* at 1392.

[121] *Id.* at 1085. *See also* A. MacAlister, *Morphology of Vertebrate Animals* (1878).

[122] *World Who's Who in Science* 1483 (A. Debus* ed. 1968).

[123] D. Heribert-Nilsson, *Synthetische Artbildung* (1954).

[124] Thompson, *Introduction*, to C. Darwin*, The Origin of Species (1956).

[125] *World Who's Who in Science* 1675 (A. Debus* ed. 1968).

[126] W. Tinkle, *Fundamentals of Zoology* (1939). He earned his Ph.D. degree in biology at Ohio State.

[127] G. O'Toole, *The Case against Evolution* (1926).

[128] F. Marsh, *Fundamental Biology* (1941). He earned his Ph.D. degree in biology from University of Nebraska.

[129] W. Roberts, The Reaction of the American Protestant Churches to the Darwinian Philosophy (1936) (unpub. Ph.D. dissertation at University of Chicago) (churches in America generally); H. Smith*, *Evolution and Presbyterianism* (1922) (Free Church of Scotland); A. Ellegard*, *Darwin and the General Reader: The Reception of Darwin's Theory of Evolution in the British Periodical Press* (1958)(Methodists in England); Holifield*, *The English Methodist Response to Darwin*, 10 Methodist History 14 (1972) (Methodists in England); R. Dietz*, *Eastern Lutheranism . . . Darwinism—Biblical Criticism—The Social Gospel* (1958) (unpublished Ph.D. dissertation at University of Pennsylvania) (Lutherans); Street*, *The Evolutionary Controversy in the Southern Presbyterian Church . . .*, 37 J. Presbyterian Historical Society 232 (1959) (Southern Presbyterians); N. Furniss*, *The Fundamentalist Controversy, 1918-1931* (1954) (Northern Baptists); Reist*, *Augustus Hopkins Strong and William Newton Clarke: A Study in Nineteenth-Century Evolutionary and Eschatological Immanentism*, 18 Foun-

dations 5 (1975) (Methodists in England); T. Simonsson*, *Logical and Semantic Structures in Christian Discourses* (A. George* trans. 1971) (Jews); Bezirgan*, *The Islamic World*, in Comparative Reception of Darwinism 375 (T. Glick* ed. 1974) (Muslims).

[130] M. Frederick (Eggleston)*, *Religion and Evolution Since 1859* at 169 (1935) (Loyola U. Press).

[131] A. McCann, *God or Gorilla* (1922).

[132] H. Paul*, *The Edge of Contingency: French Catholic Reaction to Scientific Change from Darwin to Duhem* 45 (1979).

[133] L. More*, *The Dogma of Evolution* (1925) (Princeton U. Press).

[134] L. Vialleton*, *L'Illusion Transformiste* (1929).

[135] Stebbins*, *France*, in The Comparative Reception of Darwinism 162 (T. Glick* ed. 1974).

[136] Lemoine*, *Introduction: De L'Évolution?*, in 5 Encyclopedie Francaise 06-6 (P. Lemoine* ed. 1937).

[137] *World Who's Who in Science* 339 (A. Debus* ed. 1968).

[138] A. Clark*, *The New Evolution: Zoogenesis* (1930); Clark*, *Animal Evolution*, 3 Quarterly Rev. of Biology 523, 539 (1928) ("Thus so far as concerns the major groups of animals, the creationists seem to have the better of the argument.").

[139] *See generally* H. Morris, *A History of Modern Creationism* (1984) (creationist author).

[140] de Beer*, *Book Review of Olson's Evolution of Life*, 206 Nature 331, 331 (1965). *See also* T. Morgan*, *The Scientific Basis of Evolution* 140 (1932) ("There is here no implication that natural selection itself is responsible for the appearance of new types," and (p. 127) "But only by a perverse use of the term could natural selection be interpreted to mean an active agent in nature.").

[141] R. Dawkins*, *The Blind Watchmaker* 305 (1986).

[142] T. Dobzhansky*, F. Ayala*, G. Stebbins* & J. Valentine*, *Evolution* 15 (1977) (italics in original).

[143] Gould*, *The promise of paleobiology as a nomothetic, evolutionary discipline*, 6 Paleobiology 96, 105 (1980).

[144] Gould*, *Darwinism Defined: The Difference Between Fact and Theory*, Discover, Jan. 1987, at 64, 64.

[145] Bethell*, *A Challenge to Materialism*, New Republic, Aug. 1, 1983, at 34, 36 (italics added).

[146] L. Gilkey*, *Creationism on Trial: Evolution and God at Little Rock* 21-22 (1985) (italics added).

[147] Kenyon, *The Creationist View of Biologic Origins*, NEXA Journal, Spring 1984, at 28, 28 (creationist author).

[148] *Creation Research Society*, 23 Creation Research Society Quarterly 4 (1986).

[149] *Evolution and Christian Thought Today* (R. Mixter* ed. 1959) (publication of American Scientific Affiliation).

[150] Examples are Dr. Dean H. Kenyon (Ph.D. from Stanford in biophysics, professor of biology at San Francisco State U.), Dr. Walter L. Bradley (Ph.D. from U. Texas in materials science, professor of mechanical engineering at Texas A.&M.), Dr. N. Chandra Wickramasinghe (Ph.D. from Cambridge in astronomy, chairman of applied mathematics and professor of astronomy at U. College in Cardiff), and Dr. Anthony Ostric (Ph.D. from Geneva U. in anthropology, professor emeritus of anthropology at St. Mary's College).
[151] Letter from Dr. Wernher von Braun to Dr. Vernon Grose (Sept. 14, 1972).
[152] *World Who's Who in Science* 1730 (A. Debus* ed. 1968). Von Braun earned his Ph.D. degree from U. of Berlin.
[153] De Wit earned his Ph.D. in biology.
[154] *World Who's Who in Science* 835 (A. Debus* ed. 1968).
[155] These are Dr. Henry M. Morris (Ph.D. from U. of Minnesota in hydraulics, former chairman of civil engineering at V.P.I., author of a major hydraulics textbook), Dr. Duane T. Gish (Ph.D. from U. of California at Berkeley in biochemistry, former instructor at Cornell Medical School, with major research on the tobacco mosaic virus), Dr. Steven A. Austin (Ph.D. from Pennsylvania State U. in geology), Dr. Richard B. Bliss (Ed.D. from Sarasota U. in science education, former director of science education for a Wisconsin public school district), Dr. Kenneth B. Cumming (Ph.D. from Harvard in biology), Dr. John D. Morris (Ph.D. from U. of Oklahoma in geological engineering, former professor there), and Dr. Gerald Aardsma (Ph.D. from U. of Toronto in nuclear physics). Institute for Creation Research, *Institute for Creation Research* (1982).
[156] Section 14.3 (c) (citing sources).
[157] Section 14.3 (b) (citing sources).
[158] Limoges*, *A Second Glance at Evolutionary Biology in France*, in The Evolutionary Synthesis 322, 327 (E. Mayr* & W. Provine* eds. 1980)
[159] Smith*, *Two Evolutions*, in On Nature 42, 59 (L. Rouner* ed. 1984).
[160] Note 42.
[161] Note 46.
[162] Note 45.
[163] Note 44.
[164] *Id.* at 218-19.
[165] Note 89.
[166] Note 146.
[167] Section 14.2 (citing sources).
[168] NBC News* & Associated Press*, November National Poll at 15 (Nov. 24, 1981) (76% support for teaching both creation and evolution, and 10% additional support for teaching only creation, in public schools).
[169] Stacey* & Shupe*, *Religious Values and Religiosity in the Textbook Adoption Controversy in Texas 1981*, 25 Rev. of Religious Research 321, 326 (1984).
[170] The percentage of "religious moderates" (as contrasted with "funda-

mentalists") supporting creation instruction is 73.4%, and of Roman Catholics is 72.4%, according to one scientific poll. *Id.* In another poll, 70% felt that creation should be "taught along with evolution in public schools" (22% opposed), yet 61% stated that they were not Fundamentalists or Evangelicals (15% of the rest were Fundamentalists, 6% Evangelicals, 2% both, and 16% did not know or answer). Public Policy Resources Laboratory* of Texas A. & M. University, *The Texas Poll*, Fall 1987, at 1, 19, 20. Results were accurate to 3%. *Id.* at 2.

171 *Lawpoll: Creationism and the First Amendment*, ABA Journal [of American Bar Assn.], Jan. 1, 1987, at 35 (scientific survey by New York polling firm). A still heavier majority of lawyers regard creation science instruction as constitutional (63%). *Id.*

172 Austin Analytical Consulting*, Opinion Poll for Biology Teachers question 3 (1986) (nationwide standardized survey, 95% confidence level.

173 *Finding: Let kids decide how we got here*, Am. School Board J., March 1980, at 52 (48% for teaching both, 25% for teaching just evolution, 19% for teaching only creation).

174 *See* S. Ahlstrom*, *A Religious History of the American People* 816 (1972) ("It is not inappropriate to say that the Fundamentalist movement was launched. . . . Since dispensationalism was highly esteemed by both the patrons and editors of the project, its message was prominent in every booklet, with R. A. Torrey, A. T. Pierson, Arno C. Gaebelein and even Scofield himself contributing one or more essays."); S. Cole*, *The History of Fundamentalism* 25, 32, 35, 45, 54, 89, 91, 230, 240, 248, 250, 255, 302, 316 (1931); G. Dollar, *A History of Fundamentalism in America* 4, 264-65, 279 (1973) (premillennialism, pretribulationism, reliability of King James Version, personal moral separation, ecclesiastical separatism, etc.) (creationist author); D. Beale, *In Pursuit of Purity—American Fundamentalism Since 1850* (1986) (creationist author).

175 *E.g.*, W. Most*, *Free From All Error: Authorship, Inerrancy, Historicity of Scripture, Church Teaching, and Modern Scripture Scholars* 31, 33-34 (1985) (Roman Catholic author, Franciscan Maryton Press); Pope Pius XII, *Divino Afflante Spiritu* (1943) (books of Scripture "containing revelation without error"); Pope Leo XIII, *Providentissimus Deus* (1893) ("It follows that they who think any error is contained in the authentic passages of the Sacred Books surely either pervert the Catholic notion of divine inspiration, or make God Himself the source of error.").

176 *E.g.*, Crowley, *Seven Evils of the "Two-Model Approach"*, Capitol Voice, Sept. 1, 1981, at 5, 5 ("Here are seven reasons why you will not hear me promoting the two-model approach.").

177 Hall & Hall, The Counter-Evolution Movement (1980); Robbins, *The Hoax of "Scientific Creationism,"* Trinity Rev., 1987, at 1.

178 Consequently, the demands of Fundamentalists (for deletion of evolution and for instruction in Genesis) differ markedly from the concept of balanced treatment (of the theory of creation along with evolution). L. Cole*, *Politics and the Restraint of Science* 96 (1983).

[179] Ellwanger* states, for example:

> Though I have been unable to determine just what a "fundamentalist" is, I would rather doubt that such persons would care to share that title with a *Roman Catholic*, which makes the ACLU charge all the more obscene that my legislative effort is some kind of fundamentalist conspiracy.
>
> I and my organization, CITIZENS FOR FAIRNESS IN EDUCATION, are the sole national circulators of a uniform origins act in America. We have, in fact, been *opposed by* several creationist, *fundamentalist*, and other religious groups who are against legislating for openness in science on origins.

Ellwanger, *Are Creationists Second Class Christians and Jews? Are Christians and Jews Second Class Citizens?*, Christian News, May 24, 1982, at 9, 9 (italics added).

[180] D. Young, *Christianity and the Age of the Earth* (1982).

[181] Bradley & Olsen, *The Trustworthiness of Scripture in Areas Relating to Natural Science*, in Hermeneutics, Inerrancy, and the Bible at 283 (E. Radmacher & R. Preus eds. 1984) (papers at Summit II Conference of International Council on Biblical Inerrancy).

[182] Wonderly, *Non-Radiometric Data Relevant to the Question of Age*, in Origins and Change: Selected Readings from the Journal of the American Scientific Affiliation 67 (D. Willis ed. 1978); D. Wonderly, *God's Time Records in Ancient Sediments* (1977).

[183] R. Newman & H. Eckelmann, *Genesis One and the Origin of the Earth* (1977).

[184] *Evolution and Christian Thought Today* (R. Mixter ed. 1959).

[185] J. Wiester, *The Genesis Connection* (1983).

[186] A. Custance, *Evolution or Creation?* (1976)

[187] F. Schaeffer, *Genesis in Space and Time* (1972).

[188] W. Griffith Thomas, *Genesis: A Devotional Commentary* (1946).

[189] Green, *Primeval Chronology*, in Classical Essays in Old Testament Interpretation 13 (W. Kaiser ed. 1974).

[190] Warfield, *On the Antiquity and Unity of the Human Race*, in Biblical and Theological Studies 238 (S. Craig ed. 1968).

[191] G. Archer, *Encyclopedia of Bible Difficulties* 58-65 (1983).

[192] B. Nelson, *Before Abraham* (1948).

[193] B. Ramm, *The Christian View of Science and Scripture* (1954).

[194] 1 L. Agassiz, *Essay on Classification*, in Contributions to the Natural History of the United States 53 (1857) ("this globe has been in existence for innumerable ages").

[195] D. Hull*, *Darwin and His Critics* 168 (1973).

[196] E. Larson*, *Trial and Error: The American Legal Controversy over Creation and Evolution* 12 (1985).

[197] *Id.* at 13 (Dana was a creationist until 1874).

[198] *Newton's Philosophy of Nature* 64-65 (H. Thayer* ed. 1974); 2 *Memoirs of Sir Isaac Newton* 454 (D. Brewster ed. 1850).

[199] *World Who's Who in Science* 1020 (A. Debus* ed. 1968).
[200] H. Morris, *A History of Modern Creationism* (1984) (creationist author).
[201] W. Stansfield*, *The Science of Evolution* 80-82 (1977).
[202] *Id.* at 83-84.
[203] Gould*, *On Rereading Edmund Halley*, Natural History, March 1986, at 14.
[204] R. Descartes, Principes de la Philosophie (1647) (reprinted in 3 *Oeuvres Philosophiques* (F. Alquie* ed. 1973)).
[205] W. Thomson, *The Doctrine of Uniformitarianism in Geology Briefly Refuted* (1865); Thomson, *On Geological Time*, 2 Popular Lectures and Addresses 10 (1889-94).
[206] P. Gosse, *Omphalos: An Attempt To Untie the Geological Knot* (1857).
[207] S. Toulmin* & J. Goodfield*, *The Discovery of Time* 81 (1965).
[208] Severo*, Poll Finds Americans Split on Creation Idea, N.Y. Times, Aug. 29, 1982.
[209] D. Young, *Creation and the Flood* (1977).
[210] D. Wonderly, *God's Time-Records in Ancient Sediments* (1977).
[211] P. Zimmerman, *Rock Strata and the Bible Record* (1970).
[212] Van de Fliert, *Fundamentalism and the Fundamentals of Geology*, in Origins and Change: Selected Readings from the Journal of the American Scientific Affiliation 38 (D. Willis ed. 1978).
[212A] Cuffey, *Dialogue on Paleontologic Evidence and Organic Evolution: The Position of Roger J. Cuffey*, in *id.* at 55.
[213] A. Custance, *The Flood—Local or Global?* (1979).
[214] B. Ramm, *The Christian View of Science and Scripture* (1954).
[215] W. Griffith Thomas, *Genesis: A Devotional Commentary* (1946).
[216] R. Jamieson *et al.*, 1 *Jamieson, Fausset and Brown Commentary* (1879).
[217] J. Montgomery, *The Quest for Noah's Ark* (1972).
[218] N. Gillespie*, *Charles Darwin and the Problem of Creation* 48-49 (1979).
[219] Rappaport*, *Geology and Orthodoxy: The Case of Noah's Flood in Eighteenth-Century Thought*, 11 British J. History of Science 1 (1978).
[220] *World Who's Who in Science* 1228 (A. Debus* ed. 1968).
[221] N. Gillespie*, *Charles Darwin and the Problem of Creation* 58 (1979) (italics added).
[222] *Id.* at 11.
[223] *44% Believe God Created Mankind 10,000 Years Ago*, San Diego Union, Aug. 30, 1982, §A, at 12, col. 1.
[224] *E.g.*, W. Johnson, *The Crumbling Theory of Evolution* (1976); P. Haigh, *What's Wrong with Evolution?* (1975).
[225] Schneersohn, *A Letter on Science and Judaism*, in Challenge: Torah Views on Science and Its Problems 20 (1978).
[226] *Koran* sura 50, v. 37 (E. Rhys* ed., J. Rodwell* trans. 1909) ("37. We created the heavens and the earth and all that is between them in six days, and no weariness touched us."); *id.* sura 71, v. 8 ("8. Say: Do ye indeed disbelieve in Him who in two days created the earth? and do ye assign Him

peers? The Lord of the worlds is He!").

[227] *Scofield Reference Bible* 3-4 (C. Scofield ed. 1909).

[228] D. Beale, *In Pursuit of Purity—American Fundamentalism Since 1850* 37 (1986) (Fundamentalist author).

[229] *E.g.*, P. O'Connell, *The Origin and Early History of Man* (1965); W. Johnson, *The Crumbling Theory of Evolution* (1976); P. Haigh, *What's Wrong with Evolution?* (1975).

[230] Schneersohn, *A Letter on Science and Judaism*, in Challenge: Torah Views on Science and Its Problems 20 (1978).

[231] *Koran* sura 11, v. 40-44 (E. Rhys* ed., J. Rodwell* trans. 1909) (account of Noah's ark and flood).

[232] Note 168.

[233] Notes 169-70.

[234] Note 201.

[235] S. Austin, *Catastrophes in Earth History* (1984) (creationist author).

[236] Notes 47-48.

CHAPTER 16

Theories of Evolution and Abrupt Appearance and Recent Political Activity

> *But Scopes would have difficulty recognizing the battlelines of today. Creationists are now espousing one of the arguments of Clarence Darrow's ardent defense of Scopes: that the theory of the beginning should not be taught to the exclusion of another. In short, perhaps creationism should be considered along with the evolutionary theory.*
>
> —Adell Thompson*, professor of biology and science education at University of Missouri at Kansas City[1]

Evolution advocates have generated more political pressure than the unorganized creation advocates have. No political pressure has been brought by proponents of the theory of abrupt appearance as of

*Historians and others cited in this chapter, unless otherwise indicated, are not proponents of, and their quoted statements are not intended as endorsements of, either the theory of abrupt appearance or the theory of creation. However, their quoted statements are acknowledging information that supports the parallel nonreligious nature of the thories of abrupt appearance and evolution.

the date of this book. The active lobbying and political pressure by evolutionist organizations is too often overlooked (Section 16.1), while the opposition by many leading creationists to balanced treatment legislation is conveniently ignored (Section 16.2). It is simply not accurate to say that evolutionists experiment while creationists lobby.

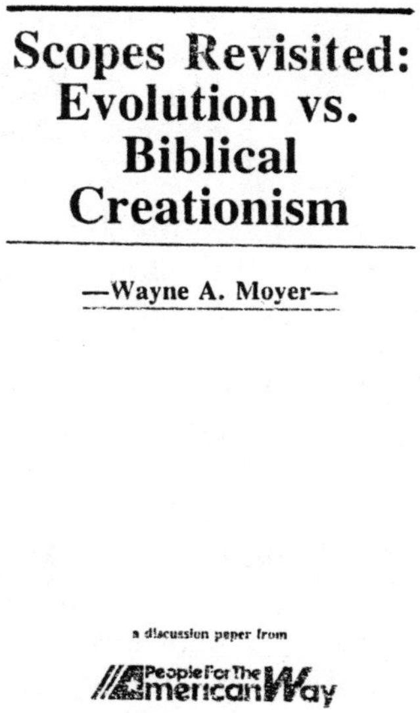
Scopes Revisited:
Evolution vs.
Biblical
Creationism

—Wayne A. Moyer—

a discussion paper from

People For The American Way

Figure 16.1
Evolutionist lobbying, such as by a polemical booklet of People for the American Way

16.1 Active Lobbying by Evolutionist Organizations in the Creation-Evolution Controversy

Most of the actual lobbying and political pressure in the creation-evolution controversy in recent years has come from evolutionist organizations, in contrast to the comparatively limited efforts of creationist organizations and the explicit opposition of many leading creationists and creationist organizations to legislative efforts such as balanced treatment legislation. Evolutionist organizations that have carried on significant lobbying against the theory of creation include the following:

It is important to note that not all or even most of the members of the science and education organizations agree with the evolutionist position of the leadership.

a. Evolutionist Lobbying in the Early Twentieth Century

Most people are aware of the antievolution laws that were enacted in six states during the 1920s, or at least of the Tennessee law that gave rise to the *Scopes* trial in 1925.[2] Few are aware that the Science League of America, with Maynard Shipley* as president,[3] lobbied actively in the 1920s in support of evolutionary instruction and in opposition to antievolution legislation, to the same extent that various creationists lobbied in support of such legislation. Shipley* described its role as follows:

> Practically every professional and scientific society, including the National Education Association, has now expressed itself as opposed to anti-evolution legislation. *The Science League of America, however, remains the only body specifically devoted to that opposition and to no other object.*[4]

b. Evolutionist Lobbying in the Late Twentieth Century

The scope of contemporary evolutionist lobbying is indicated by the existence of one organization for that sole purpose, and the major involvement of eight organizations and minor involvement of many more.

(1) Committees of Correspondence on Evolution (CCs). The Committees of Correspondence on Evolution (now called the National Center for Science Education) were formed and continue to exist for the sole purpose of opposing the theory of creation and supporting exclusive presentation of the theory of evolution, as the Georgia leader acknowledges:

> Weinberg described our nascent, national network of *anti-creationist* citizen *lobbies*. . . .
>
> The Committee network was established in earnest in the fall of 1980. By fall of 1981, a CC had been established in each of thirty-seven states. By January 1982, the number of states was forty-two and still rising, with membership in individual CCs ranging from six to three hundred.[5]

They are simply "committees active against creationism," according to the national founder, Weinberg*,[6] and "act to combat attempts that would mandate creationist teaching in our schools," Eldredge* adds.[7] Many if not most of these forty-two (or more) chapters engage in "lobbying," Weinberg* states,[8] and the CCs "cooperate informally with many proevolution societies such as the state academies of science, the National Academy of Sciences, AAAS, AIBS, . . . American Humanist Association, NABT, NSTA, Society for the Study of Evolution . . . and the like," according to Weinberg*.[9]

(2) People for the American Way (PAW). People for the American Way, which was formed to oppose the "new right," has actively opposed the theory of creation in its publications as well as its activities.[10] It most recently led the attack against adding the theory of creation and against restricting "dogmatic" teaching of evolution in Texas Board of Education hearings, with the cooperation of most of the other organizations listed in this section,[11] and there distributed a statement calling for textbooks "which exclude 'scientific creationism.' "[12]

(3) American Humanist Association (AHA). The American Humanist Association published *Humanist Manifesto II* with an explicit affirmation of evolution,[13] and later passed a resolution urging school boards, teachers, and textbook publishers to "[r]esist and oppose measures currently before several state legislatures that would require creationist views of origins be given equal treatment and emphasis in public-school biology classes and text materials."[14] Its administrator describes the activism of AHA in opposing the theory of creation and supporting the theory of evolution:

> Since 1977, when the American Humanist Association issued its precedent-setting *Statement Affirming Evolution as a Principle of Science, humanists have been involved in the issue.* This past October, the AHA was invited to send a representative to two important meetings on the subject. The first was sponsored by the National Academy of Sciences in Washington, D.C. The second was sponsored by the National Association of Biology Teachers and was held at the offices of the National Education Association, also in Washington. . . . The result was the forming of a loose network of active organizations that will cooperate

> to *combat the creationist intrusion* into public schools, public museums, national and state parks, and the government funding of scientific research.[15]

The AHA has published, and its administrator edits, a periodical entitled *Creation/Evolution*[16] for the purpose of attacking the theory of creation and defending the theory of evolution.

(4) American Civil Liberties Union (ACLU). The American Civil Liberties Union has long taken an official stand against the theory of creation,[17] and has sent representatives to testify against creationist instruction and for exclusive evolutionist instruction at numerous legislative and school board hearings and meetings. It has stated a purpose of "challenging every creationist statute in every state in which it is introduced,"[18] has filed legal actions against balanced treatment of the two theories in Arkansas and Louisiana,[19] and has threatened similar actions in many other states.

(5) The American Association for the Advancement of Science (AAAS). The American Association for the Advancement of Science has also passed an anticreationist resolution,[20] and has actively worked against the theory of creation[21] in ways that its science publication recounts:

> The *AAAS meeting* also served as a rallying ground for efforts to organize national opposition to teaching of creationism. Representatives of some *42 state "committees of correspondence" met* on 4 January [1982] to discuss ways of opposing infusion of creationist doctrine into the school curriculum.
>
> The *AAAS added its official stamp to the counterattack on creationism* by passing a resolution against "Forced teaching of creationist beliefs in public school science education."[22]

The AAAS joined as co-plaintiff in the ACLU's lawsuit against Louisiana's balanced treatment law that was considered recently by the U.S. Supreme Court.[23]

(6) National Academy of Sciences (NAS). The National Academy of Sciences hosted one of the 1981 meetings to organize scientific and political opposition to the theory of creation (attended by the AHA, AAAS, NABT, BSCS, and other activist groups)[24], which Lewin* describes as follows:

> [T]ime is more than ripe for coordinated reaction by evolutionists and their supporters. Two separate meetings held in Washington, D.C., on 19 and 20 October signal the beginnings of such a reaction. The first meeting was organized by the National Academy of Sciences (*NAS*) and the second by the National Association of Biology Teachers (*NABT*).[25]

The NAS passed a resolution affirming evolution and condemning creation (over significant dissent). It recently sponsored and sent to 40,000 school districts, superintendents, teachers, and legislators a polemic booklet attacking the theory of creation and affirming the theory of evolution:[26]

> At long last, the National Academy of Sciences has *joined the battle against the creationists*. They have published a colorful booklet, Science and Creationism: A View from the National Academy of Sciences, and sent *over forty thousand copies* nationwide to school district superintendents, secondary school science department heads, leaders of science organizations, and members of the U.S. Congress. The booklet explains why creationism is not science and presents a selection of the evidence for evolution. This book is the *outgrowth of a meeting* first called by the National Academy of Sciences in October 1981.[27]

(7) National Education Association (NEA). The National Education Association hosted at its Washington headquarters the second anticreationist meeting in 1981, which was organized by the NABT.[28] It has adopted a resolution opposing the theory of creation and defending exclusive evolutionary instruction. That resolution was not representative of all its members, however, because a professional survey revealed that 42.8 percent of high school biology teachers (and probably a large percentage of nonbiology teachers) support the presentation of a scientific theory of creation in public schools.[29]

(8) National Association of Biology Teachers (NABT). The National Association of Biology Teachers also has actively opposed creationist instruction and supported exclusive evolutionary instruction, as its executive director until recently, Moyer*, stated:

> NABT will continue to oppose introduction of creationism into biology textbooks in public, in the legislatures, and, if necessary, in the courts, as we have done in the past.[30]

It published a collection of articles extolling the theory of evolution and condemning the theory of creation,[31] and also joined as coplaintiff in the ACLU's lawsuits against the Arkansas and Louisiana balanced treatment laws.[32]

Moyer* has "lobbied against legislation regarding the teaching of creation-science in public school instruction," according to court pleadings.[33] While still executive director, Moyer* wrote and NABT published the significant 1980 article calling for evolutionist lobbying against the creationist menace,[34] and organized one of the 1981 meetings to coordinate the attack (with the AHA, AAAS, NEA, and other groups participating).[35] Moyer* wrote a booklet to the same effect for PAW,[36] and published an article listing techniques for defeating creationist scientists in debate.[37]

(9) Biological Sciences Curriculum Study (BSCS). The Biological Sciences Curriculum Study used federal funds to write three of the leading high school biology textbooks,[38] which are generally credited with introducing extensive presentation of evolution while excluding scientific evidence for creation.[39] BSCS through its president, Mayer*, has similarly "lobbied against legislation regarding the teaching of creation-science," as the ACLU has admitted.[40] While creationist organizations are sometimes charged with promoting the theory of creation for the financial purpose of selling textbooks, it is significant to note that BSCS receives a large proportion of its income (nearly $1 million in some years) from royalties and proceeds from textbook and curriculum sales of its evolutionist publications.[41]

Summary. Evolutionists have lobbied extensively for the hegemony of their viewpoint in public schools and other state institutions, something that is rarely mentioned in tales of creationist conspiracy. In the 1920s, the Science League of America fought, as hard as any creationist, in opposition to antievolution bills (Shipley*[42]). In the past two decades, nine organizations have lobbied extensively in opposition to any teaching of creation and to any restriction on dogmatic evolutionary teaching. "The AAAS [American Association for the Advancement of Science] meeting also served as a rallying ground for efforts to organize national opposition to teaching of creationism. Representatives of some 42 state 'committees of correspondence' met on 4 January [1982] to discuss ways of opposing infusion of creationist doctrine into the school curriculum" (Walsh*[43]). The Committees of Correspondence on Evolution, now renamed the National Center for Science Education, exist for that purpose as "anti-creationist citizen lobbies" (Saladin*[44]). Resolutions against teaching the theory of creation and in favor of exclusively teaching the theory of evolution have been passed by the American Humanist Association, American Civil Liberties Union, AAAS, and National Academy of Sciences; and publications taking the same position have been issued by People for the American Way, AHA, NAS, and National Association of Biology Teachers. Meetings to organize for battle were hosted by the NAS and NABT and attended by officials of all the foregoing organizations plus the National Education Association and Biological Sciences Curriculum Study (Lasen*[45], Lewin*[46]). Many more examples can be cited.

Figure 16.2 Creationist nonlobbying such as the antilegislative position of the leading creationist organization (drawing of Institute for Creation Research headquarters)

16.2 Political Noninvolvement by Leading Creationist Scientists toward Balanced Treatment Legislation

In contrast, the majority of leading creationist scientists explicitly have opposed legislation or similar requirements for balanced treatment of the theories of creation and evolution, preferring instead to persuade teachers and administrators of the scientific merit of the theory of creation without legal compulsion. That antilegislative approach is true of at least four of the five "national" creationist organizations that the *McLean* court decision described: the Institute for Creation Research (ICR), Creation-Life Publishers (CLP), the Creation Research Society (CRS), and the Bible Science Association (BSA) (the opinion also listed another organization that is much smaller than the others).[47]

The ICR position[48] is as follows:

> This is why the Institute for Creation Research, from its very beginning, has discouraged attempts by well-meaning creationists to force the teaching of scientific creationism in the public schools, even though a large part of I.C.R.'s efforts have been directed toward the promotion of creationist teaching in the schools. . . .[49]

Similarly, the administrative head of the CRS stated firmly that "CRS does not engage in any lobbying for any legislation."[50] The BSA consistently has opposed balanced treatment laws or requirements,[51] as does the Creation Social Science and Humanities Society (CSSHS).[52] One of the two officers of CSSHS wrote in its publication,

> Actually not all creationists believe in legislation-mandated teaching of creation models. The CSSHS, for example, disagrees with this approach.[53]

Some other creationists have condemned legislative or similar requirements.[54]

The only organization of a national scope that supports legislation is Citizens for Fairness in Education, an unincorporated association of Mr. Paul Ellwanger, who is not a Fundamentalist but instead is Roman Catholic.[55] His objective is to teach "scientific evidences."[56] His organization has no connection with other creationist organizations (other than by occasional correspondence), and receives no funds from such organizations.

The statement is frequently made in the anticreationist literature[57] that the Institute for Creation Research and this author fomented the balanced treatment bills that at one time were pending in over half the states:

> Shortly after the *Hendren* decision, a top Yale Law School student . . . named Wendell Bird took time out from his studies to devise a legal strategy for the creationism movement. . . . In January 1978 he published his legal strategy as a long student note in the influential *Yale Law Journal*, and won a school prize for his efforts. . . .
>
> . . ..
>
> After finishing law school, Bird joined Morris at the Institute for Creation Research, serving as a legal adviser and, for a time, as staff attorney. One of his first tasks was to update the ICR model equal-time resolution. . . .[58]

The charge is inaccurate. First, the article in the *Yale Law Journal*[59] was not a "legal strategy for creationism" but an evaluation of the First Amendment implications of the creation-evolution controversy, which was deemed sufficiently documented to merit publication (after every one of its 278 footnotes was source checked by law students) and award (with the unanimous support of the journal officers). The only contact with ICR or any other creationist organization, when the article was being written, was a request for general information along with hundreds of requests to evolutionist and other sources. Second, the resolution for "balanced presentation"[60] was written by this author without any request from ICR, before he had any association with ICR, and before he even had met anyone from ICR. Thereafter, this author provided legal representation to ICR as staff attorney from late 1980 through late 1982, and thereafter on an occasional basis along with scores of clients from his Atlanta office. Third, the resolution, published by ICR as only one of 192 monthly articles in its newsletter and not disseminated significantly more widely than the other 191 articles, clearly stated its nonlegislative purpose:

> Please note that this is a suggested *resolution*, to be adopted by boards of education, not *legislation* proposed for enactment as law. ICR has always taken the position that the route of education and persuasion on this issue is more fruitful in the long run than that of coercion.[61]

In fact, the resolution differed markedly from the subsequent balanced treatment bills, as a paragraph-by-paragraph comparison makes clear.

Summary. Thus, the "national" creationist organizations virtually all oppose balanced treatment legislation or similar requirements, and most creationist scientists take the same position (ICR,[62] CRS,[63] BSA,[64] CSSHS[65]). Their reliance instead is on noncompulsive persuasion based on their view of the inherent scientific merit of the theory of creation vis-à-vis the theory of evolution, and on the value of scientific openness.

* * *

The political dimension of the creation-evolution controversy is no different from its history. Both sides in the controversy have seen active lobbying and political pressure, but this has been far greater by evolutionist organizations than by creationists. By contrast, the theory of abrupt appearance has not been the subject of lobbying up until now.

Notes

1 A. Thompson*, *Biology, Zoology, and Genetics: Evolution Model vs. Creation Model* 127 (1983) (italics added).

2 The definitive study is E. Larson, *Trial and Error: The American Legal Controversy Over Creation and Evolution* 28-92 (1985) (Oxford U. Press).

3 Shipley*, *Growth of the Anti-Evolution Movement*, 32 Current History 330 (1930).

4 M. Shipley*, *The War on Modern Science* 384 (1927).

5 Saladin*, *Opposing Creationism: Scientists Organize*, Humanist, Mar.-Apr. 1982, at 59, 59 (italics added).

6 Weinberg*, *Committees Active against Creationism*, 64 American Geophysical Union, Aug. 23, 1983, at 514.

7 Letter from Dr. Niles Eldredge* to "Colleagues" (Apr. 22, 1981) (on letterhead of N.Y. CC on Evolution).

[8] S. Weinberg* & R. Chapman*, *What Is a Committee of Correspondence?* 5 (Dec. 1981) (listing lobbying activities); *see* Saladin*, *Sixty Years of Creationism in Georgia*, Society, Jan.-Feb. 1983, at 17, 23.

[9] S. Weinberg* & R. Chapman*, *What Is a Committee of Correspondence?* 1 (Dec. 1981). The abbreviations stand for American Association for the Advancement of Science, American Institute of Biological Studies, National Association of Biology Teachers, and National Science Teachers Association.

[10] *E.g.*, W. Moyer*, *Scopes Revisited: Evolution vs. Biblical Creationism* (PAW 1983); D. Bollier*, *Liberty and Justice for Some* 185-200 (PAW 1982) (chapter on creationism).

[11] Letter from Michael Hudson* [of PAW] to Texas Board of Education (Mar. 21, 1984) ("On behalf of the membership of PEOPLE FOR THE AMERICAN WAY, I am writing to urge the State Board to repeal its anti-evolution textbook content rules at the April Board meeting.").

[12] People for the American Way*, Statement on the Texas Content Rules (1983). The statement was signed by organizations including PAW, CC, ACLU, NABT, NEA, and BSCS.

[13] *Humanist Manifesto II*, in Humanist Manifestos I and II at 13, 14 (P. Kurtz* ed. 1973), reprinted from Humanist, Sept.-Oct. 1973, at 4.

[14] *A Statement Affirming Evolution as a Principle of Science*, Humanist, Jan.-Feb. 1977, at 4; Chambers*, *Why a Statement Affirming Evolution*, *id.* at 4.

[15] Edwords*, *Creation/Evolution Update*, Humanist, Jan.-Feb. 1982, at 46 (italics added). *See* Section 14.1(g).

[16] Saladin*, *Sixty Years of Creationism in Georgia*, Society, Jan.-Feb., 1983, at 17, 23 ("quarterly journal, *Creation/Evolution*, now edited by Frederick Edwords and Philip Osmon under the auspices of the American Humanist Association").

[17] ACLU, Amendment to Policy 71 (June 22, 1980).

[18] Letter from Isaac Asimov* for ACLU to General Public (Mar. 1982).

[19] McLean v. Arkansas Bd. of Educ., 529 F. Supp. 1255 (E.D. Ark. 1982); Aguillard v. Edwards, No. 81-4787 (E.D. La. Jan. 10, 1985).

[20] AAAS*, *Resolutions*, 215 Science 1072, 1072 (1982).

[21] Saladin*, *Opposing Creationism: Scientists Organize*, Humanist, Mar.-Apr. 1982, at 59.

[22] Walsh*, *At AAAS Meeting, a Closing of Ranks*, 215 Science 380, 380 (1982) (italics added).

[23] Amended Complaint at 1, Aguillard v. Treen, No. 81-4787 (E.D. La. Jan. 10, 1985).

[24] A. Lasen*, *Summary Report: Meeting on Creationism-Evolutionism* (NAS Oct. 19, 1981).

[25] Lewin*, *A Response to Creationism Evolves*, 214 Science 635, 635 (1981) (italics added).

[26] Committee on Science and Creationism*, *Science and Creationism: A*

View from the National Academy of Sciences (1984).

[27] Edwords*, *Creation/Evolution Update*, Humanist, May-June 1984, at 35 (italics added). *See also* Letter from Frank Press, President of National Academy of Sciences (March 1984) ("More than 40,000 copies of this booklet are being mailed to school district superintendents and secondary school science department heads, as well as to organizations such as the National Science Teachers Association and selected members of the U.S. Congress.").

[28] Heard*, *Educators, Scientists, Clergy Form Network To Get Out Message*, Educ. Week, Nov. 9, 1981, at 6.

[29] Austin Analytical Consulting*, Opinion Poll for Biology Teachers question 8 (1986).

[30] Moyer*, *Letter*, 30 BioScience 4 (1980).

[31] *A Compendium of Information on The Theory of Evolution and the Evolution-Creation Controversy* (rev. ed. J. Lightner* ed. 1978).

[32] McLean v. Arkansas Bd. of Educ., 529 F. Supp. 1255, 1257 (E.D. Ark. 1982); Amended Complaint at 1, Aguillard v. Treen, No. 81-4787 (E.D. La. Jan. 10, 1985).

[33] Brief of Defendants (ACLU) at 20, Keith v. Louisiana Dept. of Educ., 553 F. Supp. 295 (M.D. La. 1982).

[34] Moyer*, *The Problem Won't Go Away*, 42 Am. Biology Teacher 234 (1980) ("I propose we organize Committees of Correspondence on Evolution, composed of people willing to communicate the meaning and wonder of evolution to the public.").

[35] Heard*, *Educators, Scientists, Clergy Form Network To Get Out Message*, Educ. Week, Nov. 9, 1981, at 6.

[36] W. Moyer*, *Scopes Revisited: Evolution vs. Biblical Creationism* (People for the American Way 1983).

[37] Milne*, *How To Debate with Creationists—and "Win"*, 43 Am. Biology Teacher 235 (1981).

[38] Committee on Science and Technology, Report: National Science Foundation Curriculum Development and Implementation for Pre-College Science Education, 94th Cong., 1st Sess. 303 (1975).

[39] D. Nelkin*, *Science Textbook Controversies and the Politics of Equal Time* 157 (1977); Section 18.1.

[40] Brief of Defendants (ACLU) at 20, Keith v. Louisiana Dept. of Educ., 553 F. Supp. 295 (M.D. La. 1982).

[41] For example, BSCS received $732,903 in royalties and $101,553 proceeds from curriculum sales in 1977, $149,062 in royalties in 1980, $218,338 in royalties and $48,617 in curriculum sales in 1981, and $126,484 in royalties and $31,896 in curriculum sales in 1982. BSCS Form 990 (1977, 1980, 1981 & 1982) (filed with IRS).

[42] Note 4.

[43] Note 22.

[44] Note 5.

[45] Note 24.

[46] Note 25.

[47] McLean v. Arkansas Bd. of Educ., 529 F.Supp. 1255, 1259 (E.D. Ark. 1982).

[48] The official ICR position was stated as follows:

> The following summary items may help clarify ICR's position on such matters. On the negative side:
>
> (1) ICR does not initiate, promote, finance, or lobby for so-called "creation laws." Such legislation, if appropriate at all, should be entirely the responsibility of the citizens of each particular state.
>
> (2) ICR does not initiate or finance lawsuits, either to restrain evolution or to introduce creation in public institutions.

The ICR Position on Creationist Litigation and Legislation, Acts & Facts, May 1981, at 1, 1.

[49] H. Morris, *The King of Creation* 212 (1980).

[50] W. Rusch, A Brief Statement of the History and the Aims of the CRS 2 (unpub. statement by Creation Research Society 1982).

[51] *What Can We Learn from the Arkansas Decision?*, Bible-Science Newsletter, Feb. 1982, at 3 ("We feel that the real issue that creationists should bring before courts, and into legislation if they feel they have to go that route, is to demonstrate how much the teaching of mega-evolution, with all its moral and social consequences, is destroying the faith of the Christian child in the public school classroom. Because it is doing that, the government is clearly establishing a religion in its schools. Where court action and legislation are necessary, and it is necessary at times, it should be taken primarily to protect the Christian child and also the Christian teacher in the schools.").

[52] Myers, *Book Review*, Creation Social Science & Humanities Quarterly, Summer 1984, at 27, 28.

[53] *Id.*

[54] Crowley, *Seven Evils of the "Two-Model Approach"*, Capitol Voice, Sept. 1, 1981, at 5; Hall & Hall, The Counter-Evolution Movement (1980).

[55] He wrote:

> Though I have been unable to determine just what a "fundamentalist" is, I would rather doubt that such persons would care to share that title with a Roman Catholic, which makes the ACLU charge all the more obscene that my legislative effort is some kind of fundamentalist conspiracy.

Ellwanger, *Are Creationists Second Class Christians and Jews? Are Christians and Jews Second Class Citizens?*, Christian News, May 24, 1982, at 9.

[56] He wrote:

> Quite simply, scientific creationism could, just as evolution is, be called a theory, based on *scientific evidences* and inferences drawn from those evidences by creation-scientists. *Biblical creationism*, on the other hand, is a faith, based on what the Bible tells us about origins, and as such it is *prohibited by this bill.*

> . . ..
> . . .Biblical creationism, in addition to being prohibited by this bill, is really *a matter for the home and the churches*. . . . [I]t matters not an iota what a person's theological viewpoint is, simply because the *bill prohibits anyone from imposing their theology* on students in the public (K-12) schools. . . .

Letter from Mr. Paul Ellwanger to Sen. Bill Keith (Sept. 8, 1980).

[57] *E.g.*, Fleury*, *Creation and Evolution: The Rise of Scientific Creationism*, 24 Choice 1513, 1516 (1987).

[58] E. Larson, *Trial and Error: The American Legal Controversy Over Creation and Evolution* 147, 149 (1986) (Oxford U. Press, discontinuitist author) (italics in original). Larson incorrectly calls this author an "avowed creationist"; this author has only taken a public position on the constitutional merit of uncensored instruction and not on the scientific merits of the creation-evolution controversy.

[59] [Bird], *Freedom of Religion and Science Instruction in Public Schools*, 87 Yale L.J. 515 (1978).

[60] *Resolution for Balanced Presentation of Evolution and Scientific Creationism*, Impact Article, May 1979 (ICR No. 71).

[61] *Id.* at i (italics in original). The same was true of a prior and very dissimilar resolution. Morris, *Resolution for Equitable Treatment of Both Creation and Evolution*, Impact Article, Feb. 1975, at i (ICR No. 26). Larson acknowledges the disclaimer language. E. Larson, *Trial and Error: The American Legal Controversy Over Creation and Evolution* 150 (1986).

[62] Note 48.

[63] Note 50.

[64] Note 51.

[65] Note 52.

PART VIII

Whether the Theories of Abrupt Appearance and Evolution Are Educationally Valuable? The Educational Feasibility of Uncensored Instruction

Uncensored instruction in the theory of evolution and alternative scientific theories such as the theory of abrupt appearance follows the accepted educational approach of presenting contrasting explanations, an approach that is followed widely for other subjects in public schools and colleges. In fact, many evolutionist scientists and educators have advocated the teaching of scientific alternatives generally or the theory of creation specifically in science classrooms, for reasons ranging from a belief in the use of contrasting explanations as an educational tool to a belief in the fairness of alternatives on controversial topics to a belief that abrupt appearance will be rejected by students when directly compared with evolution. True education requires exactly that sort of consideration of alternatives, as Bloom* of University of Chicago states in *The Closing of the American Mind*:

> Freedom of mind requires not only, or not even especially, the absence of legal constraints but the presence of alternative thoughts. The most successful tyranny is not the one that uses force to assure uniformity but the one that removes the awareness of other possibilities, that makes it seem inconceivable that other ways are viable, that removes the sense that there is an outside. . . .[1]

Educational institutions have "an obligation to. . .students to present fairly and clearly the variety of views," according to Stratton*, who was president, chancellor, and a physics professor at Massachusetts Institute of Technology:

> The need to seek truth for its own sake must constantly be defended. *Again and again we shall have to insist upon the right to express unorthodox views reached through honest and competent study.*
>
> . . ..
>
> We ask for freedom of study and protection for the rights of those who hold unpopular views. But there is no freedom without responsibilities and obligations. The public rightfully holds the university responsible for the intellectual integrity and professional competence of its faculty. And I believe that in areas of uncertainty and dissent, the university has an *obligation to its students to present fairly and clearly the variety of views* that give body and substance to the problem.[2]

Academic freedom is often more honored in the breach than in the observance in regard to controversial viewpoints. Widespread discrimination actually exists against discontinuitist scientists, teachers, and students. Most self-designated civil libertarians conveniently overlook this phenomenon, although they would be uncontrollably exercised if the situation were reversed. True civil liberty involves the right to hear all alternatives on controversial subjects in governmental schools, rather than to suffer indoctrination in what a high or petty official or teacher has determined to be orthodox in science.

Note

1 A. Bloom*, *The Closing of the American Mind* 249 (1987).

2 J. Stratton*, *Science and the Educated Man* 77-79 (1966) (italics added).

CHAPTER 17

The Educational Method of Contrasting Explanations and the Theories of Evolution and Abrupt Appearance

For God's sake, let the children have their minds kept open—close no doors to their knowledge; shut no door from them. . . .
—Dudley Field Malone*, Scopes' attorney, during the *Scopes* trial[1]

The educational approach of contrasting explanations is an accepted method that is extensively used (Section 17.1). That approach is implemented by uncensored public school instruction in various theories of origins, such as the theory of abrupt appearance along with the theory of evolution (Section 17.2). The theories of abrupt appearance and evolution both can be, and in fact have been, implemented with strictly scientific content.

*Educators and others cited in this chapter, unless otherwise indicated, are not proponents of, and their quoted statements are not intended as endorsements of, either the theory of abrupt appearance or the theory of creation. However, their quoted statements are acknowledging information that supports the nonreligious or educationally valuable nature of the theories of abrupt appearance and evolution.

Figure 17.1
The educational "method of multiple working hypotheses," advocated by T.C. Chamberlin, president of the American Association for the Advancement of Science, and many educators*

17.1 Educational Merit of Contrasting Explanations

The presentation of alternative explanations on a nonreligious topic—"the common device of teaching by comparison and contrast"[2]—is an approach with (a) great educational merit as well as (b) major scientific advantage. (c) It is widely practiced in educational institutions.

a. Advantages of Alternative Explanations in Education

The educational benefit of contrasting explanations has long been recognized:

> It has not been our custom to think of the method of *working hypotheses* as *applicable to instruction* or to the practical affairs of life. We have usually regarded it as but a method of science. But I believe its application to practical affairs has a value coordinate with the importance of the affairs themselves. . . .
>
> Just as the investigator armed with many working hypotheses is more likely to see the true nature and significance of phenomena when they present themselves, so the instructor equipped with a full panoply of hypotheses ready for application *more readily recognizes the actuality of*

> *the situation, more accurately measures its significance, and more appropriately applies the methods which the case calls for.*[3]

The "superiority of a set of competing paradigms over the hegemony of a single school of thought" is advocated by Merton*.[4] "The Socratic method involves the notion that people clarify their thoughts by testing them against alternatives," Hyman* adds.[5] The presentation of alternatives is, in fact, an ethical obligation for teachers that the Code of Ethics of the National Education Association acknowledges: "In fulfilling his obligation to the student, the educator. . .shall not without just cause deny the student access to varying points of view."[6]

Many educational theorists state or imply the benefit of contrasting explanations. "Comparative analysis" is stressed as the first of twenty-two instructional considerations in curriculum development, by Wiles* and Bondi*:

> 1. *COMPARATIVE ANALYSIS*—A thought process, structured by the teacher, that employs the description, classification, and analysis of more than one system, group, or the like in order to ascertain and evaluate similarities and differences.[7]

A "number of solutions" are important in teaching students to think, according to Tyler*:

> There is evidence to show that help given at this point in learning is *productive of improved problem solving*. It is *helpful to show students a number of solutions* or a number of possible facts and conditions that have to be considered and to have them practice suggesting various possibilities when they are attacking problems.[8]

Alternative explanations implement the "interpretation questions" ("to compare certain ideas") and "evaluation questions" that are two of seven categories in Sanders's* taxonomy of instructional questions.[9] "Divergent questions," which give "the student a choice between more than one alternative," are also part of the questioning techniques recommended by Gallagher* and Aschner*.[10] Mathematical problem-solving abilities are best developed by asking students to explore a question in several ways, Schoenfeld* contends.[11]

The underlying reason for alternative explanations is the determination to consider all relevant information on a subject, which philosopher of science Whitehead* stressed as critical to true science:

> An unflinching determination to take the whole evidence into account is the only method of preservation against the fluctuating extremes of fashionable opinion. This advice seems so easy, and is in fact so difficult to follow.[12]

The educational benefits of presenting alternative explanations are better development of process skills of science including analytic thinking, greater student interest and class participation, better education of the student in different viewpoints, and greater respect for diverse parental viewpoints. The function of public schools in controversial subjects is to teach students how to think, not what to think.[13]

b. Advantages of Alternative Theories in Science

The scientific importance of alternative theories is even greater than their educational significance. The use of "multiple working hypotheses" in science was forcefully advocated by Chamberlin*, who was president of the American Academy for the Advancement of Science, editor of *Journal of Geology*, president of University of Wisconsin, and professor of geology at University of Chicago:

> [T]he *method of multiple working hypotheses is urged*. . . . The effort is to bring up into view every rational explanation of new phenomena, and to develop every tenable hypothesis respecting their cause and history. The investigator thus becomes the parent of a family of hypotheses; and, by his parental relation to all, he is forbidden to fasten his affections unduly upon any one. . . . Having thus *neutralized the partialities* of his emotional nature, he proceeds with a certain natural and enforced erectness of mental attitude to the investigation, knowing well that some of his intellectual children will die before maturity, yet feeling that several of them may survive the results of final investigation, since it is often the outcome of inquiry that several causes are found to be involved instead of a single one. . . .[14]

Other advantages, besides the greater impartiality of the researcher, include the following:

> *Fertility in processes* is also the natural outcome of the method. Each hypothesis suggests its own criteria, its own means of proof, its own methods of developing the truth; and if a group of hypotheses *encompass the subject on all sides*, the total outcome of means and of methods is full and rich.
>
> . . . .
>
> A special merit of the method is, that by its very nature it *promotes thoroughness*. The value of a working hypothesis lies largely in its *suggestiveness of lines of inquiry that might otherwise be overlooked*. Facts that are trivial in themselves are brought into significance by their bearings upon the hypothesis, and by their causal indications.[15]

Feyerabend*, a prominent philosopher of science at University of California at Berkeley, also makes a compelling case for "many alternative theories rather than . . . a single point of view":

> You can be a good empiricist only if you are prepared to work with *many*

> *alternative theories* rather than with a single point of view and "experience". This plurality of theories must not be regarded as a preliminary stage of knowledge which will at some time in the future be replaced by the One True Theory. *Theoretical pluralism* is assumed to be an essential feature of all knowledge that claims to be objective. Nor can one rest content with a plurality which is merely abstract and which is created by denying now this and now that component of the dominant point of view. *Alternatives must rather be developed in such detail* that problems already "solved" by the accepted theory can again be treated in a new and perhaps also more detailed manner. Such development will of course take time, and it will not be possible, for example, at once to construct alternatives to the present quantum theory which are comparable to its richness and sophistication. Still, it would be very *unwise to bring the process to a standstill in the very beginning by the remark that some suggested new ideas are undeveloped, general, metaphysical.* It takes time to build a good theory . . .; and it also takes time to develop an alternative to a good theory.[16]

The strengths of theoretical pluralism include allowing "a much sharper criticism of accepted ideas" and making possible recognition of both "the relevance and the refuting character of many very decisive facts," he adds:

> The function of such concrete alternatives is, however, this: *They provide means of criticizing the accepted theory* in a manner which goes beyond the criticism provided by a comparison of that theory "with the facts"; however closely a theory seems to reflect the facts, however universal its use, and however necessary its existence seems to be to those speaking the corresponding idiom, *its factual adequacy can be asserted only after it has been confronted with alternatives* whose invention and detailed development must therefore precede any final assertion of practical success and factual adequacy. This, then, is the methodological justification of a plurality of theories: *Such a plurality allows for a much sharper criticism of accepted ideas* than does the comparison with a domain of "facts" which are supposed to sit there independently of theoretical considerations. . . . Criticism must use alternatives. Alternatives will be the more efficient the more radically they differ from the point of view to be investigated. . . .
>
> . . ..
>
> It seems to me that this example is typical for the relation between fairly general theories, or points of view, and "the facts." *Both the relevance and the refuting character of many very decisive facts can be established only with the help of other theories* which, although factually adequate, are yet not in agreement with the view to be tested. . . .
>
> . . . Now if it is true, as has been argued in the last section, that many facts become available only with the help of such alternatives, then *the refusal to consider them will result in the elimination of potentially*

> *refuting facts*. More especially, it will eliminate facts whose discovery would show the complete and irreparable inadequacy of the theory. . . .[17]

Further, the consequence of ignoring alternative theories is "dogmatic petrification and the establishment, on so-called 'empirical grounds', of a rigid metaphysics."[18]

Popper* gives the same exhortation, to "try to construct alternative theories" even to compellingly established theories:

> Be as clear as you can about the various theories you hold, and be aware that we all hold theories unconsciously, or take them for granted, although most of them are almost certain to be false. Try again and again to formulate the theories which you are holding and to criticize them. And try to construct alternative theories—alternatives even to those theories which appear to you inescapable; for only in this way will you understand the theories you hold. Whenever a theory appears to you as the only possible one, take this as a sign that you have neither understood the theory nor the problem which it was intended to solve. And look upon your experiments always as tests of a theory—as attempts to find faults in it, and to overthrow it. If an experiment or observation seems to support a theory, remember that what it really does is to weaken some alternative theory—perhaps one which you have not thought of before. And let it be your ambition to refute and replace your own theories: this is better than defending them, and leaving it to others to refute them. . . .[19]

Glenister* and Witzke* join in the commitment "to the principle of multiple working hypotheses":

> In contrast, geologists, like scientist in general, are committed to the principle of *multiple working hypotheses*. Rather than running the risk of becoming too attached to a single hypothesis or model, geologists prefer to consider several alternatives concurrently. . . . Science, then, is a dynamic, multiple-hypothesis discipline in which old hypotheses are abandoned in the light of new evidence. . . .[20]

Many others endorse the use of alternative explanations in science. Ruse* agrees that, "given a number of basic facts, one can spin any number of explanatory hypotheses."[21] Thompson* believes that "[w]hen studying science in all fields—biology, zoology, genetics, geology, astronomy, etc.—we should use all knowledge available to us and should present all of this to our students."[22] De Bono* criticizes the tendency to "stay with one hypothesis until we can reject it," because "the existing hypothesis determines our perceptions and the sort of evidence that we look for"; and calls for "generating alternative ones . . . in order to allow us to look at things more broadly."[23] Harper* is troubled by "the absence of a multiple-hypothesis approach . . . by the biological community," and that prompts him "to regard the current uncritical acceptance of the Swarth-Lack theory as smacking of poor scholarship."[24] Ellis* states the ultimate issue: "One cannot make a rational choice between alternative explanations on the basis of an examination of only one of them."[25]

The benefit of studying minority scientific viewpoints has been discussed above, with Kerkut* calling it "a good principle to encourage the study of 'scientific heresies' " to prevent the "mental straitjacket" of dogmatism.[26] The danger of suppressed criticism is cited by Feyerabend*:

> There are, of course, *areas in which scientists agree*—but this cannot raise our confidence. *Unity* is often the result of a political decision. On other occasions, it is the result of shared prejudices. Or it may indicate a decrease in critical consciousness; *criticism remains faint if only one point of view is considered.*[27]

"Blind commitment to a theory is not an intellectual virtue: it is an intellectual crime," Lakatos* adds.[28] That is evident in the fact that all currently accepted scientific theories were once minority viewpoints, and over the history of science most majority viewpoints have been later abandoned. Minority viewpoints, to the extent they consist of relevant and additional scientific information and are formulated by members of the scientific community, may and usually should be considered and taught.

c. *Examples of Contrasting Explanations in Educational Practice*

Colleges and public schools currently teach alternate viewpoints on a variety of topics in most science and other subject disciplines.

That includes every major field of science. (i) In biology, schools and colleges generally present both Mendel's genetic theory and Lamarck's theory of inheritance of acquired characteristics,[29] and are beginning to cover the punctuated equilibria approach as well as the neo-Darwinian synthesis. The schools and colleges generally give alternative explanations for the mass extinction of the dinosaurs and other organisms as well as for other unsettled issues.[30] (ii) In chemistry, public schools generally teach the molecular orbital theory along with the covalent bonding theory of chemical bonding,[31] and the unit membrane model and the fluid mosaic model of cell membrane structure. (iii) In physics, educational institutions generally offer the inflationary universe theory or the steady state theory along with the big bang theory of the origin of the universe,[32] and the particle theory as well as the wave theory of light.[33] (iv) In earth science, schools and colleges ordinarily present continental drift and alternative viewpoints, and several explanations of the origin of the moon. (v) In astronomy, classes generally discuss the open universe viewpoint as well as the closed universe viewpoint.

The same is true in the humanities. (i) In economics classes, schools and colleges frequently present Keynesian economic views along with monetarist or free market economic views, and various theories of business cycles and of inflation. (ii) In American history, schools and colleges often offer conflicting viewpoints on the Vietnam War, and historical revisionist views as well as traditional views. (iii) In world history, classes frequently discuss alternative explanations for the decline of the Roman Empire, and both Protestant and Roman Catholic viewpoints of the Reformation. (iv) In reading, public educational institutions frequently employ both the look-say method and the phonics method, and seek to expose students to a variety of literary styles and genres.

Thus, educational practice joins educational theory in supporting the presentation of alternative explanations, including biology and every other major field of science.

Summary. Educators use "the common device of teaching by comparison and contrast" (Anderson* and Kilbourn*[34]), and it is closely related to "the method of working hypotheses" that is "applicable to instruction" (Chamberlin*[35]). Those approaches are integral to the Socratic method (Hyman*[36]), and to various teaching techniques such as comparative analysis and effective questioning (Wiles* and Bondi*[37]). Scientists also widely use "the method of multiple working hypotheses" in order to "encompass the subject on all sides" and to suggest "lines of inquiry that might otherwise be overlooked" (Chamberlin*[38]). In fact, one "can be a good empiricist only if you are prepared to work with many alternative theories rather than with a single point of view," because such "a plurality allows for a much sharper criticism of accepted ideas" and brings to light both "the relevance and the refuting character of many very decisive facts" that otherwise would be overlooked through investigator bias (Feyerabend*[39]). Popper* exhorts scientists to "try to construct alternative theories—alternatives even to those theories which appear to you inescapable; for only in this way will you understand the theories you hold" (Popper*[40]). "Blind commitment to a theory is not an intellectual virtue; it is an intellectual crime" (Lakatos*[41]). Most schools and colleges in fact use the approach of alternative explanations in various subjects, showing its feasibility. In science, they frequently contrast Mendelian genetics with Lamarckism, punctuated equilibria with neo-Darwinian gradualism, various theories of dinosaur extinction, unit membrane and fluid mosaic models of the cell, etc. In humanities, schools and colleges often present Keynesian and monetarist economics, traditional and revisionist history, and liberal and conservative political views.

Figure 17.2
The educational benefit of "fully stating and balancing the facts and arguments on both sides of each question" (Darwin)*

17.2 Educational Merit of Contrasting All Scientific Theories of Origins

Academic instruction in all scientific theories of origins implements the highly regarded education approach of presenting alternative explanations. (a) Many evolutionist scientists and educators have publicly acknowledged the resulting educational benefits, including Darwin*, Provine*, Black*, Thompson*, Scopes*, Solomon*, Alexander*, Sarich*, Anderson*, Kilbourn*, de Grazia*, and Morrow*. (b) Censoring alternative theories poses educational dangers, and (c) presenting alternative theories is educationally feasible.

a. Merit of Considering Alternative Theories of Origins

Darwin* himself argued for the educational merit of balanced instruction:

> I hope in a future work to do this. For I am well aware that scarcely a single point is discussed in this volume on which facts cannot be adduced, often apparently leading to conclusions directly opposite to those at which I have arrived. A fair result can be obtained only by fully stating and *balancing the facts and arguments on both sides of each question*; and this is here impossible.[42]

Provine*, the prominent historian of science at Cornell and the co-editor of *The Evolutionary Synthesis* (1980), acknowledges the merit of teaching "creationism . . . along with evolutionism," and regards "creationism" as "a viable, understandable and plausible theory" (although he views it as wrong):

> First of all I said that *creationism should be taught along with evolutionism in grade schools and high schools*. My motivation for wishing them to be discussed in this way is twofold. First of all I believe strongly in an *open discussion of ideas*. I do not believe that natural scientists should suppress the creationist point of view and keep it out of the science classroom when *creationism is a viable, understandable and plausible theory* for the creation point. It is my opinion that it is a wrong theory, and the reason why I would like it discussed, particularly in the science classroom, is that when we put it against evolutionism in the science classroom, creationism will gradually die out. Students will accept evolutionism rather than creationism.[43]

Black*, a former chancellor of the New York State Board of Regents, concurs:

> Monopoly in education can become *thought control*, denying the individual teacher's and student's right to read and listen and think and debate and make decisions and speak out. The views of those who hold the monopoly are exalted, while nonconforming views are suppressed or ignored. Thus education ceases to be education and becomes indoctrination.
>
> . . ..
>
> . . .I prefer to consider *both* views as theories, which is apparently all the creationists want.
>
> . . .Certainly the cause of intellectual freedom would seem to be best

> served by the inclusion rather than the exclusion of competing theories in any area of human study . . ..[44]

Thompson*, professor of biology and science education at University of Missouri, also supports the educational merit of uncensored instruction on origins as part of teaching alternative explanations generally:

> When studying science in all fields—biology, zoology, genetics, geology, astronomy, etc.—we should use all knowledge available to us and should present all of this to our students. *Students should be exposed to both sides of the coin regarding biological change*—the doctrine of creation and that of evolution—since both are based on models. . . .
>
> . . ..
>
> But Scopes would have difficulty recognizing the battlelines of today. *Creationists are now espousing* one of the arguments of Clarence Darrow's ardent defense of Scopes: that the theory of the beginning should not be taught to the exclusion of another. In short, perhaps creationism should be considered along with the evolutionary theory.[45]

His recognition of the modern reversal of the *Scopes* confrontation is interesting. In fact, John Scopes* himself "believe[d] in teaching every aspect of every problem or theory,"[46] and his attorney Malone* called on authorities to "let the children have their minds kept open—close no doors to their knowledge," as quoted at the beginning of this chapter.

Solomon*, a biologist, reaches a similar conclusion, while condemning the suppression of minority scientific viewpoints:

> We cannot imagine that the cause of truth is served by keeping unpopular or minority ideas under wraps. . .. Specious arguments can be exposed only by examining them. *Nothing is so unscientific* as the inquisition mentality that served, as it thought, the truth, by seeking to *suppress or conceal dissent* rather than by grappling with it.[47]

Alexander,* also a biologist, notes that uncensored instruction can help "to teach students to think":

> No teacher should be dismayed at efforts to present creation as an alternative to evolution in biology courses; indeed, at this moment creation is the only alternative to evolution. Not only is this worth mentioning, but a *comparison of the two alternatives can be an excellent exercise in logic and reason.* Our primary goal as educators should be *to teach students to think* and such a comparison, particularly because it concerns an issue in which many have special interests or are even emotionally involved, may accomplish that purpose better than most others.[48]

Sarich*, a noted anthropologist at University of California, concurs that the theory of creation should be taught along with the theory of evolution in the classroom.[49]

Anderson* and Kilbourn*, education professors at East York Collegiate Institute of Ontario and Ontario Institute for Studies in Education, respectively, acknowledge at least that "an argument for teaching special-creation can be made," on several grounds including the educational merit of contrasting explanations:

> Second, we believe that *an argument for teaching special-creation can be made*, but to plausibly do so requires a conscious shift to the domain of the curriculum controversy. Within that domain there seems to be at least three possibilities: a moral argument concerning the rights of minority groups, a pedagogical argument concerning the common device of teaching by comparison and contrast, and a substantive argument concerning an effort to provoke a student's understanding about the nature of explanation and how it functions. The first of these is obviously a difficult area but should be taken seriously. The last, relatively unexplored, we find genuinely interesting because of its potential for addressing broader issues about the curriculum and what it should be.[50]

De Grazia*, a professor of social theory at New York University, agrees: "Discussions of contrasting theories of the origins of life are educational."[51] Finally, Morrow*, a biochemistry and chemistry professor at Wofford College, has endorsed the educational merit of "balanced treatment":

> My professional training is that of a molecular biologist, or biochemist, and one of my research specialties is abiogenesis, which is more popularly known as "the origin of life". I am an evolutionist, and I am not a Christian.
>
> In my opinion, the Balanced Treatment for Scientific Creationism and Evolution Act is a reasonable alternative to the current state of affairs for one powerful reason: Students would have available a realistic set of options to explore, discuss, evaluate, and, if they so choose, from which to select a personal answer to the problem of the origin of life.[52]

A recent public school textbook, published by Burgess Publishing Co., also recognized the educational propriety of dual theories of origins:

> In some school systems, it is mandated that the evolution and special-creation theories be taught side by side. That seems a *healthy attitude* in the view of the tenuous nature of hypothesis.[53]

Another major textbook that is quoted below implicitly reaches the same conclusion by devoting a few paragraphs to the theory of creation.[54] Thus, the educational merit of uncensored instruction of all origins theories does not rely for justification on the testimony of creationists, although many of them also call for uncensored instruction such as the noted creationist physicist Werner von Braun (the late director of the NASA space program)[55] or educational psychologist Bergman (in a prestigious education monograph series).[56]

b. Dangers of Censoring Alternative Theories of Origins

Evolution is sufficiently hypothetical that there is room for "consideration of some other explanation of the facts," according to Good*, emeritus professor of botany at University of Hull:

> The fundamental inherent difficulty in the study of evolution is that this great natural process involves time dimensions of magnitude quite out of proportion to the duration of human life or even to the sum of human experience, and the observer has therefore to rely on indirect, or circumstantial evidence. Hence beliefs that are often referred to as theories of evolution are, more accurately, *only working hypotheses*. This is a very important matter because the essence of a hypothesis is that it is an opinion suggested by the available evidence, but *not one which precludes the possibility of some alternative*. A hypothesis may well be substantiated when more corroborative details are forthcoming, but until then there is *no logical reason for excluding the consideration of some other explanation of the facts*. So, while it may be justifiable to believe that evolution affords a reasonable explanation of the facts of nature, it is *not justifiable to maintain that no other explanation is possible or permissible*.[57]

Evolution and Darwinism pose the danger, without alternative theories, of causing other facts to be wrongfully ignored, although they have helped bring many apparently unrelated facts into useful focus, Chamberlin* adds:

> As an illustration, it is only necessary to cite the phenomenal influence which the Darwinian hypothesis has exerted upon the investigation of the past two decades. But a single working hypothesis may lead investigation along a given line to the neglect of others equally important; and thus, while inquiry is promoted in certain quarters, the investigation lacks in completeness. But if all rational hypotheses relating to a subject are worked co-equally, thoroughness is the presumptive result, in the very nature of the case.[58]

Without that balance there tends to be uncritical belief in Darwinism that "may be counterproductive," in the view of Stonehouse* of Cambridge:

> He may even convince you, as he has convinced me, that some fundamental truths about evolution have so far eluded us all, and that uncritical acceptance of Darwinism may be counterproductive as well as expedient. Far from ignoring or ridiculing the groundswell of opposition to Darwinism that is growing, for example, in the United States, we should welcome it as an opportunity to re-examine our sacred cow more closely.

> Somewhere between us may lie the grain of truth that we would all be better for knowing.[59]

Many of the transformed cladists, structuralists, nonDarwinians, and antievolutionists agree (Section 3.2(d)-(f)). Another name for refusing to consider alternatives to Darwinism is simply censorship, Pangle* implies:

> The attempts by neo-Darwinians to limit the claims to knowledge, and hence the access to the education of the young, of so-called "Creationists" are painfully stark contemporary examples of the bluster and unscientific indignation into which rationalism collapses in these cases.[60]

Instead, "[t]he obvious way to decide between rival theories is to examine the evidence," Dawkins* states,[61] and it is difficult to see why students as well as scientists should not be allowed to do so.

Legal requirements for curricular balance are not unique to the area of origins. California requires balance in sexual roles in curriculum for public schools, with the following requirements:

> Instructional materials containing references to, or illustrations of, people must refer to or illustrate both sexes approximately evenly, in both numbers and importance, except as limited by accuracy or special purpose.
>
> . . ..
>
> If professional or executive occupations, trades, or other gainful occupations are portrayed, men and women should be represented therein approximately equally.
>
> . . ..
>
> The number of traditional activities engaged in by characters of one sex should be approximately even with the number of nontraditional activities presented for characters of that sex.[62]

Most states have similar requirements for balance in racial roles and other topics. The reason is that imbalances will influence students. What, then, is the probable effect of imbalance on the subject of origins, teaching only orthodox evolution and censoring alternative theories?

c. *Feasibility of Strictly Scientific Content for Alternative Theories*

Instruction in alternative scientific theories of origins, such as the theories of evolution and abrupt appearance and of any other approaches, is feasible. The empirical evidence and scientific interpretations that constitute the theory of abrupt appearance have been summarized in Volume 1,[63] and can be taught without any inclusion of religious material, as discussed earlier in this volume.[64] There is no more need to refer to and discuss creation or a creator during instruction in the theory of abrupt appearance than during instruction in the theory of evolution,[65] and no more need of bringing religious doctrine into the one theory than into the other, in that those explanations touch equally on basic issues of the origin of the world, life, and man. Presentation of the theory of abrupt appearance will not allow or invite entanglement with any of the scores of various religious views of creation, any more than presentation of the theory of evolution allows or invites discussion of any of the scores of religious views of evolutionary origins.[66] Textbooks and other curricular materials can easily be developed based on the empirical evidence and related scientific interpretations that constitute the theory of abrupt appearance and the theory of evolution.[67]

Instruction in the theory of creation from a totally scientific standpoint, along with the theory of evolution, is also educationally feasible, as the evolutionists indicated who were cited earlier in this section. That is also evident in one current textbook for public high school science that actually does summarize various theories of development and part of the theory of creation, although it does not give space for presentation of scientific evidence on the subject. It is published by a major publisher, Prentice-Hall, and written by Webster*, a science consultant, Fichter*, former professor of zoology at Miami University, Coble*, professor of science education at East Carolina University, and Rice*, professor of education at University of South Alabama. Their summary is as follows:

> Possible Keys to the Past. The variety of organisms on the earth is astounding! No one knows how the various species came to exist. Each species may have been created separately. Or several species may have had common ancestors and diverged. . . .
>
> . . ..
>
> . . . Some people believe that evolution explains the diversity of organisms on the earth. Some people do not believe in evolution. These people believe that the various types of organisms were *created* as they appear. No one knows for sure how the many different kinds of living things came to be. *But many people have developed theories to explain how this diversity may have come about.*
>
> . . ..
>
> *SPECIAL CREATION*
>
> Besides theories of change, some people believe that the many different kinds of organisms are a result of a *special creation*. These people believe that each organism was created separately. The organisms did not change in form. Instead, they were created as they appear now. Thus, no changes were responsible for the varied appearances and varied kinds of organisms on the earth. Would people who believe in special creation say that the woolly mammoth and the elephant are related? Why?

> . . ..
> *Theories to explain the diversity of organisms have been suggested by many people.* One theory proposes that organisms changed to fit their environment. Another theory proposes a gradual change through chance variation. Still another theory proposes that mutations are solely responsible for variations of species. Many of today's scientists believe that migration and isolation, along with mutations, are factors leading to diversity. And some people believe that a special act of *creation* rather than change produced the wide variety of species.[68]

That textbook shows that alternative theories of origins can be taught, and that the theory of creation could be presented without reference to a creator and without religious content,[69] even by noncreationist authors or teachers. The theory of creation is not Genesis, and its empirical evidence is not found in Genesis.

There is no persuasive reason to think that teaching alternative scientific theories of origin would bring any significant reduction in classroom treatment of evolution; it would simply promote a more accurate treatment of weaknesses as well as strengths and of overlooked data as well as consistent data. Even if a few teachers made the individual choice to reduce emphasis on theories of origins, that would not impair the quality of science instruction for several reasons. First, many scientists believe that presentation of evolution is unnecessary and sometimes harmful,[70] such as many transformed cladists who often argue "that no evolutionary suppositions are necessary to discover the sort of 'pattern' . . . characteristic of the living world."[71] There are many antiDarwinian noncreationist scientists who oppose all evolutionary theories (as discussed earlier).[72] Second, such fields as biology were successfully taught before 1960 without heavy emphasis on evolution and without any mention at all in many textbooks,[73] and are still so taught by one high school biology textbook that totally omits evolution[74] and another that only mentions it briefly.[75]

Nevertheless, a number of legal commentators have concluded that reduction or elimination of evolutionary instruction for secular purposes would be constitutionally permissible. Justice Black* on the United States Supreme Court stated that "a state law prohibiting all teaching of human development or biology is constitutionally quite different from a law that compels a teacher to teach as true only one theory of a given doctrine," and in fact is consistent with the First Amendment.[76] Macbeth* argues for elimination of origins from public schools,[77] and Kalven* suggested in *University of Chicago Law Review* that elimination of evolution at lower educational levels would be constitutional, while Gelfand* adds in a recent legal article that elimination of all origins theories is not just constitutional but preferable to him as an Atheist, and Scheid* agrees that "elimination of evolution from biology courses" along with other theories is constitutional.[78] On that point, the decision of the Supreme Court in *Epperson v. Arkansas* is discussed in Section 20.2 (c).

Summary. Consideration and presentation of all scientific theories of origins follows the preferred educational and scientific approaches of contrasting explanations and of multiple hypotheses, as many evolutionists have acknowledged. "Discussions of contrasting theories of the origins of life are educational" (de Grazia*[79]). Some warn that "[w]e cannot imagine that the cause of truth is served by keeping unpopular or minority ideas under wraps," and that "[n]othing is so unscientific as the inquisition mentality . . . seeking to suppress or conceal dissent rather than by grappling with it" (Solomon*[80]). Others caution that "beliefs that are often referred to as theories of evolution are, more accurately, only working hypotheses," and that the evolutionary hypothesis is "not one which precludes the possibility of some alternative" (Good*[81]). Many believe that "uncritical acceptance of Darwinism may be counterproductive" and may apotheosize a "sacred cow" (Stonehouse*[82]; Section 3.2(d)-(f)). Thus, Provine* concludes "that creationism should be taught along with evolutionism in grade schools and high schools," to further "an open discussion of ideas" rather than to "suppress . . . a viable, understandable and plausible theory" of creation (Provine*[83]). Thompson* agrees that "[s]tudents should be exposed to both sides of the coin regarding biological change—the doctrine of creation and that of evolution" (Thompson*[84]). They are joined by many other scientists and educators (Black*,[85] Sarich*,[86] and Morrow*[87]), and by still others who support classroom comparison of the alternatives but not necessarily equal time (Alexander*,[88] Anderson* and Kilbourn*,[89] and Webster* *et al.*[90]).

Presentation of all scientific theories of origins is educationally feasible without any mixture of religious concepts, as most of the foregoing authors believe and as textbooks exemplify (Webster*[91]). The theory of abrupt appearance consists of empirical evidence and scientific interpretations that were summarized in Volume 1, and does not invite religious concepts of creation or a creator any more than does the theory of evolution. The scientific discussion of the theory of abrupt appearance in Chapters 2, 4, and 6 is not found in

Genesis, and did not necessitate any consideration of Genesis or other religious views, any more than the scientific discussion of the theory of evolution in Chapters 3, 5, and 7 was found in or necessitated any mention of theistic evolution or various evolutionist religions and beliefs summarized in Sections 14.1 and 13.3. Good science demands consideration of alternatives.

Notes

[1] *The World's Most Famous Court Trial* 187 (3d ed. 1925) (transcript of *Scopes* trial) (italics added).

[2] Anderson* & Kilbourn*, *Creation, Evolution, and Curriculum*, 67 Science Education 45, 53-54 (1983).

[3] Chamberlin*, *The Method of Multiple Working Hypotheses*, 148 Science 754, 757-58 (1965) (italics added).

[4] Summarized by Shulman*, *Paradigms and Research Programs in the Study of Teaching: A Contemporary Perspective*, in Handbook of Research on Teaching 3, 5 (3d ed. M. Wittrock* ed. 1986).

[5] R. Hyman*, *Ways of Teaching* 77 (1970).

[6] National Education Association*, *Code of Ethics* Principle I (1968).

[7] J. Wiles* & J. Bondi*, *Curriculum Development: A Guide to Practice* 171, 172 (1972) (italics in original).

[8] R. Tyler*, *Basic Principles of Curriculum and Instruction* 71 (1969) (italics added). A similar argument for teaching "differing points of view" has been published in the education honorary society's monograph series by educational psychologist Bergman (a creationist):

> The essential point is that we must *honestly deal with differing points of view*, regardless of our own, and regardless of the prevailing point of view. Because a small number of people accept a point of view does not necessarily make it either correct or incorrect. Our concern is, should students be aware of, or at least exposed to, differing points of view, even if they are held by a minority? The limitations of time may force a teacher to spend less time on some theories, but even if there are a number of opposing minority theories, *some exposure should be given to each*.
>
> In teaching it is important that *ideas not be forced on the student*. Many concepts in science can be supported by a tremendous amount of evidence and are accepted by virtually all researchers in the field, but nonetheless, they are still ideas and can be wrong. Establishing teacher credibility requires presenting material in nondogmatic ways according to the merits of the facts. *Ideally, the evidence, both pro and con, should be presented for both sides*. Information presented in a forceful, logical, coherent manner will be accepted by students. On the other hand, when information is forced on a student, the student either reacts against it or

accepts it without full understanding. *Information presented in a dogmatic way is learned without any strong foundation.* In essence the student has learned what but not why.

J. Bergman, *Teaching About the Creation/Evolution Controversy* 32 (1979) (Phi Delta Kappa "Fastback" monograph).

[9] N. Sanders*, *Classroom Questions: What Kinds?* (1966); J. Wiles* & J. Bondi*, *Curriculum Development: A Guide to Practice* 314 (1972).

[10] Quoted in J. Wiles* & J. Bondi*, *Curriculum Development: A Guide to Practice* 316-17 (1972).

[11] Schoenfeld*, *Explicit Heuristic Training as a Variable in Problem Solving Performance*, 10 J. Research in Mathematics Educ. 173 (1979).

[12] A. Whitehead*, *Science and the Modern World* 187 (1925). *See also* C. Patterson*, *Evolution* 147 (1978) ("But the *essence of scientific method* is not testing a single theory to destruction; it is testing two (or more) *rival theories*, like Newton's and Einstein's, and accepting the one that passes more or stricter tests until a better theory turns up. So we must look at evolution theory and natural selection theory in terms of their performance against their competitors.").

[13] Michalik*, *Enhancing Critical Thinking Skills*, 72 Liberal Education (1986); Wolff*, *According to Whom—Helping Students Analyze Contrasting Views on Reality*, Educational Leadership, Oct. 1986, at 36.

[14] Chamberlin*, *The Method of Multiple Working Hypotheses*, 148 Science 754, 756 (1965) (italics added).

[15] *Id.* (italics added).

[16] Feyerabend*, *How To Be a Good Empiricist—A Plea for Tolerance in Matters Epistemological*, in The Philosophy of Science 12, 14 (P. Nidditch* ed. 1968) (Oxford U. Press) (italics added, original italics deleted).

[17] *Id.* at 14-15, 29-30 (italics added, original italics deleted).

[18] *Id.* at 29.

[19] K. Popper*, *Objective Knowledge* 26 (1972).

[20] Glenister* & Witzke*, *Interpreting Earth History*, in Did the Devil Make Darwin Do It? Modern Perspectives on the Creation-Evolution Controversy 55, 56 (D. Wilson* ed. 198..) (italics in original). Note that they make an exception for evolution and creation: they regard evolution as sufficiently established as to preclude alternatives, and creation as too inflexible to be a viable alternative.

[21] Ruse*, *The Ideology of Darwinism*, in Darwin Today 233 (E. Geisler* & W. Scheler* eds. 1983).

[22] A. Thompson*, *Biology, Zoology, and Genetics: Evolutionary Model vs. Creation Model* 2, 127 (1983).

[23] E. de Bono*, *De Bono's Thinking Course* 28 (1982).

[24] Harper*, *A critical review of theories concerning the origin of the Darwin finches*, 14 J. Biogeography 391, 401 (1987).

[25] Ellis*, *Alternatives to the Big Bang*, 22 Ann Rev. Astronomy & Astrophysics 157, 158 (1984).

[26] G. Kerkut*, *Implications of Evolution* 157 (1960); Section 9.7.

[27] Feyerabend*, *The Expert as Con Man*, Science Digest, Feb. 1984, at 83, 83 (italics added).

[28] 1 I. Lakatos*, *The Methodology of Scientific Research Programmes* 1 (J. Worrall* & G. Currie* eds. 1978) ("Indeed, the hallmark of scientific behaviour is a certain skepticism even towards one's most cherished theories.")

[29] Describing Lamarckism is not just a historical comparison, because Lamarckians still exist as a minority viewpoint. *E.g.*, M. Wolsky* & A. Wolsky*, *The Mechanism of Evolution: A New Look at Old Ideas* (1976); E. Steele*, *Somatic Selection and Adaptive Evolution: On the Inheritance of Acquired Characters* 1 (2d ed. 1981).

[30] *E.g.*, S. Luria*, S. Gould* & S. Singer*, *A View of Life* 653-54 (1981) (Permian extinction). Other examples of alternative explanations in Gould's* college textbook are dual explanations for the Cambrian explosion, *id.* at 651-52; alternative approaches to taxonomy (pheneticist, cladistic, and classical evolutionary), *id.* at 684; multiple approaches to the number of kingdoms, *id.* at 693-94; dual views on whether life arose once or several times, *id.* at 711; and dual approaches on the origin of multicellular life, *id.* at 712.

[31] *E.g.*, R. Hulsizer* & D. Lazarus*, *The World of Physics* 295-304 (1977); A. Greenstone* & S. Harris*, *Concepts in Chemistry* 92-102 (3d ed. 1975).

[32] *E.g.*, W. Stansfield*, *The Science of Evolution* 53 (1977) ("Two major hypotheses are currently popular in the explanation for evolution of matter in the universe: (1) the 'big-bang' hypothesis and (2) the 'steady-state' hypothesis."); J. Silk*, *The Big Bang* 316 (1979) ("alternative theories to the Big Bang"). A modified steady state theory still remains as a minority viewpoint. *E.g.*, Oldershaw*, *The Continuing Case for a Hierarchical Cosmology*, 92 Astrophysics & Space Science 347 (1983); Chapter 7.

[33] *E.g.*, J. Murphy*, *Physics: Principles and Problems* 267-69 (1982); R. Hulsizer* & D. Lazarus*, *The World of Physics* 474-87 (1977).

[34] Note 2.

[35] Note 3.

[36] Note 5.

[37] Note 7.

[38] Note 14.

[39] Note 16.

[40] Note 19.

[41] Note 28.

[42] C. Darwin*, *The Origin of Species* 2 (1st ed. 1859, repr. 1964).

[43] *Scientists Abandon Evolution*, Contrast, Mar.-Apr. 1982, at 1, 3 (Provine* describes himself as an Atheist).

[44] T. Black*, *Straight Talk about American Education* 40, 276 (1982) (chancellor 1979-80, member 1969-80).

[45] A. Thompson*, *Biology, Zoology, and Genetics: Evolution Model vs.*

Creation Model 2, 271 (1983) (although he does not view the theory of creation as scientific).

[46] Quoted in P. Davis & E. Solomon*, *The World of Biology* 414 (1974).

[47] P. Davis & E. Solomon*, *The World of Biology* 414 (1974) (Solomon* is an evolutionist, while Davis is a creationist).

[48] R. Alexander*, *Evolution, Creation, and Biology Teaching*, in Evolution versus Creationism 90, 91 (J. Zetterberg* ed. 1983) (although he does not support legislation of curriculum or regard the theory of creation as scientific).

[49] Lecture by V. Sarich* at Bakersfield, California (May 18, 1986).

[50] Anderson* & Kilbourn*, *Creation, Evolution, and Curriculum*, 67 Science Education 45, 53-54 (1983) (although they do not regard the theory of creation as scientific).

[51] A. de Grazia*, Quantavolution and Creation in Arkansas 4 (unpub. ms. 1982).

[52] Letter from Dr. W. Scot Morrow* to Dr. Major Rhodes* (Jan. 1, 1980) (he does regard the theory of creation as scientific).

[53] A. Wiggins* & C. Wynn*, *Natural Science: Bridging the Gap* (1981) (although that text does not itself present the theory of creation).

[54] V. Webster* *et al.*, *Life Science* 409, 436-37, 441-42, 444 (1980).

[55] Von Braun said:

> [T]he scientific method does not allow us to exclude data which lead to the conclusion that the universe, life and man are based on design. To be forced to believe only one conclusion—that everything in the universe happened by chance—would violate the very objectivity of science itself . . ..
>
> . . .. It is in that same sense of scientific honesty that I endorse the presentation of alternative theories for the origin of the universe, life and man in the science classroom. It would be an error to overlook the possibility that the universe was planned rather than happened by chance.

Letter from Dr. Wernher von Braun to Dr. Vernon Grose (Sept. 14, 1972).

[56] That Phi Delta Kappan monograph says:

> Probably the strongest pedagogical argument for teaching both theories is that it *permits comparisons and contrasts*. Teaching by contrasts helps the student to integrate new knowledge within the total framework of the subject. Also, by teaching with an open-ended approach where problems are not solved or "closed" and students are left on their own, students are stimulated to continue searching.

J. Bergman, *Teaching About the Creation/Evolution Controversy* 35-36 (1979).

[57] R. Good*, *Features of Evolution in the Flowering Plants* 2 (1974) (not speaking of the theory of creation).

[58] Chamberlin*, *The Method of Multiple Working Hypotheses*, 148 Science 754, 756 (1965).

[59] Stonehouse*, *Introduction*, to M. Pitman, Adam and Evolution 9, 12 (1984).
[60] Pangle*, *Introduction*, to L. Strauss, Studies in Platonic Political Philosophy 21-22 (1983) (U. of Chicago Press).
[61] R. Dawkins*, *The Blind Watchmaker* 287 (1986).
[62] California State Dep't of Educ.*, *Standards for Evaluation of Instructional Materials with Respect to Social Content* 5, 6, 7 (1982).
[63] Chapters 2, 4 & 6.
[64] Chapters 12-14.
[65] Sections 13.2 & 13.3.
[66] Sections 14.1-14.2.
[67] Chapters 2, 4 & 6.
[68] V. Webster* *et al.*, *Life Science* 409, 436-37, 441-42, 444 (1980) (emphasis added) (the references to creation of "kinds" and "species" are inaccurate).
[69] Except for the mistaken reference to kinds.
[70] Section 3.2(d)-(f).
[71] Beatty*, *Classes and cladists*, 31 Systematic Zoology 25, 29 (1982).
[72] Section 3.2(f).
[73] Grabiner* & Miller*, *Effects of the Scopes Trial: Was It a Victory for Evolutionists?*, 185 Science 833, 833-34 (1974); Troost*, *Evolution in Biological Education Prior to 1960*, 52 Science Education 300 (1968); G. Skoog*, *The Topic of Evolution in Secondary School Biology Textbooks: 1900-1968*, at 31 (diss. 1969); Skoog*, *The Coverage of Evolution in High School Biology Textbooks Published in the 1980's*, 68 Science Education 117 (1984); Skoog*, *Topic of Evolution in Secondary School Biology Textbooks: 1900-1977*, 63 Science Education 621 (1979); Skoog*, Coverage of Evolution in Secondary School Biology Textbooks: 1900-1982, at 2, 4-5 (unpublished ms. Oct. 16, 1982).
[74] P. Bauer* *et al.*, *Experiences in Biology* (1981). The authors are Bauer*, associate professor of botany at Colorado State; Magnoli*, professor of science education at Mobile College; Alvarez*, a science curriculum specialist for a public school system; Chang-Van Horn*, a science resource teacher and adviser for a public school system; and Gomes*, an administrator of a public school.
[75] V. Webster* *et al.*, *Life Science* (1980); G. Skoog*, Coverage of Evolution in Secondary School Biology Textbooks: 1900-1982, at 5 (unpublished ms. Oct. 16, 1982) ("Since 1959, only a popular 1960 textbook and a 1981 textbook failed to include the word evolution in either the text, glossary, or index. A 1980 textbook used the word evolution only once and that was in the last sentence of the chapter on evolution. Evolution was not listed in the glossary of this textbook."). The authors of those textbooks are competent science professors and educators, who evidently have the professional opinion that it is not scientifically or educationally necessary for evolution to be taught in those high school science courses.
[76] Epperson v. Arkansas, 393 U.S. 97, 111 (1968) (Black*, J., concurring).

[77] Macbeth*, *A Third Position in the Textbook Controversy*, 38 Am. Biology Teacher 495 (1976).

[78] Kalven*, *A Commemorative Case Note*: Scopes v. State, 27 U. Chi. L. Rev. 505, 517 (1960); Gelfand*, *Of Monkeys and Men—An Atheist's Heretical View of the Constitutionality of Teaching the Disproof of a Religion in the Public Schools*, 16 J. Law & Educ. 271, 276, 318 (1987); Scheid*, *Evolution and Creationism in the Public Schools*, 9 J. Contemp. L. 81, 115-16 (1983).

[79] Note 51.

[80] Note 47.

[81] Note 57.

[82] Note 59.

[83] Note 43.

[84] Note 45.

[85] Note 44.

[86] Note 49.

[87] Note 52.

[88] Note 48.

[89] Note 50.

[90] Note 54.

[91] Note 68.

CHAPTER 18

The Current Educational Bias in Favor of the Theory of Evolution and Against the Theory of Abrupt Appearance

Education, you know, means broadening, advancing, and if you limit a teacher to only one side of anything the whole country will eventually have only one thought, be one individual. I believe in teaching every aspect of every problem or theory.
—John Scopes*, in connection with the *Scopes* trial[1]

Current public schools and colleges generally present evolution extensively and exclude alternative scientific theories in biology and some other courses (Section 18.1). The typical classroom and its impact is described by one noncreationist as follows:

> When I learned my basic Darwin in high school—and neo-Darwinism and new genetics in college—I learned it as dogmatic truth, as I might have learned a religious catechism. Not in the sense that no physical evidence was adduced—there was enough of that—but in the sense that

*Educators and others cited in this chapter, unless otherwise indicated, are not proponents of, and their quoted statements are not intended as endorsements of, either the theory of abrupt appearance or the theory of creation. However, their quoted statements are acknowledging information that supports the nonreligious or educationally valuable nature of the theories of abrupt appearance and evolution.

> *no alternative theory of the evidence was ever introduced, no critical examination of assumptions and incongruities ever encouraged.* Indeed, I was led to believe that the only alternative to orthodox biology was biblical fundamentalism and the 'creationist' movement.[2]

That bias is related to a widespread bias against discontinuitist and particularly creationist scientists and educators by many educational institutions and technical publications (Section 18.2).

Figure 18.1
The educational danger of "limit-[ing] a teacher to only one side of anything," rather than "teaching every aspect of every . . . theory" (Scopes, pictured the year of the trial)*

18.1 Extensive Treatment of the Theory of Evolution and Exclusion of the Theory of Abrupt Appearance in Most Public Educational Institutions

a. Indoctrination from Exclusion of Alternative Theories

Indoctrination, which has been defined in many ways, is tied directly to suppression of alternatives by Schofield*:

> The one word which we can use to describe the characteristic of indoctri-

nation, then, is "irrationality," a deliberate attempt to remove understanding. Far from encouraging the use of evidence to substantiate, it actually *suppresses all evidence which is in any way likely to undermine the beliefs* and ideas it is attempting to inculcate. Suppression of evidence, the doctrinaire approach and the authoritarian manner are all deliberate, and it is the intention of the indoctrinator that all these features shall be characteristic of the process. His aim is to *suppress all possible criticism* of the beliefs he transmits. *One line of argument will be put so forcefully, so repeatedly, so uncompromisingly*, that the victim of the indoctrination will *never be able to consider an alternative because none appears to be available. . . .*

. . . .

The teacher is more obviously an indoctrinator and his conduct reprehensible when he *attempts to inculcate into the minds of his pupils his own beliefs and attitudes*, and also ideas which are by no means certain *without the suggestion of possible alternatives*. This does not mean that no teacher should teach anything unless it is one hundred percent certain. . . . The intentions of the teacher, as distinct from the indoctrinator, are based on reason. He puts forward an idea and adduces evidence from his own experience and from that of other people to show what can be said in favour of the idea *and what must be said against it*.[3]

Similarly, White* defines indoctrination as teaching with the intent that a pupil believe what is taught such that nothing will shake that belief,[4] and Snook* finds that "a person indoctrinates P if he teaches with the intention that the pupil or pupils believe P regardless of the evidence."[5]

The harms of indoctrination are "rigidity, narrowness, and dogmatism," which are "certainly characteristics of poor teaching."[6] Beck* elaborates on the dangers:

The important point about these definitional exercises is not that they have captured for us the "essence" of indoctrination. Rather it is that they have displayed before us more clearly than before a number of things to be on guard against in education: peddling false beliefs; adopting authoritarian, inculcative intentions with respect to students; using methods that do not engage the free spirit and critical faculties of students; and producing in students a state of *mindless acceptance of conventional attitudes and beliefs*.[7]

Siegel* sees similar harm amounting to educational child abuse.

The child has an overwhelming interest in avoiding *indoctrination*. To be so shackled, and *to have her options and future so limited*, is to narrow her life in a way that is as unacceptable as it is out of her control. In being indoctrinated, *the child is cut off from all but a narrow band of possibilities*. Her freedom and her dignity are short-circuited, her autonomy is denied, her control over her own life and her ability to contribute to community life are truncated, her mental life is impoverished. This is a

> description more apt of child abuse than of acceptable education. . . . [T]he child should be thought of as having the right, in having the right to be a critical thinker, to avoid it.[8]

Thus, indoctrination is excoriated by educational theorists, such as de Bono*,[9] Gribble*,[10] Passmore*,[11] Wilson*,[12] and Perry*.[13]

The consequence of indoctrination from teaching a single viewpoint is magnified by the influence of the teacher, the pressure from peers, and the authoritativeness of the textbook. Teachers enjoy influence from their position of authority, superiority in education, and difference in age, as Zander* *et al.*[14] and Van Alst*[15] note. That authority is described by Schofield*:

> The teacher, as Peters stresses, as we shall see later, is an "authority figure". He has tremendous influence because of the knowledge he has acquired and because of the power vested in him by those who accept him into their society as a teacher. This authority can be used for good or ill. It can make harmful content harmless or harmless content "potential dynamite" as Mussolini realized. . . .[16]

Mussolini's* exact words were as follows:

> One will say that geography and mathematics are by nature nonpolitical. Such may be the case, but also the contrary. Their teaching can do good or harm. From the elevation of his chair, certain words, an intonation, an allusion, a judgment, a bit of statistics, coming from the professor suffice to produce a political effect. That is why a professor of mathematics plays a political role and should be a fascist.[17]

That teacher authority is particularly powerful toward vulnerable values such as religious convictions, as Brown* and Pallant* find,[18] and in technical subjects such as science, Patel* and Gordon*[19] and Stone* and James*[20] add. The instructor's influence also derives from authority over grades and class discussion, including the ability to count discrepant responses "wrong" and thereby to penalize disagreement, Battle*,[21] Bartlett*,[22] and Thompson*[23] find. Thus, students sometimes alter their personal beliefs when they conflict with the official classroom view, Sereno*[24] and Berenda*[25] conclude.

Peers also can exert pressure to conform to the classroom orthodoxy of a single view. Particularly in elementary and secondary schools, the individual's need for group acceptance and social approval influences development of his values, according to Berenda*,[26] Hurlock*,[27] and Argyle*,[28] and particularly of religious and similar values.[29] Compliance with peer pressure may involve forsaking opinions and values that differ significantly from other students, Asch*[30] and Festinger*[31] state, and may include adopting beliefs that conform to those of fellow students, Berenda*,[32] Dashiell*,[33] and Lasseigne*[34] conclude. If a student does not conform to the peer group, fellow students may seek to dissuade and influence him, as Hare*[35] and Festinger* *et al.*[36] demonstrate, and that normally causes conformity.[37] If the pupil withstands that pressure, the peer group may reject him as a deviant and stigmatize him in various ways, as Emerson*[38] and Rosenberg*[39] observe. If expression of nonconforming views must occur in front of teachers and fellow students, the cumulative pressure to conform and the deterrent toward nonconformity is greater, Hare*,[40] Hovland* *et al.*,[41] and Argyle*[42] note.

Secondary and elementary school students are most sensitive to teacher influence and peer pressure. Their critical and abstract thinking are not advanced and mature, as Marek* and Renner*[43] and Goldman*[44] find in their studies. Their personal values are quite vulnerable to outside influence, Vergote*,[45] Goldman*,[46] Hurlock*,[47] and Hyde*[48] state.

Textbooks carry substantial influence as well, as Chall* of Harvard points out:

> Textbooks are more potent forces in what and how teachers teach and in what and how children learn than we are ready to admit. Textbooks select for study a content, an emphasis, a method of instruction and learning, and a level of difficulty. This power is held jealously by the government and dominant party of nondemocratic countries. No totalitarian country would chance the consequences of freedom in textbook development and selection. Even the choice of first story in the first reading text must pass the approval of political and educational committees.[49]

One study of reading books, with one group using texts with characters from various ethnic and racial groups and another group using books with all-white characters, showed that "the children using the multiethnic readers responded significantly more favorably toward Negroes than the children using the regular readers."[50] Studies of the roles of Indians and Eskimos in texts revealed that textbook presentation influenced students' attitudes toward those groups, according to the Commission on Civil Rights*,[51] Uribe* and Martinez*,[52] and Bains* *et al.*[53] Studies of the roles of women in textbooks support the same conclusion, according to Scott* and Schau*[54] and Campbell* and Wirtenberg*.[55] The content of science textbooks particularly influences the instruction in the classroom, Kastrinos*[56] and Voss*[57] note.

b. Indoctrination from Exclusive Treatment of Evolution

"Presently, the concepts of evolutionary theory . . . permeate the public school textbooks," a court opinion acknowledged,[58] at least in biology and for some textbooks in other fields. Evolution receives an average of 14,055 words in each of eight major biology textbooks published between 1980 and 1982, and seven devote at least 11,000 words to evolution.[59] By contrast, neither the theory of abrupt appearance nor the theory of creation receives more than a paragraph in any but one of the roughly thirty textbooks for public school biology, neither is mentioned in most, and neither is mentioned in the rest except in criticism. And no other alternative scientific view of origins receives a reference as an existing theory, except for a few highly critical references to panspermia.

The teacher's guidebook for three leading biology texts describes evolution as "pervasive and comprehensive" and "interwoven":

> Because of its *pervasive and comprehensive character*, *evolution* is treated in three ways in the BSCS materials. There are specific chapters on evolution as the history of living things. There are specific chapters on evolution as a process. And third, evolution either as history or as process is *interwoven in all other chapters* where it has a place: in the treatment of cell chemistry, ecology, taxonomy, and so on.
>
> Evolution is another *pervasive theme* that is *developed throughout the book*, but its main treatment comes in Chapters 31-34. The student must have a good background in genetics, as well as some knowledge of the diversity of animals, before evolution can have its full impact. Chapters 33 and 34 deal specifically with the physical and cultural evolution.
>
> The *entire course*—indeed, any modern biology course—can be regarded as a *summary of the evidence for evolution*. The main objective of Chapter 18, "Evolution," then, is not to give the evidence for evolution; that has already been done in several ways, *both implicit and explicit*. Instead the chief aim is to give the student some idea of the mechanism of evolution.[60]

The former chairman of the board of the Biological Sciences Curriculum Study (BSCS) agreed that "evolution is not only one of the major themes but is, in fact, central,"[61] and others have concurred.[62] In the late 1970's and early 1980's, "fifty percent of American school children currently use BSCS books directly and the curriculum is incorporated indirectly in virtually all biology texts," the *McLean* court decision[63] and Mayer*[64] conclude.

Those BSCS textbooks concede that Darwinian evolution is "the most inclusive of the great unifying principles of biology."[65] Another of the five leading biology texts, *Modern Biology*,[66] is also pervasively evolutionary,[67] as are nearly all of the competing books.[68] The content of the textbooks is very significant, not only because it is what students read, but because it heavily influences what teachers teach in science.[69] Although many evolutionist scientists defend that exclusive and pervasive presentation of evolution,[70] others express concern about the consequence of indoctrination.

That exclusive presentation of Darwinian evolution is condemned by most structuralists, such as Lambert*, Millar*, and Hughes*:

> Indeed, we think that *most textbooks appear dedicated to the idea that the material with which they deal should be beyond discussion.* To us, such an approach does not convince students that our science is alive, instead it portrays a discipline devoid of life and one in which there are absolute facts, which besides being true are theory independent. Such a process then *leads only to reinforce our belief in the correctness of our own views.* Indeed there seems to be a fine line between learning as a liberatory experience and learning as a method of reinforcement of our own personal and sometimes communal orthodoxy.
>
> Industrial melanism is a good example of this type of approach. However, Jones (1981 p. 109) was quite correct when he remarked:
>
>> Industrial melanism is the textbook example of natural selection in action. Like most such examples it is *usually presented in a way which is both incomplete and inaccurate.*[71]

Similar condemnations come from most transformed cladists, antiDarwinians, and antievolutionists.[72]

The exclusion of alternative theories amounts to indoctrination. Omission of alternatives is indeed endemic, Harper* notes:

> At this stage, alternatives to Darwinism are not usually mentioned, and even if they appear later during secondary education they are often presented so poorly and unconvincingly that many children cannot understand them, let alone imagine how they might originally have been firmly believed. . . .
>
> . . ..
>
> . . . It may be objected by some that there is no need to mention alternatives to Darwinism because none of the alternatives is widely believed. This argument might be acceptable if we were also prepared to accept the same argument from a Soviet indoctrinator—that he doesn't teach capitalism because so few people in the USSR believe in it.[73]

That amounts to indoctrination under any widely accepted definition:

> For some time it has seemed to me that *our current methods of teaching Darwinism are suspiciously similar to indoctrination.* To try to establish whether there is indoctrination, I have used two approaches. The first involves a brief survey of the methods we use; the second is a more philosophical approach—namely to apply a criterion or means of identifying indoctrination to our teaching of Darwinism.
>
> . . ..
>
> A review of methods used to put across Darwinism to children gives

cause for concern. The following will be considered: (i) we expose children at an early age to the theory we want them to learn; (ii) we do not present alternative theories, or if we do then inadequately; (iii) if alternatives are presented, this happens at a later age; (iv) we state that the theory or parts of it are proved; (v) we make statements and ask questions which implicitly assume the theory to be true; (vi) we suggest that the theory is validated by a method which is inapplicable; (vii) we cast aspersions on those who do not conform. *All this adds up to a catalogue of the methods we would expect to be used in the case of well attested political or religious indoctrination.* As a battery of methods, they are formidable. It forms, in my view, reasonable grounds for suspecting that *we are indoctrinating.* The seven techniques will be discussed in a little more detail.

. . ..

Snook's criterion is now applied to the teaching of Darwin's theory in the following way. In terms of the criterion it would be far-fetched to claim that teachers of Darwin's theory do not have the intention that pupils should believe in Darwin's theory. Perhaps only some actively desire that the pupils should believe, though this presumably includes all teachers of Darwin's theory who believe it themselves and want their pupils to believe in truths and not falsehoods: and among those teachers who do not fall into this category, many would fulfil the "intention" criterion simply because they realize that, as a result of their teaching, their pupils' belief in Darwinism is likely.

We get into a bit of difficulty when we try to apply "regardless of evidence". . . . I believe, however, that Snook intended it to apply to this kind of situation. There is a close similarity for instance, between the Darwinist and the Marxist in the example quoted earlier. Both can take any relevant information whatever, true or false, and reconcile it with their theory. The Darwinist can always make a plausible reconstruction of what took place during the supposed evolution of a species. . . . Secondly, Snook characterized the "educator" as the teacher who is primarily concerned with evidence and the handling of it, while the indoctrinator is primarily concerned to put across a set of conclusions. Looked at in this way the teacher of Darwin's theory corresponds with the latter since he undoubtedly is concerned to put across the conclusion that natural selection causes evolution, while he cannot be concerned to any great extent with real evidence because there isn't any.

If it is accepted that (i) proposition II is a fair rendering of Darwin's theory, (ii) Snook's criterion is acceptable, and (iii) it is applicable, then *indoctrination is demonstrated.*[74]

The only rationale for excluding alternatives (or for ostensibly inviting them but never finding them satisfactory) is a prior decision accepting the radical definition of science (Sections 9.3-9.6) and an indoctrinatory view of education. The assessment of Anderson* and Kilbourn* is as follows:

> It should again be noted that an argument showing that the special-creation position lies outside the domain of science is an argument within the theoretical debate because it depends on an articulation of a position on the nature of science. Moving from that argument to the conclusion that special-creation should not be taught *assumes that resolution of the theoretical debate is sufficient grounds for making a curricular decision.* This assumption is tenable, we suggest, *only if science teaching is narrowly conceived as inculcation* and training in the discipline itself. *At its pedagogical extreme, this would be a form of indoctrination.* The function of science teaching would be to insure that the student adopt and believe a scientific point of view. This position implies that science provides the correct (if not the only) explanations. Philosophically, of course, the position runs into difficulty (as with creationists) since the only grounds for arguing the position are within the position itself and we are once again confronted with *competing metaphysical systems.*[75]

They could have added that the criticized approach to science teaching seeks to insure that the student adopt an evolutionary instead of a nonevolutionary scientific point of view, which implies that evolution provides the correct (if not the only) explanation. Pangle* denounces such "attempts by neo-Darwinians to limit the claims to knowledge, and hence the access to the education of the young, of so-called 'creationists' . . .."[76]

c. *Result of Effectively Teaching Evolution as Fact*

The usual effect of presenting evolution exclusively is to present it as fact or "dogmatic truth," as Roszak* was quoted as saying above. References to evolution as "theory" still amount to its presentation as "fact," if it is the only viewpoint taught, as the teachers' guidebook for BSCS texts admits:

> A special word is necessary concerning our habit of referring to the "theory of evolution." This usage is often taken to mean that evolution is but an envisaged possibility, something uncertain and unproved.
>
> This sense of "theory" no longer holds in science, if it ever did . . .. Evolution is a theory in this sense, yes—a body of interrelated *facts*. As new *facts* about evolution are discovered, the organization may be changed in order to include them, but this would not mean that the present organization of facts now known is unsound.[77]

Thus, "evolution continues to be presented in textbooks . . . as if it were . . . fact," according to Klein*, a regent emerita of the New York State Board of Regents:

> Reseachers in the field of evolution, however, have produced no verifiable facts which would validate their theory conclusively. From time to

> time evolutionists have even admitted ignoring real facts and altering the theory to fit selected data. In spite of these grossly unscientific tactics, the theory of evolution continues to be presented in textbooks, encyclopedias, and research papers as if it were a proven and verifiable scientific fact.[78]

The tendency of public school texts is to present concepts as certain truth (unless an alternative is also presented), as Nelkin* notes:

> Textbooks especially tend to convey a *message of certainty*, for in the process of simplification, findings may become explanations, explanations may become axioms, and tentative judgments may become definitive conclusions. Preoccupied with communicating a scientific view of nature, textbooks often neglect to convey concepts of critical inquiry.[79]

The textbooks present evolution not only as fact, but as erroneous fact, in the views of many evolutionist scientists such as Kerkut*:

> At present, however, it is a matter of faith that the textbook pictures are true, or even that they are the best representations of the truth that are available to us at the present time.[80]

Textbooks present "stories . . . replete with phantoms" for animal evolution, according to Patterson*:

> To me one of the most astonishing consequences of the furor over cladistics is the realization that the current account of tetrapod [four-legged vertebrate] evolution, shown in a thousand diagrams and everywhere acknowledged as the centerpiece of historical biology, is a will-o'-the wisp. For nowhere can one find a clear statement of how and why the Recent groups are interrelated, and the *textbook stories* are *replete with phantoms*—extinct, uncharacterizable groups giving rise one to another.[81]

The misleading dogmatism of textbooks on evolution, particularly of plants, is noted by Corner* who, although an evolutionist, finds that "[t]extbooks hoodwink" one:

> Much evidence can be adduced in favour of the theory of evolution—from biology, bio-geography and palaeontology, but I still think that, to the unprejudiced, the fossil record of plants is in favour of special creation. . . . The evolutionist must be prepared with an answer, but I think that most would break down before an inquisition.
>
> *Textbooks hoodwink.* A series of more and more complicated plants is introduced—the alga, the fungus, the bryophyte, and so on, and examples are *added eclectically* in support of one or another theory—and that is held to be a presentation of evolution. If the world of plants consisted only of these few textbook types of standard botany, the idea of evolution might never have dawned . . ..[82]

"Neo-Darwinist textbooks on evolution keep citing the same comparatively few examples" that Saunders* and Ho* find nonpersuasive,[83] and on "phylogeny our textbooks are . . . a festering mass of unsupported assertions" in the estimation of Bonner*.[84] The texts give a misleading picture of biochemical evolution as well, Cairns-Smith* observes.[85] Thus, Stansfield* finds a significant "contribution creationist scientists are currently making to science" in "their recognition of 'creeping dogmatism' in the science of evolution."[86]

Summary. (a) Indoctrination occurs when a teacher "attempts to inculcate into the minds of his pupils his own beliefs and attitudes, and also ideas which are by no means certain without the suggestion of possible alternatives" (Schofield*[87]). That produces "mindless acceptance of conventional attitudes and beliefs" (Beck*[88]), and "the child is cut off from all but a narrow band of possibilities" (Siegel*[89]).

Indoctrination in schools and universities is particularly effective (and thus dangerous) because of the influence of the teacher, the peer group, and the text. "The teacher . . . is an 'authority figure' " with "tremendous influence because of the knowledge he has acquired and because of the power vested in him" (Schofield*[90]). Peers offer great pressure toward conformity, because the student "is 'cut off' from the rest of society, forced inward toward his own age group, made to carry out his whole social life with others his own age," as "a small society" (Coleman*[91]). "Textbooks are more potent forces in what and how teachers teach and in what and how children learn," because they "select for study a content, an emphasis, a method of instruction" (Chall*[92]).

(b) In the typical classroom addressing evolution, "no alternative theory of the evidence was ever introduced, no critical examination of assumptions and incongruities ever encouraged" (Roszak*[93]). The average biology textbook in public schools devotes 14,055 words to evolution (Skoog*[94]), but not more than an unfavorable paragraph to any current alternative theory. The leading textbooks admit that "[e]volution is another pervasive theme that is developed throughout the book," so that the "entire course—indeed, any modern biology course—can be regarded as a summary of the evidence for evolution" (Klinckmann*[95]). The textbooks not only are what students read, but generally determine what teachers teach in science (Kastrinos*[96]).

(c) To teach the theory of evolution without alternatives effectively is to teach it as fact. As the teacher handbook for three leading texts informs teachers, "referring to the 'theory of evolution' " does not mean merely "an envisaged possibility, something uncertain and unproved," because "[e]volution is a theory in this sense . . . a body of interrelated facts" (Klinckmann*[97]). Yet many scientists and educators find evolution to involve "no verifiable facts" or necessary interpretations, and object to the way "the theory of evolution continues to be presented in textbooks . . . as if it were a proven and verifiable scientific fact" (Klein*[98]). They argue that "it is a matter of faith that the textbook pictures are true" (Kerkut*[99]), that on animal evolution texts are "replete with phantoms" (Patterson*[100]), that on plant evolution "[t]extbooks hoodwink" (Corner*[101]), that on fossil relations "textbooks are . . . a festering mass of unsupported assertions" (Bonner*[102]), and that on biochemical evolution texts are misleading (Cairns-Smith*[103]).

Most modern classrooms simply indoctrinate students in evolutionary theory and censor alternative scientific theories. In presenting evolution, "most textbooks appear dedicated to the idea that the material with which they deal should be beyond discussion," and only "reinforce our belief in the correctness of our own views" (Lambert*, Millar*, and Hughes*[104]). In the classroom, "alternatives to Darwinism are not usually mentioned, and even if they appear later during secondary education they are often presented so poorly and unconvincingly that many children cannot understand them" or believe them, so that "our current methods of teaching Darwinism are suspiciously similar to indoctrination" (Harper*[105]).

Figure 18.2
Wegener's theory of continental drift "took geologists and geophysicists almost forty years . . . to accept," and then only after much ridicule and hostility (Broad* and Wade*); discontinuitist theories might expect worse*

18.2 Discrimination against Discontinuitist Scientists and Educators by Educational Institutions and Publications

One product of indoctrination in evolution and censorship of alternative scientific theories is discrimination, not only by public universities and schools, but by science publications. Because discrimination typically is difficult to prove, the normal presumption applies that documented instances represent only the tip of an iceberg.

a. Discrimination against Discontinuitists by Universities and Schools

Significant discrimination does exist against discontinuitist theories of origins, particularly against the theory of creation. The "intolerant" attitude toward the theory of creation among "most" evolutionary biologists is acknowledged by Provine*:

> [M]ost biological scientists are intolerant of creationism and do not understand the reasons for the great attraction of the creationist's position.[106]

Other acknowledgments of intolerance toward the theory of creation were cited in Section 9.7(d). That intolerance is not shared by the eighty-six percent of the public that supports public school instruction in the theory of creation,[107] but it is a serious problem for creationist scientists and teachers and students.

Many creationist scientists have been denied tenure[108] or discharged by universities effectively because of their scientific conclusions about the theory of creation.[109] Patterson* of Iowa State University concedes that "their chances of achieving or retaining prestigious academic positions" are undermined:

> Were biologists, geologists, or paleontologists to endorse publicly a pseudoscience such as creationism their *chances of achieving or retaining prestigious academic positions would be greatly undermined*, as would their chances for high office in professional societies. Only in Bible colleges, seminaries, and creationist ministries can the latter succeed as outspoken creationists.[110]

Many creationist students have been denied earned degrees, prevented from completing academic programs[111], or denied entrance into graduate study for which they otherwise qualified, because of similar discrimination.[112] For example, Patterson* states that he would fail a creationist student who otherwise passed his course but did not give valid scientific evidence for the theory of creation to Patterson's* satisfaction, and would place a disparaging reference on the college transcript of a creationist student (which probably would preclude graduate study in science) who could state evolutionist arguments while personally rejecting them:

> I would not fail a student outright simply on the basis of the above answers but would certainly consider it necessary to check further into his/her command of the subject. The best way to do this, in my view, would be to request that they detail their scientific arguments and reasons for their answers. If those arguments turned out to be *scientifically counterfeit or badly fallacious, as are those of the present day creation scientists (sic)*, or if their reasons were contradictory to scientific facts or contradictory to certain other theories of science (e.g. thermodynamics), then I would consider these persons to either be [*sic*] *imposters or seemingly hopeless incompetents* (probably due their being misled by evangelists from the creationist movement). Moreover, I would keep their answers on file as powerful evidence of their incompetence and then proceed to submit a *failing grade . . . even if their success on the memorization parts of the quizzes etc. were enough to carry them into the passing range* (on paper). In other words, I would use my professional judgment in a case like this and if I thought the new findings superseded the overall averages on exams (which are always incomplete barometers of competence anyway and should only be used as guidelines when more definitive information is lacking), then I would *overrule those scores* on the basis of the answers I got from the special investigation.
>
> Another case is worth noting here. Suppose the student gives the correct scientific answers in his or her science course and suppose he/she also knows and gives the *correct scientific arguments and reasons* for the follow-up question, but still *insists on rejecting* all this for reasons of incompatibility with his/her religious beliefs. In this case, I would prefer to pass the student strictly according to the usual scoring criteria but with the proviso that his rejection of the subject matter for religious reasons be *noted on his transcript* of grades.[113]

b. Discrimination against Discontinuitist Scientists and Educators by Science Publications

Many discontinuitist, and particularly creationist, scientists have had manuscripts rejected by the major science publications because of antidiscontinuitist and anticreationist discrimination, and many more have not submitted manuscripts because of inevitable discriminatory rejection by most journals.[114] Strike*, professor of philosophy of education at New York State College of Agricultural and Life Sciences of Cornell University, bluntly admits that "[t]he referee system has rejected creationism," and that "it is not seen as an acceptable scientific option by the referee system of science . . . ."[115]

For example, Dr. Stefan Marinov suffered rejection of his papers opposing cosmic evolution by thirty-seven journals as reported in *Nature* (the publication of the leading British science organization):

> For some years, Dr. Marinov has submitted papers and proposals concerning 'absolute spacetime' to such bodies, with—by his own account—a rather small degree of success. Literal copies of this correspondence make up the bulk of his book and are absorbing reading.
>
> Between these two lie the responses of some 35 other journals and the National Science Foundation (four referee reports followed by formal appeals up successive rungs of the hierarchy).
>
> All readers should note how, in this case at least, the system seems to have ensured that orthodoxy prevails—deciding for themselves whether by malevolent conspiracy, inertia or good sense.[116]

Similarly, Robert V. Gentry published a dozen scholarly articles on radiohalos in refereed science journals,[117] but has had every manuscript rejected since publicly stating his creationist interpretation of his polonium halo research as an affirmative evidence for the theory of creation.[118] Earlier, after successfully publishing one article on his research in *Applied Physics Letters*,[119] Gentry submitted another article on further research but made the mistake of including the following creationist interpretation:

> It is difficult to reconcile these results with current cosmological theories which envision long time periods between nucleosynthesis and [the earth's] crustal formation. It is suggested these [polonium] halos are more nearly in accord with a cosmological model which would envision an instantaneous fiat creation of the earth.[120]

The editor of *Applied Physics Letters* rejected the manuscript on the basis of the negative comments of peer reviewers, and attached their comments:

> Failing to think of any other possible explanations, he concludes that the earth was formed by instantaneous fiat. In one blow he implicitly rejects all the carefully accumulated evidence of decades which is in complete conflict with his remarkable conclusion.
>
> He is undoubtedly well aware of the findings of the modern science of geochronology. The scientific approach would be to use all these results to his advantage and try to find a compatible explanation.
>
> Without going into a long harangue about "pseudoscience", let me simply say that X X X X and I regard the reasoning displayed in this manuscript in its present form as *unworthy of publication. The experimental observations, minus any wild speculation, might be appropriately reported* in a journal such as Nature.[121]

From those reviewer comments, the reason for rejection clearly was disagreement with the discontinuitist interpretation ("wild speculation") of "instantaneous fiat" and not with the quality of scientific research, which "might be appropriately reported." Gentry revised the manuscript and deleted the creationist interpretation, and it promptly passed peer review and was published in *Nature*.[122]

Gentry submitted a different manuscript on further research to *Science*, a journal published by the American Association for the Advancement of Science. Reviewers had no objection to the experimental work but recommended rejection because of the following discontinuitist interpretation, which one reviewer labelled a "very weak and contradictory argument":[123]

> the experimental evidence indicates the inclusions of the polonium halos contained the specific alpha emitters responsible for the halos (or possibly in certain cases beta decaying lead precursors) at the time when the mica crystallized, and as such these particular halos represent extinct radioactivity.[124]

Gentry requested new reviewers and removed the discontinuitist interpretation, and the article was approved and published in *Science*.[125] However, as word of his creationist views spread, he was unable to attain approval for publication in scholarly journals, and suffered cancellation of his research contract with Oak Ridge National Laboratory (the reason was not budgetary because its annual payment was a mere $1.00).

This great difficulty encountered by discontinuitist scientists in publishing science articles on origins is evident in the active participation in the anticreationist meetings of many of the scientific organizations that sponsor scientific journals, such as the 1981 meeting sponsored by the National Academy of Sciences (publisher of *Proceedings of the NAS*) and attended by representatives of the American Association for the Advancement of Science (publisher of *Science*), American Museum of Natural History (publisher of *Natural History*), National Association of Biology Teachers (publisher of *American Biology Teacher*), National Science Teachers Association, American Institute of Biological Sciences, American Geological Institute (publisher of *Geotimes* and *Earth Science*), American Society of Biological Chemists (publishers of *Journal of Biological Chemistry*), American Anthropological Association (publisher of *American Anthropologist*, *American Ethnologist*, *Anthropology and Education Quarterly*, and *Anthropology and Humanism Quarterly*), and Federation of American Societies for Experimental Biology (an organization of seven scientific societies such as American Physiological Society, American Association of Immunologists, and American Society for Cell Biology).[126]

Noncreationists with unorthodox theories confront similar problems. Arp* "observed at first hand many of the factors overriding the objective criteria of what research programs were best," and at last fell victim himself to termination of his telescope use at major observatories.[127] Hoyle and Wickramasinghe "received hints and even warnings from friends and colleagues that our views on these matters are generally repugnant to the scientific world," and were "disturbed to discover how little attention is generally paid to fact and how much to myths and prejudice."[128] Velikovsky* encountered incredible vilification.[129]

Summary. Discrimination exists widely against discontinuitist views, which is closely related to the strong bias in favor of the theory of evolution and against the theory of abrupt appearance (Section 9.7(c)-(d)). Similarly, "most biological scientists are intolerant of creationism" (Provine*[130]). (a) In universities and schools, "[w]ere biologists, geologists, or paleontologists to endorse publicly a pseudoscience such as creationism their chances of achieving or retaining prestigious academic positions would be greatly undermined" (Patterson*[131]). Many examples of denial of tenure, termination of employment, denial of earned degrees, or exclusion from graduate study can be cited. Similarly, an outspoken evolutionist professor admits that if students embraced a nonevolutionary theory and gave defenses that "turned out to be scientifically counterfeit or badly fallacious, as are those of the present day creation scientists . . ., then I would consider those persons to either be [*sic*] imposters or seemingly hopeless incompetents," and would "then proceed to submit a failing grade . . . even if their success on the memorization part of the quizzes etc. were enough to carry them into the passing range (on paper)" (Patterson*[132])!

(b) In science journals, the "referee system has rejected creationism" (Strike*[133]) and generally shows that intolerance toward most theories of discontinuity. For example, Gentry's manuscripts based on his radiohalo research were publishable and published when discontinuitist conclusions were deleted (Gentry[134]), but were "unworthy of publication" because of "wild speculation" in the eyes of peer reviewers when discontinuitist conclusions were included (Myers*,[135] *Science*[136]).

Notes

1 P. Davis & E. Solomon*, *The World of Biology* 414 (1974) (italics added).

2 T. Roszak*, *Unfinished Animal* 99-100 (1975).

3 H. Schofield*, *The Philosophy of Education* 178, 181 (1972) (italics added, original italics deleted).

4 White*, *Indoctrination*, in The Concept of Education (R. Peters* ed. 1967).

5 I. Snook*, *Indoctrination and Education* 47 (1972).

6 H. Schofield*, *The Philosophy of Education* 198 (1972).

7 C. Beck*, *Educational Philosophy and Theory: An Introduction* 190-91 (1974) (italics added).

8 Siegel*, *Critical Thinking as an Intellectual Right*, in Children's Intellectual Rights 39, 46 (D. Moshman* ed. 1986).

9 de Bono*, *The Cognitive Research Trust (CoRT) Thinking Program*, in Thinking: The Expanding Frontier 115 (1983).

10 J. Gribble* *Introduction to Philosophy of Education* 29-40 (1969).

11 J. Passmore*, *The Philosophy of Teaching* 179-80 (1980).

12 Wilson*, *Education and Indoctrination*, in Aims in Education 24 (T. Hollins* ed. 1964).

13 Perry*, *Education and the Science of Education*, in Philosophy and Education 17, 27 (2d ed. I. Scheffler* ed. 1966).

14 A. Zander*, T. Curtis* & H. Rosenfeld*, *The Influence of Teachers and Peers on Aspirations of Youth* 25, 78-79 (U.S. Office of Educ. 1961) (high school sophomores and seniors).

15 Van Alst*, *The Effects of Influenced Teacher and Student Expectations on Student Performance in Tenth Grade Science*, 34 Dissertation Abstracts 1732A (1973) (unpublished dissertation for Boston University) (high school sophomores in biology course).

16 H. Schofield*, *The Philosophy of Education* 182 (1972).

17 Mussolini*, *Scuola Fascista*, Le Temps (Aug. 31, 1932), quoted in Perry*, *Education and the Science of Education*, in Philosophy and Education 17, 27-28 (2d ed. I. Scheffler* ed. 1966).

18 Brown* & Pallant*, *Religious Belief and Social Pressure*, 10 Psych. Rep. 813, 814 (1962) ("Positive pressure produced a significant change in stated beliefs towards an 'expert's' opinion, showing that religious beliefs are susceptible to social influences.") (high school-aged individuals).

19 Patel* & Gordon*, *Some Personal and Situational Determinants of Yielding to Influence*, 61 J. Abnormal & Soc. Psych. 411, 414, 417 (1960) (prestige of source governs suggestibility in high school students).

20 Stone* & James*, *Interval Scaling of the Prestige of Selected Secondary Education Teacher Specialities*, 20 Perceptual & Motor Skills 859, 860 (1965) (science teachers possess particularly high prestige).

[21] *See* Battle*, *Relation between Personal Values and Scholastic Achievement*, J. Experimental Educ., Sept. 1957, at 27.

[22] Bartlett*, *Teacher Perception and Labeling of Discrepant Behavior*, 33 Dissertation Abstracts 5825A, 5825A-26 (1973) (unpublished dissertation for Peabody College).

[23] Thompson*, *High School Students and Their Values*, 16 Cal. J. Educ. Research 217, 219 (1965).

[24] Sereno*, *Ego-Involvement, High Source Credibility, and Response to a Belief-Discrepant Communication*, 35 Speech Monographs 476 (1968) (attitude change results from belief-discrepant situation created by high-credibility source) (college students).

[25] *See* R. Berenda*, *The Influence of the Group on the Judgments of Children* 49 (1950) (students aware of teacher's opinion in classroom, even if obviously wrong, will limit range of their views and conform their beliefs more to that opinion) (elementary school students).

[26] *Id.* at 30 ("very strong need to remain a member of one's group" and "fear of being accused by the others of wanting to be 'different' ").

[27] E. Hurlock*, *Child Development* 218 (1942) (elementary school-age individuals).

[28] Argyle*, *Social Pressure in Public and Private Situations*, 54 J. Abnormal & Soc. Psych. 172, 174 (1957) ("norm formation is connected with the need for acceptance") (high school students).

[29] Pressure from peers carries particular influence upon religious convictions, because "strong social support is required for the maintenance of a system of religious belief." Brown*, *A Study of Religious Belief*, 53 Brit. J. Psych. 259, 268 (1962).

[30] Asch*, *Effects of Group Pressure upon the Modification and Distortion of Judgments*, in Group Dynamics Research and Theory 189, 191, 193, 194 (2d ed. D. Cartwright* & A. Zander* eds. 1960) (some minority individuals come "to perceive the majority estimates as correct," others believe "that their perceptions are inaccurate," while others "suppress their observations" though aware of majority's error).

[31] Festinger*, *A Theory of Social Comparison Processes*, 7 Human Rel. 117, 137 (1954) (group has power to influence the member effectively and, in the case of opinion difference . . . to eliminate the difference of opinion").

[32] R. Berenda*, *The Influence of the Group on the Judgments of Children* 32, 60 (1950) ("There is a statistically significant change in the judgments of the minority children in the direction of the group," even if it is plainly wrong, which reflects "a strong tendency to follow the majority.").

[33] Dashiell*, *Experimental Studies of the Influence of Social Situations on the Behavior of Individual Human Adults*, in A Handbook of Social Psychology 1148 (C. Murchison* ed. 1935) (individuals given information about majority student opinion shift to greater conformity) (high school students).

[34] Lasseigne*, *A Study of Peer and Adult Influence on Moral Beliefs of Adolescents*, 10 Adolescence 227, 229 (1975) (adolescents become "extremely

vulnerable" to peer group influence in moral beliefs, and this influence "significantly" exceeds parent influence) (high school students).

[35] A. Hare*, *Handbook of Small Group Research* 44 (1962) (group pressures deviant member and "will make overt attempts to secure the conformity of the deviant").

[36] Festinger*, Gerard*, Hymovitch*, Kelley* & Raven*, *The Influence Process in the Presence of Extreme Deviates*, 5 Human Rel. 327, 344, 345 (1952) (group seeks to obtain conformity).

[37] *Id.* at 344 (pressure toward uniformity in cohesive group increases change in deviant opinions); Festinger*, *A Theory of Social Comparison Processes*, 7 Human Rel. 117, 127 (1954) (group influence and pressure induces deviant "to change [his] own opinion to agree more with the others in the group").

[38] Emerson*, *Deviation and Rejection: An Experimental Replication*, 19 Am. Soc. Rev. 688 (1954) (conforming group members reject deviants) high school students).

[39] Rosenberg*, *The Dissonant Religious Context and Emotional Disturbance*, 68 Am. J. Soc. 1, 4 (1962) (majority labels nonconformist in group inferior, "excluding the minority-group member from participation in activities, taunting him, hurling derogatory epithets at him, or using the abundant variety of instruments of cruelty") (high school students).

[40] A. Hare*, *Handbook of Small Group Research* 35 (1962) (an individual "is more apt to conform if his alternative is to go on record as a deviant in a group . . . whose influential members disagree with him," so "views expressed in public or with a possibility of being made public are more conforming" (emphasis omitted)).

[41] C. Hovland*, I. Janis* & H. Kelley*, *Communication and Persuasion: Psychological Studies of Opinion Change* 168 (1953) (openly expressed opinions tend to be more conforming than privately expressed opinions).

[42] Argyle*, *Social Pressure in Public and Private Situations*, 54 J. Abnormal & Soc. Psych. 172, 174 (1957).

[43] Marek* & Renner*, *Operational Thinking and the Tenth Grade Student*, Sci. Tchr., Sept. 1972, at 32 ("73 percent of the tenth-graders interviewed cannot do formal operational thinking," *i.e.*, critical or analytical thinking, as in biology course) (high school sophomores).

[44] R. Goldman*, *Religious Thinking from Childhood to Adolescence* 239 (1964) (conceptual thought about religious questions does not reach full development during adolescence).

[45] A. Vergote*, *The Religious Man: A Psychological Study of Religious Attitudes* 297, 298 (M. Said* trans. 1969) ("[A]dolescence is the age of doubts about faith" since an individual then must "make his own critical synthesis of life," which "leads him to reconsider his religious convictions.").

[46] R. Goldman*, *Religious Thinking from Childhood to Adolescence* 242 (1964) ("many adolescents jettison their theological framework as childish . . . because it cannot apparently be reconciled with science").

[47] E. Hurlock*, *Child Development* 357, 360 (1942)(one major cause of

"adolescent doubt" and "discarding of . . . beliefs" is "the disturbing influence that comes from the *study of science*" that contradicts religious beliefs (italics in original)).

[48] K. Hyde*, *Religious Learning in Adolescence* 92 (1965) ("[C]ritical powers may be emotionally orientated against religious beliefs, while the assertions of a popular humanism, with its mechanical explanation of life and its rejection of the spiritual, is uncritically accepted. Thus a prejudice against religion becomes firmly established while religious ideas remain confused and inadequate.").

[49] Chall*, *Middle and Secondary School Textbooks*, in The Textbook in American Society 24, 26 (J. Cole* & T. Sticht* eds. 1981).

[50] Litcher* & Johnson*, *Changes in Attitudes Toward Negroes of White Elementary School Students after Use of Multiethnic Readers*, 60 J. Educ. Psychology 148, 149 (1969).

[51] 11 U.S. Comm'n on Civil Rights*, *Characters in Textbooks: A Review of the Literature* 15-16 (1980).

[52] O. Uribe* & J. Martinez*, *Analyzing Children's Books From a Chicano Perspective* 10 (1975).

[53] Bains*, Altman* & Vasquez*, *A Black American Perspective*, in Perspectives on School Print Materials: Ethnic, Non-Sexist and Others 29-30 (L. Beckum*, J. Vasquez* & W. Rosenoff* eds. 1975).

[54] Scott* & Schau*, *Sex Equity and Sex Bias in Instructional Materials*, in Handbook for Achieving Sex Equity Through Education 218, 220-21 (S. Klein* ed. 1985).

[55] Campbell* & Wirtenberg*, *How Books Influence Children: What the Research Shows*, 11 Interracial Books for Children Bull. 3, 4 (1980).

[56] Kastrinos*, *Survey of the Teaching of Biology in Secondary Schools*, 98 Sch. & Society 241, 242 (1970).

[57] Kastrinos* & Voss*, *Influence of the Textbook on Topics Remembered by Students Who Took College Boards in Biology*, 32 Am. Biology Teacher 227, 233 (1970).

[58] McLean v. Arkansas Bd. of Educ., 529 F. Supp. 1255, 1272 (E. D. Ark. 1982).

[59] G. Skoog*, Coverage of Evolution in Secondary School Biology Textbooks: 1900-1982, at 12 (unpublished ms. Oct. 16, 1982).

[60] E. Klinckmann*, *Biology Teachers' Handbook* 16 (2d ed. 1970).

[61] Lee*, *The BSCS Position on the Teaching of Biology*, BSCS Newsletter, Nov. 1972, at 5.

[62] A. Grobman*, *The Changing Classroom: The Role of the Biological Sciences Curriculum Study* viii (1969).

[63] McLean v. Arkansas Bd. of Educ., 529 F. Supp. 1255, 1259 (E.D. Ark. 1982).

[64] Mayer*, *The BSCS Process of Curriculum Development*, BSCS Newsletter, Sept. 1976, at 4, 8 ("While more than 50 percent of the American high school students now *use BSCS materials* directly, 100 percent of them are

using materials that have been *influenced* by the BSCS, as publishers have followed the curriculum study lead.").

[65] Biological Sciences Curriculum Study, *Biological Science: Molecules to Man* 105 (3d ed. 1976).

[66] Leonard* & Lowery*, *A Criterion for Biology Textbook Selection*, 38 Am. Biology Teacher 477, 478 (1976).

[67] *E.g.*, J. Otto* & A. Towle*, *Modern Biology* 14-50, 150-61, 163-64, 166-67, 182, 252-53, 257, 260-61, 262, 264-66, 268, 272, 341, 367, 374, 412-23, 437-38, 441, 452, 454, 456-57, 458, 459, 465, 467, 468, 469, 471-73, 486, 488, 490, 493, 496, 500, 503, 516, 517-21 (1977).

[68] R. Oram*, *Biology: Living Systems* 118, 248-67, 277-94, 602-23, 73T-80T, 142T-45T (3d ed. Teacher's Ed. 1979).

[69] Kastrinos*, *Survey of the Teaching of Biology in Secondary Schools*, 98 School & Society 241, 242 (1970).

[70] *E.g.*, Huxley*, *At Random*, in 3 *Evolution after Darwin* 41-65 (S. Tax* ed. 1960) ("I would turn the argument the other way around and hold that it is essential for evolution to become the central core of any *educational system*, because it is evolution, in the broad sense, that links inorganic nature with life, and the stars with earth, and matter with mind, and animals with man. Human history is a continuation of biological evolution in a different form.").

[71] Lambert*, Millar* & Hughes*, *Teaching the classic case of natural selection*, 79 Rivista di Biologia (Biology Forum) 117, 117-18 (1986) (italics added, capitalized name lower cased).

[72] Sections 3.2(d)-(f).

[73] Harper*, *Darwinism and Indoctrination*, 59 School Science Rev. 258, 259, 267-68 (1977).

[74] *Id.* at 258, 259, 265 (italics added).

[75] Anderson* & Kilbourn*, *Creation, Evolution, and Curriculum*, 67 Science Education 45, 51 (1983) (italics added, original italics deleted).

[76] Pangle*, *Introduction*, to L. Strauss, Studies in Platonic Political Philosophy 21-22 (1983) (U. of Chicago Press).

[77] E. Klinckmann*, *Biology Teachers' Handbook* 16 (2d ed. 1970) (italics added).

[78] Klein*, *Preface*, to L. Sunderland, Darwin's Enigma 5, 5 (1985).

[79] D. Nelkin*, *Science Textbook Controversies and the Politics of Equal Time* 148 (1977) (italics added) (not speaking specifically of evolution or creation).

[80] G. Kerkut*, *Implications of Evolution* 148 (1960).

[81] Patterson*, *Book Review*, 29 Systematic Zoology 216, 217 (1980) (italics added).

[82] Corner*, *Evolution*, in Contemporary Botanical Thought 95, 97 (A. MacLeod* & L. Cobley* eds. 1961).

[83] Saunders* & Ho*, *Is Neo-Darwinism Falsifiable?—And Does It Matter?*, 4 Nature & System 179, 191 (1982) ("Neo-Darwinist textbooks on evolu-

tion keep citing the same comparatively few examples: industrial melanism, sickle cell anaemia, DDT resistance. All are comparatively minor evolutionary changes; all involve variations in which a large and obvious selective advantage can be obtained by a single allele substitution.").

[84] Bonner*, *Book Review*, 49 Am. Scientist 240 (1961) ("In the case of phylogeny our textbooks are little help; in fact they are, as a rule, a festering mass of unsupported assertions.").

[85] A. Cairns-Smith*, *Genetic Takeover and the Mineral Origins of Life* 56 (1986).

[86] W. Stansfield*, *The Science of Evolution* 11 (1977).

[87] Note 3.

[88] Note 7.

[89] Note 8.

[90] Note 16.

[91] J. Coleman*, *The Adolescent Society* 3 (1961).

[92] Note 49.

[93] Note 2.

[94] Note 59.

[95] Note 60.

[96] Note 69.

[97] Note 77.

[98] Note 78.

[99] Note 80.

[100] Note 81.

[101] Note 82.

[102] Note 84.

[103] Note 85.

[104] Note 71.

[105] Note 73.

[106] W. Provine*, Theories of Creationism and Evolution from a Historical Perspective (unpublished lecture before Sigma Xi Chapter at Corning, N.Y., Nov. 17, 1981). *E.g.*, Schafersman*, *Letter*, Geotimes, Aug. 1981, at 11, 11 (credentialed creationist scientists are by his definition "not scientists").

[107] NBC News & Associated Press, November National Poll at 15 (Nov. 24, 1981).

[108] Examples of denial of tenure to creationists are Dr. Norbert Smith (Ph.D. in biology from Northeastern Oklahoma State University) at that institution; Dr. David A. Warriner (Ph.D. in chemistry from Cornell) at Michigan State University; Dr. J. Harold Ellens (Ph.D. in psychology) at Oakland University; Dr. Alvin Bytwork (Ph.D.) at Western Michigan State University; and Dr. Gerald R. Bergman (Ph.D. in educational psychology from Wayne State University) at Bowling Green State University.

[109] Examples of discharge of creationists are Dr. Joseph Arnett (Ph.D. in psychology) at University of Illinois; and Prof. Robert Gentry (M.S.) at Oak Ridge National Laboratories. Examples of discharge of creationists at the public school level are Mr. Lloyd Dale, who had been named "South Dakota

Outstanding Teacher of the Year," yet was dismissed as a science teacher by the Lemmon Public Schools. Many cases are listed in J. Bergman, *The Criterion* (1984) (creationist author).

110 Patterson*, *An Engineer Looks at the Creationist Movement*, 89 Proc. Iowa Academy of Sciences 57 (1982).

111 Examples of denial of earned degrees to creationists are Byron Nelson at Rutgers University being denied his M.S. in genetics; Professor Richard Culp at University of Michigan being denied his Ph.D. in zoology; Professor George Mulfinger being denied his Ph.D. in science education at Syracuse University; Clifford Burdick (after completing his dissertation) being denied his Ph.D. in geology at University of Arizona; and Erville Clark being denied his Ph.D. in biology at Stanford.

112 Examples of denials of entrance into graduate programs to creationist students are Thomas Jungman being excluded from the Ph.D. program (despite academic success in the M.S. program) at various institutions because of an unfavorable and anticreationist letter of recommendation from San Jose State University; and David McQueen being excluded from the Ph.D. program (despite academic success in the M.S. program) at a Michigan university.

113 Letter from Professor John W. Patterson* [of Iowa State University] to Mr. Kevin Wirth (Feb. 7, 1984).

114 The *McLean* opinion found that "not one recognized scientific journal . . . has published an article espousing the creation science theory," although no evidence was there provided of rejection of creationist articles by scientific journals. McLean v. Arkansas Bd. of Educ., 529 F. Supp. 1255, 1268 (E.D. Ark. 1982).

115 Strike*, *The Status of Creation-Science: A Comment on Siegel and Hahn*, 63 Phi Delta Kappan 555, 556 (1982).

116 *Unorthodox assessments*, 300 Nature 566, 566 (1982).

117 Chapter 6, note 149 (Gentry publications before his public creationist stance).

118 R. Gentry, *Creation's Tiny Mystery* (1986) (record of discrimination and publication rejections after his public creationist stance).

119 Gentry, *Abnormally Long Alpha-Particle Tracks in Biotite*, 8 Applied Physics Letters 65 (1966).

120 R. Gentry, *Creation's Tiny Mystery* 38 (1986) (creationist author).

121 Letter from Frank E. Myers* (Editor) to Robert V. Gentry (June 7, 1966) (on letterhead of J. Applied Physics and Applied Physics Letters, rejecting ms. and attaching reviewer comments that are quoted).

122 Gentry, *Extinct Radioactivity and the Discovery of a New Pleochroic Halo*, 213 Nature 487 (1967).

123 Reviewer response on *Science* form (n.d.).

124 R. Gentry, *Creation's Tiny Mystery* 41, 43 (1986).

125 Gentry, *Fossil Alpha-Recoil Analysis of Certain Variant Radioactive Halos*, 160 Science 1228 (1968).

126 A. Lasen*, *Summary Report: Meeting on Creationism-Evolutionism*

(National Academy of Sciences Oct. 19, 1981).

[127] H. Arp*, *Quasars, Redshifts, and Controversies* 166 (1987).

[128] F. Hoyle & N. Wickramasinghe, *Evolution from Space* 147 (1981).

[129] Section 9.7(b).

[130] Note 106.

[131] Note 110.

[132] Note 113.

[133] Note 115.

[134] Notes 122 & 125.

[135] Note 121.

[136] Note 123.

PART IX

Whether Instruction in All Scientific Theories of Origins Is Constitutional? Academic Freedom and Separation of Church and State

The constitutional freedom of students is by definition advanced by teaching additional scientific information along with evolution, thereby satisfying their constitutional right to receive information. Censorship and indoctrination by definition occur when that additional scientific information is excluded from the classroom because of someone's intolerance. Yet that is precisely the case in the great majority of American public schools and state universities.

The academic freedom of teachers to teach alternative scientific theories to evolution is also implicated in the widespread intolerance of the educational establishment against any challenge to the theory of evolution, and particularly against the theory of creation. Yet, forty-two percent of the public school teachers want to teach alternative scientific theories as well as evolution, and generally are prohibited or chilled from doing so; doubtless a larger percentage still would like to teach the theory of abrupt appearance or particular scientific alternatives to evolution.

The First Amendment of the United States Constitution provides that the government "shall make no law respecting an establishment of religion." Interpretation of those nine words has generated as contradictory a multitude of approaches as has definition of science and definition of religion. For example, the Supreme Court of the United States has sustained public school reference to a creator or God, but has struck down a requirement for teaching the theory of "creation-science" along with the theory of evolution at least if the legislative purpose is religious, and yet there recognized the constitutionality of teachers electing "to supplant the present science curriculum with the presentation of theories, besides evolution, about the origin of life."

The primary test used by the Supreme Court, in construing the Establishment Clause, focuses on the primary effect, legislative purpose, and excessive entanglement arising from a law. For teaching all scientific theories of origins, the secular purpose and primary effect are to advance students' constitutional freedom to hear additional scientific information. No entanglement results because no religious organizations are involved in public school and college classrooms.

CHAPTER 19

The Academic Freedom of Students To Receive and of Teachers To Teach Scientific Information

> *[T]he search for knowledge and understanding of the physical universe and of the living things that inhabit it should be conducted under conditions of intellectual freedom, without religious, political or ideological restrictions. . . . [F]reedom of inquiry and dissemination of ideas require that those so engaged be free to search where their inquiry leads . . . without political censorship and without fear of retribution in consequence of unpopularity of their conclusions. Those who challenge existing theories must be protected from retaliatory reactions.*
>
> —Resolution of National Academy of Sciences (1976)[1]

Students enjoy a constitutional right to receive information, including scientific information, in public schools and universities

(Section 19.1). Teachers enjoy academic freedom[2] to teach, particularly at the public university level and to a lesser degree at the public school level, which includes teaching scientific information in appropriate courses (Section 19.2). Those constitutional rights arise under the First Amendment, which protects freedom of speech. They are jeopardized by the sort of indoctrination and censorship described in the preceding chapter.

Figure 19.1
The "'State may not . . . contract the spectrum of available knowledge'," and "the Constitution protects the right to receive information and ideas'" (U.S. Supreme Court, whose seal is pictured)

19.1 Advancement of Students' Right To Receive Information by Uncensored Instruction

a. Advancement of Students' Right To Receive Scientific Information

Students in public schools and universities enjoy the constitutional right, as part of freedom of speech, to receive information, as the Supreme Court of the United States stated in *Board of Education of Island Trees v. Pico*:[3]

> And we have recognized that "*the State may not*, consistently with the spirit of First Amendment, *contract the spectrum of available knowledge*." *Griswold v. Connecticut*, 381 U.S. 479, 482 (1965). In keeping with this principle, we have held that in a variety of contexts "the Constitu-

> tion protects the *right to receive information and ideas.*" *Stanley v. Georgia*, 394 U.S. 557, 564 (1969); see *Kleindienst v. Mandel*, 408 U.S. 753, 762-763 (1972) (citing cases). This right is *an inherent corollary of the rights of free speech and press* that are explicitly guaranteed by the Constitution, in two senses. First, the right to receive ideas follows ineluctably from the sender's First Amendment right to send them: "The right of freedom of speech and press . . . embraces the right to distribute literature, and necessarily protects the right to receive it." *Martin v. Struthers*, 319 U.S. 141, 143 (1943). . . .
>
> *More importantly*, the right to receive ideas is a *necessary predicate to the recipient's meaningful exercise of his own rights* of speech, press, and political freedom. . . .[4]

The Court acknowledged that "right of the public to receive suitable access to social, political, esthetic, moral, and other ideas and experiences," in *Red Lion Broadcasting Co. v. FCC*.[5] The same right was described in *Virginia State Board of Pharmacy v. Virginia Citizens Consumer Council, Inc.*,[6] *Kleindienst v. Mandel*,[7] *Stanley v. Georgia*,[8] *Marsh v. Alabama*,[9] and *Martin v. City of Struthers*.[10] That student right to receive information is sometimes described as student academic freedom.[11]

The student right to receive information certainly includes scientific information, and in that area the Constitution forbids public schools and universities from seeking to " 'contract the spectrum of available knowledge' " or from otherwise censoring information about alternative theories of origins. For example, Professor Joseph Goldstein of Yale Law School suggested

> that the freedom of speech and religion clauses of the *First Amendment would prohibit establishment by the state, in Lysenko-like fashion, of any single scientific theory*, doctrine, or dogma as to what it means to be "adult," "mature," "wise," or "ethical." . . .
>
> It is not far-fetched to read "non-religion" and "militant opposite" to include the sciences and thus to entitle them to the neutrality that secular law guarantees to the religions. Indeed, science may be less different from religion than most would care to acknowledge. In any event, the First Amendment is essential to the life of *science* which *must always remain free of official orthodoxies and thus able to challenge and to modify the scientific truths of the moment*. . . .[12]

Even the National Education Association has agreed with the general principle that "an educator shall not unreasonably deny students access to varying points of view,"[13] and various legal commentators see a violation of the student right to receive information "if he is denied the opportunity to consider a controversial subject in supervised classroom discussion."[14]

b. Advancement of Students' Rights to Balanced Instruction, a Marketplace of Ideas, and Freedom from State Orthodoxy

That right of students to receive information includes a corresponding obligation of government schools to "provide a fairly balanced exposition of various relevant theories and points of view, and of alternatives open to action," Professor Emerson of Yale Law School contends in his landmark *The System of Freedom of Expression*:

> Secondly, to the extent that the government undertakes to lay down educational policy, it must conform to the concept of balanced presentation. This means that *it must provide a fairly balanced exposition of various relevant theories and points of view, and of alternatives* open to action. The first principle grows out the nature of the university; the second out of the obligation of the government in a closed or substantially closed system.
>
> If these principles had been applied in the *Epperson* case, the Arkansas statute would have been struck down on First Amendment (freedom of expression) grounds. The proscription upon the teaching of a particular theory of man's development invades the area of academic policy. The requirement of balanced presentation is not met when the teaching of a theory that falls within the area of recognized academic or scientific standards is forbidden. Other kinds of government regulation would undoubtedly pose more complex problems. But the development of some principles for solving these important issues could begin.[15]

He made the same point in a legal article on the centennial of Darwin's *Origin of Species*.[16] Nahmod makes a similar point about "unbalanced presentation on a controversial subject" in public schools:

> An *unbalanced presentation* on a controversial subject also *may be harmful* to the education of students. It deprives them of the opportunity to consider as many relevant facts and opinions as possible. Moreover, a classroom is one of the few places where controversial subjects can be discussed in a supervised and reasonably thorough manner. In making an unbalanced presentation, a teacher *impedes the development of critical and other faculties*; the point of view espoused and perhaps received so uncritically may in fact be erroneous and ultimately harmful to the students. Although this may also occur in the context of a balanced presentation, students at least will have had the opportunity to decide otherwise.[17]

The right of students to enjoy the classroom as a "marketplace of ideas" is an important element of their constitutional rights, as the Supreme Court stated in *Keyishian v. Board of Regents*:[18]

> The classroom is peculiarly the "marketplace of ideas." The Nation's future depends upon leaders trained through wide exposure to that robust exchange of ideas which discovers truth "out of a multitude of tongues, [rather] than through any kind of authoritative selection." *United States v. Associated Press*, 52 F. Supp. 362, 372.[19]

Other decisions have reiterated the point.[20] A marketplace of ideas necessarily includes presentation of alternatives, and that is effectuated by teaching all scientific theories of origins and frustrated by teaching just the theory of evolution. A marketplace of ideas is "in direct opposition" to court decisions striking down the alternative of the theory of creation, Greenburg suggests:

> The traditional judicial treatment of the balanced treatment legislation, however, appears to be in direct opposition to the Court's description of the classroom as the "marketplace of ideas." The reluctance of the courts to uphold laws which require treatment of divine creation in the classroom whenever evolution is taught appears to be a direct deprivation of students to gain total knowledge of all the prevalent theories of man's creation, and imposes a straightjacket upon scholastic freedom to learn and teach.[21]

The right of students to be free of officially-prescribed orthodoxy is also an important part of the constitutional right of students to receive information, as the Supreme Court held in *West Virginia State Board of Education v. Barnette*:[22]

> If there is any fixed star in our constitutional constellation, it is that no official, high or petty, can prescribe what shall be orthodox in politics, nationalism, religion, or other matters of opinion or force citizens to confess by word or act their faith therein.[23]

Schools and universities may not indoctrinate students in only what is "officially approved," the Court said in *Tinker v. Des Moines School District*:

> In our system, *state-operated schools may not be enclaves of totalitarianism.* School officials do not possess absolute authority over their students. Students in school as well as out of school are "persons" under our Constitution. They are possessed of fundamental rights which the State must respect, just as they themselves must respect their obligations to the State. In our system, *students may not be regarded as closed-circuit recipients of only that which the State chooses to communicate.* They may not be confined to the expression of those sentiments that are *officially approved.* In the absence of a specific showing of constitutionally valid reasons to regulate their speech, students are entitled to freedom of expression of their views. . . .[24]

That right has been reiterated in a number of subsequent decisions of the Supreme Court.[25] Official prescription of orthodoxy is best avoided by public educational institutions covering all scientific theories of origins, and is best accomplished by exposing students only to the theory of evolution while censoring all heterodox alternatives.

Figure 19.2
Teachers possess "flexibility . . . to supplant the present science curriculum with the presentation of theories, besides evolution, about the origin of life" (U.S. Supreme Court, whose courtroom is pictured)

19.2 Advancement of Many Teachers' Academic Freedom by Uncensored Instruction

Teachers in public schools and public universities enjoy a constitutional right to academic freedom.[26] At the elementary and secondary school level, that right is narrow to correspond with the broad governmental power to prescribe curriculum. Although some have argued that academic freedom is limited to institutions,[27] there is a clear constitutional right enjoyed by teachers particularly at the university level.

a. Advancement of Teachers' Academic Freedom

The academic freedom of teachers at the university level is quite broad, as the Supreme Court of the United States stressed in *Shelton v. Tucker*:[28]

> The vigilant protection of constitutional freedoms is nowhere more vital than in the community of American schools. "... But, in view of the nature of the teacher's relation to the effective exercise of the rights which are safeguarded by the Bill of Rights and by the Fourteenth Amendment, inhibition of freedom of thought, and of action upon thought, in the case of teachers brings the safeguards of those amendments vividly into operation. Such unwarranted *inhibition upon the free spirit of teachers* ... has an unmistakable tendency to chill that free play of the spirit which all teachers ought especially to cultivate and practice; it makes for caution and timidity in their associations by potential teachers." *Wieman v. Updegraff*, 344 U.S. 183, 195 (concurring opinion). "Scholarship cannot flourish in an atmosphere of suspicion and distrust. Teachers and students must always remain free to inquire, to study and to evaluate . . . ." *Sweezy v. New Hampshire*, 354 U.S. 234, 250.[29]

Academic freedom of a less expansive nature applies to teachers at the elementary and secondary levels, as stated in *Pickering v. Board of Education*:[30]

> To the extent that the Illinois Supreme Court's opinion may be read to suggest that teachers may constitutionally be compelled to relinquish the *First Amendment rights* they would otherwise enjoy as citizens to comment on matters of public interest in connection with the operation of the public schools in which they work, it proceeds on a premise that has been unequivocally rejected in numerous prior decisions of this Court. *E.g. Wieman v. Updegraff*, 344 U.S. 183 (1952); *Shelton v. Tucker*, 364 U.S. 479 (1960); *Keyishian v. Board of Regents*, 385 U.S. 589 (1967). . . . At the same time it cannot be gainsaid that the *State has interests as an employer in regulating the speech of its employees* that differ significantly from those it possesses in connection with regulation of the speech of the citizenry in general. The problem in any case is to arrive at a balance between the interests of the teacher, as a citizen, in commenting upon matters of public concern and the interest of the State, as an employer, in promoting the efficiency of the public services it performs through its employees.[31]

In that case, the board of education had dismissed a teacher for writing and publishing in a newspaper a letter criticizing school spending.

Many science teachers in public educational institutions want to teach scientific alternatives to evolution because, in their professional judgment, alternative theories are educationally valuable as multiple working hypotheses or as better scientific explanations. At the secondary school level, a professional poll revealed that 42.3% of public school biology teachers so conclude that the theory of creation should be taught.[32] Most of those teachers are deterred from teaching that alternative or the theory of abrupt appearance, as is evident in the paucity of instruction in either the theory of creation or the theory of abrupt appearance.[33] Probably the percentage is higher at the elementary school level and lower at the university level. Uncensored instruction in alternative theories of origins allows room for the academic freedom of those teachers.

b. Limitations on Teachers' Academic Freedom in Public Schools

Legislatures have broad authority to prescribe curriculum for public schools at the pre-college level, as the U.S. Supreme Court has repeatedly recognized. It said the following in *West Virginia State Board of Education v. Barnette*:

> [T]he State may "require teaching by instruction and study of all in our history and in the structure and organization of our government, including the guaranties of civil liberty, which tend to inspire patriotism and love of country."[34]

The Court, in two major older decisions, emphasized that "[n]o question is raised concerning the power of the state . . . to require . . . that certain studies plainly essential to good citizenship must be taught,"[35] or concerning "the State's power to prescribe a curriculum for institutions which it supports."[36] The Supreme Court also summarily affirmed a decision that stated the same rule:

> The State may establish its curriculum either by law or by delegation of its authority to the local school boards and communities. This is a long recognized system of operation within our Nation.[37]

An article in *Willamette Law Review* entitled "Legislative Control over Public School Curriculum" has summarized the virtually unanimous authority supporting legislative prescription of courses of study and specification of guidelines.[38] One of the two legal encyclopedias that are most widely used describes the general rule that legislatures have power "to select the system of instruction and course of study to be pursued in the public schools":

> §283. Power to prescribe courses of instruction.
>
> The fundamental power to *select the system of instruction and course of study* to be pursued in the public schools is in the *legislature*, and its mandate is final and binding on all persons . . ..
>
> The power of the legislature to impose a system of public school education upon local communities is not limited to the *common branches*. Hence, the *legislature* may, in its discretion, *provide for courses in agriculture, home economics, and driver training*, and may also provide for the establishment of kindergartens as a part of the public school system.[39]

The other such legal encyclopedia similarly acknowledges the state or school board "power to prescribe the curriculum and studies":

> §485. Curriculum and Studies
>
> . . ..
>
> While the *State* has power to *prescribe the curriculum and studies* in public schools, in the absence of such regulations the local board has discretion to provide for the teaching of such branches as it deems best.
>
> The *State* has power to require that *certain studies* plainly essential to good citizenship be taught and that nothing be taught which is manifestly inimical to the public welfare. . . .
>
> . . .Statutes specifically prescribing that certain courses be given or maintained, or certain subjects taught, are mandatory on school boards . . ..[40]

State court decisions are consistent with that general rule. The North Carolina Supreme Court entered the following decision:

> The General Assembly has the power, which we think cannot be questioned, to prescribe by statute the subjects to be taught and the methods of instruction to be followed in the public schools of the state . . ..[41]

Similar decisions have been made by the Idaho,[42] South Dakota,[43] Alaska,[44] Pennsylvania,[45] Nebraska,[46] Indiana,[47] Minnesota,[48] New York,[49] North Dakota,[50] and Wisconsin[51] Supreme Courts, and the California[52] and Missouri[53] Courts of Appeals. Court precedents have upheld legislative prescriptions of specific courses of study, such as languages, German, vocational education, driver training, health and physical education, health and sex education, music, agriculture, hygiene and physiology, and patriotic exercises, in Georgia,[54] California,[55] Connecticut,[56] Illinois,[57] Pennsylvania,[58] California,[59] Michigan,[60] Massachusetts,[61] Arizona,[62] Kansas,[63] Indiana,[64] and Ohio.[65] Course prescriptions have included not only subjects but guidelines for content, which have been upheld by California,[66] North Carolina[67] and Connecticut[68] precedents. In general, legislatures have "plenary power . . . in the field of public education," as the Idaho Supreme Court said,[69] concurring with the South Dakota,[70] Alaska,[71] Kentucky,[72] Nebraska,[73] Oregon,[74] Indiana,[75] and other Supreme Courts.[76]

States indeed have exercised their power to prescribe what is taught. Twenty-six states have statutes prescribing courses of study in traditional academic areas, thirty-two states have statutes prescribing courses of study on the economic system, forty-eight states have statutes prescribing courses of study in government or history or related subjects, and forty-eight states have statutes prescribing courses of study in various character-related subjects.[77] In summary, legislatures have prescribed courses in the following numbers of states:

English	23
Reading	23
Literature	8
Geography	21
Science	10
Spelling and writing	23
Arithmetic	23
Art and music	11
U.S. history	35
State history	31
U.S. Constitution	44
State Constitution	20
Contributions of minorities	12
Government	37
Patriotic exercise	26
Citizenship and patriotism	30
Health	35
Fire prevention	16
Safety	20
Free enterprise	11
Conservation of resources	22
Consumer education	8
Vocational education	7
Agriculture	9
Driver education	11
Alcohol, tobacco and drugs	46
Physical education	31
Humane treatment of animals	14
Moral virtues	20

School districts and individual public schools prescribe all additional courses beyond the core curriculum prescribed by the legislatures.

The academic freedom of public school teachers is necessarily limited by such "plenary power" of legislatures and school boards, at the secondary and elementary levels. That limited scope of academic freedom in public schools has been affirmed by the Supreme Court: "nothing . . . gives a person employed to teach the Constitutional right to teach beyond the scope of the established curriculum."[79] Similar limitations on academic freedom have been noted by the U.S. Courts of Appeals for the Fourth,[80] Seventh,[81] and Tenth Circuits,[82] by U.S. District Courts,[83] and by legal commentators such as Goldstein,[84] Schauer,[85] and others.[86] One commentator concludes as follows:

> The right of teachers to structure course content has been broadened at the university level, but in secondary schools, the final decision still rests with the school board. Finally, even though the rights of intellectual individualism and academic freedom have been recognized, they have played a role only when fundamental rights of students also have been infringed.[87]

Thus, the U.S. Supreme Court has mentioned academic freedom primarily at the university level, as its decisions[88] and legal commentators[89] indicate. "Significantly, the Court's rule is applicable at the university level and is generally not a public school principle."[90] The primary reasons, besides legislative authority under state constitutions, are the nonresearch role of public school teachers and the immaturity of public school students in contrast with the university level:

> "A teacher works in a sensitive area in a schoolroom. There he shapes the attitude of young minds towards the society in which they live. In this, the state has a vital concern." *Adler v. Board of Education*, 342 U.S. 485, 493.[91]

A further reason is the "right to receive information," and not to be indoctrinated, on the part of public school students. All of this is consistent with teaching scientific "theories, besides evolution, about the origin of humankind" and of plants and animals, which the Supreme Court has approved.[92]

Summary. Students in public educational institutions hold a constitutional "right to receive information and ideas" (*Board of Education of Island Trees v. Pico*[93]). Corollaries of the right to receive information are a prohibition against "establishment by the state, in Lysenko-like fashion, of any single scientific theory" (Goldstein[94]), an obligation for government schools to "provide a fairly balanced exposition of various relevant theories and points of view" (Emerson[95]), a role of the classroom as a "marketplace of ideas" (*Keyishian v. Board of Regents*[96]), and a right to be free of official prescription of "what shall be orthodox in . . . matters of opinion" (*West Virginia State Board of Education v. Barnette*[97]). That right to receive information is furthered by more scientific information such as alternative theories of origins.

Teachers at the university level in particular enjoy a constitutional right to academic freedom, and those teachers whose professional judgment favors instruction in scientific theories, besides evolution, on origins are within their academic freedom in following that professional judgment in appropriate science classes. Teachers at the elementary and secondary school levels have "First Amendment rights" but "at the same time . . . the State has interests as an employer in regulating the speech of its employees" (*Pickering v. Board of Education*[98]). Also "the State has power to prescribe the curriculum and studies in public schools" (*Corpus Juris Secundum*[99]), and all states have restricted teacher rights by extensively prescribing courses of study (Sheldon[100]). States and school districts have every right to protect the students' right to receive information, such as alternative scientific theories of origins, and many teachers hope for that opportunity (Austin Analytical Consulting[101]).

Notes

1 National Academy of Sciences, *Resolution* (April 1976).

2 "Academic freedom, though not a specifically enumerated constitutional right, long has been viewed as a special concern of the First Amendment." Regents of Univ. of Cal. v. Bakke, 438 U.S. 265, 312 (1978) (plurality opinion). *See also* Keyishian v. Board of Regents, 385 U.S. 589, 603 (1967).

3 Board of Educ. of Island Trees Union Free Sch. Dist. v. Pico, 457 U.S. 853 (1982) (plurality opinion).

4 *Id.* at 867 (italics added except case names, original italics deleted).

5 395 U.S. 367, 390 (1969).

6 425 U.S. 748, 756 (1976).

7 408 U.S. 753, 762-63 (1972).

8 394 U.S. 557, 564 (1969).

9 326 U.S. 501, 504-05 (1946).

10 319 U.S. 141, 143 (1943).

11 *E.g.*, Van Alstyne, *The Judicial Trend Toward Student Academic Freedom*, 20 U. Fla. L. Rev. 290 (1968); R. Hofstadter & W. Metzger, *The Development of Academic Freedom in the United States* 386, 397 (1955); Keyishian v. Board of Regents, 385 U.S. 589, 603 (1967) ("Teachers and students"); Sweezy v. New Hampshire, 354 U.S. 234, 250 (1957) (same).

12 Goldstein, *On Being Adult and Being an Adult in Secular Law*, 105 Daedalus 69, 70 (Fall 1976) (italics added).

13 National Education Association, *Code of Ethics* ..... (19..).

14 Nahmod, *Controversy in the Classroom: The High School Teacher and Freedom of Expression*, 39 Geo. Wash. L. Rev. 1032, 1054 (1971).

15 T. Emerson, *The System of Freedom of Expression* 624 (1970) (italics added except case name). Emerson is speaking of state universities rather

than of public schools, but his rationale of a closed system and government content control applies to both.

[16] Emerson & Haber, *The* Scopes *Case in Modern Dress*, 27 U. Chi. L. Rev. 522, 527 (1960).

[17] Nahmod, *Controversy in the Classroom: The High School Teacher and Freedom of Expression*, 39 Geo. Wash. L. Rev. 1032, 1048 (1971) (italics added).

[18] 385 U.S. 589 (1967).

[19] *Id.* at 603.

[20] *E.g.*, Grayned v. City of Rockford, 408 U.S. 104, 117 (1972); Tinker v. Des Moines School Dist., 393 U.S. 503, 512-13 (1969); Red Lion Broadcasting Co. v. FCC, 395 U.S. 367, 390 (1969).

[21] Note, *The Constitutional Issues Surrounding the Science-Religion Conflict in Public Schools: The Anti-Evolution Controversy*, 10 Pepperdine L. Rev. 461, 486 (1983).

[22] 319 U.S. 624 (1943).

[23] *Id.* at 642.

[24] 393 U.S. 503, 511 (1969) (italics added), cited in Board of Island Trees Union Free Sch. Dist. v. Pico, 457 U.S. 853, 868 (1982) (plurality opinion).

[25] *E.g.*, Wooley v. Maynard, 430 U.S. 705 (1977).

[26] S. Goldstein, *Law and Public Education* 71-110 (1974); T. Emerson, *The System of Freedom of Expression* 593-626 (1970); R. Hofstadter & W. Metzger, *The Development of Academic Freedom in the United States* (1955); Van Alstyne, *The Constitutional Rights of Teachers and Professors*, 1970 Duke L.J. 841; Nahmod, *Controversy in the Classroom: The High School Teacher and Freedom of Expression*, 39 Geo. Wash. L. Rev. 1032 (1971); Note, *Academic Freedom in the Public Schools: The Right To Teach*, 48 N.Y.U.L.Rev. 1176 (1973); Van Alstyne, *The Specific Theory of Academic Freedom and the General Issue of Civil Liberties*, 404 Annals 140 (1972).

[27] Regents of University of Cal. v. Bakke, 438 U.S. 265, 312-13 (1978) (plurality opinion); Sweezy v. New Hampshire, 354 U.S. 234, 263 (1957) (Frankfurter, J., concurring); Finken, *On Institutional Academic Freedom*, 61 Tex. L. Rev. 817 (1983).

[28] 364 U.S. 479 (1960).

[29] *Id.* at 487 (italics added except case names).

[30] 391 U.S. 563 (1968).

[31] *Id.* at 568 (italics added except case names).

[32] Austin Analytical Consulting, Opinion Poll for Biology Teachers (1986).

[33] Section 18.1(a).

[34] West Virginia State Bd. of Educ. v. Barnette, 319 U.S. 624, 631 (1943).

[35] Pierce v. Society of Sisters, 268 U.S. 510, 534 (1924).

[36] Meyer v. Nebraska, 262 U.S. 390, 402 (1923).

[37] Mercer v. Michigan State Bd. of Educ., 379 F. Supp. 580, 585 (D. Mich. 1974), *aff'd*, 419 U.S. 1081 (1975).

[38] Sheldon, *Legislative Control over Public School Curriculum*, 15 Willamette L. Rev. 473 (1979).
[39] 68 Am. Jur. 2d *Schools* §283, at 602-03 (italics added).
[40] 79 C.J.S. *Schools and School Districts* §485, at 428 (italics added).
[41] Posey v. Board of Education, 199 N.C. 306, 154 S.E. 393, 397 (1930).
[42] Thompson v. Engelking, 96 Idaho 793, 537 P.2d 635, 644 (1975).
[43] Anderson v. South Dakota High School Activities Association, 247 N.W. 2d 481, 483 (S.D. 1976).
[44] Macauley v. Hildebrand, 491 P. 2d 120, 122 (Alas. 1971).
[45] Ehret v. School District, 333 Pa. 518, 5 A.2d 188, 190-91 (1939).
[46] Ratigan v. Davis, 175 Neb. 416, 122 N.W.2d 12, 16 (1963), *appeal dismissed*, 375 U.S. 394 (1964).
[47] Indiana v. Haworth, 122 Ind. 462, 23 N.E. 946 (1890).
[48] Associated Schools v. School District, 122 Minn. 254, 142 N.W. 325 (1924).
[49] People ex rel. Fish v. Sandstrom, 279 N.Y. 523, 18 N.E. 2d 840, 843 (1939).
[50] North Dakota v. Totten, 44 N.D. 557, 175 N.W. 563 (1919).
[51] Morrow v. Wood, 35 Wis. 59 (1881).
[52] California Teachers Association v. Board of Trustees, 82 Cal. App. 3d 249, 14 Cal. Rptr. 850, 854 (1978).
[53] Roach v. St. Louis Public Schools, 7 Mo. App. 567 (1879).
[54] Concerned School Patrons v. Ware County Board of Education, 245 Ga. App. 202, 263 S.E.2d 925, 927 (1980) (health and physical education).
[55] California Teachers Association v. Board of Trustees, 82 Cal. App. 3d 249, 146 Cal. Rptr. 850, 852-54 (1978) (driver training); Citizens for Parental Rights v. San Mateo County Board of Education, 124 Cal. Rptr. 68, 51 Cal. App. 3d 1 (1975), *appeal dismissed*, 425 U.S. 908 (1976) (sex education).
[56] Hopkins v. Hamden Board of Education, 29 Ct. Super. 397, 289 A.2d 914, 918 (1971) (health and sex education).
[57] Moyer v. Board of Education, 391 Ill. 156, 62 N.E.2d 802, 804 (1945) (health and physical education).
[58] In re Ganaposki, 332 Pa. 550, 2 A.2d 742, 744 (1939) (physical education and athletics).
[59] Jones v. Board of Trustees, 8 Cal. App. 2d 146, 47 P.2d 804, 805 (1935) (music); Bales v. Escondido Union High School District, 133 Cal. App. 725, 24 P. 2d 884 (1933) (agriculture).
[60] Prevey v. School District, 263 Mich. 622, 249 N.W. 15 (1933) (hygiene and physiology).
[61] Commonwealth v. Johnson, 309 Mass. 476, 35 N.E. 2d 801, 805 (1929) (patriotic exercises).
[62] Alexander v. Phillips, 31 Ariz. 503, 254 P. 1056 (1927) (physical education and athletics).
[63] Epley v. Hall, 97 Kan. 549, 155 P. 1083 (1916).
[64] W.P. Myers Publishing Co. v. White River School Township, 28 Ind.

App. 91, 62 N.E. 66 (1901); School Commissioners v. Indiana, 129 Ind. 14, 28 N.E. 61 (1891) (German); Indiana ex rel. Andrew v. Webber, 108 Ind. 31, 8 N.E. 708 (1886).

[65] Mercure v. Board of Education, 49 Oh. App.2d 409, 361 N.E.2d 273, 277 (1976).

[66] California Teachers Association v. Board of Trustees, 82 Cal. App. 3d 249, 146 Cal. Rptr. 850, 854 (1978).

[67] Posey v. Board of Education, 199 N.C. 306, 154 S.E. at 397.

[68] Hopkins v. Hamden Board of Education, 29 Ct. Super. 397, 289 A.2d 914, 918 (1971).

[69] Thompson v. Engelking, 96 Idaho 793, 537 P.2d 635, 644 (1975). *See also* Andrus v. Hill, 73 Idaho 196, 249 P.2d 205, 207 (1952); In re Community School Districts, 52 Idaho 363, 15 P.2d 732, 733 (1932).

[70] South Dakota High School Interscholastic Activities Association v. St. Mary's Inter-Parochial High School, 82 S.D. 84, 141 N.W.2d 477, 480 (1966); Anderson v. South Dakota High School Activities Association, 247 N.W.2d 481, 483 (S.D. 1976).

[71] Macauley v. Hildebrand, 491 P. 2d 120, 122 (Alas. 1971).

[72] Shields v. Wilkins, 449 S.W. 2d 220, 222 (Ky. 1969).

[73] Campbell v. Area Vocational Technical School, 183 Neb. 318, 159 N.W. 2d 817, 821 (1968).

[74] Grant v. School District, 244 Ore. 131, 415 P.2d 165, 166 (1966), *cert. denied*, 385 U.S. 1010 (1967).

[75] Indiana ex rel. Clark v. Haworth, 122 Ind. 462, 23 N.E. 946 (1890).

[76] *E.g.*, Jackson v. Ellington, 316 F.Supp. 1071, 1074 (W.D. Tenn. 1970), *cert. dismissed*, 404 U.S. 811 (1971).

[77] Sheldon, *Legislative Control over Public School Curriculum*, 15 Willamette L. Rev. 473, 504-05 (1979).

[78] *Id.*

[79] Mercer v. Michigan State Bd. of Educ., 379 F.Supp. 580 (E.D. Mich.), *aff'd mem.*, 419 U.S. 1081 (1974). *See* Epperson v. Arkansas, 393 U.S. 97, 113-14 (1968) (Black, J., concurring).

[80] Parker v. Board of Educ., 237 F.Supp. 222, 229-30 (D. Md.), *aff'd*, 348 F.2d 464 (4th Cir. 1965), *cert. denied*, 382 U.S. 1030 (1966).

[81] Zykan v. Warsaw Comm. School Corp., 631 F.2d 1300 (7th Cir. 1980); Palmer v. Board of Education, 603 F.2d 1271 (7th Cir. 1979), *cert. denied*, 444 U.S. 626 (1980); Brubaker v. Board of Educ., 502 F.2d 973, 984-85 (7th Cir. 1974), *cert. denied*, 421 U.S. 965 (1975).

[82] Adams v. Campbell County School Dist., 511 F.2d 1242 (10th Cir. 1975) (teacher has no constitutional right to employ unorthodox teaching methods).

[83] Mailloux v. Kiley, 323 F.Supp. 1387, 1392 (D. Mass.), *aff'd*, 448 F.2d 1242, 1242 (1st Cir. 1971); Birdwell v. Hazelwood School Dist., 352 F. Supp. 613 (E.D. Mo. 1972), *aff'd*, F.2d 490 (8th Cir. 1974) (teacher may not discuss his opposition to campus visitation by military recruiters in algebra class);

Ahern v. Board of Educ., 327 F.Supp. 1931 (D. Neb. 1971), *aff'd*, 456 F.2d 399 (8th Cir. 1972) (teacher may not discuss politics in economics class); *see also* Millikan v. Board of Directors, 93 Wash. 2d 522, 611 P.2d 414 (1980).

[84] Goldstein, *The Asserted Constitutional Right of Public School Teachers To Determine What They Teach*, 127 U.Pa.L. Rev. 1293, 1339-49, 1355-56 (1976).

[85] Schauer, *School Books, Lesson Plans, and the Constitution*, 78 W. Va. L. Rev. 287, 305 (1976).

[86] Comment, *The Dwindling Rights of Teachers and the Closing Courthouse Door*, 44 Fordham L. Rev. 511, 521-34 (1975).

[87] *Id.* (footnotes omitted).

[88] Healy v. James, 408 U.S. 169, 180-81 (1972).

[89] T. Emerson, *The System of Freedom of Expression* 598-611 (1970); Goldstein, *The Asserted Constitutional Right of Public School Teachers To Determine What They Teach*, 124 U. Pa. L. Rev. 1293 (1976); Kemerer & Hirsh, *The Developing Law Involving the Teacher's Right To Teach*, 84 W. Va. L. Rev. 31 (1981); Smalls, *A Legal Framework for Academic Freedom in Public Secondary Schools*, 12 J. Law & Educ. 529 (1983); Van Alstyne, *The Constitutional Rights of Teachers and Professors*, 1970 Duke L.J. 841; *Developments: Academic Freedom*, 81 Harv. L. Rev. 1045 (1968).

[90] Caudill, *Law and Worldview: Problems in the Creation-Science Controversy*, 3 J. Law & Religion 1, 21 n. 109 (1985).

[91] Shelton v. Tucker, 364 U.S. 479, 485 (1960).

[92] Edwards v. Aguillard, 482 U.S. ____, 96 L.Ed. 2d 510, 521 (1987).

[93] Note 3.

[94] Note 12.

[95] Note 15.

[96] Note 19.

[97] Note 23.

[98] Note 31.

[99] Note 40.

[100] Note 78.

[101] Note 32.

CHAPTER 20

The Constitutionality under the Establishment Clause of Public Instruction in "All Scientific Theories of Origins"

> *What is needed is a new theory of the requirements imposed by the first amendment. Possibly such a theory may be found in the concept of* balanced presentation. *Essentially the obligation of the government must be to present a* fairly balanced exposition of various relevant theories and points of view, and of alternatives open for action. *Only through enforcing a concept of this nature can individual members of society develop their full potential or exercise their sovereign right to govern themselves. The concept of* balanced presentation *is, of course, an extremely broad and vague one. But more specific elements which would enter into the solution of particular problems in these terms could be developed and refined. Thus, one essential element of the general doctrine might be that views or theories within the area of recognized academic or scientific standards could not be proscribed, and conversely views or theories outside such area could not be exclusively imposed. . . .*
>
> —Professor Thomas Emerson, Yale Law School[1]

The Establishment Clause of the First Amendment, which is often described as the requirement for separation of church and state, provides that "Congress shall make no law respecting an establishment of religion . . .." This chapter discusses the application of that requirement to the origins issue. Section 20.1 assesses the historical test by which the Establishment Clause is sometimes interpreted, while Section 20.2 addresses the tripart test for the Establishment Clause that focuses on the effect, purpose, and entanglement of governmental action.

The Supreme Court of the United States recently decided a case, *Edwards v. Aguillard*,[2] involving a Louisiana "Act for Balanced Treatment of Creation-Science and Evolution" in public schools.[3] The Court struck down the law on the basis that the legislative purpose for its passage was unconstitutional, but did not hold that the theory of creation is inherently religious.

The Supreme Court expressly stated that teachers may present scientific "theories, besides evolution, for the origin of life":

> [T]eaching a variety of scientific theories about the origins of humankind to schoolchildren might be validly done with the clear secular intent of enhancing the effectiveness of science instruction.[4]

The Court recognized that teachers "already possess" a "flexibility . . . to supplant the present science curriculum with the presentation of theories, besides evolution, about the origin of life,"[5] and are "free to teach any and all facets of this subject" of "all scientific theories about the origins of humankind."[6] That ruling sustained the finding of a three-judge panel of the U.S. Court of Appeals:

> No court of which we are aware has prohibited voluntary instruction concerning purely scientific evidence that happens, incidentally, to be consistent with a religious doctrine or tenet. It simply does not follow that science instruction violates the Establishment Clause merely because it "happens to coincide or harmonize with the tenets of some or all religions." *McGowan*, 366 U.S. at 442 . . ..[7]

On review of that three-judge decision, the U.S. Court of Appeals divided by a narrow 8-7 margin; the eight judges did not enter an opinion on the merits, but the seven dissenting Court of Appeals judges sharply argued that teaching alternate scientific theories, and that even the Louisiana law, did "not infringe the Constitution."[8]

Many legal commentators have agreed with the permissibility of teaching scientific alternatives, such as Caudill[9] and Strossen:

> Absent the statute, nothing would have prevented any school teacher who so chose from discussing any scientific shortcomings in evolutionary theory or any scientific evidence supporting a different theory of origins, including a creation theory.[10]

Scheid concurs:

> We have been assuming, as suggested in Section II, that a creationism model could be advocated as any other scientific theory. . . . Biology teachers should be permitted to teach a scientific creationism model if they want to—perhaps as a way of challenging students, by way of a contrasting hypothesis to a deeper understanding of the evidentiary support for evolution. From the point of view of science and education, however, a creationism model should not be required as a matter of law. . . .[11]

Some scientists, such as Zimmerman[11A] and even Gould, agree that "absolutely nothing prevents such a presentation, if evidence there be."[11B]

Thus, there is no constitutional problem with presentation in public educational institutions, at least without compulsion, of scientific "theories, besides evolution, for the origin" of the living world. That principle applies to instruction in the scientific theory of abrupt appearance, and applies to instruction in the theory of creation as long as it is fully scientific and nonreligious.[12] Any other rule would deny the "balanced exposition of various relevant theories and points of view, and of alternatives," that Emerson called for at the beginning of this chapter; and would indoctrinate students in one theory while censoring others. That would deprive students of some scientific information that they have a constitutional right to receive, when schools elect to teach the subject of origins, and would deprive teachers of the academic freedom to teach that scientific information that they professionally judge to be appropriate to the subject of origins, when schools allow the teaching of origins, as discussed in Chapter 19. The constitutionality of teaching all scientific theories of origins can be further seen by application of the historical test and of the tripart test for the Establishment Clause.

20.1 The Constitutionality under the Historical Test for the Establishment Clause of Teaching All Scientific Theories of Origins

The U.S. Supreme Court occasionally has used a historical test to apply the Establishment Clause to a particular case, especially when issues are raised that had counterparts at or just after the adoption of the Establishment Clause. Such a historical test clearly shows the constitutionality of teaching even the most controversial alternative theories of origins in public educational institutions.

Figure 20.1 The constitutional convention, in the context that "all men are created," and with the last words "In the Year of Our Lord" (painting by Christy of The Signing of the Constitution)

a. Supreme Court Recognition of Alternate Approaches to the Tripart Test

The Supreme Court explicitly has recognized alternative approaches to the Establishment Clause besides the tripart test, and has repeatedly said that the tripart test is not an exclusive approach to that Clause, in *Lynch v. Donnelly*,[13] *Marsh v. Chambers*,[14] *Mueller v. Allen*,[15] *Larson v. Valente*,[16] *Jones v. Wolf*,[17] *Tilton v. Richardson*,[18] and elsewhere.[19] An alternative test was specifically employed by the Court in *Marsh v. Chambers*,[20] and that was a historical test that generally upholds governmental actions that were accepted as constitutional at the time the First Amendment was adopted.[21] Such a historical test also was used in *Walz v. Tax Commission*,[22] *McGowan v. Maryland*,[23] *Everson v. Board of Education*,[24] and other Establishment Clause decisions.

That historical test was stated as follows in *Marsh*:

> historical evidence sheds light not only on what the draftsmen intended the Establishment Clause to mean, but also on how they thought that Clause applied to the practice authorized by the First Congress—their actions reveal their intent. An Act "passed by the first Congress assembled under the Constitution, many of whose members had taken part in framing that instrument, . . . is contemporaneous and weighty evidence of its true meaning."[25]

That holding recently was cited with approval in *Lynch v. Donnelly*.[26] In *Walz*, the Court described the importance of history, and apparently found it decisive (while also discussing the tripart test):

> Mr. Justice Holmes said that "[i]f a thing has been practised for two hundred years by common consent, it will need a strong case for the Fourteenth Amendment to affect it * * *." Jackman v. Rosenbaum Co., 260 U.S. 22,31 (1922). For almost 200 years the view expressed in the actions of legislatures and courts has been that tax exemptions for churches do not threaten "those consequences which the Framers deeply feared" or "tend to promote that type of interdependence between religion and state which the First Amendment was designed to prevent." ...[27]

b. Historical Evidence under the Alternative Test for the Constitutionality of Teaching All Scientific Theories of Origins

The theory of evolution and the theory of abrupt appearance are wholly scientific and nonreligious, and should not be viewed as raising any Establishment Clause issues at all.

The theory of creation is more controversial from an Establishment Clause standpoint, and the primary attacks are that creation is an inherently religious concept and that a creator is necessarily incorporated or implied. Creation is not inherently religious, as discussed in Chapters 12-14, and can be wholly scientific, as shown in Chapters 9-10, as its history reflects, in Chapter 15. A creator is not a necessary element of the theory of creation, and is no more mentioned by creationists than by evolutionists, as Sections 13.2-13.3 and 14.1-14.3 demonstrate. By *a fortiori* logic, if reference to a creator in public educational institutions does not violate the Establishment Clause (the theory of creation does not require or embody such a reference), then the theory of creation with its reference to creation does not violate the Establishment Clause, and it is all the more clear that the theory of abrupt appearance (which does not involve the concept of creation) is not constitutionally impermissible.

The historical meaning of the Establishment Clause has been discussed in a number of interpretivist[28] and noninterpretivist[29] studies. That meaning is illuminated by extensive historical evidence. The Constitution itself closes with "in the year of our Lord."[30] It was written in the historical context of the Declaration of Independence, and the Declaration refers to "creation" as well as to a "Creator,"[31] and was written by the same Jefferson who coined the "wall of separation" phrase long afterwards in 1802. The broader context was the philosophy of Locke, Blackstone, and a few others. Locke grounded his philosophy in "the law of Nature—i.e., to the will of God":

> The law of Nature stands as an eternal rule to all men, legislators as well as others. The rules that they make for man's actions must . . . be conformable to the law of Nature—i.e., to the will of God.[32]

Blackstone also built upon natural law, defined as the "eternal immutable laws of good and evil, to which the Creator himself . . . conforms . . .."[33]

The first Congress in 1789, which approved the Establishment Clause, prescribed a statutory oath for some public officials, which included the phrase "so help me God."[34] That First Congress also passed a resolution asking the president "to set aside a Thanksgiving Day to acknowledge 'the many signal favors of Almighty God,' "[35] and did so on the very day that "final agreement was reached on the language of the Bill of Rights," as the Supreme Court stressed in *Marsh v. Chambers*.[36] President Washington complied by issuing a Thanksgiving proclamation eight days later, which referred in part to the "author" of the world as well as to "God."[37] The first Congress also authorized chaplains and prayers to God three days earlier,[38] and James Madison voted for that chaplaincy appropriation and was on the committee designing the chaplain's functions.[39] "Clearly the men who wrote the First Amendment Clauses did not view paid legislative chaplains and opening prayers as a violation of that Amendment . . .," the Supreme Court concluded in *Marsh*.[40] Earlier during the First Congress, on April 30, 1789, President Washington gave his first inaugural address to Congress, and referred to the "Author" of the world as well as to the "Almighty Being":[41]

> [I]t would be peculiarly improper to omit in this first official act my fervent supplications to that Almighty Being who rules over the universe, who presides in the councils of nations, and whose providential aids can supply every human defect, that His benediction may consecrate to the liberties and happiness of the people of the United States a Government instituted by themselves for these essential purposes, and may enable every instrument employed in its administration to execute with success the functions allotted to his charge. In tendering this homage to the Great Author of every public and private good, I assure myself that it expressed your sentiments not less than my own . . ..
>
> . . ..
>
> Having thus imparted to you my sentiments as they have been awakened by the occasion which brings us together, I shall take my present leave; but not without resorting once more to the benign Parent of the Human Race in humble supplication that, since He has been pleased to favor the American people with opportunities for deliberating in perfect tranquility, and dispositions for deciding with unparalleled unanimity

> on a form of government for the security of their union and the advancement of their happiness, so His Divine blessing may be equally conspicuous in the enlarged views, the temperate consultations, and the wise measures on which the success of this Government must depend.[42]

In fact, "God is mentioned or referred to in all inaugural addresses but Washington's second, which is a very brief . . . acknowledgment," Bellah notes.[43]

An early Congress established public schools in the District of Columbia in 1804, and those schools did teach about a "Creator" as well as referring to "God," with Jefferson's support as the first president of the District of Columbia school board.[44] Jefferson's own curricular plan for a state university, the University of Virginia, while intentionally omitting theology instruction, included "a professor of ethics who was to treat 'the proof of the being of a God, the Creator' . . . ."[45] Jefferson obviously saw theology as religious but the concept of creation or even a creator as nonreligious. The first Congress also reenacted the Northwest Ordinance, which provided land for schools that was used by both public and nonpublic schools, and that not only permitted but encouraged religious uses.[46]

Jefferson did not write the Establishment Clause or even attend the constitutional convention, but his views have figured prominently in recent discussions of the Clause because he wrote the "separation of church and state" phrase thirteen years later, in 1802.[47] Jefferson did write the Virginia Act for Establishing Religious Freedom, adopted in 1786 and the most significant precursor to the religion clauses; and it began with a reference to "God" and "created" that Jefferson obviously viewed as consistent with nonestablishment:

> WHEREAS, Almighty God hath created the mind free; that all attempts to influence it by temporal punishments or burthens, or by civil incapacitations, tend only to beget habits of hypocrisy and meanness, and are a departure from the plan of the Holy author of our religion . . . .[48]

Jefferson also argued that all liberties are created by God, and again saw nonestablishment as consistent with reference to God, in words that are engraved on the Jefferson Memorial:

> The God who gave us life, gave us liberty at the same time. . . . Can the liberties of a nation be thought secure when we have removed their only firm basis, a conviction in the minds of the people that these liberties are the gift of God?[49]

Besides what he permitted as president of the public school board for the District of Columbia, Jefferson approved of the setting aside of a room at the University of Virginia "for religious worship," and "proposed to encourage various denominations to situate their theological schools near the University" to " 'give to their students ready and convenient access and attendance on the scientific lectures of the University' " while "enabling the students of the University to attend religious exercises," as rector of the University of Virginia.[50] And Jefferson saw the concept of creation (although in a metaphysical sense that is different from the scientific theory of creation) as not dependent on revelation but as independent of religion:

> Indeed I think that every Christian sect gives a great handle to Atheism by their general dogma that, without a revelation, there would not be sufficient proof of the being of a god. . . . I hold (without appeal to revelation) that when we take a view of the Universe, in it[s] parts general or particular, it is impossible for the human mind not to perc[e]ive and feel a conviction of design, consummate skill, and indefinite power in every atom of it[s] composition. The movements of the heavenly bodies, so exactly held in their course by the balance of centrifugal and centripetal forces, the structure of our earth itself, with it[s] distribution of lands, waters and atmosphere, animal and vegetable bodies, examined in all their minutest particles, insects mere atoms of life, yet as perfectly organized as man or mammoth, the mineral substance, their generation and uses, it is impossible, I say, for the human mind not to believe that there is, in all this, design, cause and effect, up to an ultimate cause, a fabricator of all things from matter and motion, their preserver and regulator while permitted to exist in their present forms, and their regenerator into new and other forms. We see, too, evident proofs of the necessity of a superintending power to maintain the Universe in it[s] course and order. . . .[51]

Early legal commentators agreed that the Establishment Clause is not inconsistent with reference to creation or even to a creator. Justice Story interpreted the Clause much more narrowly,[52] as did Chancellor Kent.[53] Judge Cooley found "no provisions which prohibit the authorities from such solemn recognition of a superintending Providence in public transactions and exercises as the general religious sentiment of mankind inspires," and that "all must acknowledge the fitness of recognizing in important human affairs the superintending care and control of the Great Governor of the Universe."[54] The "Supreme Court, for more than a century and a half, showed no reticence in invoking the Deity in its own decisions," Pfeffer* concedes.[55] Extensive further evidence could be cited.

The point is that the Establishment Clause is not violated by public school teaching of scientific evidence that points to evolution, abrupt appearance, or even creation, simply because the authors of that Clause saw the concept of creation as being nonreligious and saw even the concepts of a creator or God as being permissible subjects of governmental reference. Moreover, the first public schools and Jefferson provided for teaching about a creator or God, and treated it as nonreligious. Finally, the Supreme Court recently has upheld public school reference to God or a creator (which instruction in the theory of creation does not necessitate), as discussed next. *A fortiori*, it is constitutional to refer to creation in a scientific sense.

Summary. The Establishment Clause of the First Amendment does not prevent teachers in public schools (or universities) from presenting scientific "theories, besides evolution, for the origin of humankind" and of plants and animals (*Edwards v. Aguillard*[56]). Instead, it requires government "to present a fairly balanced exposition of various relevant theories and points of view, and of alternatives," on all unsettled subjects that are addressed (Emerson and Haber[57]).

The historical test for the Establishment Clause has been endorsed and used occasionally by the Supreme Court (*Marsh v. Chambers*[58]), and permits instruction by public institutions in the theories of evolution and of abrupt appearance, and even in a scientific theory of creation. The Constitution itself finds the Establishment Clause not to be inconsistent with reference to "in the year of our Lord," and the Declaration of Independence refers to "creation" and a "Creator." The very Congress that wrote the Clause made many references to the same concepts, and Jefferson distinguished between religion and "a professor of ethics who was to treat 'the proof of the being of a God, the Creator' . . ." (C. Antieau *et al.*[59]). Those things are different from the theory of creation, but *a fortiori* show its constitutionality. That theory of creation is less clearly nonreligious than the theory of abrupt appearance, and its constitutionality *a fortiori* shows the constitutionality of the theory of abrupt appearance.

20.2 The Constitutionality under the Tripart Test for the Establishment Clause of Teaching All Scientific Theories of Origins

Teaching the theory of evolution and the theory of abrupt appearance, from a strictly scientific vantage point, seems clearly to come under the recent recognition of the Supreme Court of the United

Figure 20.2
Teachers are "free to teach any and all facets of this subject" of "all scientific theories about the origins of humankind" and life (U.S. Supreme Court, whose building is pictured)

States that teachers may teach alternative scientific theories of origins, as the last chapter discussed.

Even teaching the theory of creation, from such a scientific basis and without any reference to a creator, appears to come under the same rule. Even if the theory of creation required reference to a creator (it does not), that would not violate the Establishment Clause, as earlier Supreme Court decisions indicate.

The Court recognized the constitutionality of public school "references to the Deity . . . or Supreme Being, or . . . God," in the very *Engel v. Vitale*[60] decision that held mandatory prayer unconstitutional in public schools:

> There is of course nothing in the decision reached here that is inconsistent with the fact that *school children* and others are officially encouraged to express love for our country by reciting historical documents such as the Declaration of Independence which contain *references to the Deity* or by singing officially espoused anthems which include the composer's professions of faith in a *Supreme Being*, or with the fact that there are many manifestations in our public life of belief in *God*. Such patriotic or ceremonial occasions bear no true resemblance to the unquestioned religious exercise [mandatory classroom prayer] that the State of New York has sponsored in this instance.[61]

The Declaration of Independence, which the Court cited as appropriate for public school study, explicitly refers to a "Creator" and "God," as well as "creation," in several places.[62] The Constitution refers to "our Lord."[63] The national anthem, which the Court said may be constitutionally sung in the schools, says "[m]ay the heaven-rescued land praise the Power that hath made and preserved us a nation," and refers to "God".[64] The Supreme Court[65] and other courts[66] unanimously have upheld the public school pledge to the flag, with its reference to "one nation under God,"[67] and with its purpose to affirm the dependence of "our Government upon the moral directions of the Creator."[68] Lower courts have sustained singing the national anthem in public schools.[69] The Supreme Court has repeatedly stated that America's "institutions presuppose a Supreme Being," in *Lynch v. Donnelly*,[70] *Walz v. Tax Commission*,[71] *Zorach v. Clauson*,[72] and *Holy Trinity Church v. United States*,[73] referring with approval to a number of widespread practices including some in public schools. Two federal appellate courts have upheld the national motto, "In God We Trust,"[74] and the Supreme Court has agreed.[75] *A fortiori*, reference to a scientific theory of creation, without any reference to a creator, is constitutional under those precedents. That was one thesis of an article published in the *Yale Law Journal* by this author.[76]

The tripart test, or the *Lemon* test,[77] consists of the following three requirements:

> It is well settled that "a legislative enactment does not contravene the establishment clause if it has *a* secular legislative purpose, if its *principal or primary* effect neither advances nor inhibits religion, and if it does not foster an *excessive* governmental entanglement with religion.[78]

After definitions are discussed, the effect, purpose, and entanglement aspects of the tripart test are assessed separately.

a. The Scientific and Nonreligious Nature of Theories of Origins

(1) The Definitions of Theories of Origins. The theory of abrupt appearance is the theory that the universe, first life, and plant and animal natural groups appeared abruptly and discontinuously in complex form. That theory consists of empirical evidence and scientific interpretations, as discussed in Chapters 2, 4, and 6.

The theory of creation is a specific variant within the broad category of the theory of abrupt appearance, just as theories of saltationism and theistic evolution are scientific and nonscientific variants within the broad category of the theory of evolution. The "theory of

*Scientists, theologians, and philosphers cited in Section 20.2(a), unless otherwise indicated, are not advocates of, and their quoted statements are not intended as endorsements of, either the theory of abrupt appearance or the theory of creation.

creation" as a scientific term was used over a century ago by such scientists as Professor Louis Agassiz of Harvard, who was "America's leading biologist"[79] as well as the leading creationist scientist of his time,[80] and by Charles Darwin* himself.

The theory of evolution also addresses the origin and development of the universe, the first life, and organisms.[81] Biological evolution includes "common ancestry" of all organisms[82]—or macro-evolution—which involves evolution "from primordial life, through unicellular and multicellular organisms, invertebrate and vertebrate animals, to man . . .."[83] Biochemical evolution involves the development of life from nonlife, and cosmic evolution involves the development of the universe from the big bang.

(2) The Scientific Nature of Theories of Origins. The theory of abrupt appearance is scientific, in postulating that the universe, the first life, and plants and animals appeared abruptly in complex form discontinuously from other forms, on the basis of affirmative scientific evidence in such fields as paleontology, morphology, information theory, probability, genetics, and classification.[84] That evidence is summarized in Chapters 2, 4, and 6, and the scientific nature of the theory is discussed in Chapters 9-10. For example, the paleontology argument for the biological theory of abrupt appearance is based on two empirical facts that the fossil record generally reflects: the abrupt appearance of fossil categories of complex organisms and the systematic gaps between different categories of fossil organisms. Those facts are acknowledged by many evolutionist scientists, such as Gould* of Harvard and Raup* of the Field Museum, although they interpret abrupt appearance within the context of continuity rather than discontinuity:

> New species almost always *appeared suddenly* in the fossil record with *no intermediate links* to ancestors in older rocks of the same region.[85]
>
> Unfortunately, the origins of most higher categories are shrouded in mystery; commonly new higher categories *appear abruptly* in the fossil record *without* evidence of *transitional ancestral forms.*[86]

In fact, some evolutionists have conceded that this fossil record is an affirmative scientific evidence for views of abrupt appearance:

> Rather than supporting evolution, the *breaks* in the known fossil record *support the creation* of major groups with the possibility of some limited variation within each group.[87]

Hundreds of similar scientific citations can be and were made for the other elements of the theory of abrupt appearance, and are summarized in Chapters 2, 4, and 6.

"[E]volution theory is in crisis," and is far from being compellingly established, as scientists Saunders* and Ho* have observed.[88] The same conclusion has been reached by many other noncreationist scientists such as Grassé*[89] ("the most distinguished of French zoologists"[90]), Kerkut* (editor of a major physiology series),[91] Patterson* (senior paleontologist at the British Museum),[92] Sermonti* (professor of genetics at University of Perugia) and Fondi* (professor of paleontology at University of Siena),[93] Denton* (a molecular biologist who recently wrote the book *Evolution: A Theory in Crisis*),[94] Løvtrup* (professor of biology at University of Umea who recently wrote the book *Darwinism: The Refutation of a Myth*),[95] and many others.[96] Biochemical evolution (of the first life)[97] and cosmic evolution (of the universe) have problems equally as serious as has biological evolution.[98] Many hundreds of similar concessions by noncreationist scientists are cited in Chapters 3, 5, and 7, demonstrating that evolution is not compellingly substantiated or impervious to alternative scientific interpretations. The seven dissenting judges on the U.S. Court of Appeals agreed in *Edwards v. Aguillard*:

> As I noted at the outset, the record contains affidavits—some of them by highly-qualified scientists who there proclaim themselves agnostics and believers in evolution as a theory—which affirm that the above propositions are correct: that *evolution is not established fact* and that there is strong evidence that life and the universe came about in a different manner, one perhaps less inconsistent with religious doctrine. . . . For purposes of reviewing the summary judgment which our panel's opinion affirms, then, the propositions stated above must be taken as established . . .. *There are two bona fide views.*[99]

Justice Scalia and Chief Justice Rehnquist of the U.S. Supreme Court also agreed, in their dissent:

> Infinitely less can we say (or should we say) that the scientific evidence for evolution is so *conclusive* that no one could be gullible enough to believe that there is any real scientific evidence to the contrary, so that the legislation's stated purpose must be a lie.[100]

The theory of creation can consist of scientific evidence, although some of its proponents present it in a religious manner, and in fact is as scientific as evolution, as discussed in Chapters 9 and 10 (on the demarcation between science and other fields). There are many examples, cited in Chapter 17 and elsewhere, such as the following:

> I am not a creationist or a religious Fundamentalist, and instead am an evolutionist and Agnostic.
>
> . . .My conclusions are that creation-science is *scientific*, non-religious, and educationally worthwhile in comparison with evolution. It can be taught and can be presented in a textbook *without any religious content.*

> It is affirmative *scientific evidence* that supports creation-science, and the evidence is not compellingly persuasive that supports evolution.
>
> . . ..
>
> . . .Creationist scientists offer several areas of what can properly be called affirmative evidence and analysis . . .. These involve *scientific data* and do *not involve religious concepts*.[101]

An Agnostic physicist, to whom the theory of creation is "anathema," recently concluded that the "experimental evidence" actually better supports it than evolution:

> I think however that we must go further than this and admit that *the only acceptable explanation is creation*. I know that this is anathema to physicists, as indeed it is to me, but we must not reject a theory that we do not like if the *experimental evidence supports it*.[102]

The U.S. Supreme Court in *Edwards v. Aguillard* did not enter a holding that the theory of "creation-science" is inherently religious, although the Court implied it in dictum. Justice Scalia and Chief Justice Rehnquist disagreed sharply with that implication in their dissent:

> The Act's reference to "creation" is not convincing evidence of religious purpose. The Act defines creation science as "scientific evidenc[e]," and Senator Keith and his witnesses repeatedly stressed that the subject can and should be presented without religious content. . . . We have no basis on the record to conclude that creation science need be anything other than a collection of scientific data supporting the theory that life abruptly appeared on earth. . . . Creation science, its proponents insist, no more must explain whence life came than evolution must explain whence came the inanimate materials from which it says life evolved.[103]

Although an eight judge majority of the U.S. Court of Appeals for the Fifth Circuit refused to review (without opinion) the three judge decision finding the theory of "creation-science" religious,[104] a seven judge dissent excoriated the three judges for their decision:

> The statute which concerns us today is quite different: it has *no direct religious reference whatever* and *merely requires that the whole scientific truth be taught* on the subject if any is.
>
> . . ..
>
> That was to provide, as my summary of the statute indicates, that neither evolution nor creation be presented as finally established scientific fact and that when evolution is taught as a theory, the *scientific evidence* . . . for the sudden appearance of highly developed forms of life be given equal time (and vice versa).
>
> . . ..
>
> It follows that the Louisiana statute requires no more than that neither theory about the origins of life and matter be misrepresented as fact, and

> that if *scientific evidence supporting either view* of how these things came about be presented in public schools, *that supporting the other* must be—so that within the reasonable limits of the curriculum, the subject of origins will be discussed in a balanced manner if it is discussed at all. . . .[105]

The issue is *not* which explanation of origins is correct, but whether any is so compellingly established and universally accepted that it ought to be taught to the exclusion of other scientific explanations. Because no theory is so unquestionably true, all scientific views should be taught to protect the student right to receive scientific information and the teacher right to academic freedom by offering the "whole scientific truth."

(3) The Nonreligious Nature of Theories of Origins. The theory of abrupt appearance is nonreligious, as discussed in Chapters 12-16. It does not include any religious concepts, is different from the theory of creation, and centers around the widely used scientific term of "abrupt appearance."

The theory of creation also is nonreligious, and in fact is as nonreligious as the theory of evolution, as also discussed in Chapters 12-16. That is the conclusion not only of creationist scientists, but of many noncreationists such as Fr. Dr. William G. Most*, an evolutionist theologian:

> My professional opinion is that creation-science is *not religious*. It appears to me to be scientific.
>
> . . ..
>
> . . .The concept of *creation is not inherently religious and is nonreligious* when defined as abrupt appearance in complex form. The concept of a creator is also not inherently religious, although it can be stated in religious terms; and it is not religious in its relation to creation-science. Creation-science is no more supportive of religious concepts of a creator or other religious doctrines than evolution is in its theistic evolutionist formulations.[106]

The term "creation," both in philosophical and scientific usage, is nonreligious and scientific in signifying an origination, as Leslie*,[107] Gillespie*,[108] and even Darwin*[109] acknowledged. It so appears in the writings of leading proponents of the big bang,[110] inflationary universe,[111] quantum and particle creation, and continuous creation theories[112] about the origin of the universe, of directed panspermia advocates about the origin of the first life, and of others about the origin of organisms.[113] The concept of creation also appears in Ambrose's* and Heribert-Nilsson's approaches, all of which firmly reject *Genesis*.[114]

Further, the concept of a creator is not a necessary part of presenting the scientific theory of creation and is not central to it in any event, because the empirical evidence that constitutes the theory of creation indicates occurrences of creation but not the sources or causes of those occurrences.[115] Just as the theory of evolution cannot resolve and often does not address the question of who or what originated matter and energy in the cosmos and what mechanism brought about macroevolution, the scientific theory of creation does not properly address the question of the source or cause of creation. The noncentrality of a creator to the scientific theory of creation is evident in the absence of a creator from definitions of "creation" given by several public school textbooks produced by secular national publishers.[116] In fact, the role of a creator in evolutionist writings and thought is greater than in creation-related writings and thought.[117] Moreover, the concept of a creator is not necessarily religious, but often is philosophical or historical instead.[118] In any event, reference to creation or even to a creator does not bring violation of the Establishment Clause, as discussed earlier in this chapter.

The Supreme Court has defined "religion" as involving an "ultimate concern,"[119] and as not being centered in and not even requiring belief in God or a Supernatural Being.[120] The theory of creation simply does *not* constitute such an "ultimate concern" or religious belief system. Similarly, it lacks all or certainly most of the characteristics of religion in theological definitions described in Chapter 12, or in philosophical definitions such as in the *Encyclopedia of Philosophy*[121] and *Encyclopaedia Britannica.*[122]

The theories of evolution and of abrupt appearance, while both are scientific explanations, are comparably "consistent" or "harmonious" with various religions, and are parallel in every other aspect that might be alleged to be religious. Each scientific explanation is consistent with (although different from) various religions that span the full theological spectrum:

Theological Category	*Creationist Religions*	*Evolutionist Religions*
a. Protestant:	Conservative Evangelicalism and Fundamentalism; Church of Christ and Seventh-day Adventism	Theological Liberalism and Neo-Orthodoxy;[123] Religious Humanism and Unitarianism[124]

Theological Category	*Creationist Religions*	*Evolutionist Religions*
b. Catholic:	Much Orthodox Roman Catholicism and Eastern Orthodoxy	Neo-Modernist Roman Catholicism[125]
c. Jewish:	Orthodox Judaism	Reform Judaism[126]
d. Non-Judeo-Christian:	Islam (Muslims) and some Hinduism.	Buddhism and Hinduism;[127] Secular Humanism and other Humanist faiths;[128] and Atheism.[129]

The religions with which the theory of abrupt appearance is consistent are not just Fundamentalist but many other Protestant, Catholic,[130] Jewish,[131] and nonJudeo-Christian faiths.[132] Such harmony between scientific explanation and religious belief does not violate the Establishment Clause: "the 'Establishment' Clause does not ban federal or state regulation whose reason or effect merely happens to coincide or harmonize with the tenets of some or all religions."[133] Moreover, each scientific explanation is antagonistic to some religious beliefs in the view of some people.[134] An example is the recent book entitled *Is God a Creationist? The Religious Case Against Creation-Science.*[135]

b. The Secular Primary Effect of Furthering Students' Right To Receive Additional Scientific Information and Uncensored Instruction

The primary effect of teaching "all scientific theories of origins" is to advance students' First Amendment right to receive all the scientific information on the subject of origins. That can be seen in the support given to balanced treatment by a number of evolutionists[136] (others are cited in Section 17.2), as well as by Darwin and Scopes (as quoted later).

Teaching the theory of abrupt appearance along with the theory of evolution produces that primary effect of advancing students' right under the First Amendment to receive more scientific information on the topic of origins. To deny that is to ignore the scientific evidence outlined in Chapters 2, 4, and 6, and possibly also to insist on indoctrination in the theory of evolution and on censorship of any scientific alternative.

Even teaching the theory of creation along with the theory of evolution might produce that secular effect, which may be why the Supreme Court in *Edwards v. Aguillard* did not enter a holding that a nonsecular effect would necessarily arise when it found a Louisiana law to have a nonsecular legislative purpose. Quinn, a philosopher of science formerly at Brown University and now at Notre Dame University, criticized an earlier court decision about a partially nonscientific theory of creation on precisely that ground, and found a secular primary effect:

> As I mentioned before, the Opinion does contain an argument for (1) [that an Arkansas law had "the advancement of religion as a major effect"]. . . . The more specific argument aims to show both that Section 4(a) as a whole is congruent with the literal interpretation of Genesis favored by fundamentalist Christians and that the ideas in 4(a)(1) in particular are identical to the ideas in the Genesis creation story as literally interpreted. . . . First, though there may be a technical, legal sense in which any use of the concept of a supreme being counts as religious, this is not a sense in which any such use advances or promotes religion. After all, that concept is used in purely theoretical discussions in works of metaphysics that have no tendency to promote or advance religious belief or practice by any individual or group. . . . Third, though there are extensive parallels between Section 4(a) and Genesis, it is doubtful that this by itself is sufficient to show that a major effect of Act 590 is to advance particular religious beliefs. After all, there are also extensive parallels between parts of the criminal law and Deuteronomy. Both the Decalogue in Deuteronomy 5 and the criminal law prohibit such things as murder, theft and perjury. But surely this does not suffice to show that a major effect of the criminal law is to advance particular religious beliefs. Hence, I think there are solid rational grounds for doubting that Judge Overton's argument for (1) is successful.[137]

Thus, Quinn finds the judge's effort logically unsuccessful and philosophically incorrect:

> There are two conclusions I wish to draw from this portion of my discussion. First, because Judge Overton's Opinion does not provide adequate justification for any of (1)-(3), it is not a rationally persuasive argument for the claim that Act 590 fails the second part of the three-pronged test. Second, because the argument (6)-(20) [that the theory of creation does not advance science] is demonstrably unsound, philosophy of science contributed nothing of positive value to the quality of Judge Overton's Opinion. . . .[138]

The insufficiency of "parallels" between a concept and religion to produce a religious primary effect is a significant element in Supreme Court analysis under the Establishment Clause.

(1) Permissibility of Such Secondary Effects as Mere Consistency with and Incidental Benefits to Religion. The Establishment Clause

prohibits, under the tripart test, a "primary" effect but not a secondary or tertiary effect of advancing religion.

State actions such as public school curricula that merely "coincide or harmonize with the tenets of some or all religions" do not violate the primary effect requirement, and instead are a permissible secondary effect, as the Supreme Court recognized in *Harris v. McRae* (upholding restrictions on federal funding of Medicaid abortions)[139] and *Lynch v. Donnelly* (sustaining a nativity scene in a city holiday display).[140] The Court said the following in *McGowan v. Maryland*,[141] in upholding Sunday closing laws:

> However, it is equally true that the "Establishment" Clause does not ban federal or state regulation of conduct whose reason or effect merely happens to coincide or harmonize with the tenets of some or all religions. In many instances, the Congress or state legislatures conclude that the general welfare of society, wholly apart from any religious considerations, demands such regulation. Thus, for temporal purposes murder is illegal. And the fact that this agrees with the dictates of the Judaeo-Christian religions while it may disagree with others does not invalidate the regulation. So too with the questions of adultery and polygamy. *Davis v. Beason*, 133 U.S. 333; *Reynolds v. United States*, *supra*. The same could be said of theft, fraud, etc., because those offenses were also proscribed in the Decalogue.[142]

The theory of evolution and the theory of abrupt appearance each is consistent with—but different from—various religious beliefs in theistic evolution and creation (Sections 13.3 and 14.1-14.2). Neither scientific theory has a primary effect of advancing religion.

Governmental activities such as school curricula that offer "incidental benefits to religion" similarly do not have an impermissible primary effect of advancing religion, as the Supreme Court has said in *Lynch v. Donnelly*,[143] *Committee for Public Education v. Nyquist*,[144] and other decisions. For example, the Court said the following in *Nyquist*:

> It is equally well established, however, that not every law that confers an "indirect," "remote," or "incidental" benefit upon religious institutions is, for that reason alone, constitutionally invalid. *Everson*, *supra*; *McGowan v. Maryland*, *supra*, at 450; *Walz v. Tax Comm'n*, 397 U.S. 664, 671-672, 674-675 (1970). What our cases require is careful examination of any law challenged on establishment grounds with a view to ascertaining whether it furthers any of the evils against which that Clause protects. . . .[145]

The theory of evolution and the theory of abrupt appearance at most provide that sort of incidental benefit to religion, and have a primary effect of advancing students' access to scientific information.

(2) Analogous Supreme Court Decisions on Secular Primary Effects. Many decisions of the Supreme Court involving analogous governmental activities lend support to the constitutionality of teaching all scientific theories of origins in state-funded schools. Those decisions were summarized in *Lynch v. Donnelly*, as follows:

> But to conclude that the *primary effect* of including the creche is to advance religion in violation of the Establishment Clause would require that we view it as more beneficial to and more an endorsement of religion, for example, than expenditure of large sums of public money for textbooks supplied throughout the country to students attending church-sponsored schools, *Board of Education v. Allen, supra*; expenditure of public funds for transportation of students to church-sponsored schools, *Everson v. Board of Education, supra*; federal grants for college buildings of church-sponsored institutions of higher education combining secular and religious education, *Tilton, supra*; noncategorical grants to church-sponsored colleges and universities, *Roemer v. Board of Public Works*, 426 U.S. 736 (1976); and the tax exemptions for church properties sanctioned in *Walz, supra*. It would also require that we view it as more of an endorsement of religion than the Sunday Closing Laws upheld in *McGowan v. Maryland*, 366 U.S. 420 (1961); the released time program for religious training in *Zorach, supra*; and the legislative prayers upheld in *Marsh, supra*.
>
> We are unable to discern a greater aid to religion deriving from inclusion of the creche than from these benefits and endorsements previously held not violative of the Establishment Clause.[146]

Other decisions could be added whose primary effects as well as whose legislative purposes the Supreme Court has upheld: equal use of veterans' benefits for religious higher education,[147] equal access to public university facilities for religious groups,[148] and judicial resolution of church property disputes through neutral principles.[149] Teaching all scientific theories instead offers at most the sort of secondary effect of "coinciding or harmonizing" with various religions that was sustained in connection with funding for abortions and with Sunday closing laws.[150]

c. *The Legislative Purpose of Advancing Students' Right To Receive Additional Scientific Information and to Uncensored Instruction*

The governmental purpose for teaching all scientific theories of origins, like the primary effect, is to advance the constitutional right of students to receive scientific information and to end indoctrination and censorship. Professor Laurence Tribe* of Harvard Law

School proposed the basic principle that "anything '*arguably non-religious*' should not be considered religious in applying the establishment clause."[151] Some legal commentators have gone further to argue that the legislative purpose is irrelevant: an otherwise valid governmental requirement should not be overturned because of the purpose behind it.[152]

(1) Violation Only by an Exclusively Religious Purpose. The Supreme Court recently stated that the legislative purpose requirement is violated "only" when the governmental activity was "motivated wholly by religious considerations":

> The Court has invalidated legislation or governmental action on the ground that a secular purpose was lacking, but *only* when it has concluded there was no question that the statute or activity was motivated *wholly* by religious considerations. See, *e.g.*, *Stone v. Graham, supra*, at 41; *Epperson v. Arkansas*, 393 U.S. 97, 107-109 (1968); *Abington School District v. Schempp, supra*, at 223-224; *Engel v. Vitale*, 370 U.S. 421, 424-425 (1962). Even where the benefits to religion were substantial, as in *Everson, supra*; *Board of Education v. Allen*, 392 U.S. 236 (1968), *Walz, supra*, and *Tilton, supra*, we saw a secular purpose and no conflict with the Establishment Clause.[153]

It is important to note that the Court cited *Epperson v. Arkansas* in support of that point; that key case is discussed in a few pages. *Wallace v. Jaffree*[154] reiterated that the purpose requirement is violated only if a law "is entirely motivated by a purpose to advance religion," and is not violated if "motivated in part by a religious purpose."[155] *McGinnis v. Royster*[156] expressly disclaims any judicial need or ability to distinguish impermissible primary purposes and permissible secondary purposes under the analogous Equal Protection Clause:

> The search for legislative purpose is often elusive enough, Palmer v. Thompson, 403 U.S. 217 (1971), without a requirement that primacy be ascertained. . . The Equal Protection Clause does not countenance such speculative probing into the purposes of a coordinate branch. We have supplied no imaginary basis or purpose for this statutory scheme, but we likewise refuse to discard a clear and legitimate purpose because the court below perceived another to be primary.[157]

The Court also has stressed a "reluctance to attribute unconstitutional motives to the states, particularly when a plausible secular purpose" appears on "the face of the statute."[158]

There clearly is "a secular purpose" for teaching all scientific theories of origins, and for teaching the theory of evolution and the theory of abrupt appearance. The theory of abrupt appearance is not just "arguably non-religious" but manifestly nonreligious, and no more advances any religion than does the theory of evolution. Charles Darwin acknowledged the secular reason for balancing both sides of the issue:

> For I am well aware that scarcely a single point is discussed in this volume on which *facts* cannot be adduced, often apparently leading to conclusions directly opposite to those at which I have arrived. A fair result can be obtained only by fully stating and *balancing the facts and arguments on both sides of each question* . . ..[159]

John Scopes joined in that thinking:

> Education, you known, means broadening, advancing, and if you limit a teacher to *only one side* of anything the whole country will eventually have only one thought, be one individual. I believe in *teaching every aspect of every problem or theory*.[160]

There may even be a secular purpose for instruction in the theory of creation along with the theory of evolution. There was a secular purpose to advance students' right to receive scientific information that undergirded the Louisiana law for balanced treatment of the theories of creation and evolution, according to Justice Scalia and Chief Justice Rehnquist in dissent:

> In this case, however, it seems to me the Court's position is the repressive one. The people of Louisiana . . . are quite entitled, as a secular matter, to have whatever scientific evidence there may be against evolution presented in their schools, just as Mr. Scopes was entitled to present whatever scientific evidence there was for it. . . . Yet that illiberal judgment, that *Scopes*-in-reverse, is ultimately the basis on which the Court's facile rejection of Louisiana Legislature's purpose must rest.[161]

Seven dissenting judges of the U.S. Court of Appeals for the Fifth Circuit also explicitly found that balanced treatment has "a credible secular purpose" of "advancing academic freedom,"[162] as the Louisiana law expressly stated as its purpose, and thus "does not infringe the Constitution":[163]

> Such authorities [*Stone v. Graham, Wallace v. Jaffree, Lemon v. Kurtzman, Karen B. v. Treen*] treat of statutes having a direct and clear religious connection, either by way of granting public assistance to religious schools or by requiring religious activities in public ones. The statute which concerns us today is quite different: it has no direct religious reference whatever and *merely requires that the whole scientific truth be taught* on the subject if any is.
>
> . . ..
>
> I should have thought that *requiring the truth to be taught* on any subject displayed its own secular warrant, one at the heart of the scientific method itself. Put another way, I am surprised to learn that a state

> cannot forbid the teaching of half-truths in its public schools, whatever its motive in doing so. . . . It comes as news to me, however, that the Constitution forbids a state to require the teaching of truth—any truth, for any purpose, and whatever the effect of teaching it may be.[164]
>
> . . ..
>
> . . . By *requiring that the whole truth be taught*, Louisiana aligned itself with Darrow; striking down that requirement, the panel holding aligns us with Bryan.[165]

Those seven judges were sharply disagreeing with a narrow eight-judge majority of the court, who in a two-sentence procedural order declined to review a three-judge decision that balanced treatment is unconstitutional.

Larson, a legal commentator and historian of science who wrote the authoritative history of the creation-evolution controversy, concurred that "it is difficult to entirely discount the Balanced Treatment Act's express legislative purpose of 'protecting academic freedom' *if* creation-science is, in fact, scientific."[166] That secular purpose is evident in the widespread (86%) public support for teaching the theory of creation along with the theory of evolution, which at the 86% level is far too high to be attributable to Fundamentalist religious demands.[167] Provine compares the polls with the courts:

> In this particular case, since public opinion polls show consistently that a majority of people want to have creationism taught along with evolution in the public schools, the courts are clearly out of synchronization with popular views.[168]

Similar results of other polls were cited in Section 15.3(a).

(2) Deference to the Stated Purpose and Legislative History and Irrelevance of Nonlegislative Purposes. The Supreme Court has stressed that a law's stated purpose should not lightly be disregarded.[169] Besides the text of a law, its official legislative record should be the primary if not the only source for the law's purpose,[170] particularly when the alternative is a focus on *non*legislative purposes.

The purpose, motive, or assessment of one or more individual legislators is not controlling or even indicative of the "legislative purpose," which is the purpose of the entire legislature. The Court has recently stated, in *CPSC v. G.T.E. Sylvania*,[171]

> ordinarily even the contemporaneous remarks of a single legislator who sponsors a bill are not controlling in analyzing legislative history.[172]

Many other Supreme Court decisions[173] and U.S. Court of Appeals decisions support the same point,[174] and Gedicks summarizes the law on the issue:

> Although relevant statements by an individual member of such a body constitute evidence that is highly probative of the motivations of that member, *they tell little about the motivations of other members*, and, thus, little about the motivations of the decision-making body as a whole:
>
> > Admissions by individual members . . . are relevant to institutional motivation only because the individual is part of the institution and his admission . . . therefore tells us something about his role in the institution's action. However, such statements . . . have *little independent probative value concerning institutional motivation*, for one member's motivation, standing alone, provides no information about others' motives.[175]

The views of "adherents of particular faiths and individual churches" on such "public issues" are not generally relevant to the legislature's purpose, as the Supreme Court has held in *Walz v. Tax Commission*:[176]

> Adherents of particular faiths and individual churches frequently take strong positions on public issues including, as this case reveals in the several briefs amici, vigorous advocacy of legal or constitutional positions. Of course, churches as much as secular bodies and private citizens have that right. No perfect or absolute separation is really possible; the very existence of the Religion Clauses is an involvement of sorts—one that seeks to mark boundaries to avoid excessive entanglement.[177]

That holding was reaffirmed in *Lemon v. Kurtzman*,[178] and by Justice Brennan a few years later in *McDaniel v. Paty*,[179] quoting Tribe:

> "In much the same spirit, American courts have not thought the separation of church and state to require that religion be totally oblivious to government or politics; *church and religious groups in the United States have long exerted powerful political pressures on state and national legislatures*, on subjects as diverse as slavery, war, gambling, drinking, prostitution, marriage, and education. *To view such religious activity as suspect, or to regard its political results as automatically tainted, might be inconsistent with first amendment freedoms of religious and political expression*—and might not even succeed in keeping religious controversy out of public life, given the political ruptures caused by the alienation of segments of the religious community.' " L. Tribe, [*American Constitutional Law*]§ 14-12, pp. 866-867 (footnotes omitted).[180]

Commentators such as Choper agree:

> Surely, legislation is not invalid simply because a religious organization supported or opposed it. . . . Religious groups have differed concerning a wide variety of political issues—including Sunday closing, gambling, pornography, drug control, gun control, the draft, prohibition, abolition of slavery, racial integration, prostitution, overpopulation, sterilization, abortion, birth control, marriage, divorce, the Equal Rights Amendment,

> and capital punishment, to name but a few. Undoubtedly, organized churches and other religious groups have markedly influenced the resolution of some of these issues. . . .[181]

He is joined by Gedicks,[182] Seldman,[183] and Goldstein.[184]

(3) Analogous Supreme Court Decisions on Secular Purposes. The governmental purpose for teaching all scientific theories of origins is manifestly constitutional in comparison with other governmental activities for which the Supreme Court has found sufficient secular purposes. The Court has found secular purposes for and upheld much financial aid to religious schools or their students or parents,[185] a governmental Christmas display with a nativity crèche,[186] public school references to a creator or God,[187] legislative chaplaincies and prayers,[188] equal access by religious organizations to public university facilities,[189] judicial resolution of church property disputes by neutral principles,[190] tax exemptions to religious organizations,[191] and certain released time from public schools for religious instruction.[192] Decisions have sustained the governmental purposes for cessation of federal funding to abortions[193] and for prohibition of commercial activities on Sundays.[194]

(4) Significance of the Edwards and Epperson Decisions. There have been two Supreme Court decisions involving the subject of origins. *Epperson v. Arkansas*[195] overturned an Arkansas law prohibiting public schools from teaching human evolution, while *Edwards v. Aguillard*[196] struck down a Louisiana law requiring "balanced treatment for creation-science and evolution-science," with both decisions finding no secular legislative purpose.

The recent Court decision in *Edwards v. Aguillard* has been widely misinterpreted and even misrepresented. Its language was cited at the beginning of this chapter that teachers "already possess" a "flexibility . . . to supplant the present science curriculum with the presentation of theories, besides evolution, about the origin of life," and are "free to teach any and all facets of this subject" of "all scientific theories about the origins of humankind."[197] Its holding did not rest on the primary effect or excessive entanglement facets of the tripart test, but only on the legislative purpose facet, as the majority opinion made clear:

> In this case, the *purpose* of the Creationism Act was to restructure the science curriculum to conform with a particular religious viewpoint. Out of many possible science subjects taught in the public schools, the legislature chose to affect the teaching of the one scientific theory that historically has been opposed by certain religious sects. As in *Epperson*, the legislature passed the Act to give preference to those religious groups

> which have as one of their tenets the creation of humankind by a divine creator. The "overriding fact" that confronted the Court in *Epperson* was "that Arkansas' law selects from the body of knowledge a particular segment which it proscribes for the sole reason that it is deemed to conflict with. . .a particular interpretation of the Book of Genesis by a particular religious group." 393 U.S., at 103. Similarly, the Creationism Act is designed *either* to promote the theory of creation science which embodies a particular religious tenet by requiring that creation science be taught whenever evolution is taught *or* to prohibit the teaching of a scientific theory disfavored by certain religious sects by forbidding the teaching of evolution when creation science is not also taught. The Establishment Clause, however, "forbids *alike* the preference of a religious doctrine *or* the prohibition of theory which is deemed antagonistic to a particular dogma." *Id.*, at 106-107 (emphasis added). Because the *primary purpose* of Creationism Act is to advance a particular religious belief, the Act endorses religion in violation of the First Amendment.[198]

Thus, the Court never held that the Louisiana law was unavoidably religious in effect, or that another legislature could not have a secular purpose for enacting it. Nevertheless, the theory of creation involved in *Edwards* is different from the theory of abrupt appearance, and that theory of abrupt appearance logically is one of the "scientific theories about origins" that the Court permitted.

The Supreme Court decision in *Epperson v. Arkansas* is not relevant to the issue of teaching alternative scientific theories of origins, for several reasons. First, the *Epperson* law forbade instruction in evolution rather than adding scientific alternatives, and it unneutrally forbade one viewpoint rather than "excis[ing] . . . all discussion of the origin of man."[199] Second, *Epperson* involved a "sole reason" (legislative purpose) of excluding evolution and teaching the "Genesis account" of creation, rather than a purpose of offering more scientific information.[200] Third, it involved the "Book of Genesis" and the "biblical account of creation," rather than a scientific theory of abrupt appearance.[201] Fourth, the decision stressed the Establishment Clause requirement of "neutrality between religion and religion, and between religion and non-religion,"[202] which is precisely what uncensored instruction in scientific alternatives produces and precisely what exclusive instruction in evolution thwarts. The *Epperson* decision has been criticized on a number of legal grounds by Choper,[203] Goldstein,[204] Gelfand,[205] and on the basis of its dishonest use of history by Larson.[206]

d. The Absence of Excessive Entanglement from Public School Presentation of Additional Scientific Information and Uncensored Instruction

No excessive entanglement would arise from teaching all scientific theories of origins in state schools and colleges, under court precedents and in view of the definition of entanglement.

(1) Nonentanglement from the Same Activities. First, the same level of screening texts and classrooms that might be required has already been upheld by the Supreme Court, in *Board of Education v. Allen,*[207] *Mueller v. Allen,*[208] and other decisions.[209] The first of those decisions said the following:

> Although the books loaned are those required by the parochial school for use in specific courses, each book loaned must be approved by the public school authorities; only secular books may receive approval. The . . . record contains no suggestion that religious books have been loaned. Absent evidence, we cannot assume that school authorities, who constantly face the same problem in selecting textbooks for use in the public schools, are unable to distinguish between secular and religious books or that they will not honestly discharge their duties under the law. . . .[210]

In fact, greater screening is permissible when "the Bible [religious material] may constitutionally be used [in public schools] in an appropriate study of [nonreligious subjects such as] history, civilization, ethics, comparative religion, or the like," without excessive entanglement.[211] *A fortiori*, the lesser screening necessary for the use of nonreligious material (such as the scientific evidence of the theory of evolution and of the theory of abrupt appearance) for teaching nonreligious subjects (such as biology and physics) does not produce impermissible entanglement. Moreover, a "real threat" of excessive entanglement must exist, rather than merely an imagined possibility.[212]

Second, the same sort of screening already occurs in public schools to avoid impermissible religious content, and can apply to science instruction as easily as to other curricula. The Supreme Court has said it is "not prepared to read into the plan as an inevitability the bad faith upon which any future excessive entanglement would be predicated."[213]

Teachers should be presumed to teach curricular material in good faith without introducing religious doctrine.[214] In fact, one survey of teachers showed them split almost evenly (53.7% to 42.3%) over teaching just the theory of evolution or also teaching the theory of creation.[215] There is no more reason to think one half will bring religion into the theory of abrupt appearance or even into the theory of creation than to think the other half will bring religion into the theory of evolution.

Curricular materials will become available when more schools offer alternate scientific theories of origins. One or more national secular textbook companies can be expected to meet demand by publishing suitable secular texts or supplements, and in fact one already has with limited treatment of two theories.[216] The scientific content of which those texts can consist is exemplified by Chapters 2-8 of this book.

Third, the very same screening is already necessary for instruction in evolution, to ensure that theistic evolution is not taught[217] and that impermissible religious discussion does not occur.[218] The theory of evolution has the same types and degrees of implications for religion and world views as does the theory of abrupt appearance, because each is consistent with various religions and world views.[219] Neither scientific theory requires the teaching of religious views.

(2) Nonentanglement with Religion by Definition. Moreover, that screening by definition cannot constitute any entanglement with churches or other religious institutions; at most it involves interrelations between public education officials and public schools.[220] The Supreme Court made that point in a recent Establishment Clause case involving parochial school aid:

> Neither will there be any excessive entanglement arising from supervision of public employees to insure that they maintain a neutral stance. It can hardly be said that the supervision of public employees performing public functions on public property creates an excessive entanglement between church and state.[221]

A philosophy professor-lawyer who opposes balanced treatment reached the same conclusion of no excessive entanglement:

> In the Supreme Court case of *Board of Education v. Allen*, a New York statute provided for the lending of state approved secular textbooks free of charge to all students, including those in parochial schools. . . . Although each book loaned had to be approved by public school authorities and only secular books could be approved, the Court did not think this continual monitoring of textbooks would involve excessive entanglement. . . . *Certainly, no more would be required of school boards in the monitoring of textbooks* under [balanced treatment]. The monitoring of *classroom discussion* would be troublesome as a practical administrative matter. It would, however, not involve entanglement *with religion*, as would the state's monitoring of classroom discussion in a parochial

> school. The state might become excessively entangled with the administration of its own public schools. *This, however, is not an entanglement with religion.* Furthermore, it is *doubtful that much monitoring of classroom discussion would have to be done* in any case. Public school teachers have no constitutional right to disregard the planned curriculum.[222]

Another legal commentator made much the same point.[223]

e. *The Errors of the McLean Decision on the Arkansas Balanced Treatment Law*

The 1982 court decision of *McLean v. Arkansas Board of Education*[224] involved the constitutionality of the Arkansas "Balanced Treatment for Creation-Science and Evolution-Science Act."[225] A U.S. District Court judge (one of nearly 500 nationally) held that the act violated each facet of the tripart test for the Establishment Clause, through "the specific purpose of advancing religion," "a major effect" of "the advancement of particular religious beliefs," and "excessive and prohibited entanglement with religion."[226] To reach those conclusions, the court concluded "that creation science is inspired by the Book of Genesis and that Section 4(a) [its definition] is consistent with a literal interpretation of Genesis,"[227] that "[s]ince creation science is not science, the conclusion is inescapable that the *only* real effect of Act 590 is the advancement of religion,"[228] and that "the essential characteristics of science are: (1) It is guided by natural law; (2) It has to be explanatory by reference to natural law; (3) It is testable against the empirical world; (4) Its conclusions are tentative . . .; and (5) It is falsifiable."[229]

A number of writers have called the *McLean* decision simply wrong in its pivotal holdings. The following paragraphs are not meant to repeat the sections in this book that analyze various basic errors in the opinion, but to refer to earlier sections and to cite other critics, on the questions of whether the theory of "creation-science" is nonscientific, religious, and unconstitutional. The point is not that the theory of creation-science is necessarily scientific and nonreligious, but that the *McLean* inquisition is not intellectually defensible, and that its attacks do not apply to the theory of abrupt appearance.

(1) Science and Theories of Origins. A number of opponents have conceded that the theory of creation is scientific, such as Lipson, a physicist and Fellow of the Royal Society:

> I think however that we must go further than this and admit that *the*

> *only acceptable explanation is creation.* I know that this is anathema to physicists, as indeed it is to me, but we must not reject a theory that we do not like if *the experimental evidence supports it.*[230]

Other acknowledgments are quoted in the beginning of Chapter 2 and in Section 9.4. It is not necessarily the case that the "proof in support of creation-science consisted almost entirely of efforts to discredit the theory of evolution," as the *McLean* court alleged,[231] although even that would be scientific under normal definitions of science.

The theory of abrupt appearance manifestly consists of affirmative evidence rather than mere negative evidence. Eighteen categories of that affirmative evidence are summarized in Chapters 2, 4, and 6, such as the paleontology arguments of the abrupt appearance of complex life and the systematic gaps in the fossil record, the morphology argument of the systematic similarity between fossil organisms and modern day counterparts, the information science argument of the vast information content of all living forms, and the genetics argument of the genetic limits on viable change. The "only source of this information" is not "ultimately contained in the book of Genesis,"[232]—which does not mention paleontology, comparative morphology, information content, genetics, or thirteen other areas—but in the data of science.

The theory of evolution was not allowed by the judge to be evaluated or compared with the theory of creation. Yet the theory of evolution shares most of the characteristics on which the theory of creation was criticized, as discussed in Chapters 10 and 13-16, and is not compellingly established, as hundreds of noncreationists showed in Chapters 3, 5, and 7. Moreover, the court asserted that "the scientific community does not consider origins of life a part of evolutionary theory,"[233] contrary to the orthodox view that biochemical evolution is an integral part of evolution as stated by Dobzhansky, Ayala, Stebbins, and Valentine:

> [T]he concept of evolution has been applied not only to the living world but to the nonbiological as well. Thus, we speak of the evolution of the entire universe, the solar system and the physical earth, apart from the organisms that inhabit it. As we shall show in Chapter 11 ("Cosmic Evolution and the Origin of Life"), the origin of life is best explained as the outcome of precellular chemical evolution, which took place over millions of years.[234]

Scores of similar definitions of biochemical evolution and cosmic evolution are cited at the beginnings of chapters 5 and 7, and are referred to by Caudill in criticism of the *McLean* decision:

> In addition, the court was not always clear in its terminology. "Evolution-science," as defined in the Act, included naturalistic origins of life. Yet, the court seemed to narrow its discussion of evolution to post-origin development of species. While this may be consistent with the popular use of the term "evolution," and an acceptable move to avoid the question of origin of life, neither biology as a discipline taught in public schools nor the equal time bill under consideration is limited in scope to mechanisms after life appeared. This is important because inquiry into "naturalistic origins of life" is much more controversial than the general theory of evolution. . . .[235]

The reason that the court excluded most testimony on the scientific evidence for evolution was obviously that the judge had prejudged evolution to be unassailable and true, ignoring that "evolution theory is in crisis"[236] and that evolution is "a theory in crisis."[237] The widespread scientific rejection of Darwinism, macroevolution, biochemical evolution, and the cosmic evolutionary big bang is shown by hundreds of citations in Sections 3.2, 7.1, and Chapters 3, 5, and 7 generally.

The definition of science given by the *McLean* court is "remote from well-founded opinion in the philosophy of science" according to Laudan,[238] and "demonstrably false" in the assessment of Quinn.[239] The numerous specific reasons that support those conclusions are discussed in Chapter 9, and the comparably scientific natures of the theory of evolution and the theory of abrupt appearance, and even the theory of creation, are treated in Chapter 10. Many philosophers and scientists concede that the theory of creation meets the faulty *McLean* test of science as well as does the theory of evolution. The unfairness of a double standard is scored by Caudill:

> Second, the court's assessment of the scientific character of creationist research was *determined at the outset by the presumption that creationism was wholly religious* and the corollary presumption that evolution was not. The court emphasized the creationists' belief in supernatural intervention and the certitude of the Biblical account, and contrasted these beliefs with science's emphasis on natural law and empirical, tentative, and falsifiable explanations. Yet creation scientists affirm natural laws, and attempt to do empirical, tentative, and falsifiable research. It is an unfair characterization of creation-science research to suggest that all laboratory or field research is guided by primarily supernatural explanations and all conclusions are made in advance. Granted, the creation scientist has a pre-theoretical position that he or she hopes to verify, but so does the evolutionist. The greatest weakness in the *McLean* decision appears to be the court's unwillingness to distinguish the scien-

tific from the religious aspects of either creationism or evolutionism. . . .[240]

Many other aspects of the *McLean* decision on science can be criticized as well.

(2) Religion and Theories of Origins. The *McLean* court found the theory of creation to be religious because "the definition of 'creation science' contained in 4(a) has as its unmentioned reference the first 11 chapters of the Book of Genesis" and particularly because of its reference to "creation from nothing."[241] That objection is simply "amusing" to Tipler, a prominent cosmologist and an Atheist:

> The sections of the opinion on cosmology make amusing reading for cosmologists. The 1981 Arkansas equal time law defined "creation-science" as "science" that involved, among other things, "Sudden creation of the universe, energy, and life from nothing." (Overton 1982, p. 30). The judge thought such an idea inherently unscientific:
>
> > The argument that creation from nothing. . . does not involve a supernatural deity has no evidentiary or rational support. To the contrary, "creation out of nothing" is a concept unique to Western religions. In traditional Western religious thought, the [conception of a creator of the world is a] conception of God. Indeed, creation of the world "out of nothing" is the ultimate religious statement because God is the only actor. . . . The idea of [sudden creation from nothing, or] creatio ex nihilo, is an inherently religious concept. (Overton, 1982). . . .
>
> *The problem* with this is that, as I pointed out in section 2, *the standard big bang theory has the Universe coming into existence out of nothing*, and *cosmologists use the phrase "creation of the universe" to describe this phenomenon*. Thus if we accepted Judge Overton's idea that creation out of nothing is inherently religious, and his ruling that inherently religious ideas cannot be taught in public educational institutions, it would be illegal to teach the big bang theory at state universities. . . . Dave Schramm, who was one of the expert witnesses in the Arkansas case, remarked to me that he and the other cosmologists in the case were unhappy with this part of Overton's opinion. . . .[242]

The many other scientific uses of the term "creation" are discussed in Sections 13.1 and 13.4, and the noncentrality of any concept of a creator to the theory of creation is shown in Sections 13.2 and 13.3. In general, "there is also plenty of room to doubt Judge Overton's claim that the ideas of 4(a)(1) are identical, and not merely similar, to the ideas in the Genesis creation story as literally interpreted," Quinn concludes.[243]

The theory of abrupt appearance does not incorporate the concepts of creation or creator, and involves natural groups rather than kinds of plants and animals, allows for either a long or short time scale for the universe and life, allows for either uniformitarianism or catastrophism, and does not single out from evolution generally the evolution of humans. Those were other areas in which the *McLean* opinion found the theory of creation to support Genesis,[244] although the problem areas are not necessarily religious and are not necessarily part of the theory of creation.

The *McLean* court also stressed the religious motivation of many creationist scientists. However, philosophers have long recognized that the "context of discovery" is irrelevant to the "context of justification."[245] Raup writes that "whether a body of reasoning is scientific or not should be decided independently of the question of whether the adherents are committed to one ideology or another."[246] That point is discussed in Sections 9.6(b) and 14.3(b), and the similar problems of some evolutionists' motivations are outlined in Sections 13.3(a), 13.5, 14.1, and 14.3(b)-(c). That additional double standard is identified by Caudill:

> Finally, to deny any criticism of evolutionary theory on the basis that the critics are religiously motivated is the *equivalent of "religious" dogmatism in science*.... The fact that many early scientists were motivated by religious beliefs does not render their contributions to science useless.
>
> The radical separationism represented in the *McLean* position is *not genuinely neutral* regarding religion.[247]

(3) The Constitution and Theories of Origins. The *McLean* approach to the tripart test for the Establishment Clause can be summarized in several steps:

> (1) Act 590 does have the advancement of religion as a major effect.
> (2) Act 590 does not have the advancement of science as an effect.
> (3) Act 590 does not have the advancement of any other thing as an effect.
> (4) Hence, Act 590 has the advancement of religion as its only effect.
> (5) Whence, Act 590 has the advancement of religion as its primary effect.[248]

The third point, as well as many others in the court's analysis, is excoriated by Quinn:

> It is curious that Judge Overton says nothing at all to justify (3). Indeed, the Opinion shows no indication that he is aware of the need to assume (3), or something very much like it, to insure the validity of its argument. . . .
>
> . . ..
>
> The second part of the three-pronged test for establishment reaches only those statutes having their primary effect the advancement of religion. Secondary effects which advance religion are not constitutionally fatal. Since creation science is not science, the conclusion is inescapable that the only real effect of Act 590 is the advancement of religion.
>
> But the conclusion is very far indeed from being inescapable.

> Though it does not rest on the specious claim that since creation science is not science it must be religion, it does rest on the claim that since creation science advances religion but not science it advances only religion. This claim is certainly not obvious and needs to be supported by argument. To argue for it would be to argue in support of something like (3) which would rule out other possibilities. This the Opinion does not do, and the failure to do it is a serious flaw in the Opinion. As long as the possibility that creation science is, above and beyond being religion and not science, some other thing as well (perhaps, for example, speculative philosophy) has not been ruled out, it remains an open question whether Act 590 also has the advancement of some such other thing as a major effect, and hence it remains an open question whether Act 590 has the advancement of this other thing as its primary effect and the advancement of religion only as its secondary effect. Since, as Judge Overton says, secondary effects which advance religion are not constitutionally fatal, such questions cannot be left open. . . .[249]

Thus, the *McLean* opinion is "remote from well-founded opinion" in constitutional law, just as it is in philosophy of science.

The secular legislative purpose requirement of the tripart test, whether or not truly violated by the Arkansas legislature in *McLean*, need not be violated by laws or school policies for teaching the theory of creation. The nonentanglement requirement cannot be violated by "supervision of public employees to insure that they maintain a neutral stance," under *Wolman v. Walter*.[250]

The theory of abrupt appearance does not and need not have any of the constitutional flaws that the *McLean* opinion found or imagined in the theory of creation. Its primary effect and secular purpose are to further students' rights to receive information by providing more scientific information and by ending indoctrination and censorship.

Summary. The tripart test for the Establishment Clause, which focuses on the primary effect, legislative purpose, and excessive entanglement of state action, is not violated by teaching alternative scientific theories of origins. The theory of evolution and the theory of abrupt appearance are comparably scientific and nonreligious; the latter consists of such scientific evidence that the universe, life, and plants and animals abruptly appeared with discontinuity and in complex form, as was summarized in the paleontology, morphology, information science, genetics, classification, comparative anatomy and biochemistry, and eleven other arguments in Chapters 2, 4, and 6.

The primary effect and legislative purpose for teaching the theory of evolution, the theory of abrupt appearance, and any other scientific theories of origins in public schools and universities would be to advance students' rights under the First Amendment to receive scientific information, and thus to retard indoctrination in one view and censorship of alternative theories. Secondary or tertiary effects of advancing religion would be permissible under the Establishment Clause, as would be state requirements that merely "coincide or harmonize with the tenets of some or all religions" (*McGowan v. Maryland*[251]) or that merely confer "incidental benefits to religion" (*Committee for Public Education v. Nyquist*[252]). Secondary or even primary purposes of advancing religion do not violate the secular purpose requirement of the tripart test (*Wallace v. Jaffree*[253]), and positions of religious groups (which split on the origins issue) do not invalidate consistent state actions (Choper[254]). The *Epperson* and *Edwards* decisions are not inconsistent with teaching the theory of abrupt appearance along with the theory of evolution.

No excessive entanglement arises from uncensored instruction. The Supreme Court already has found no entanglement where "each book loaned must be approved by the public school authorities; only secular books may receive approval" (*Board of Education v. Allen*[255]). The Court also has ruled that "[i]t can hardly be said that the supervision of public employees performing public functions on public property creates an excessive entanglement between church and state" (*Wolman v. Walter*[256]).

Notes

1 Emerson & Haber, *The Scopes Case in Modern Dress*, 27 U. Chi.L. Rev. 522, 527 (1960).

2 482 U.S., 96 L.Ed.2d 510 (1987).

3 La. Rev. Stat.§ 17:286.1 *et seq*. (1981).

4 482 U.S., 96 L.Ed.2d 510, 526 (1987).

5 *Id* at 521.

6 *Id* at 522.

7 Aguillard v. Edwards, 765 F. 2d 1251, 1257 (5th Cir. 1985).

8 Aguillard v. Edwards, 778 F. 2d 225, 226 (5th Cir. 1985) (en banc, Gee, J., dissenting with Clark, C.J. and Reavley, Garwood, Higginbotham, Hill & Jones, JJ.).

9 Caudill, *Law and Worldview: Problems in the Creation-Science Controversy*, 3 J. Law & Religion 1, 21 (1985).

[10] Strossen, *"Secular Humanism" and "Scientific Creationism": Proposed Standards for Reviewing Curricular Decisions Affecting Students' Religious Freedom*, 47 Ohio St.L.J. 333, 403-04 (1986).

[11] Scheid, *Evolution and Creationism in the Public Schools*, 9 J. Contemp. L. 81, 118-19 (1983).

[11A] Zimmerman, *Keep guard up after evolution victory*, 37 BioScience 636, 636 (1987) ("The Supreme Court ruling did not, in any way, outlaw the teaching of 'creation-science' in public school classrooms. . . . 'Creation-science' can still be brought into science classrooms if and when teachers and administrators feel that it is appropriate.")

[11B] Gould, *Justice Scalia's Misunderstanding*, Natural History, Oct. 1987, at 14, 20. *Accord*, Gould, *The Verdict on Creationism*, N.Y. Times Magazine, July 19, 1987, at 32, 34 ("But no statute exists in any state to bar instruction in 'creation science.' It could be taught before, and it can be taught now.")

[12] Even if the concept of creation were found to be inherently religious contrary to the discussion in this chapter, its mention as part of instruction in scientific data would not violate the Establishment Clause. The Supreme Court similarly held in *Lynch* that inclusion of a nativity scene "in the context of the Christmas season" in a municipal Christmas display does not violate the Establishment Clause: "Focus exclusively on the religious component of any activity would inevitably lead to its invalidation under the Establishment Clause." 465 U.S. 668, 680 (1984). For another example, the Court in *Schempp* said that "study of the Bible or of religion, when presented objectively as part of a secular program of education," is consistent with the Establishment Clause, although the Bible is clearly religious when considered alone. School Dist. of Abington Township v. Schempp, 374 U.S. 203, 225 (1963). *See also* Witters v. Washington Dep't of Svcs. for the Blind, 474 U.S. 481, 486-88 (1986).

[13] Lynch v. Donnelly, 465 U.S. 668, 679 (1984).

[14] Marsh v. Chambers, 463 U.S. 783 (1983).

[15] Mueller v. Allen, 463 U.S. 388, 394 (1983).

[16] Larson v. Valente, 456 U.S. 288 (1982).

[17] Jones v. Wolf, 443 U.S. 595 (1979).

[18] Tilton v. Richardson, 403 U.S. 672, 677-78 (1971).

[19] *See* Committee for Pub. Educ. v. Nyquist, 413 U.S. 756, 773 (1973).

[20] 463 U.S. 783 (1983).

[21] *E.g.*, *id.* at 786-91. *Accord*, Lynch v. Donnelly, 465 U.S. at 674-75, 678.

[22] Walz v. Tax Comm'n, 397 U.S. 664, 671 (1970) (historical basis for tax exemptions).

[23] McGowan v. Maryland, 366 U.S. 420, 431-41 (1961) (historical basis for Sunday closing laws).

[24] 330 U.S. 1, 8-16 (1947).

[25] 463 U.S. at 790, quoting Wisconsin v. Pelican Ins. Co., 127 U.S. 265, 297 (1888).

[26] Lynch v. Donnelly, 465 U.S. at 674.

[27] 397 U.S. at 686.

[28] *E.g.*, C. Antieau, A. Downey & E. Roberts, *Freedom from Federal Establishment* 111-203 (1964); R. Cord, *Separation of Church and State: Historical Fact and Current Fiction* 2-83 (1982); M. Malbin, *Religion and Politics: The Intentions of the Authors of the First Amendment* 1-18 (1978); J. McClellan, *Joseph Story and the American Constitution* 118-59 (1971); 2 J. Story, *Commentaries on the Constitution* § § 1870-1879 (1833); Kurland, *The Irrelevance of the Constitution*, 24 Vill. L. Rev. 3, 5-9 (1978).

[29] *E.g.*, L. Pfeffer, *Church, State, and Freedom* 135-80 (rev. ed. 1967); L. Tribe, *American Constitutional Law* 812-34 (1978); T. Emerson, *The System of Freedom of Expression* 21-27 (1971); Giannella, *Religious Liberty, Nonestablishment, and Doctrinal Development*, 80 Harv. L. Rev. 1381 (1967); Choper, *Religion Clauses of the First Amendment: Reconciling the Conflict*, 41 U. Pitt. L. Rev. 673 (1980).

[30] U.S. Const. (after art. VII and before signatures).

[31] 1 Stat. 1 (1789).

[32] J. Locke, *Second Essay Concerning Civil Government* 56 (Great Books of the Western World ed. 1952).

[33] W. Blackstone, 2 *Commentaries on the Laws of England* 40 (8th ed. 1778).

[34] 1 Stat. 73, 76 (1789).

[35] 1 *Annals of Cong.* 914 (1789).

[36] 463 U.S. at 788 & n.9.

[37] 1 *A Compilation of the Messages and Papers of the Presidents* 64 (J. Richardson ed. 1901).

[38] 1 *Annals of Cong.* 2180 (1789), 1 Stat. 71. *See also* Marsh v. Chambers, 463 U.S. at 787-88.

[39] Id. at 788 n.8.

[40] 463 U.S. at 788.

[41] 1 *A Compilation of the Messages and Papers of the Presidents* 51, 52 (J. Richardson ed. 1901).

[42] *Id.* at 52, 53-54.

[43] R. Bellah, *Beyond Belief* 187 (1970).

[44] *See* Wilson, *Eighty Years of the Public Schools of Washington*, in 1 Recs. of Colum. Hist. Soc. 119, 122-23, 127 (1897); Comment, *Jefferson and the Church-State Wall*, 1978 B.Y.U.L. Rev. 645.

[45] C. Antieau, A. Downey & E. Roberts, *Freedom from Federal Establishment* 200 (1964).

[46] Northwest Ordinance, 1 Stat. 52 (July 13, 1789) ("Religion, morality, and knowledge, being necessary to good government and the happiness of mankind, schools and the means of education shall forever be encouraged . . . .").

[47] Letter from Thomas Jefferson to Danbury Baptists (Jan. 1, 1802), in 8 *Writings of Thomas Jefferson* 113 (H. Washington ed. 1861).

[48] An act for establishing religious freedom, 12 Hening's Laws of Virginia 84, 84 (1786).

[49] T. Jefferson, *Notes on Virginia* (1781), reprinted in *The Real Thomas*

Jefferson 523 (1983).

[50] C. Antieau, A. Downey & E. Roberts, *Freedom from Federal Establishment* 200-01 (1964).

[51] Letter from Thomas Jefferson to John Adams (Apr. 11, 1823), in 2 *The Adams-Jefferson Letters* 591, 591-92 (L. Cappon ed. 1959).

[52] J. Story, *Commentaries on the Constitution* §1874 (1st ed. 1833).

[53] 2 J. Kent, *Commentaries on American Law* 34-39 (6th ed. 1848).

[54] T. Cooley, *Constitutional Limitations* 470-71 (1868).

[55] Pfeffer, *The Deity in American Constitutional History*, 23 J. Church & State 215, 238 (1981); *id.* at 219-28 (citing decisions).

[56] Note 4.

[57] Note 1.

[58] Note 20.

[59] Note 45.

[60] 370 U.S. 421 (1962).

[61] *Id.* at 435 n.21 (emphasis added). *Accord*, Lynch v. Donnelly, 465 U.S. 668, 676 *passim* (1984); *see* Zorach v. Clauson, 343 U.S. 306, 312-13 (1952).

[62] Declaration of Independence 1, 2, 32 (1776), in 1 Stat. 1 (1789).

[63] *Supra* note 30.

[64] *See* 36 U.S.C. §170.

[65] *E.g.*, Lynch v. Donnelly, 465 U.S. at 676; Engel v. Vitale, 370 U.S. at 435 n. 21.

[66] Aronow v. United States, 432 F.2d 242, 243 (9th Cir. 1970); Smith v. Denny, 280 F. Supp. 651, 654 (E.D. Cal. 1968), *appeal dismissed*, 417 F. 2d 614 (9th Cir. 1969); Opinion of the Justices, 108 N.H. 97, 101, 228 A.2d 161, 164 (1967); Lewis v. Allen, 5 Misc. 2d 68, 159 N.Y.S.2d 807 (1957), *aff'd*, 11 App. Div. 2d 447, 207 N.Y.S.2d 862 (1960), *aff'd*, 14 N.Y.2d 867, 200 N.E.2d 767, 252 N.Y.S.2d 80, *cert. denied*, 379 U.S. 923 (1964); Lanner v. Wimmer, 662 F.2d 1349 (10th Cir. 1981); Bogen v. Doty, 456 F. Supp. 983 (D. Minn. 1978), *aff'd*, 598 F.2d 1110 (8th Cir. 1979); Reed v. Van Hoven, 237 F. Supp. 48, 56 (W.D. Mich. 1965).

[67] 36 U.S.C.§ 172.

[68] H.R. Rep. No. 1693, 83d Cong., 2d Sess. 2, reprinted in [1954] U.S. Code Cong. & Ad. News 2339, 2340.

[69] *E.g.*, Sheldon v. Fannin, 221 F. Supp. 766, 774 (D. Ariz. 1963); Opinion of the Justices, 108 N.H. at 102, 228 A.2d at 164; Bogen v. Doty, 456 F. Supp. 983 (D. Minn. 1978), *aff'd*, 598 F.2d 1110 (8th Cir. 1979); Reed v. Van Hoven, 237 F. Supp. at 56.

[70] 465 U.S. at 675-76.

[71] 397 U.S. 664, 672 (1970).

[72] 343 U.S. at 313.

[73] 143 U.S. 457, 470 (1892).

[74] O'Hair v. Blumenthal, 588 F.2d 1144 (5th Cir. 1979), *cert. denied*, 442 U.S. 930 (1979) (*aff'g* 462 F. Supp. 19, 19-20 (W.D. Tex. 1978)); Aronow v. United States, 432 F.2d at 243.

[75] Lynch v. Donnelly, 465 U.S. at 676.

[76] [Bird], *Freedom of Religion and Science Instruction in Public Schools*, 87 Yale L.J. 515, 554-65 (1978).

[77] Lemon v. Kurtzman, 403 U.S. 602, 612-13 (1971).

[78] Harris v. McRae, 448 U.S. 297, 319 (1980) (italics added).

[79] *E.g.*, Gould*, *Catastrophes and Steady State Earth*, Natural History, Feb. 1975, at 15, 15-16.

[80] *E.g.*, *Prof. Agassiz on the Origin of Species*, 30 Am.J. of Science 142, 149 (1860).

[81] *E.g.*, T. Dobzhansky*, F. Ayala*, G. Stebbins* & J. Valentine*, *Evolution* 9 (1977); Mayr*, *Evolution*, Scientific Am., Sept. 1978, at 47, 47, 51.

[82] *E.g.*, F. Ayala* & J. Valentine*, *Evolving: The Theory and Processes of Organic Evolution* 1 (1979); W. Stansfield*, *The Science of Evolution* 3 (1977).

[83] *E.g.*, Dobzhansky*, *Evolution*, 10 Encyclopedia Americana 734, 748 (1982).

[84] The biological theory of abrupt appearance, for example, includes the following affirmative evidence: (a) paleontology argument of fossil record of systematic abrupt appearance and systematic gaps; (b) comparative morphology argument of systematic similarity between fossil organisms and their modern counterparts, and of systematic stasis; (c) information content argument about vast information, in complex molecules and organs; (d) probability argument concerning the high probability of abrupt appearance of complex organisms, complex molecules, and symbiotic relationships; (e) genetics argument of the genetic limits on biological change; (f) comparative discontinuity argument about systematic anomalies in classification, anatomy, and biochemistry.

[85] *E.g.*, Gould*, *Evolution's Erratic Pace*, Natural History, May 1977, at 12, 12 (italics added). *Accord*, id. at 14 ("The extreme rarity of transitional forms in the fossil record persists as the trade secret of paleontology.").

[86] *E.g.*, D. Raup* & S. Stanley*, *Principles of Paleontology* 382 (2d ed. 1978) (italics added). *Accord*, G. Simpson*, *The Major Features of Evolution* 360 (1953) (italics added) ("In spite of these examples, it remains true, as every paleontologist knows, that *most* new species, genera, and families and that *nearly all* new categories above the level of families *appear in the record suddenly* and are *not* led up to by known, gradual, completely continuous *transitional sequences*.").

[87] A. Thompson*, *Biology, Zoology, and Genetics: Evolution Model vs. Creation Model* 2, 76 (1983) (italics added). *Accord*, Clark*, *Animal Evolution*, 3 Quarterly Rev. of Biology 523, 539 (1928) (curator of paleontology at the Smithsonian Institution) ("On the basis of the paleontological record, the creationist has the better of the argument.").

[88] Ho* & Saunders*, *Preface*, to Beyond Neo-Darwinism ix, ix (M. Ho* & P. Saunders* eds. 1984).

[89] P. Grassé*, *The Evolution of Living Organisms* 202 (trans. 1977) ("the

explanatory doctrines of biological evolution do not stand up to an objective, in-depth criticism").

[90] Dobzhansky*, *Book Review*, 29 Evolution 376, 376 (1975).

[91] G. Kerkut*, *Implications of Evolution* 150 (1961) ("What conclusions, then, can one come to concerning the validity of the various implications of the theory of evolution? . . . [T]he evidence is still lacking for most of them.").

[92] Address by Dr. Colin Patterson*, Am. Museum of Natural Hist., tr. at 4 (Nov. 5, 1981) ("The second theme is that evolution not only conveys no knowledge but seems somehow to convey antiknowledge . . ..").

[93] G. Sermonti* & R. Fondi*, *Dopo Darwin: Critica all' Evoluzionismo* (1980). *Accord*, M. Vernet*, *Revolution en Biologie* (1969).

[94] M. Denton*, *Evolution: A Theory in Crisis* 75, 77 (1985) ("Darwin's model of evolution is still very much a theory and still very much in doubt when it comes to macroevolutionary phenomena." It is "a highly speculative hypothesis entirely without direct factual support . . ..").

[95] S. Løvtrup*, *Darwinism: The Refutation of a Myth* (1987).

[96] *E.g.*, Olson*, *Morphology, Paleontology, and Evolution*, 1 Evolution after Darwin 523, 523 (S. Tax* ed. 1960) ("some among the biologists who feel that much of the [macroevolutionary] theory accepted by the majority today is actually false"); Patterson*, *Cladistics and Classification*, 94 New Scientist 303, 306 (1982) ("Thus cladistics calls into question much of conventional evolutionary history."); Ball*, *On Groups, Existence and the Ordering of Nature*, 32 Systematic Zoology 446, 446 (1983) (Transformed cladists are "neutral or opposed to evolutionary theorizing of any kind in systematics," operating instead "in a non-evolutionary domain."); Lipson*, *A Physicist Looks at Evolution*, 31 Physics Bull. 138, 138 (1980) ("I have therefore tried to see whether biological discoveries over the last thirty years or so fit in with Darwin's theory. I do not think that they do. . . . To my mind, the theory does not stand up at all.").

[97] *E.g.*, Yockey*, *A Calculation of the Probability of Spontaneous Biogenesis by Information Theory*, 67 J. Theoretical Biology 377, 377 (1977) ("belief in currently accepted scenarios of spontaneous biogenesis is based on faith, contrary to conventional wisdom").

[98] *E.g.*, F. Hoyle, *The Intelligent Universe* 186 (1983):

> [A] sickly pall now hangs over the big bang theory. As I have mentioned earlier, when a pattern of facts becomes set against a theory, experience shows that it rarely recovers. Jayant Narlikar, an Indian professor of cosmology, is a leading theoretical physicist who also shares this view.

[99] 778 F.2d at 226 (italics added).

[100] 482 U.S. . . ., 96 L. Ed. 2d 510, 552 (1987).

[101] Affidavit of W. Morrow* at 2-3, Edwards v. Aguillard, 482 U.S. . . . ., 96 L. Ed. 2d 510 (1987) (R.D. 77 Ex. 2, R.544) (italics added).

[102] Lipson*, *A Physicist Looks at Evolution*, 31 Physics Bull. 138, 138 (1980) (italics added).

[103] 482 U.S. . . ., 96 L. Ed. 2d at 549 (italics added).

[104] Aguillard v. Edwards, 765 F. 2d at 1253, 1256, 1257.
[105] Aguillard v. Edwards, 778 F. 2d at 226 (italics added).
[106] Affidavit of W. Most* at 2, Edwards v. Aguillard, 482 U.S., 96 L. Ed. 2d 510 (1987) (R.D. 77 Ex. 4, R.544) (italics added).
[107] Leslie*, *Cosmology, Probability, and the Need To Explain Life*, in Scientific Explanation and Understanding 53, 56 (N. Rescher* ed. 1983).
[108] N. Gillespie*, *Charles Darwin and the Problem of Creation* 32 (1979) ("the conventional practice of using the term creation as a synonym for 'appear' or 'originate' "); *id.* at 158 n. 10 (same).
[109] 2 *The Life and Letters of Charles Darwin* 202-03 (F. Darwin* ed. 1903) ("creation, by which I really meant 'appeared' "); *see* C. Darwin*, *The Origin of Species* 486 (1st ed. 1859, repr. 1964) ("Our classifications will come to be . . . genealogies; and will truly give what may then be called the plan of creation.").
[110] *E.g.*, G. Gamow*, *The Creation of the Universe* 20 (1955) ("cosmogony can be formulated as an attempt to reconstruct the evolutionary process which led from simplicity of the early days of creation to the present immense complexity"); J. Trefil*, *The Moment of Creation: Big Bang Physics* (1983); J. Silk*, *The Big Bang* 144 (1979) ("the singularity when creation of matter possibly occurred"); Trefil*, *Matter vs. Antimatter*, Science 81, Sept. 1981, at 66, 66 ("One argument is that more matter than antimatter was created during the Big Bang").
[111] Tryon*, *What Made the World?*, New Scientist, Mar. 8, 1984, at 14, 16 ("I proposed that our Universe had been created spontaneously from nothing (*ex nihilo*), as a result of established principles of physics."—inflationary universe theory); Guth* & Steinhardt*, *The Inflationary Universe*, Scientific Am., May 1984, at 116, 128 ("the actual creation of the universe is describable by physical laws" and is "from absolutely nothing").
[112] H. Bondi*, *Cosmology* 143 (1968) ("the continual creation of matter"); F. Hoyle*, *The Nature of the Universe* 124 (1950) ("Continuous creation, on the other hand, can be represented by mathematical equations . . . and compared with observation.").
[113] *E.g.*, F. Hoyle & N. Wickramasinghe, *Evolution from Space: A Theory of Cosmic Creationism* (1984); F. Hoyle, *The Intelligent Universe: A New View of Creation and Evolution* (1984); Raloff*, *They Call It Creation Science*, Science News, Jan. 16, 1982, at 44, 46 (Quoting Dr. N. Chandra Wickramasinghe [Chairman of Dep't of Applied Mathematics, University College at Cardiff]: "But the general concept of creation, that could be separated from the theological arguments, was one that I felt some sympathy for." The author quotes Dr. Wickramasinghe as "raised a Hindu" who now "doesn't even share the basic premise of the Christian faith, much less the Christian fundamentalists' trust in . . . the book of Genesis . . ..").
[114] *E.g.*, E. Ambrose*, *The Nature and Origin of the Biological World* 143 (1982) ("We conclude therefore that recent hypotheses about the origin of species fall to the ground, unless it is accepted that an intensive input of new

information is introduced .... This can be explained in terms of the operation of creative intelligence."); Gray*, *Alternatives in Science: The Secular Creation of Heribert-Nilsson*, Kronos, Summer 1982, at 8, 8, 13-14 ("a strictly secular theory of special creation has been worked out in some detail by a fully certified academic biologist").

115 *E.g.*, Etkin, *Science and Creation*, in Challenge: Torah Views on Science and Its Problems 241, 250-51 (rev. ed. 1978) (by former professor of biology at Columbia and Chicago); *see* V. Webster* *et al.*, *Life Science* 41-42 (1980).

116 *E.g.*, V. Webster* *et al.*, *Life Science* 409, 436-37, 441-42, 444 (1980).

117 *E.g.*, Provine*, *Implications of Darwin's Ideas on the Study of Evolution*, 32 BioScience 501, 506 (1982); C. Darwin*, *The Origin of Species* 343, 753, 757, 758, 759 *passim* (variorum ed. M. Peckham* 1959) (Darwin's* references to a "Creator").

118 *E.g.*, Quinn*, *The Philosopher of Science as Expert Witness*, in Science and Reality: Recent Work in the Philosophy of Science 32, 39-40 (J. Cushing*, C. Delaney* & G. Gutting* eds. 1984) ("that concept is used in purely theoretical discussions in works of metaphysics that have no tendency to promote or advance religious belief"); F. Copleston*, *A History of Philosophy* 317 (1946) (Aristotle's "First Unmoved Mover"); Leslie*, *Anthropic Principle, World Ensemble, Design*, 19 Am. Philos. Q. 141, 141 (1982) ("calling it evidence of Design . . . does not always indicate belief in a Designer"; a "creative force").

119 *E.g.*, United States v. Seeger, 380 U.S. 163, 187 (1965) (construction of term "religion" in statute); Choper, *Defining "Religion" in the First Amendment*, 1982 U. Ill. L. Rev. 579, 594-604 (suggesting "ultimate concerns," "extratemporal consequences," or "transcendent reality").

120 *E.g.*, Torcaso v. Watkins, 367 U.S. 488, 495 & n. 11 (1961) (nontheistic religions); Everson v. Board of Educ., 330 U.S. 1, 16 (1947) (protection of "Non-believers"); *see* Gillette v. United States, 401 U.S. 437, 443 (1971) (Free Exercise Clause); Welsh v. United States, 398 U.S. 333 (1970) (statutory construction); United States v. Seeger, 380 U.S. at 166 (same, ethical creed with skepticism toward existence of God).

121 *E.g.*, Alston*, *Religion*, in 7 Encyclopedia of Philosophy 140, 141-42 (P. Edwards* ed. 1967).

122 *E.g.*, Ramsey*, *Religion, Philosophy of*, in 15 Encyclopaedia Britannica: Macropaedia 592, 594 (15th ed. 1974); *Religion*, 8 Oxford English Dictionary 410 (1971).

123 *E.g.*, K. Cauthen*, *The Impact of American Religious Liberalism* 7, 22 (1962) (importance of evolution to Theological Liberalism); Meland*, *Liberalism, Theological*, in 13 Encyclopaedia Britannica 1021, 1022 (W. Preece* ed. 1965) (same); J. Moore*, *The Post-Darwinian Controversies* 304-05 (1979) (same historically).

124 *E.g.*, *Humanist Manifesto I*, in Humanist Manifestos I and II (P. Kurtz* ed. 1973) (importance of evolution to Religious Humanism); Wilson*, *The*

Religious Element in Humanism Pervades Its Origin, Inspiration and Support, 22 Humanist 173, 173 (1962) (same).

[125] *E.g.*, R. Cross*, *The Emergence of Liberal Catholicism in America* 149 (1958) (important role of evolution in Neo-Modernist Catholicism); P. Teilhard de Chardin*, *Christianity and Evolution* 183-84 (R. Hague* trans. 1971) (same).

[126] *E.g.*, L. Barish* & R. Barish*, *Basic Jewish Beliefs* 11 (1961) (important role of evolution in Reform Judaism); W. Plaut*, *The Torah: A Modern Commentary* 6, 16 (1974) (same).

[127] K. Nakamura*, *Buddhist Philosophy*, in 3 Encyclopaedia Britannica: Macropaedia 425, 425 (15th ed. 1975) (important role of evolution in Buddhism).

[128] *E.g.*, Kurtz*, *A Secular Humanist Declaration*, Free Inquiry, Winter 1980-81, at 3, 6 (important role of evolution in Secular Humanism); *Humanist Manifesto II*, in Humanist Manifestos I and II 13, 14 (P. Kurtz* ed. 1973) (same); Huxley*, *Evolutionary Humanism: Part I*, Humanist, Sept.-Oct. 1952, at 201, 208 (important role of evolution in Evolutionary Humanism "Religion").

[129] *E.g.*, Bozarth*, *The Meaning of Evolution*, Am. Atheist, Sept. 1978, at 19; Bock*, *Some Thoughts on Evolution*, Am. Atheist, Dec. 1981, at 4.

[130] *E.g.*, Pope Paul VI, *Original Sin and Modern Science*, in 11 The Pope Speaks (1966) (creationist rather than evolutionist belief of Orthodox Roman Catholicism); P. Fehlner, *In the Beginning* 30-32 (1987) (same).

[131] *E.g.*, Perlman, *Science vs. Evolution?*, in A Science and Torah Reader 28, 28 (Y. Komreich ed. 1970) (creationist belief of Orthodox Judaism); L. Spetner, Evolution: An Analysis from the Torah Premises 1 (unpub.ms. 1987) (same).

[132] *E.g.*, Rahman*, *Islam*, in 9 Encyclopaedia Britannica: Macropaedia 911, 912 (1974).

[133] McGowan v. Maryland, 366 U.S. 420, 442 (1961). *Accord*, Lynch v. Donnelly, 465 U.S. 668, 682 (1984); Harris v. McRae, 448 U.S. 297, 319 (1980).

[134] *E.g.*, Dencer, *The Establishment Clause, Secondary Religious Effects, and Humanistic Education*, 91 Yale L.J. 1196, 1214 n.90 (1982) ("The theory of evolution both indirectly inhibits some religions and indirectly advances others."); Epperson v. Arkansas, 393 U.S. 97, 113 (1968) (Black, J., concurring).

[135] *E.g.*, *Is God a Creationist? The Religious Case Against Creation-Science* (R. Frye* ed. 1983); *supra* notes 130-32.

[136] *E.g.*, Affidavits of W. Morrow & W. Most, Edwards v. Aguillard, 482 U.S. . . . . , 96 L. Ed. 2d 510 (1987) (R.D. 77 Ex. 2 & 4, R. 544); A. Thompson, *Biology, Zoology, and Genetics: Evolution Model vs. Creation Model* 2 (1983) ("Students should be exposed to both sides of the coin regarding biological change—the doctrine of creation and that of evolution"); *Scientists Abandon Evolution*, Contrast, Mar.-Apr. 1982, at 1, 3 (Dr. William Provine [a self-described Atheist]: "[C]reationism is a viable, understanda-

ble and plausible theory for the creation point. It is my opinion that it is a wrong theory . . . I would like it discussed, particularly in the science classroom . . ..''); Section 17.2.

[137] Quinn, *The Philosopher of Science as Expert Witness*, in Science and Reality: Recent Work in the Philosophy of Science 32, 38-40 (J. Cushing, C. Delaney & G. Gutting eds. 1984) (although Quinn does find a nonsecular purpose).

[138] *Id.* at 45.

[139] 448 U.S. at 319-20.

[140] 465 U.S. at 663.

[141] 366 U.S. 420 (1961).

[142] *Id.* at 442 (italics in original).

[143] 465 U.S. at 663.

[144] 413 U.S. 756, 771 (1973).

[145] *Id.* at 771-72 (italics in original).

[146] 465 U.S. at 681-82.

[147] Witters v. Washington Dep't of Svcs. for the Blind, 474 U.S. 481 (1986).

[148] Widmar v. Vincent, 454 U.S. 263 (1981).

[149] Jones v. Wolf, 443 U.S. 595 (1979).

[150] *E.g.*, Harris v. McRae, 448 U.S. at 319-20; McGowan v. Maryland, 366 U.S. 420, 442 (1961).

[151] L. Tribe, *American Constitutional Law* §14-6, at 828 (1978) (not discussing theories of origins; italics in original).

[152] Comment, *Establishment Clause Analysis of Legislative and Administrative Aid to Religion*, 74 Colum. L. Rev. 1175, 1178-81 (1974); Tussman & tenBroek, *The Equal Protection of the Laws*, 37 Calif. L. Rev. 341, 360 (1949); *see* Palmer v. Thompson, 403 U.S. 217, 224 (1971); United States v. O'Brien, 391 U.S. 367, 383-84 (1968); McCray v. United States, 195 U.S. 27, 56 (1904); Fletcher v. Peck, 10 U.S. (6 Cranch) 87, 130 (1810).

[153] Lynch v. Donnelly, 465 U.S. at 680 (emphasis added). *Accord, e.g.*, Harris v. McRae, 448 U.S. 297, 319 (1980); McGinnis v. Royster, 410 U.S. 263, 276 (1973) (under equal protection clause); *see* McGowan v. Maryland, 366 U.S. 420, 444-49 (1961)(upholding Sunday closing laws despite partly religious purpose for enactment); Karen B. v. Treen, 653 F. 2d 897, 900 (5th Cir. 1981), *aff'd mem.*, 455 U.S. 913 (1982) ("a secular legislative purpose"); Florey v. Sioux Falls Sch. Dist. 49-5, 619 F.2d 1311, 1314-15 (8th Cir.), *cert. denied*, 449 U.S. 987 (1980).

[154] 472 U.S. 38 (1985).

[155] *Id.* at 56. *Accord, id.* at 58, 60.

[156] McGinnis v. Royster, 410 U.S. 263 (1973).

[157] *Id.* at 276.

[158] *E.g.*, Mueller v. Allen, 463 U.S. at 394-95 (1983).

[159] C. Darwin, *The Origin of Species* 2 (1st ed. 1859, repr. 1964) (italics added).

[160] Quoted in P. Davis & E. Solomon, *The World of Biology* 414 (1974) (italics added).
[161] Edwards v. Aguillard, 482 U.S. . . ., 96 L. Ed. 2d at 552 (italics in original).
[162] Aguillard v. Edwards, 778 F. 2d at 227.
[163] Aguillard v. Edwards, 778 F. 2d at 226.
[164] *Id.* at 227, 228 (italics added).
[165] *Id.* at 1332 (italics added).
[166] Larson, *Textbooks, Judges, and Science*, 17 Cumberland L. Rev. 116, 130 (1986).
[167] NBC News & Associated Press, November National Poll 15 (Nov. 24, 1981).
[168] Provine, *Book Review of Trial and Error: The American Controversy over Creation and Evolution*, Academe, Jan.-Feb. 1987, at 50, 51.
[169] *E.g.*, Witters v. Washington Dep't of Svcs. for the Blind, 474 U.S. 481, 496 (1986) ("the secular purpose articulated by the legislature"); Committee for Pub. Educ. v. Regan, 444 U.S. at 654 ("here, as in *Wolman*, there is clearly a secular purpose behind the legislative enactment: '[quoting the stated purpose]' "); Board of Educ. v. Allen, 392 U.S. at 243 ("express purpose"); McGowan v. Maryland, 366 U.S. 420, 445 (1961) (same); Brest, *Palmer v. Thompson: An Approach to the Problem of Unconstitutional Legislative Motive*, 1971 Sup. Ct. Rev. 95, 130 (should not invalidate law for illicit purpose unless "clear and convincing evidence"); *see generally* Seldman, *The Establishment Clause and Religious Influence on Legislation*, 75 Nw. U. L. Rev. 944 (1980).
[170] *E.g.*, Wallace v. Jaffree, 472 U.S. 38, 58 (1985) ("The unrebutted evidence of legislative intent contained in the legislative record"); Committee for Pub. Educ. v. Regan, 444 U.S. at 654.
[171] 447 U.S. 102 (1980).
[172] *Id.* at 118.
[173] *E.g.*, Chrysler Corp. v. Brown, 441 U.S. 281 (1979); United States v. Emmons, 410 U.S. 396 (1973); Palmer v. Thompson, 403 U.S. 217, 224 (1971); United States v. O'Brien, 391 U.S. 367, 383-84 (1968); McCaughan v. Hershey Chocolate Co., 283 U.S. 488, 493 (1931); United States v. Trans-Mo. Freight Ass'n, 166 U.S. 290, 318 (1897).
[174] Karen B. v. Treen, 653 F. 2d 897, 901 (5th Cir. 1981), *aff'd mem.*, 455 U.S. 913 (1982) ("In fact, the personal testimony of individual proponents, given in court after enactment of the statute, . . . reflects on the partial perspectives of those legislators and not the collective intention of the entire legislative body."); Marchese v. United States, 126 F. 2d 671 (5th Cir. 1942) ("Its meaning ought justly to be gathered from its words as promulgated to the public rather than from the expressions of legislators or even of their committees pending its passage.").
[175] Gedicks, *Motivation, Rationality, and Secular Purpose in Establish-*

ment Clause Review, 1985 Ariz. St. L. J. 677, 712 (italics added, footnote deleted).

[176] Walz v. Tax Comm'n, 397 U.S. 664 (1970).

[177] *Id.* at 670.

[178] Lemon v. Kurtzman, 403 U.S. 602, 623 (1971).

[179] 435 U.S. 618 (1978).

[180] *Id.* at 641-42 n.25 (Brennan, J. concurring) (italics added).

[181] Choper, *The Religion Clauses of the First Amendment*, 41 U. Pitt. L. Rev. 673, 684 (1980).

[182] Gedicks, *Motivation, Rationality, and Secular Purpose in Establishment Clause Review*, 1985 Ariz. St. L. J. 677, 712-13.

[183] Seldman, *The Establishment Clause and Religious Influence on Legislation*, 75 Nw. U. L. Rev. 944, 948-49 (1980).

[184] Goldstein, *The Asserted Constitutional Right of Public School Teachers To Determine What They Teach*, 127 U. Pa. L. Rev. 1293, 1311 n. 57 (1976).

[185] *E.g.*, Mueller v. Allen, 463 U.S. 388 (1983); Committee for Pub. Educ. v. Regan, 444 U.S. 646 (1980); Wolman v. Walter, 433 U.S. 229 (1977); Roemer v. Board of Pub. Works, 426 U.S. 736 (1976) (plurality op.); Meek v. Pittenger, 421 U.S. 349 (1975); Tilton v. Richardson, 403 U.S. 672 (1971); Board of Educ. v. Allen, 392 U.S. 236 (1968); Everson v. Board of Educ., 330 U.S. 1 (1947).

[186] Lynch v. Donnelly, 465 U.S. at 661-85.

[187] Section 20.1.

[188] Marsh v. Chambers, 463 U.S. 783 (1983).

[189] Widmar v. Vincent, 454 U.S. 263, 271-72 (1981).

[190] Jones v. Wolf, 443 U.S. 595 (1979).

[191] Walz v. Tax Comm'n, 397 U.S. 664 (1970).

[192] Zorach v. Clauson, 343 U.S. 306 (1952).

[193] Harris v. McRae, 448 U.S. at 319-20.

[194] McGowan v. Maryland, 366 U.S. at 442.

[195] 393 U.S. 97 (1968).

[196] 482 U.S. . . ., 96 L. Ed. 2d 510 (1987).

[197] 96 L. Ed. 2d at 521-22.

[198] *Id.* at 525 (italics in original except first and last).

[199] 393 U.S. at 109.

[200] *Id.* at 103, 107. *Accord*, Lynch v. Donnelly, 465 U.S. at 680.

[201] 393 U.S. at 103, 107-09.

[202] *Id.* at 104.

[203] Choper, *The Religion Clauses of the First Amendment: Reconciling the Conflict*, 41 U. Pitt. L. Rev. 673, 694 (1980).

[204] Goldstein, *The Asserted Constitutional Right of Public School Teachers To Determine What They Teach*, 127 U. Pa. L. Rev. 1293, 1311 n. 57 (1976).

[205] Gelfand, *Of Monkeys and Men—An Atheist's View of the Constitutionality of Teaching the Disproof of a Religion in the Public Schools*, 16 J. Law & Educ. 271 (1987).

[206] E. Larson, *Trial and Error: The American Legal Controversy over*

Creation and Evolution 113-16 (1985) (Oxford U. Press).

207 392 U.S. 236, 244-45 (1968). This decision upheld state textbook loans to religious school students, despite the necessary screening of textbooks.

208 463 U.S. 388, 403 (1983). *Mueller* sustained state tax deductions and audits for religious school textbooks if secular texts and if not "instructional books and material used in the teaching of religious tenets." 463 U.S. at 390 n.1.

209 *E.g.*, Committee for Pub. Educ. & Religious Liberty v. Regan, 444 U.S. 646 (1980). *Regan* upheld state reimbursement of parochial teacher time in grading secular tests and keeping secular records. *Id.* at 657-59.

210 Board of Educ. v. Allen, 392 U.S. at 244-45.

211 *E.g.*, Lynch v. Donnelly, 465 U.S. at 679, quoting Stone v. Graham, 449 U.S. 39, 42 (1981). *Accord*, School Dist. of Abington Township v. Schempp, 374 U.S. 203, 225 (1963).

212 *E.g.*, Marsh v. Chambers, 463 U.S. at 795.

213 *E.g.*, Committee for Pub. Educ. v. Regan, 444 U.S. 646, 660-61 (1980). *See also* Marsh v. Chambers, 463 U.S. at 795.

214 *E.g.*, Board of Educ. v. Allen, 392 U.S. at 243.

215 Austin Analytical Consulting, Opinion Poll for Biology Teachers question 8 (1986).

216 V. Webster *et al.*, *Life Science* (1980) (Prentice-Hall, Inc.).

217 Sections 13.3(a) and 14.1 (theistic evolutionist religions).

218 The same classroom questions or statements that theoretically could be asked or made about the theory of abrupt appearance could equally well be asked of the theory of evolution, such as "who caused" abrupt appearances or evolution. That mere possibility does not produce excessive entanglement from either abrupt appearance or evolution; teachers in either case are presumed to act in good faith and to decline to allow impermissible religious discussion. *See* Committee for Pub. Educ. v. Regan, 444 U.S. at 660-61; Board of Educ. v. Allen, 392 U.S. at 245.

219 Sections 14.1-14.2

220 *E.g.*, Lynch v. Donnelly, 465 U.S. at 683-85 (no entanglement from crèche in city Christmas display because no city contact with church authorities over its design or content); Roemer v. Board of Pub. Works, 426 U.S. at 766 (entanglement test requires "entanglement of church and state"); Meek v. Pittenger, 421 U.S. at 370 (same).

221 Wolman v. Walter, 433 U.S. 229, 248 (1977) (majority opinion in that Part VI).

222 Scheid, *Evolution and Creation in the Public Schools*, 9 J. Contemp. L. 81, 99 (1983) (although Prof. Scheid sees effect and purpose problems).

223 Lines, *Scientific Creationism in the Classroom*, 28 Loyola L. Rev. 35, 50-51 (1982).

224 529 F. Supp. 1255 (E.D. Ark. 1982).

225 Ark. Stat. Ann. §80-1663 *et seq.* (1981 Supp.).

226 529 F. Supp. at 1264, 1266, 1272.

[227] *Id.* at 1266.
[228] *Id.* at 1272.
[229] *Id.* at 1267.
[230] *E.g.*, Lipson, *A Physicist Looks at Evolution*, 31 Physics Bull. 138, 138 (1980) (italics added).
[231] 529 F. Supp. at 1272.
[232] *Id.*
[233] *Id.* at 1266.
[234] T. Dobzhansky, F. Ayala, G. Stebbins & J. Valentine, *Evolution* 9 (1977).
[235] Caudill, *Law and Worldview: Problems in the Creation-Science Controversy*, 3 J. Law & Religion 1, 15 (1985).
[236] Ho & Saunders, *Preface*, to Beyond Neo-Darwinism ix, ix (M. Ho & P. Saunders 1984).
[237] M. Denton, *Evolution: A Theory in Crisis* (1985).
[238] Laudan, *Commentary: Science at the Bar—Causes for Concern*, Science, Technology & Human Values, Fall 1982, at 16, 19.
[239] Quinn, *The Philosopher of Science as Expert Witness*, in Science and Reality: Recent Work in the Philosophy of Science 32, 42 (J. Cushing, C. Delaney & G. Gutting eds. 1984).
[240] Caudill, *Law and Worldview: Problems in the Creation-Science Controversy*, 3 J. Law & Religion 1, 35-36 (1985) (italics added except case name).
[241] 529 F. Supp. at 1264-65.
[242] Tipler, *How to Construct a Falsifiable Theory in Which the Universe Came Into Being Several Thousand Years Ago*, 2 Philosophy of Science Association 873, 893-94 (1984) (italics added).
[243] Quinn, *The Philosopher of Science as Expert Witness*, in Science and Reality: Recent Work in the Philosophy of Science 32, 40 (J. Cushing, C. Delaney & G. Gutting eds. 1984).
[244] 529 F. Supp. at 1265 & n. 19.
[245] H. Reichenbach, *Experience and Prediction* 6-7, 382-84 (1938).
[246] Raup, *The Geological and Paleontological Arguments against Creationism*, in Scientists Confront Creationism 147, 159 (L. Godfrey ed. 1983).
[247] Caudill, *Law and Worldview: Problems in the Creation-Science Controversy*, 3 J. Law & Religion 1, 43 (1985) (italics added except case name).
[248] Quinn, *The Philosopher of Science as Expert Witness*, in Science and Reality: Recent Work in the Philosophy of Science 32, 37 (J. Cushing, C. Delaney & G. Gutting eds. 1984). Note that Quinn agrees with *McLean* about an unconstitutional purpose by the Arkansas legislature.
[249] *Id.*
[250] 433 U.S. 229, 248 (1977) (majority opinion in that Part VI).
[251] Note 142.
[252] Note 145.

[253] Note 153.
[254] Note 181.
[255] Note 210.
[256] Note 221.

CHAPTER 21

Summary of the Philosophy, Theology, Education, and Constitution Issues: The Theory of Abrupt Appearance and the Theory of Evolution

The truth always wins and we are not afraid of it. The truth is no coward. The truth does not need the law. The truth does not need the forces of government. The truth does not need Mr. Bryan. The truth is imperishable, eternal and immortal and needs no human agency to support it. We are ready to tell the truth as we understand it and we do not fear all the truth that they can present as facts. We are ready. We are ready. We feel we stand with progress. We feel we stand with science. We feel we stand with intelligence. We feel we stand with fundamental freedom in America. We are not afraid. Where is the fear? We meet it, where is the fear? We defy it, we ask your honor to

*Philosophers, theologians, historians, educators, and others cited in this chapter, unless otherwise indicated, are not proponents of, and their quoted statements are not intended as endorsements of, either the theory of abrupt appearance or the theory of creation. However, their quoted statements are acknowledging information that supports the nonreligious or educationally valuable nature of the theories of abrupt appearance and evolution.

admit the evidence as a matter of correct law, as a matter of sound procedure and as a matter of justice to the defense in this case. (Profound and continued applause.)
—Dudley Field Malone*,
attorney for John Scopes*,
from transcript of the
Scopes trial[1]

The theory of evolution is widely believed, but it also is widely under internal and external attack as a "theory in crisis."[2] Referring to the same critics and skeptics who were cited in volume 1, Holbrook* recently describes the strengthening attack:

> How long will it be before the doubts expressed by many biologists are enough to put evolutionary theory seriously in question? The molecular biologists and geneticists, as we shall see, believe they have found the solution to the problem (talking even of 'automatic foresight'). But as we should see, there are many doubts as to whether the belief to which Darwin refers can be sustained at all. If they cannot, then perhaps we in the Humanities may claim our release from the daunting metaphysical attitudes into which Darwini[an] mechanism has trapped us?[3]

Løvtrup*, in his new book, contends that "the currently accepted theory of evolution—called 'neo-Darwinism' or 'the modern synthesis'—is false," and that "Darwinism was refuted from the moment it was conceived."[4] Midgley* takes offense to several aspects of evolution, in words that many scientists and philosophers would find applicable to the whole theory:

> It cannot be more excusable to peddle groundless predictions to the defenceless general public, who will take them to have the full authority of science, than to one's professional colleagues, who know much better what bees infest one's bonnet. These bold prophecies of an escalating future are often combined, as they are here, with the vision of one's own Science in a gold helmet finally crushing its academic rivals: again, scarcely a monument to scientific balance and caution.[5]

Many, some of whom are cited at the end of this chapter, simply contend that Darwinism is dying or dead.

The widespread attacks on part or all of biological evolution, biochemical evolution, or cosmic evolution logically imply the possibility of scientific alternatives. Feyerabend*, the prominent philosopher of science, emphasizes the importance of alternative theories in science. He is not specifically discussing the field of origins, but many researchers would see his words as directly applicable to evolutionary theory and alternative theories:

I want to discuss an example which shows very clearly the *function of alternatives in the discovery of facts.*

. . ..

It seems to me that this example is typical for the relation between fairly general theories, or points of view, and 'the facts'. Both the relevance and the refuting character of many very decisive facts can be established only with the help of *other theories* which, although factually adequate, are yet not in agreement with the view to be tested. This being the case, the production of such refuting facts may have to be preceded by the invention and articulation of *alternatives* to that view. Empiricism demands that the empirical content of whatever knowledge we possess be increased as much as possible. Hence the invention of *alternatives* in addition to the view that stands in the centre of discussion constitutes an essential part of the empirical method. . . .

. . ..

. . . Now if it is true, as has been argued in the last section, that many facts become available only with the help of such *alternatives*, then *the refusal to consider them will result in the elimination of potentially refuting facts*. More especially, it will eliminate facts whose discovery would show the complete and irreparable inadequacy of the theory. Such facts having been made inaccessible, the theory will appear to be free from blemish and it will seem that 'all the evidence points with merciless definiteness' . . .. More than ever the theory will appear to possess tremendous empirical support. The chances for the consideration of alternatives are now very slight indeed. . . .

At the same time it is evident, on the basis of the considerations in the last section, that this appearance of success cannot in the least be regarded as a sign of truth and correspondence with nature. Quite the contrary, the suspicion arises that the absence of major difficulties is a result of the decrease of empirical content brought about by the *elimination of alternatives*, and of facts that can be discovered with the *help of these alternatives* only. In other words, the suspicion arises that this alleged success is due to the fact that in the process of application to new domains the theory has been turned into a metaphysical system. . . .[6]

The danger of refusing to consider alternative theories is great:

At this point an 'empirical' theory of the kind described . . . becomes almost indistinguishable from a *myth.* In order to realize this, we need only consider that on account of its all-pervasive character a myth such as the myth of witchcraft and of demonic possession will possess a high degree of confirmation on the basis of observation. Such a myth has been taught for a long time; its content is enforced by fear, prejudice, and ignorance as well as by a jealous and cruel priesthood. It penetrates the most common idiom, infects all modes of thinking and many decisions which mean a great deal in human life. . . . The only way of investigating such all-embracing principles is to *compare them with a different set of*

> *equally all-embracing principles*—but this way has been excluded from the very beginning. The myth is therefore of no objective relevance, it continues to exist solely as the result of the effort of the community of believers and of their leaders, be these now priests or Nobel prize winners. Its 'success' is entirely man-made. . . .[7]

The primary category of scientific alternatives to the theory of evolution is the theory of abrupt appearance. The alternatives can be outlined as follows:

The Theory of Evolution	*The Theory of Abrupt Appearance*
Theory of continuity (macroevolution, biochemical evolution, cosmic evolution)	Theory of discontinuity (steady state, natural group systematics, nineteenth century systematics or typology, etc.)
Theories of Darwinian evolution (either neo-Darwinian/natural selection or punctuated equilibria)	Theory of abrupt appearance (biological abrupt appearance, biochemical abrupt appearance, cosmic abrupt appearance
Theories of non-Darwinian evolution (saltations, macromutations, neutral mutations, structuralism, some transformed cladistics, neo-Lamarckism)	Theories of panspermia and directed panspermia
	Theories of nontheistic forces (creative intelligence, great origins thesis, vitalism, etc.)
Theories of theistic evolution	Theory of creation (nomothetic or miraculous)

Whichever theory is ultimately shown to be correct, science will benefit from consideration of alternatives in place of evolutionary dogmatism (Section 10.5(a)) and materialistic faith (Section 13.5(a)).

This chapter summarizes the scientific (Sections 21.1-21.3), nonreligious (Sections 21.4-21.6), historical (Section 21.7), educational (Section 21.8), and constitutional (Sections 21.9-21.10) reasons for considering alternative theories of origins. The following citations should be read in their full context that was given earlier in this volume.

Figure 21.1
Many evolutionists have made "a frontal assault on all forms of Darwinism" (Grassé); "evolution theory is in crisis" (Saunders* and Ho*)*

21.1 The Accepted Definitions of Science and the Radical Definition

a. Prevailing Definitions and the McLean Case Definition

"[I]t can be said fairly uncontroversially that there is no demarcation line between science and non-science . . . which would win assent from a majority of philosophers" (Laudan*[8]). One reason is that the drawing of a demarcation line involves "values entering into biology" and other sciences (Ruse*[9]). Instead, there are many widely-accepted definitions of science and lines of demarcation from nonscience, such as various approaches to inductivism, vocationalism, falsificationism, sociological approaches, empiricism, other approaches, definitional agnosticism, and epistemological anarchy. A radical positivist and materialist approach is only one minority viewpoint. The most generally accepted definition, in contrast to the radical definition, is something like that "science arrives at truth by logical inferences from empirical observations" (Ziman*[10]).

The *McLean* case definition of science consists of four "essential elements": explanation and guidance by natural law, testability, falsifiability, and tentativeness. That definition has been sharply criticized by such philosophers of science as Laudan* of Virginia Polytechnic Institute, Quinn* of Notre Dame University (formerly of Brown University), and Gross* of City University of New York. Respectively, they describe the *McLean* definition as "remote from well-founded opinion in the philosophy of science" (Laudan*[11]), "demonstrably false" (Quinn*[12]), and "not rigorous, . . . redundant, and . . . tak[ing] no account of many distinctions nor of historical cases" (Gross*[13]).

b. Natural Laws and the Demarcation of Science

"[E]ither being a natural law or being explainable by a natural law is not a necessary condition for scientific status" (Quinn*[14]), and "is an altogether inappropriate standard for ascertaining whether a claim is scientific" (Laudan*[15]), even though it indeed is a frequent and presumed characteristic of science. An absolute natural laws requirement is "simply outrageous" in overlooking the classic "difference between establishing the existence of a phenomenon and explaining that phenomenon in a lawlike way" (Laudan*[16]), and also is guilty of overlooking that some scientific phenomena "can have no explanation in terms of laws" (Quinn*[17]) or are "not lawlike" such as "mathematical statements, explicit definitions, tautologies, and singular or numerical statements restricted to either individual objects or times" (Walters*[18]). Moreover, such a natural laws requirement may artificially limit science by forbidding it to consider nonnaturalistic events even if true, while compelling it to adopt naturalistic explanations even if totally improbable, because only the latter are left in the limited field. Yet, in quantum theory and elsewhere some events "can have no explanation in terms of laws if contemporary quantum theory is correct" (Quinn*[19]), and in cosmology and perhaps elsewhere science "has proven that forces are at work that . . . are outside the body of natural law" (Jastrow*[20]). One major category of events excluded by an absolute natural laws requirement is singularities, even though they are widely accepted in connection with theories of origins such as the big bang theory (Pagels*[21]), and even though occasional changes in the laws of nature are widely allowed (Sagan*[22]). Such an absolute natural laws requirement itself is based in a "faith in the order of nature" (Whitehead*[23]), and "it is not at all natural that 'natural laws' exist" (Wigner*[24]). Finally, positivist and materialist presuppositions produce the absolute natural laws requirement (Gillespie*[25]), and are themselves open to a number of philosophical difficulties (Passmore*[26]).

c. *Testability, Falsifiability, Tentativeness, and the Demarcation of Science*

"[B]eing testable and being falsifiable are not necessary for individual statements to have scientific status" (Quinn*[27]), and are not "essential characteristics of science" in the view of many specialists.

"To rely on testing as a mark of science is to miss what scientists mostly do" (Kuhn*[28]), particularly in relation to origins where limited testing is possible.[29] "It is now widely acknowledged that many scientific claims are not testable in isolation, but only when imbedded in a larger system of statements, *some* of whose consequences can be submitted to test"—and some of which cannot be (Riddiford* and Penny*[30]).

Falsifiability is probably less widely accepted as a demarcation criterion, and less related to the real world of science, than testability. Scientists, instead of "reject[ing] the core theory," more often "adjust the protective belt of auxiliary theories" (Sparkes*[31]). Many parts of science, such as "virtually every singular existential statement" and definition, are not falsifiable (Laudan*[32]). Finally, the falsifiability criterion itself may have been falsified (Sparkes*[33])!

Tentativeness is not an "essential characteristic"—or a characteristic at all—of science. "Numerous historians and philosophers of science (e.g., Kuhn, Mitroff, Feyerabend, Lakatos) have documented the existence of a certain degree of dogmatism about core commitments in scientific research and have argued that such dogmatism plays a constructive role in promoting the aims of science. . . . [O]ne does not even begin to get at those differences by pretending that science is characterized by an uncompromising open-mindedness" (Laudan*[34]). In fact, normal science is characterized by "dogmatism" rather than tentativeness (Lakatos*[35]). Nevertheless, "whether a belief is held tentatively or dogmatically is completely irrelevant to whether or not it is scientifically or in any other way epistemically respectable" (Quinn*[36]).

d. *Majority Assessments and the Demarcation of Science*

A large majority of scientists today embrace the theory of evolution, but the number of scientists who believe a theory "has no bearing on the problem" of whether a theory is scientific (Brady*[37]). Despite widespread popular beliefs to the contrary, "scientific knowledge is not objective" (Bartels*[38]). There are many benefits from "try[ing] to construct alternative theories" (Popper*[39]), particularly because every majority theory now was once a minority theory, while nearly every majority theory of the past is now a discarded theory. Yet a majority scientific theory readily "becomes the context within which that community understands the world," and "[d]oubt comes to be regarded as something less than legitimate" (Brady*[40]). General scientific biases, besides theory coloring perception, include "resistance on the part of scientists themselves to scientific discovery" (Barber*[41]), and a "mechanistic materialist philosophy explicitly or implicitly shared by most of the present 'establishment' in the biological sciences" (Dobzhansky*[42]). Twentieth-century examples of scientific bias include hostility to continental drift for forty years (Broad* and Wade*[43]), suppression of Velikovsky's* proposals (de Grazia* *et al.*[44]), Soviet enforcement of Lysenko* genetics (Joravsky*[45]), and many others.

"[E]volutionary theory" has become "an entrenched dogma" (Patterson*[46]) and "a dogmatic approach" (Brady*[47]). Neo-Darwinians "see the world in the context of our belief," and "evidence . . . will be interpreted by our theory," so that the "theory is unbeatable because it is allowed to interpret our observations" (Brady*[48]). Questioning of neo-Darwinian evolution brings an "attack with quite remarkable ferocity" (Saunders* and Ho*[49]), and "complain[ts] of inability to get a hearing for their views" (Dobzhansky*[50]). Thus, "orthodox scientists loathe scientific creationism and do all in their power to oppose it" (Ruse*[51]), and "the very concept of the creation of the Universe at such a singular beginning is philosophically objectionable to some scientists" (Ellis*[52]). The pervasiveness of that strong bias reaffirms the philosophic principle that applying a definition of science should not be done by majority vote of scientists.

21.2 The Theories of Evolution and Abrupt Appearance and the Various Definitions of Science

a. Comparable Satisfaction of Prevailing Definitions

The theory of abrupt appearance meets most of the various definitions of science (summarized in Section 9.1) as well as does the

Figure 21.2
"Darwinism is under attack"; "doubts about Darwinism represent a potential revolt from within" (Leith)*

theory of evolution. It involves empirical data and scientific interpretation (as the theory of abrupt appearance is defined in Chapters 2, 4, and 6, and summarized in Chapter 8). This book does not argue that the theory of abrupt appearance is right or that the theory of evolution is wrong, but simply that the former is a possible alternative and that the latter is not so compelling as to exclude alternatives. The theory of abrupt appearance involves Baconian induction as well as hypothesis and deduction,[53] qualified scientists under the vocational approach,[54] and falsifiability comparable to evolution under Popper's* approach.[55] The theory of abrupt appearance incorporates a new paradigm that seeks to explain anomalies in the old Darwinian and macroevolutionary paradigm consistent with Kuhn's* sociological approach,[56] involves testability comparable to evolution under the Hempel* and other empiricist approaches,[57] and in general conforms to the various definitions of science to a degree comparable to the theory of evolution's conformity.[58]

On the other hand, Popper* and others have concluded that evolution itself does *not* meet the testability-falsifiability criterion that in its most rigorous form was added to the radical definition and pulled into the *McLean* test. Popper* concludes that "Darwinism is not a testable scientific theory, but a metaphysical research programme";[59] although he has modified his earlier position that natural selection is nonscientific and almost tautologous,[60] he has *not* published any modification of his statement that in significant part "Darwinism is not a testable scientific theory."[61] Scores of other philosophers and scientists have agreed in applying Popper's* criteria to Darwinism and to macroevolution (who are cited in Sections 10.3 and 10.4), such as Patterson*[62] and Cartmill.*[63] In either case, the theory of abrupt appearance and the theory of evolution are parallel in relation to the various definitions of science, including the radical definition and *McLean* test.

b. Comparable Explanation by Natural Laws

The natural laws requirement is partially met by both the theory of evolution and the theory of abrupt appearance. Evolution is not guided by natural law in its critical origin events, because cosmic evolution includes the singularity of "the primary origin of matter or energy" (Stansfield*[64]) and the "big bang singularity when . . . we expect general relativity to break down" (Wald*[65]). Biochemical evolution similarly centers around a singularity of the origin of life "so extremely improbable that nothing can 'explain' why it originated" (Popper*[66]), and is a "unique event" that possibly "becomes an impenetrable barrier to science" (Popper*[67]). Biological evolution also confronts such information theory and probability problems that "an adequate scientific theory of [macro]evolution must await the discovery of new natural laws" (Eden*[68]).

Evolution is also not explanatory by natural laws in several basic senses. Macroevolution "cannot . . . explain any particular evolutionary change" in a plausible sense (Popper*[69]), although at the same time it "is so all-embracing that it can explain any outcome, and so is . . . an unscientific explanation," only explaining in a superficial sense (Sparkes*[70]). Darwinism similarly "explains nothing because it explains everything" (Lewontin*[71]). Natural selection shares the same fault in that it "fails to explain the origin of evolutionary novelties" and "fails to explain evolutionary diversity" (Rosen*[72]), so that many scientists and philosophers criticize it as nonexplanatory; and "[n]atural selection . . . turns out on closer inspection to be a tautology" that "the fittest individuals in a population (defined as those which leave the most offspring) will leave most offspring" (Waddington*[73]), as dozens of others criticize it. Not only is evolution nonexplanatory in critical areas, but "a number of critics" have claimed "that there can be no evolutionary laws" (Riddiford* and Penny*[74]), and that Darwinian theories do not " 'explain' in the sense that they enable events to be deduced from a set of initial conditions together with universal laws, in the way that physics and chemistry explain their respective fields" (Manser*[75]).

The theories of abrupt appearance and of evolution are comparable in their extent of guidance and explanation by natural laws. The theory of abrupt appearance is guided by natural laws in that it explains certain natural processes and empirical evidence. Biological abrupt appearance rests on the natural laws of information science, those measured by probability laws, and the laws of genetics; and it builds on the empirical evidence of paleontology, comparative morphology, classification, comparative anatomy, and comparative biochemistry. Biochemical and cosmic abrupt appearance similarly are founded on the natural laws of information science, probability, biogenesis, and thermodynamics; and on the empirical evidence of isomers, anthropic considerations, galaxy and star formation, and polonium halo origin. The theory of abrupt appearance does not involve any more singularities than, but all the regularities of, the theory of evolution. Furthermore, a natural law of abrupt appearance may well exist, and that concept has a venerable history in the nomothetic theories of creation of Owen*, Sedgwick, and other great scientists (Gillespie*[76]). Thus, Good* concludes that "new biological type[s]" may "arise in some way within the meaning of the words *de novo*," and that there is a "possibility that occasionally in time and space, if no more frequently, there may have been involved an event of a different kind" from biological evolution (Good*[77]).

The theory of abrupt appearance also explains by natural laws, beyond the possibility of nomothetic abrupt appearances and beyond the scientific evidence of which the theory consists. Thus, "aspects of description and explanation (mechanism) are usually distinguished in science" (Riddiford* and Penny*[78]), and the "discovery of the patterns of nature may not necessitate a theory of their mechanism" (Brady*[79]). The theory of evolution lacks a mechanism to the same extent as does the theory of abrupt appearance, in that biologists "plead ignorance of the means of transformation" (Patterson*[80]), while cosmologists concede that a big bang involved "a discontinuity which has often been said to constitute a limit to that which may be known" or explained causally (North*[81]). In the field of origins, singularities pose "a barrier to further retrodiction"

(Tipler*[82]), and "[s]cientific explanations . . ., in the old causal sense, are out of the question" (North*[83]). Even where singularities need not be posited, singular events generally limit investigation and proof.

On each point, the theories of evolution and abrupt appearance are parallel, incompletely guided by natural laws and not fully explainable by natural laws. The incomplete aspects arise from singularities, singular events, and possibly other features inherent in origin events, which also are parallel for the two theories.

c. *Comparable Testability*

The theories of abrupt appearance and of evolution are comparably testable: Strike* notes that "[a] strict application of a criterion of testability might rule out both," but "[a] loose application will include both" (Strike*[84]).

The theory of abrupt appearance is testable in central elements that correspond to the eighteen lines of affirmative scientific evidence described in Chapters 2, 4, and 6. Its eighteen central claims that are testable are listed in Section 10.3(a). Those evolutionists who claim that the theory of abrupt appearance is false or falsified thereby concede that it makes central empirical claims and is testable in regard to those claims. Even the theory of creation "clearly satisfies" the requirement of testability (Quinn*[85]), "make[s] a wide range of testable assertions about empirical matters of fact" (Laudan*[86]), "offer[s] some testable statements" (Gould*[87]), makes "a few . . . arguments" that "are 'scientific' in the sense that they use the basic methods of testing hypotheses" (Raup*[88]), and was viewed by Darwin* as testable in numerous areas (Mayr*[89]).

A scientific theory or model need not be, and rarely is, completely testable. The "core theory" often cannot be tested directly or even indirectly, while the "protective belt of auxiliary theories" typically is testable (Sparkes*[90]). "[M]any scientific claims are not testable in isolation, but only when embedded in a larger system of statements" (Laudan*[91]). Incomplete testability is typical of the historical sciences, because "the historical sciences try to explain unique occurrences" or singular events (Gould*[92]) and use "different methods" that "don't match stereotypes of 'the scientific method' " (Gould*[93]). Partial nontestability is particularly typical of theories of origin, because they involve singularities as well as singular events that not only are nonrepeatable but were governed by potentially different laws (Section 9.4(a)(3)).

The theory of evolution is "a historical theory, about unique events, and unique events are, by definition, . . . unrepeatable and so not subject to test" (Patterson*[94]). It has an "untested central thesis" as well as "testable part[s] of the theory" (Brady*[95]). As for Darwinism, the "theory does not allow itself to be tested" (Saunders* and Ho*[96]), and "there have been recent views expressing serious doubts about the theory of natural selection, or at least the ways in which it may be tested and placed on a scientific plane" (Forey*[97]). For neo-Darwinism, there is "an abundance of untestable statements in the literature" (Cracraft*[98]). For punctuated equilibria and species selection just as for neo-Darwinism and natural selection, the argument that "selection operated with greatest effect exactly where it was least likely to be documented—in small, localized, transitory populations—would have seemed to render [the] new theory nontestable" (Stanley*[99]). Other evolutionary elements such as adaptation involve "untestable *ad hoc* speculations" (Wassermann*[100]) and " 'just so' stories because the possibilities are limited only by the imagination" (Brady*[101]).

d. Comparable Falsifiability

The theory of abrupt appearance and the theory of evolution are comparably falsifiable, as would be expected from their comparable testability.

The theory of abrupt appearance, which consists of at least eighteen empirical lines of evidence, is falsifiable on each point. For example, its paleontology argument of abrupt appearances of natural groups and higher categories can be falsified by fossils showing systematic nonabrupt appearances of natural groups and of higher taxons. Each of the other seventeen arguments is also falsifiable, as listed in Section 10.4(a). Those who argue that the theory is false in significant parts thereby concede that it is falsifiable in significant aspects. Even the theory of creation, which is different from the theory of abrupt appearance, is "falsifiable and, thence, testable" (Quinn*[102]), and is "testable and falsifiable" (Laudan*[103]), although those authors regard it as false.

Partial unfalsifiability is as permissible for a scientific theory or hypothesis as partial testability. The core of many scientific research programs is unfalsifiable, while the belt of auxiliary hypotheses is falsifiable (Lakatos*[104]), and "the general formula is not subject to falsification although its concrete interpretations are" (Bradie* and Gromko*[105]). Partial unfalsifiability is particularly characteristic of historical sciences and origins, as a corollary of the partial nontestability of those fields.

The theory of evolution is only partially falsifiable. Macroevolution "seems to have difficulty in establishing its scientific credentials" because "experimental falsification of the theory [is] very difficult" (Sparkes*[106]). "Neo-Darwinism . . . is not falsifiable," because "[m]any of the potential falsifiers that have been suggested turn out to be tests not of Neo-Darwinism but of something else," while "[o]thers, such as those having to do with non-adaptedness and gradualism, are inherently incapable of providing conclusive tests," and "[t]he remainder . . . are so hedged about with qualifications as to make the theory invulnerable" (Saunders* and Ho*[107]). Natural selection is widely criticized as unfalsifiable (Wassermann*[108]), as are other elements of Darwinism, biochemical evolution, and cosmic evolution.

e. Comparable Tentativeness

The theory of abrupt appearance is generally more tentatively held than the theory of evolution: "today it is the conventional neo-Darwinians who appear as the conservative bigots and the unorthodox neo-Sedgwickians who rate as enlightened rationalists prepared to contemplate the evidence" (Leach*[109]). Many evolutionists proclaim that "Evolution is a fact, *fact*, *FACT*!" (Ruse*[110]), without forthrightly proclaiming that only microevolution is a fact (accepted by discontinuitists too) while macroevolution and Darwinism are theories subject to reasonable dispute (Section 3.1(c), Dobzhansky* *et al.*[111]). Further, "Darwinism is a creed not only with scientists committed to document the all-purpose role of natural selection," but "with masses of people who have at best a vague notion of the mechanism of evolution as proposed by Darwin, let alone as further complicated by his successors" (Jaki*[112]).

21.3 The Theories of Evolution and Abrupt Appearance and Other Theories of Origins

Dozens of evolutionist scientists and educators have published the conclusion that the theories of abrupt appearance or creation and the theory of evolution are the sole alternatives. A typical statement is that Darwinian evolution "has long been perceived as the only legitimate theory of evolution, and thus the only alternative to creationism" (O'Grady*[113]). That was the view of Darwin's* contemporaries as well on both sides of the issue (Lyell*[114], Bron[115]).

Figure 21.3
Cairns-Smith finds prevailing theories of biochemical evolution to add "another dimension of unreality to an already unreal line of thought"; Brady* finds biological evolution to involve many " 'just so' stories because the possibilities are limited only by imagination"*

Logic also supports that duality, under the law of the excluded middle (Mayr*[116]). However, the theory of abrupt appearance does not depend on that assumption, because that theory is based on affirmative lines of scientific evidence.

Figure 21.4
Grene concludes that it is "as a religion of science that Darwinism chiefly held, and holds men's minds,...an orthodoxy preached by its adherents with religious fervor"; Burton* sees a " 'dogma,' in their worship of the principle of natural selection" that amounts to "religion not science"*

21.4 The Theories of Evolution and Abrupt Appearance and the Prevailing Definitions of Religion

Although there are many proposed definitions of religion, various factors such as belief in a deity "neither singly nor in combination constitute tight necessary and sufficient conditions for something being a religion" (Alston*[117]). None of the cited definitions, whether in encyclopedias (*Britannica*[118]) or by theologians (Tillich*[119]), says that belief in God or a Supreme Being necessarily constitutes religion, and each of those definitions finds belief in God nonessential to religion. "Beliefs in supernatural beings can be whittled away to nothing, as in certain forms of Unitarianism, or may never be present, as in certain forms of Buddhism" (Alston*[120]).

The theories of evolution and of abrupt appearance are not religious, under the prevailing definitions of religion offered by philosophers of religion, theologians, and judges. Even the theory of creation can be nonreligious under those standards, although it is a more difficult case to assess.

Figure 21.5
Leith finds that "post-Darwinian biology is being carried out by people whose faith is in, almost, the deity of Darwin"*

21.5 The Theories of Evolution and Abrupt Appearance and the Concepts of Abrupt Appearance, Creation, and a Creator

a. Nonreligious Nature of Scientific Evidence Supporting the Theories

The term "abrupt appearance" is wholly scientific, and means in a discontinuous sense what is meant in a continuous sense by the "abrupt appearance" of complex life in punctuated equilibria (Sections 2.1 and 3.2(c)), the "abrupt appearance" of vast information content in information theory (Sections 2.4 and 4.1), the "abrupt appearance" of the earth because of polonium halos without uranium decay (Section 6.6), and the "abrupt appearance" of the universe because of the first two laws of thermodynamics (Section 6.1) and of the structure of the universe in the big bang theory (Section 13.1(b)).

Even the term "creation," although different, is nonreligious and can be scientific in meaning " 'appeared' by some wholly unknown process" (Darwin*[121]), "an act whereby some or other material is 'transformed' " (North*[122]), or coming into existence as "cosmologists use the phrase 'creation of the universe' " (Tipler*[123]). It so appears in the writings of leading proponents of the big bang, inflationary universe, quantum and particle creation, and continuous creation theories about the origin of the universe; in the writings of directed panspermia advocates and some biochemical evolutionists about the origin of the first life; and in the writings of others about the origin of organisms.

In philosophy and history, "creation" is used in the nonreligious sense of "creative art with the activity of a Demiurge or artificer" (Foster*[124]), and is "indispensable in any adequate moral and aesthetic philosophy" (Hepburn*[125]).

In cosmic evolution, "cosmologists use the phrase 'creation of the universe' to describe this phenomenon" (Tipler*[126]). Among big bang theorists, "the creation idea was soon to be frequently and quite casually applied to the appropriate discontinuity" (North*[127]). The inflationary universe theory proposes "a creation *ex nihilo*," and "[n]o law of physics prevents a creation *ex nihilo*" (Pagels*[128]). Quantum creation theory involves "models based on the laws of physics which described the creation of the universe out of nothing" (Pagels*[129]), while particle creation theory involves "creation of matter" (Grib* and Mamaev*[130]), and creation field theory is a "natural way for creating the matter" of the universe (Narlikar* and Padmanabhan*[131]). The continuous creation (or steady state) theory involved "creation out of nothing" described by physical laws (Bondi*[132]).

In biological and biochemical evolution, panspermia is "a theory of cosmic creationism" (Hoyle and Wickramasinghe[133]). Various nonreligious theories propose that exceedingly high information content is only explained by "creative intelligence" (Ambrose*[134]), that an unknown force requires the "Great Origins Thesis" (Smith*[135]), and that mechanistic evolution must be replaced by "creative evolution" (Bergson*[136]). The "process of creation" is a widely used synonym for evolution (Gould*[137]).

b. Noncentrality of a Creator to the Theories

The theories of evolution and of abrupt appearance do not involve any necessary reference to or concept of a creator. The theory of abrupt appearance, like the theory of evolution, instead consists of scientific evidence such as the abrupt appearance of complex life in the fossil record, of vast information content, and of the matter and energy of the universe (Chapters 2, 4, and 6). That is evident in advocacy of some of those empirical data and scientific interpretations by Agnostics (Lipson*[138] and for the thermodynamics argument Jastrow*[139]) and by Atheists (Hoyle and Wickramasinghe[140]). On the other hand, some advocates of each theory add a theistic gloss (religious creationism and theistic evolution).

Even for the theory of creation, that gloss is not a necessary element, as is evident in some textbook presentations (Webster* *et al.*[141]). Neither the theory of creation nor any scientific theory of origins must address questions of ultimate origins or can provide a complete mechanism. Many scientists who draw a conclusion of "creation" do not believe in a creator and do not think that creation requires a creator, and their reference to creation does not necessitate reference to a creator, as in the case of the big bang, inflationary universe, quantum creation, particle creation, and continuous creation (steady state) theories (Sections 13.1(b)-(e)). The many references in evolutionist writings do not unavoidably evoke discussion of a creator (Section 13.1).

Nevertheless, the concept of a creator is not inherently religious. The history of philosophy and of art underscores that point, as do the skeptical scientists who see creation without a creator.

c. Nonreligious Parallel Relation to a Creator and Creation of the Theories

Advocates of the theory of evolution and of the theory of abrupt appearance to the same extent make inferences about and references to a creator. Among evolutionists, the "great majority of modern evolutionary biologists are now atheists or something very close to that" (Provine*[142]), just as "almost all the early proponents of Darwinism were atheistic materialists—or their near relatives" (Hull*[143]). Darwin* himself moved "into an agnosticism tending at times toward atheism" (Moore*[144]), as do many leading proponents of his theory (Sagan*, Gould*, Ruse*, Simpson*, etc.). On the other hand, a minority of evolutionist scientists add a creator to their viewpoint; that does not make the theory of evolution inherently religious any more than a parallel addition by many discontinuitists makes the theory of abrupt appearance inherently religious.

Just as Darwin's* *The Origin of Species* "had a surprising amount of positive theological content" (Gillespie*[145]), and many Darwinians through the years have written heavily religious books (Section 15.1), evolutionist textbooks often take the theistic evolutionist position that "evolution is 'God's plan' " (Heimler*[146]). Evolutionist books and articles frequently refer to religion (Eldredge*[147]).

In view of such widespread inferences by evolutionists, "the truce between science and religion, based on the assumption that they deal with separate domains, may be a convenient but unrealistic myth" (Nelkin*[148]), as many scientists and philosophers concede. That "two spheres" approach has serious historical, epistemological, theological, and moral difficulties and is simply wrong (Miller* and Fowler*[149]), and may be "intellectual dishonesty" (Provine*[150]). In fact, the two spheres approach is based on the theological assumptions of Neo-Orthodoxy and Existentialism (Cooray*[151]).

d. Nonreligious Role in Scientific History of a Creator and Creation

Many historians of science have made the point "that religion was conducive to the advent of modern science, specifically that belief in divine creation was a major presupposition in the emergence of natural science in seventeenth-century England" (Klaaren*[152]). Thus, "Robert Boyle, Isaac Newton, and the early members of the Royal Society were religious men" who were creationists (Trevelyan*[153]). The other founders of most branches of modern science—such as "Descartes, Kepler, Galileo, Newton, and Leibnitz"—were also creationist scientists (Lakatos*[154]). Although their beliefs differ from the theory of abrupt appearance, they show that even a theory of creation can be nonreligious in nature and consistent with scientific inquiry.

e. Nonreligious Parallel Relation to World Views of the Theories

Science "drips" with values (Ruse*[155]), and evolution "is just as much a reflector and propagator of values, as anything to be named in the 'softer sciences', or in the humanities" (Ruse*[156]). Those values often take the form of an "evolutionary world view"

(Greene*[157]), which is often materialistic, naturalistic, or neo-positivistic. Evolution has "help[ed] to foster atheistic materialism" (Hull*[158]), and there is a "materialist philosophy explicitly or implicitly shared by most of the present 'establishment' in the biological sciences" (Dobzhansky*[159]). Darwinism "appears as the very keystone of the naturalistic universe" (Grene*[160]), and "Naturalism was a major premise of Darwin's thinking" (Oldroyd*[161]). Darwin* moved "to a general acceptance of positivism as a tool for such work and as a world view" (Gillespie*[162]), and the scientific world generally followed to a positivistic episteme.

Evolutionary values have also borne fruit in controversial political views, and "the extrapolations from Darwinism to either humanity or society are not separable from Darwin's own views, nor are they chronologically subsequent. They are integral" (Young*[163]). Social Darwinism arose as an economic "survival of the fittest" (Hofstadter*[164]). "Marxism . . . has a good deal in common with the evolutionist faith" (Midgley*[165]), as Marx* recognized in saying that *The Origin of Species* "contains the basis in natural history for our view," and in offering "to dedicate volume 2 of *Das Kapital* to Darwin" (Gould*[166]). "Biological arguments for racism . . . increased by orders of magnitude following the acceptance of evolutionary theory" (Gould*[167]), as Darwin* categorized "the negro" as among "the savage races" (Darwin*[168]). Naziism defended genocide on an evolutionary survival of the fittest races (Gasman*[169]), and Hitler* "consciously sought to make the practice of Germany conform to the theory of evolution" (Keith*[170]).

The theories of evolution and of abrupt appearance are parallel in their consistency with but distinctiveness from various world views. If it is at all relevant that the theory of abrupt appearance is consistent with some religious faiths (although different from them), it logically must be equally relevant that the theory of evolution is consistent with Marxism, racism, and Naziism, as well as with a comparable number of other religious faiths. The world views with which the theory of abrupt appearance is consistent are not peculiar or narrow, but are the world views from which modern science arose and that most great scientists held before the late nineteenth century. The materialistic, naturalistic, and neo-positivistic world view with which evolution is consistent has much to say about religious things, because it rules out the existence of God or of a creator and bars any actual miracle, as many philosophers and historians have observed.

Figure 21.6
Denton concludes in biological evolution that "the myth has created a widespread illusion that the theory of evolution was all but proved one hundred years ago," and Shapiro* and others* find in biochemical evolution the "myth of the prebiotic soup" (Shapiro*) and stages that "shared much with imaginative literature"*

21.6 The Theories of Evolution and Abrupt Appearance and Consistency with Religion

a. Nonreligious Nature of the Consistency of the Theories with Various Religions

Both the theory of evolution and the theory of abrupt appearance are different from religion, but are comparably consistent with various theistic evolutionist and creationist religions. "Most people would characterize one or more of the following as religions: Secular Humanism, Theological Liberalism and Buddhism. Evolution is an important doctrine of each of these religions" (Scheid*[171]). In its many varieties, "Humanism is one of the vital religions, perhaps no longer growing but very much alive. It is the dominant religion of our time" (Ehrenfeld*[172]). Humanism is religious in organization (Kurtz*[173]), profession (*Humanist Manifestos I and II*,[174] *Secular Humanist Declaration* [175]), and publications (Kurtz*[176]). It is a pervasively evolutionist faith (*Humanist Manifesto I*,[177] *Humanist Manifesto II*,[178] *Secular Humanist Declaration* [179]), and one sect is the "religion of evolutionary humanism" (Huxley*[180]). Theological Liberalism also embodies evolutionist doctrines: "Liberal religious leaders and theologians . . . proclaim the compatibility of religion and evolution" (Provine*[181]), and by "the liberal theologians, the 'prescientific science' of the biblical account of creation has at last been separated out. . ." (Gilkey*[182]). Neo-Modernist Catholics generally came to "believe in indefinite evolution 'onward and upward' " (Cross*[183]). Reform Jews generally follow evolution (Plaut*[184]), as does Humanistic Judaism (Wine*[185]). The same is true of other faiths such as Buddhism, Scientology, Theosophy, Anthroposophy, and Atheism.

The theories of evolution and of abrupt appearance are parallel in their consistency with but difference from various religions. In fact, the religious faiths in the United States divide almost evenly between theistic evolutionist and creationist ones, and that division internally splits Protestant, Catholic, Jewish, and nonJudeo-Christian faiths. That consistency does not make either the theory of abrupt appearance or of evolution religious.

b. Nonreligious Nature of Other Parallels between the Theories

The theories of evolution and of abrupt appearance are parallel in several aspects besides consistency with various religions, although most of the following points only are relevant to the theory of abrupt appearance by virtue of its rough consistency with the theory of creation. Both the theory of evolution and the theory of creation were originally presented in religious texts: the Enuma Elish, or Babylonian Genesis, describes "an evolution from chaos" (Spence*[186]), and Empedocles* was "the father of evolution" (Lull*[187]). Both theories are championed by some people with strong religious beliefs and religious motivations: Darwin* himself rejected the Old Testament, miracles, Christianity as revealed, and finally God (Gillespie*[188]), and Marxist evolutionists today are "attempting with some success to guide our research by a conscious application of Marxist philosophy" (Lewontin* and Levins*[189]). The context of discovery is irrelevant to the context of justification, both in the case of Darwin* and Marxist evolutionists and in the case of discontinuitist and creationist scientists. Both the theory of evolution and the theory of creation are defended by scientists who have written religious works. Both theories involve elements of faith, and necessarily so because origins events are not subject to absolute proof: many scientists believe in "evolution as faith" (Patterson*[190]) and macroevolution as "a fundamental article of biological faith" (Good*[191]). Finally, both theories involve teleology: "teleological explanations in biology are not only acceptable but indeed indispensable" (Ayala*[192]). None of those parallels renders either theory religious.

Figure 21.7
Vernet sees evolution facing a "revolution in biology," and Dolby* foresees possible "revolutionary changes in the further development of science"*

21.7 The Theories of Evolution and Abrupt Appearance and the History of Religious Involvement and Political Activity

a. Religious Involvement on the Evolutionist Side of the Creation-Evolution Controversy

Religious support has been at least as great for the evolutionist side as for the creationist side of the creation-evolution controversy over the last century. The point is not that this makes the scientific theories of evolution, abrupt appearance, or creation religious, but that the history of religious support for the theories of evolution and creation is essentially parallel. Darwin* himself in *The Origin of Species* "frequently condemned special creation on theological grounds" (Gillespie*[193]), and the first generation of Darwinists consisted heavily of clergymen who held evolutionary religious doctrines (Moore*[194]). In the ensuing split, some religious denominations became "sympathetic to organic evolution" (Numbers*[195]), as part of Theological Liberalism and Neo-Orthodoxy, and "[i]n the 1920s, many, probably most, evolutionists were religious" (Provine*[196]). Today, there is an unlikely combination "of atheistic evolutionists and liberal theologians, whose understanding of the evolutionary process is demonstrable nonsense, joining together with the ACLU" to defend evolutionary hegemony and to oppose creationist scientific claims (Provine*[197]).

b. Scientific Involvement on the Creationist Side of the Creation-Evolution Controversy

"[C]ontrary to what is widely assumed by evolutionary biologists today, it has always been the anti-evolutionists, not the evolutionists, in the scientific community who have stuck rigidly to the facts and adhered to a more strictly empirical approach" (Denton*[198]). The "pre-Darwinian creationists" were "true 'scientific creationists' " (Gould*[199]), who accepted a theory of creation because it "was commonly recognized by them to have strong empirical evidence in the fossil series" (Gillespie*[200]). At and just after the publication of *The Origin of Species*, many of the most eminent scientists were creationists such as Agassiz, Pasteur, Sedgwick, Maxwell, Silliman, Hitchcock, Faraday, Brewster, Joule, Kelvin, Dawson, etc. (Moore*[201]); and many other leading scientists were antievolutionists such as Owen*, Mendel*, Cope*, Virchow*, etc. Their arguments were scientific rather than religious (Moore*[202]); "it was the absence of factual evidence which was the primary source of their scepticism and not religious prejudice" (Denton*[203]). In the early twentieth century, the same was true on a smaller scale with distinguished creationist scientists including Fleischmann, Fabre, Strutt (a Nobel Prize recipient), Maunder, Carver, Fleming, Heribert-Nilsson, Thompson, etc.; and antievolutionist scientists such as More*, Vialleton*, and Lemoine*. In recent years, "the persons who have formulated, elaborated, and defended creation science are not 'preachers' . . .—as most of the media and certainly the established academic and scientific communities have assumed"—but "these are 'scientists' by any normal, useful, or descriptive definition of that word" (Gilkey*[204]). Examples are von Braun, de Wit, Hoyle, and Kenyon, as well as a large number of antievolutionists (Sections 3.2(e)-(f)). It is simply not historically accurate to say that the theory of evolution is exclusively propounded by scientists while the theory of creation is exclusively or even primarily advocated by theologians.

c. Parallel Religious Involvement on the Creationist Side of the Creation-Evolution Controversy

The theory of creation is not a Fundamentalist phenomenon, just as it is not a religious phenomenon in comparison with the theory of evolution and its substantial religious support. Instead, most support for the theory of creation is manifestly nonreligious because eighty-six percent of the American public supports its teaching (NBC News-Associated Press*[205]), and even its religious support is comparable among Protestants and Catholics (Stacey* and Shupe*[206]) and is primarily nonFundamentalist (Public Policy Resources Laboratory*[206A]).

Advocates of the theory of creation are not unified on issues of the age for the universe and earth and of a worldwide flood and flood geology. Neither were they in the past century, when an old age was championed by Agassiz, Sedgwick, Hitchcock, and Dana while a young age was defended by Kelvin and Gosse, and catastrophism was propounded by Agassiz and Murchison while flood geology was vigorously opposed by Sedgwick and Owen. Nor are those Fundamentalist issues, because the advocates of a young age rely on empirical analysis (Stansfield*[207]) as proponents of catastrophism do (Austin[208]) and did (Gould*[209]), and some Fundamentalists reject those positions while many nonFundamentalist religions embrace them (many Orthodox Roman Catholics, Orthodox Jews, and Muslims). Mere consistency with religion is different from identity with religion, and the context of discovery is irrelevant to the context of justification, as discussed in earlier sections. In any event, all of these issues differ from the theory of abrupt appearance, which has neither a religious dimension nor an age or geological column dimension.

d. Active Lobbying by Evolutionist Organizations but Not by Creationist Organizations in the Modern Creation-Evolution Controversy

Evolutionists have lobbied extensively for the hegemony of their viewpoint in public schools and other state institutions, something that is rarely mentioned in tales of creationist conspiracy. In the 1920s, the Science League of America fought, as hard as any creationist, in opposition to anti-evolution bills (Shipley*[210]). In the past two decades, nine organizations have lobbied extensively in opposition to any teaching of creation and to any restriction on dogmatic evolutionary teaching. "The AAAS [American Association for the Advancement of Science] meeting also served as a rallying ground for efforts to organize national opposition to teaching of creationism. Representatives of some 42 state 'committees of correspondence' met on 4 January [1982] to discuss ways of opposing infusion of creationist doctrine into the school curriculum" (Walsh*[211]). The Committees of Correspondence on Evolution, now renamed the National Center for Science Education, exist for that purpose as "anti-creationist citizen lobbies" (Saladin*[212]). Resolutions against teaching the theory of creation and in favor of exclusively teaching the theory of evolution have been passed by the American Humanist Association, American Civil Liberties Union, AAAS, and National Academy of Sciences; and publications taking the same position have been issued by People for the American Way, AHA, NAS, and National Association of Biology Teachers. Meetings to organize for battle were hosted by the NAS and NABT and attended by officials of all the foregoing organizations plus the National Education Association and Biological Sciences Curriculum Study (Lasen*[213], Lewin*[214]). Many more examples can be cited.

By contrast, the "national" creationist organizations virtually all oppose balanced treatment legislation or similar requirements, and most creationist scientists take the same position (ICR,[215] CRS,[216] BSA,[217] CSSHS[218]). Their reliance instead is on noncompulsive persuasion based on their view of the inherent scientific merit of the theory of creation vis-à-vis the theory of evolution, and on the value of scientific openness.

Figure 21.8
Hsü believes that for Darwinism "the foundation is about to topple"*

21.8 The Theories of Evolution and Abrupt Appearance and the Educational Method of Contrasting Explanations

a. Educational Merit of Contrasting Explanations

Educators use "the common device of teaching by comparison and contrast" (Anderson* and Kilbourn*[219]), and it is closely related to "the method of working hypotheses" that is "applicable to instruction" (Chamberlin*[220]). Those approaches are integral to the Socratic method (Hyman*[221]), and to various teaching techniques such as comparative analysis and effective questioning (Wiles* and Bondi*[222]). Scientists also widely use "the method of multiple working hypotheses" in order to "encompass the subject on all sides" and to suggest "lines of inquiry that might otherwise be overlooked" (Chamberlin*[223]). In fact, one "can be a good empiricist only if you are prepared to work with many alternative theories rather than with a single point of view," because such "a plurality allows for a much sharper criticism of accepted ideas" and brings to light both "the relevance and the refuting character of many very decisive facts" that otherwise would be overlooked through investigator bias (Feyerabend*[224]). Popper* exhorts scientists to "try to construct alternative theories—alternatives even to those theories which appear to you inescapable; for only in this way will you understand the theories you hold" (Popper*[225]). "Blind commitment to a theory is not an intellectual virtue; it is an intellectual crime" (Lakatos*[226]).

Most schools and colleges in fact use the approach of alternative explanations in various subjects, showing its feasibility. In science, they frequently contrast Mendelian genetics with Lamarckism, punctuated equilibria with neo-Darwinian gradualism, various theories of dinosaur extinction, unit membrane and fluid mosaic models of the cell, etc. In humanities, schools and colleges often present Keynesian and monetarist economics, traditional and revisionist history, and liberal and conservative political views.

b. Educational Merit of Contrasting All Scientific Theories of Origins

Consideration and presentation of all scientific theories of origins follows the preferred educational and scientific approaches of contrasting explanations and of multiple hypotheses, as many evolutionists have acknowledged. "Discussions of contrasting theories of the origins of life are educational" (de Grazia*[227]). Some warn that "[w]e cannot imagine that the cause of truth is served by keeping unpopular or minority ideas under wraps," and that "[n]othing is so unscientific as the inquisition mentality . . . seeking to suppress or conceal dissent rather than by grappling with it" (Davis and Solomon*[228]). Others caution that "beliefs that are often referred to as theories of evolution are, more accurately, only working hypotheses," and a hypothesis is "not one which precludes the possibility of some alternative" (Good*[229]). Many believe that "uncritical acceptance of Darwinism may be counterproductive" and may apotheosize a "sacred cow" (Stonehouse*[230]; Section 3.2(d)-(f)). Thus, Provine* concludes "that creationism should be taught along with evolutionism in grade schools and high schools," to further "an open discussion of ideas" rather than to "suppress . . . a viable, understandable and plausible theory" of creation (Provine*[231]). Thompson* agrees that "[s]tudents should be exposed to both sides of the coin regarding biological change—the doctrine of creation and that of evolution" (Thompson*[232]). They are joined by many other scientists and educators (Black*,[233] Sarich*,[234] and Morrow*[235]), and by still others who support classroom comparison of the alternatives but not necessarily equal time (Alexander*,[236] Anderson* and Kilbourn*,[237] and Webster* *et al.*[238]). None of those authors agrees with the theory of creation.

Presentation of all scientific theories of origins is educationally feasible without any mixture of religious concepts, as most of the foregoing authors believe and as textbooks exemplify (Webster* *et al.*[239]). The theory of abrupt appearance consists of empirical evidence and scientific interpretations that were summarized in Volume 1, and does not invite religious concepts of creation or a creator any more than does the theory of evolution. The scientific discussion of the theory of abrupt appearance in Chapters 2, 4, and 6 is not found in Genesis, and did not necessitate any consideration of Genesis or other religious views, any more than the scientific discussion of the theory of evolution in Chapters 3, 5, and 7 was found in or necessitated any mention of theistic evolution or various evolutionist religions and beliefs summarized in Sections 14.1 and 13.3. Good science demands consideration of alternatives.

c. *Extensive Treatment of the Theory of Evolution and Exclusion of the Theory of Abrupt Appearance*

Indoctrination occurs when a teacher "attempts to inculcate into the minds of his pupils his own beliefs and attitudes, and also ideas which are by no means certain without the suggestion of possible alternatives" (Schofield*[240]). That produces "mindless acceptance of conventional attitudes and beliefs" (Beck*[241]), and "the child is cut off from all but a narrow band of possibilities" (Siegel*[242]).

Indoctrination in schools and universities is particularly effective (and thus dangerous) because of the influence of the teacher, the peer group, and the text. "The teacher . . . is an authority figure'" with "tremendous influence because of the knowledge he has acquired and because of the power vested in him" (Schofield*[243]). Peers offer great pressure toward conformity, because the student "is 'cut off' from the rest of society, forced inward toward his own age group, made to carry out his whole social life with others his own age," as "a small society" (Coleman*[244]). "Textbooks are more potent forces in what and how teachers teach and in what and how children learn," because they "select for study a content, an emphasis, a method of instruction" (Chall*[245]).

In the typical classroom addressing evolution, "no alternative theory of the evidence was ever introduced, no critical examination of assumptions and incongruities ever encouraged" (Roszak*[246]). The average biology textbook in public schools devotes 14,055 words to evolution (Skoog*[247]), but not more than an unfavorable paragraph to any current alternative theory. The leading textbooks admit that "[e]volution is another pervasive theme that is developed throughout the book," so that the "entire course—indeed, any modern biology course—can be regarded as a summary of the evidence for evolution" (Klinckmann*[248]). The textbooks not only are what students read, but generally determine what teachers teach in science (Kastrinos*[249]).

To teach the theory of evolution without alternatives effectively is to teach it as fact. As the teacher handbook for three leading texts informs teachers, "referring to the 'theory of evolution' " does not mean merely "an envisaged possibility, something uncertain and unproved," because "[e]volution is a theory in this sense . . . a body of interrelated facts" (Klinckmann*[250]). Yet many scientists and educators find evolution to involve "no verifiable facts" or necessary interpretations, and object to the way "the theory of evolution continues to be presented in textbooks . . . as if it were proven and verifiable scientific fact" (Klein*[251]). They argue that "it is a matter of faith that the textbook pictures are true" (Kerkut*[252]), that on animal evolution texts are "replete with phantoms" (Patterson*[253]), that on plant evolution "[t]extbooks hoodwink" (Corner*[254]), that on fossil relations "textbooks are . . . a festering mass of unsupported assertions" (Bonner*[255]), and that on biochemical evolution texts are misleading (Cairns-Smith*[256]).

Most modern classrooms simply indoctrinate students in evolutionary theory and censor alternative scientific theories. In presenting evolution, "most textbooks appear dedicated to the idea that the material with which they deal should be beyond discussion," and only "reinforce our belief in the correctness of our own views" (Lambert*, Millar*, and Hughes*[257]). In the classroom, "alternatives to Darwinism are not usually mentioned, and even if they appear later during secondary education they are often presented so poorly and unconvincingly that many children cannot understand them" or believe them, so that "our current methods of teaching Darwinism are suspiciously similar to indoctrination" (Harper*[258]).

d. Discrimination against Discontinuitist Scientists and Educators by Educational Institutions and Publications

Discrimination exists widely against discontinuitist views, which is closely related to the strong bias in favor of the theory of evolution and against the theory of abrupt appearance (Section 9.7(c)-(d)): "most biological scientists are intolerant of creationism" (Provine*[259]). In universities and schools, "[w]ere biologists, geologists, or paleontologists to endorse publicly a pseudoscience such as creationism their chances of achieving or retaining prestigious academic positions would be greatly undermined" (Patterson*[260]). Many examples of denial of tenure, termination of employment, denial of earned degrees, or exclusion from graduate study can be cited. Similarly, if students embraced a nonevolutionary theory and gave defenses that "turned out to be scientifically counterfeit or badly fallacious, as are those of the present day creation scientists . . ., then I would consider those persons to either be [*sic*] imposters or seemingly hopeless incompetents," and would "then proceed to submit a failing grade . . . even if their success on the memorization part of the quizzes etc. were enough to carry them into the passing range (on paper)" (Patterson*[261])!

In science journals, the "referee system has rejected creationism" (Strike*[262]) and generally shows that intolerance toward most theories of discontinuity. For example, Gentry's manuscripts based on his radiohalo research were publishable and published when discontinuitist conclusions were deleted (Gentry[263]), but were "unworthy of publication" because of "wild speculation" in the eyes of peer reviewers when discontinuitist conclusions were included (Myers*,[264] *Science*[*265]).

Figure 21.9
Koestler observes that the evolutionary "citadel they are defending lies in ruins," and denies that "a bad theory is better than no theory"*

21.9 The Theories of Evolution and Abrupt Appearance and the Academic Freedom of Students and Teachers

a. Advancement of Students' Right To Receive Information

Students in public educational institutions hold a constitutional "right to receive information and ideas" (*Board of Education of Island Trees v. Pico*[266]). Corollaries of the right to receive information are a prohibition against "establishment by the state, in Lysenko-like fashion, of any single scientific theory" (Goldstein*[267]), an obligation for government schools to "provide a fairly balanced exposition of various relevant theories and points of view" (Emerson*[268]), a role of the classroom as a "marketplace of ideas" (*Keyishian v. Board of Regents*[269]), and a right to be free of official prescription of "what shall be orthodox in . . . matters of opinion" (*West Virginia State Board of Education v. Barnette*[270]). That right to receive information is furthered by more scientific information such as alternative theories of origins.

b. Advancement of Many Teachers' Academic Freedom

Teachers at the university level in particular enjoy a constitutional right to academic freedom, and those teachers whose professional judgment favors instruction in scientific theories, besides evolution, of origins are within their academic freedom in following that professional judgment in appropriate science classes. Teachers at the elementary and secondary school levels have "First Amendment rights" but "at the same time . . . the State has interests as an employer in regulating the speech of its employees" (*Pickering v. Board of Education*[271]). Also "the State has power to prescribe the curriculum and studies in public schools" (*Corpus Juris Secundum*[272]), and all states have restricted teacher rights by extensively prescribing courses of study (Sheldon*[273]). States and school districts have every right to protect the students' right to receive information, such as alternative scientific theories of origins, and nearly half the teachers hope for that opportunity (Austin Analytical Consulting*[274]).

Figure 21.10
Hsü concludes that "[we] have had enough of the Darwinian fallacy. It is about time that we cry: 'The emperor has no clothes' "

21.10 The Theories of Evolution and Abrupt Appearance and the Constitutionality of Teaching "All Scientific Theories of Origins"

a. Constitutionality under the Historical Test for the Establishment Clause

The Establishment Clause of the First Amendment does not prevent teachers in public schools (or universities) from presenting scientific "theories, besides evolution, for the origin of humankind" and of plants and animals (*Edwards v. Aguillard*[275]). Instead, it requires government "to present a fairly balanced exposition of various relevant theories and points of view, and of alternatives," on all unsettled subjects that are addressed (Emerson* and Haber*[276]).

The historical test for the Establishment Clause has been endorsed and used occasionally by the Supreme Court (*Marsh v. Chambers*[277]), and permits instruction by public institutions in the theories of evolution and of abrupt appearance, and even in a scientific theory of creation. The Constitution itself finds the Establishment Clause not to be inconsistent with reference to "in the year of our Lord," and the Declaration of Independence refers to "creation" and a "Creator." The very Congress that wrote the Clause made many references to the same concepts, and Jefferson distinguished between religion and "a professor of ethics who was to treat 'the proof of the being of a God, the Creator' . . ." (C. Antieau* *et al.*[278]). Those things are different from the theory of creation, but *a fortiori* show its constitutionality. That theory of creation is less clearly nonreligious than the theory of abrupt appearance, and its constitutionality *a fortiori* shows the constitutionality of the theory of abrupt appearance.

b. Constitutionality under the Tripart Test for the Establishment Clause

The tripart test for the Establishment Clause, which focuses on the primary effect, legislative purpose, and excessive entanglement of state action, is not violated by teaching alternative scientific theories of origins. The theory of evolution and the theory of abrupt appearance are comparably scientific and nonreligious; the latter consists of scientific evidence that the universe, life, and plants and animals abruptly appeared with discontinuity and in complex form, as was summarized in the paleontology, morphology, information science, genetics, classification, comparative anatomy and biochemistry, and eleven other arguments in Chapters 2, 4, and 6.

The primary effect and legislative purpose for teaching the theory of evolution, the theory of abrupt appearance, and any other scientific theories of origins in public schools and universities would be to advance students' rights under the First Amendment to receive scientific information, and thus to retard indoctrination in one view and censorship of alternative theories. Secondary or tertiary effects of advancing religion would be permissible under the Establishment Clause, as would be state requirements that merely "coincide or harmonize with the tenets of some or all religions" (*McGowan v. Maryland*[279]) or that merely confer "incidental benefits to religion" (*Committee for Public Education v. Nyquist*[280]). Secondary or even primary purposes of advancing religion do not violate the secular purpose requirement of the tripart test (*Wallace v. Jaffree*[281]), and positions of religious groups (which split on the origins issue) do not invalidate consistent state actions (Choper*[282]). The *Epperson* and *Edwards* decisions are not inconsistent with teaching the theory of abrupt appearance along with the theory of evolution.

No excessive entanglement arises from uncensored instruction. The Supreme Court already has found no entanglement where "each book loaned must be approved by the public school authorities; only secular books may receive approval" (*Board of Education v. Allen*[283]). The Court also has ruled that "[i]t can hardly be said that the supervision of public employees performing public functions on public property creates an excessive entanglement between church and state" (*Wolman v. Walter*[284]).

The purpose of this book is not to defend the theory of creation. It has flaws that have been discussed earlier. However, many evolutionists agree with Darwin* that the theory of creation should be taught (Section 17.2), and many such as Dolby* see benefits to science from even the theory of creation:

> In the light of this general discussion, is creationism to be regarded as science or pseudo-science? Most of the people who have taken up this issue seem to have had strong ideological commitments for or against it. I have tried to avoid such taking of sides. I am quite prepared to allow creationists to try to produce genuine science. If they succeed, I think it would in principle be quite a healthy development if children were not taught Darwinian science as unassailable dogma but were made aware that some of the fundamental ideas on which much of what they learn is built could conceivably be rejected by revolutionary changes in the further development of science, as has happened in the past. I think teaching science as a system which is open to revision would be a good idea in principle . . . .[285]

Dolby* recognizes the similarity between modern creationism and nineteenth century creationism, and perhaps the discourse was more constructive then. Darwin* criticized the "theory of creation" on scientific grounds in *The Origin of Species*, rather than ridiculing and misstating it or defining it out of science by gerrymandering the demarcation lines, and Hooker* and other evolutionists recognized the scientific legitimacy of nomothetic creation:

> Now it must be borne in mind that both these views are mere hypotheses

in a scientific point of view; neither has any inherent or prescriptive right to a preference in the mind of the impartial inquirer; but the most superficial observation will show that the hypothesis of original creations is incapable of absolute proof, except the operation be witnessed by credible naturalists, and can only be supported by facts that are either not conclusive against the opposite doctrine, or may be regarded as equally favourable to it. . ..[286]

Figure 21.11 Gould, Macbeth*, and Platnick* find neo-Darwinism "dead"*

Holmes* admired Spencer* so much that Holmes* found it doubtful that "any writer of English except Darwin has done so much to affect our whole way of thinking about the universe."[287] Many others have made similar statements about various intellectual figures. A few generations later, Spencer* and most of the others are forgotten or remembered only by historians. A few generations from now, will the same be true of Darwin*?

Darwin's* tomb, which was pictured at the beginning of this book, may someday represent a dead idea as well as a dead body. Hsu*, an evolutionist professor at the Geological Institute in Zurich E.T.H., and former president of the International Association of Sedimentologists, concludes that "the foundation is about to topple" underneath Darwinism:

> Biologists have indeed built their advances in evolutionary theory on the Darwinian foundation, not realizing that the foundation is about to topple because of Darwin's three mistakes.
>
> . . ..
>
> George Bernard Shaw wisecracked once that Darwin had the luck to please everybody who had an axe to grind. Well, I also have an axe to grind, but I am not pleased. We have suffered through two world wars and are threatened by an Armageddon. We have had enough of the

> Darwinian fallacy. *It is about time that we cry: "The emperor has no clothes."*[288]

The many antiDarwinians and antievolutionists (Section 3.2(d)-(f)) generally concur that "the emperor has no clothes." The leading punctuationists, who profess to be faithful to the emperor, still say (away from public television interviews) that the neo-Darwinian synthesis is "effectively dead, despite its persistence as textbook orthodoxy" (Gould*[289]), and many cladists believe that it has had its "obituary" written (Platnick*[290]) and is not just "dead" but "incoherent" (Cracraft*[291]). AntiDarwinian evolutionists such as Macbeth* conclude that neo-Darwinism is "dead,"[292] while Løvtrup* believes "that one day the Darwinian myth will be ranked the greatest deceit in the history of science."[293] Smith* concurs that "Darwinism is in fact dying, and its death signals the close of our age."[294]

Perhaps modern science classrooms are only Plato's cave in *The Republic*, and their certain truths are only deceptive images on the wall. Perhaps modern scientists are only Aristophanes' scientists contemplating gnats' anuses in *The Clouds*, or Swift's scientists soberly focusing microscopes on breasts and modifying objects to fit distorted mathematical laws in *Gulliver's Travels*. The dominant science mixes the hemlock to kill its rivals oftentimes; it disestablishes the priests only to don their mantles, as Rousseau warned.

Darwin's* own closing to *The Origin of Species* lends itself to paraphrase to close this defense of pluralism in theories of origins:

> Thus, from the war of nature, from famine and death, the most exalted object which we are capable of conceiving, namely, the production of man and the higher animals, remains incompletely explained and subject to alternative theories. There is grandeur in this view of life, with its several powers, having been originally breathed into all natural groups or into one; and that, whilst this planet has gone cycling on according to the fixed law of gravity, from so scientifically unresolved a beginning endless speculations most beautiful and most wonderful have been, and are being, evolved.[295]

Notes

1 *The World's Most Famous Court Trial* 187-88 (3d ed. 1925) (transcript of *Scopes* trial) (italics added).

[2] M. Denton*, *Evolution: A Theory in Crisis* (1985); Ho* & Saunders*, *Preface*, to Beyond Neo-Darwinism ix (M. Ho* & P. Saunders* eds. 1984).

[3] D. Holbrook*, *Evolution and the Humanities* 8 (1987).

[4] S. Løvtrup*, *Darwinism: The Refutation of a Myth* ix (1987).

[5] M. Midgley*, *Evolution as a Religion* 67 (1985).

[6] Feyerabend*, *How To Be a Good Empiricist—A Plea for Tolerance in Matters Epistemological*, in The Philosophy of Science 12, 27, 29-31 (P. Nidditch* ed. 1968) (Oxford U. Press) (italics added, original italics deleted).

[7] *Id.* at 31-33 (italics added, original italics deleted).

[8] Laudan*, *The Demise of the Demarcation Problem*, in 2 Working Papers in Science and Technology 7, 9 (R. Laudan* ed. 1983).

[9] Ruse*, *The Ideology of Darwinism*, in Darwin Today 233, 249 (E. Geissler* & W. Scheler* eds. 1983).

[10] Ziman*, *What is Science?*, in Introductory Readings in the Philosophy of Science 35, 37 (E. Klemke*, R. Hollinger* & A. Kline* eds. 1980).

[11] Laudan*, *Commentary: Science at the Bar—Causes for Concern*, Science, Technology & Human Values, Fall 1982, at 16, 19.

[12] Quinn*, *The Philosopher of Science as Expert Witness*, in Science and Reality: Recent Work in the Philosophy of Science 32, 42 (J. Cushing*, C. Delaney* & G. Gutting* eds. 1984).

[13] Gross*, *Commentary: Philosophers at the Bar—Some Reasons for Restraint*, in Science, Technology & Human Values, Fall 1983, at 30, 36.

[14] Quinn*, *The Philosopher of Science as Expert Witness*, in Science and Reality: Recent Work in the Philosophy of Science 32, 43 (J. Cushing*, C. Delaney* & G. Gutting* eds. 1984).

[15] Laudan*, *Commentary: Science at the Bar—Causes for Concern*, Science, Technology & Human Values, Fall 1982, at 16, 17-18.

[16] *Id.*

[17] Quinn*, *The Philosopher of Science as Expert Witness*, in Science and Reality: Recent Work in the Philosophy of Science 32, 43 (J. Cushing*, C. Delaney* & G. Gutting* eds. 1984).

[18] Walters*, *Laws of Science and Lawlike Statements*, 4 Encyclopedia of Philosophy 410, 411 (P. Edwards* ed. 1967).

[19] Quinn*, *The Philosopher of Science as Expert Witness*, in Science and Reality: Recent Work in the Philosophy of Science 32, 42-43 (J. Cushing*, C. Delaney* & G. Gutting* eds. 1984).

[20] Jastrow*, *The Astronomer and God*, in The Intellectuals Speak Out About God 15, 19 (R. Varghese* ed. 1984).

[21] H. Pagels*, *Perfect Symmetry: The Search for the Beginning of Time* 338 (1985).

[22] C. Sagan*, *Cosmos* 260 (1980).

[23] A. Whitehead*, *Science and the Modern World* 18 (1925).

[24] E. Wigner*, *The Unreasonable Effectiveness of Mathematics in the Natural Sciences*, 13 Communications in Pure and Applied Mathematics 227 (1960).

[25] N. Gillespie*, *Charles Darwin and the Problem of Creation* 3 (1979).

[26] Passmore*, *Logical Positivism*, 5 Encyclopedia of Philosophy 52 (P. Edwards* ed. 1967).

[27] Quinn*, *The Philosopher of Science as Expert Witness*, in Science and Reality: Recent Work in the Philosophy of Science 32, 43 (J. Cushing*, C. Delaney* & G. Gutting* eds. 1984).

[28] Kuhn*, *Logic of Discovery or Psychology of Research?*, in Criticism and the Growth of Knowledge 1, 10 (I. Lakatos* & A. Musgrave* eds. 1970).

[29] Section 10.3(b).

[30] Riddiford* & Penny*, *The scientific status of modern evolution theory*, in Evolutionary Theory: Paths into the Future 1, 32 (J. Pollard* ed. 1984).

[31] Sparkes*, *What is this thing called science?*, 89 New Scientist 156, 156 (1981).

[32] Laudan*, *The Demise of the Demarcation Problem*, in 2 Working Papers in Science and Technology 7, 23 (R. Laudan* ed. 1983).

[33] Sparkes*, *What is this thing called science?*, 89 New Scientist 156, 157 (1981).

[34] Laudan*, *Commentary: Science at the Bar—Causes for Concern*, Science, Technology & Human Values, Fall 1982, at 16, 17.

[35] 1 I. Lakatos*, *The Methodology of Scientific Research Programmes* 89-90 (J. Worrall* & G. Currie* eds. 1978).

[36] Quinn*, *The Philosopher of Science as Expert Witness*, in Science and Reality: Recent Work in the Philosophy of Science 32, 44 (J. Cushing*, C. Delaney* & G. Gutting* eds. 1984).

[37] Brady*, *Natural Selection and the Criteria by Which a Theory Is Judged*, 28 Systematic Zoology 600, 617 (1979).

[38] Bartels*, *Commentary: It's Good Enough for Science, but Is It Good Enough for Social Action?*, Science, Technology & Human Values, Fall 1985, at 69, 72-73.

[39] K. Popper*, *Objective Knowledge* 266 (1972).

[40] Brady*, *Dogma and doubt*, 17 Biological J. Linnean Society 79, 79 (1982).

[41] Barber*, *Resistance by Scientists to Scientific Discovery*, 134 Science 596, 596, 597 (1961).

[42] Dobzhansky*, *A Biologist's World View*, 175 Science 49, 49 (1972).

[43] W. Broad* & N. Wade*, *Betrayers of the Truth: Fraud and Deceit in the Halls of Science* 134-35 (1982).

[44] *The Velikovsky Affair: Scientism vs. Science* 1, 7 (A. de Grazia*, R. Juergens* & L. Stecchini* eds. 1966).

[45] D. Joravsky*, *The Lysenko Affair* (1970) (Harvard U. Press); Joravsky*, *The Lysenko Affair*, Scientific Am., Nov. 1962, at 41.

[46] C. Patterson*, *Evolution* 150 (1977).

[47] Brady*, *Dogma and doubt*, 17 Biological J. Linnean Society 79, 95-96 (1982).

[48] *Id.* at 91-92.

[49] Saunders* & Ho*, *Is Neo-Darwinism Falsifiable?—And Does It Matter?*, 4 Nature & System 179, 192 (1982).
[50] Dobzhansky*, *Evolutionary and Population Genetics*, 142 Science 1131, 1134 (1963).
[51] Ruse*, *The Ideology of Darwinism*, in Darwin Today 233, 255 (E. Geissler* & W. Scheler* eds. 1983).
[52] Ellis*, *Alternatives to the Big Bang*, 22 Ann. Rev. Astronomy & Astrophysics 157, 162 (1984).
[53] Each affirmative line of evidence for the theory of abrupt appearance combines induction and deduction. This can be seen in the paleontology, comparative morphology, information content, genetics (heavily deductive), and comparative discontinuity (heavily inductive) arguments of biological abrupt appearance (Chapter 2); the information content, isomers (heavily inductive), biogenesis (highly deductive), and thermodynamics (highly deductive) arguments of biochemical abrupt appearance (Chapter 4); etc.
[54] Section 15.2(c).
[55] Section 10.4(a).
[56] Each affirmative line of evidence for the theory of abrupt appearance builds on evolutionary anomalies, addresses underemphasized data, or reinterprets acknowledged data. *See* Chapters 2, 4 & 6.
[57] Section 10.3(a).
[58] *See* Section 9.1.
[59] Popper*, *Intellectual Autobiography*, in 2 The Philosophy of Karl Popper 3, 134, 137 (P. Schilpp* ed. 1974).
[60] Popper*, *Natural Selection and the Emergence of Mind*, 32 Dialectica 339, 344-45 (1978).
[61] Popper*, *Letter*, 87 New Scientist 611, 611 (1980).
[62] C. Patterson*, *Evolution* 149 (1978).
[63] Cartmill*, *Hypothesis Testing and Phylogenetic Reconstruction*, in Zeitschrift für Zoologische Systematik und Evolution 73, 90 (1981).
[64] W. Stansfield*, *The Science of Evolution* 53 (1977).
[65] R. Wald*, *Space, Time, and Gravity: The Theory of the Big Bang* 51 (1971).
[66] Popper*, *Intellectual Autobiography*, in 2 The Philosophy of Karl Popper 3, 134-35 (P. Schilpp* ed. 1974).
[67] Popper*, *Reduction and the Incompleteness of Science*, in Studies in the Philosophy of Biology 259, 270 (1974).
[68] Eden*, *Inadequacies of Neo-Darwinian Evolution as a Scientific Theory*, in Mathematical Challenges to the Neo-Darwinian Interpretation of Evolution 109, 110 (P. Moorhead* & M. Kaplan* eds. 1967).
[69] Popper*, *Intellectual Autobiography*, in 2 The Philosophy of Karl Popper 3, 138 (P. Schilpp* ed. 1974).
[70] Sparkes*, *What is this thing called science?*, 89 New Scientist 156, 156 (1981).

[71] R. Lewontin*, *The Genetic Basis of Evolutionary Change* 11-12 (1974).

[72] Rosen*, *Book Review*, 27 Systematic Zoology 370, 372 (1978).

[73] Waddington*, *Evolutionary Adaptation*, in 1 Evolution After Darwin 381, 385 (S. Tax* ed. 1960).

[74] Quoted in Riddiford* & Penny*, *The scientific status of modern evolutionary theory*, in Evolutionary Theory: Paths into the Future 1, 30 (J. Pollard* ed. 1984).

[75] Quoted in *id.* at 1-2.

[76] N. Gillespie*, *Charles Darwin and the Problem of Creation* 21 (1979) (U. of Chicago Press).

[77] R. Good*, *Features of Evolution in the Flowering Plants* 384 (1974).

[78] Riddiford* & Penny*, *The scientific status of modern evolutionary theory*, in Evolutionary Theory: Paths into the Future 1, 4 (J. Pollard* ed. 1984).

[79] Brady*, *Natural Selection and the Criteria by Which a Theory Is Judged*, 28 Systematic Zoology 600, 620 (1979).

[80] Address of Dr. Colin Patterson* at Am. Museum of Natural History, tr. at 3-4 (Nov. 5, 1981).

[81] J. North*, *The Measure of the Universe* 400 (1965).

[82] Tipler*, *How to Construct a Falsifiable Theory in Which the Universe Came Into Being Several Thousand Years Ago*, 2 Philosophy of Science Association 873, 874-75 (1984).

[83] J. North*, *The Measure of the Universe* 400-01 (1965).

[84] Strike*, *The Status of Creation-Science: A Comment on Siegel and Hahn*, 63 Phi Delta Kappan 555, 555-56 (1982) (proposing a process test that he believes the theory of creation fails in its current form).

[85] Quinn*, *The Philosopher of Science as Expert Witness*, in Science and Reality: Recent Work in the Philosophy of Science 32, 43 (J. Cushing*, C. Delaney* & G. Gutting* eds. 1984).

[86] Laudan*, *Commentary: Science at the Bar—Causes for Concern*, Science, Technology & Human Values, Fall 1982, at 16, 16-17.

[87] Gould*, *Creationism: Genesis v. Geology*, Atlantic Monthly, Sept. 1982, at 10, 13.

[88] Raup*, *The Geological and Paleontological Arguments of Creationism*, in Scientists Confront Creationism 147, 159 (L. Godfrey* ed. 1983).

[89] Mayr*, *Introduction*, to C. Darwin*, The Origin of Species xii, xiii (1st ed. 1859, repr. 1964).

[90] Sparkes*, *What is this thing called science?*, 89 New Scientist 156, 156 (1981).

[91] Laudan*, *Commentary: Science at the Bar—Causes for Concern*, Science, Technology & Human Values, Fall 1982, at 16, 17.

[92] Gould*, *The Wisdom of Casey Stengel*, Discover, Mar. 1983, at 62, 64-65.

[93] Gould*, *Darwinism Defined: The Difference Between Fact and Theory*, Discover, Jan. 1987, at 64, 69-70.

[94] C. Patterson*, *Evolution* 147 (1978).
[95] Brady*, *Dogma and doubt*, 17 Biological J. Linnean Soc. 79, 89 (1982).
[96] Saunders* & Ho*, *Is Neo-Darwinism Falsifiable?—And Does It Matter?*, 4 Nature & System 179, 185 (1982).
[97] Forey*, *Neontological Analysis Versus Palaeontological Stories*, in Problems of Phylogenetic Reconstruction 119, 124 (K. Joysey* & A. Friday* eds. 1982).
[98] Cracraft*, *The Use of Functional and Adaptive Criteria in Phylogenetic Systematics*, 21 Am. Zoologist 21, 34 (1981).
[99] S. Stanley*, *Macroevolution* 6 (1979) (speaking of natural selection). *See* Section 3.3(f).
[100] Wassermann*, *Testability of the Role of Natural Selection within Theories of Population Genetics and Evolution*, 29 British J. Philosophy of Science 223, 240 (1978).
[101] Brady*, *Dogma and doubt*, 17 Biological J. Linnean Society 79, 88 (1982).
[102] Quinn*, *The Philosopher of Science as Expert Witness*, in Science and Reality: Recent Work in the Philosophy of Science 32, 43 (J. Cushing*, C. Delaney* & G. Gutting* eds. 1984).
[103] Laudan*, *More on Creationism*, in Science, Technology & Human Values, Winter 1983, at 36, 38.
[104] Quoted in Riddiford* & Penny*, *The scientific status of modern evolutionary theory*, in Evolutionary Theory: Paths into the Future 1, 11 (J. Pollard* ed. 1984).
[105] Bradie* & Gromko*, *The Status of the Principle of Natural Selection*, 3 Nature & System 3, 9 (1981).
[106] Sparkes*, *What is this thing called science?*, 89 New Scientist 156, 158 (1981).
[107] Saunders* & Ho*, *Is Neo-Darwinism Falsifiable?—And Does It Matter?*, 4 Nature & System 179, 180, 191 (1982).
[108] Wassermann*, *Testability of the Role of Natural Selection Within Theories of Population Genetics and Evolution*, 29 British J. Philosophy of Science 223, 223-24 (1978).
[109] Leach*, *Men, bishops and apes*, Nature, Sept. 3, 1981, at 19, 20.
[110] M. Ruse*, *Darwinism Defended* 58 (1982).
[111] T. Dobzhansky*, F. Ayala*, G. Stebbins* & J. Valentine*, *Evolution* 5 (1977).
[112] S. Jaki*, *Cosmos and Creator* (1982).
[113] O'Grady*, *Evolutionary Theory and Teleology*, 107 J. Theoretical Biology 563, 575 (1984).
[114] 2 C. Lyell*, *Principles of Geology* 330 (11th ed. 1873).
[115] Bron, *Book Review*, Neues Jahrbuch für Mineralogie 112-16 (1860), reprinted in D. Hull*, *Darwin and His Critics* 120, 122 (1973).
[116] Mayr*, *Introduction*, to C. Darwin*, The Origin of Species vii, xii (1st ed. 1859, repr. 1964).

[117] Alston*, *Religion*, in 7 Encyclopedia of Philosophy 140, 141 (P. Edwards* ed. 1967).

[118] Smart*, *Religions, The Study and Classification of*, Encyclopaedia Britannica: Macropaedia 548, 548 (16th ed. 1984).

[119] P. Tillich*, *Theology of Culture* 7 (1959) (Oxford U. Press).

[120] Alston*, *Religion*, in 7 Encyclopedia of Philosophy 140, 142 (P. Edwards* ed. 1967).

[121] 2 *The Life and Letters of Charles Darwin* 202-03 (F. Darwin* ed. 1903); D. Hull*, *Darwin and His Critics* 53 (1973).

[122] J. North*, *The Measure of the Universe* 399 (1965).

[123] Tipler*, *How to Construct a Falsifiable Theory in Which the Universe Came Into Being Several Thousand Years Ago*, 2 Philosophy of Science Association 873, 894 (1984).

[124] Foster*, *The Christian Doctrine of Creation and the Rise of Modern Natural Science*, 43 Mind 446, 462 (1934).

[125] Hepburn*, *Creation, Religious Doctrine of: Creation in the Context of Scientific Cosmological Theories*, 2 Encyclopedia of Philosophy 255, 256 (P. Edwards* ed. 1967).

[126] Tipler*, *How to Construct a Falsifiable Theory in Which the Universe Came Into Being Several Thousand Years Ago*, 2 Philosophy of Science Association 873, 894 (1984).

[127] J. North*, *The Measure of the Universe* 401 (1965).

[128] H. Pagels*, *Perfect Symmetry: The Search for the Beginning of Time* 338-40 (1985).

[129] *Id.* at 347, 349.

[130] Grib* & Mamaev*, *Creation of Matter in the Friedmann Model of the Universe*, 14 Soviet J. Nuclear Physics 450, 450 1972).

[131] Narlikar* & Padmanabhan*, *Creation-field cosmology: A possible solution to singularity, horizon, and flatness problems*, 32 Physical Rev. D 1928, 1929, 1928 (1985).

[132] H. Bondi*, *Cosmology* 143-44 (1968).

[133] F. Hoyle & N. Wickramasinghe, *Evolution from Space: A Theory of Cosmic Creationism* (1984).

[134] E. Ambrose*, *The Nature and Origin of the Biological World* 143 (1982).

[135] Smith*, *Two Evolutions*, in On Nature 42, 47 (L. Rouner* ed. 1984).

[136] H. Bergson*, *L'Evolution Creatrice* (1907).

[137] Gould*, *The Return of Hopeful Monsters*, Natural History, June-July 1977, at 28.

[138] Lipson*, *A Physicist Looks at Evolution*, 31 Physics Bulletin 138, 138 (1980)

[139] R. Jastrow*, *God and the Astronomers* 11-12 (1978).

[140] F. Hoyle & N. Wickramasinghe, *Evolution from Space: A Theory of Cosmic Creationism* (1984) (panspermia advocates).

[141] V. Webster* *et al.*, *Life Science* 41-42 (1980).

[142] Provine*, *Book Review of Trial and Error: The American Controversy*

over Creation and Evolution, Academe, Jan.-Feb. 1987, at 50, 52.

143 Hull*, *Darwin and Historiography,* in The Comparative Reception of Darwinism 388, 391 (T. Glick* ed. 1974).

144 J. Moore*, *The Post-Darwinian Controversies* 314-15, 344 (1979).

145 N. Gillespie*, *Charles Darwin and the Problem of Creation* xi (1979).

146 *E.g.*, C. Heimler*, *Focus on Life Science* 431 (Teacher's Ed. 1981).

147 *E.g.*, N. Eldredge*, *The Monkey Business* 7-9 (1982).

148 D. Nelkin*, *Science Textbook Controversies and the Politics of Equal Time* 1 (1977).

149 Miller* & Fowler*, *What's Wrong with the Creation/Evolution Controversy?*, CTNS Bulletin, Autumn 1984, at 1, 7.

150 Provine*, *Book Review of Trial and Error: The American Controversy over Creation and Evolution*, Academe, Jan.-Feb. 1987, at 50, 51-52.

151 Schoch* & Prins*, *Letter*, Geotimes, May 1984, at 7.

152 E. Klaaren*, *Religious Origins of Modern Science* v, vii, 1 (1977).

153 G. Trevelyan*, *English Social History* 257 (1942).

154 1 I. Lakatos*, *The Methodology of Scientific Research Programmes* 195 (J. Worrall* & G. Currie* eds. 1978).

155 Ruse*, *The Ideology of Darwinism*, in Darwin Today 233, 247-49 (E. Geissler* & W. Scheler* eds. 1983).

156 *Id.* at 234.

157 J. Greene*, *Science, Ideology and World View* 133 (1981).

158 Hull*, *Darwinism and Historiography*, in The Comparative Reception of Darwinism 388, 391 (T. Glick* ed. 1974).

159 Dobzhansky*, *A Biologist's World View*, 175 Science 49, 49 (1972).

160 Grene*, *The Faith of Darwinism*, Encounter, Nov. 1959, at 48, 48-49.

161 D. Oldroyd*, *Darwinian Impacts* 254 (1980).

162 N. Gillespie*, *Charles Darwin and the Problem of Creation* 8-9 (1979).

163 Young*, *Darwinism Is Social*, in The Darwinian Heritage 609 (D. Kohn* ed. 1985).

164 R. Hofstadter*, *Social Darwinism in American Thought* 31, 45 (1955).

165 M. Midgley*, *Evolution as a Religion* 112 (1985).

166 S. Gould*, *Ever Since Darwin* 26 (1977).

167 S. Gould*, *Ontogeny and Phylogeny* 126-27, 130 (1977).

168 C. Darwin*, *The Descent of Man* 241-42 (1901).

169 D. Gasman*, *The Scientific Origins of National Socialism: Social Darwinism in Ernst Haeckel and the German Monist League* xvi (1971).

170 A. Keith*, *Evolution and Ethics* 10, 230 (1947).

171 Comment*, *Evolution and Creationism in the Public Schools*, 9 J. Contemp. Law 51, 106-07 (1983).

172 D. Ehrenfeld*, *The Arrogance of Humanism* 3 (1978)

173 P. Kurtz*, *The New Inquisition in the Schools*, Free Inquiry, Winter 1986-87, at 45.

174 *Humanist Manifesto I*, in Humanist Manifestos I and II (P. Kurtz* ed. 1973), reprinted from *A Humanist Manifesto*, New Humanist, May-June 1933, at 1.

175 *A Secular Humanist Declaration*, Free Inquiry, Winter 1980-81, at 3.
176 P. Kurtz*, *In Defense of Secular Humanism* 135 (1983).
177 *Humanist Manifesto I*, in Humanist Manifestos I and II, at 8 (P. Kurtz* ed. 1973).
178 *Humanist Manifesto II*, in Humanist Manifestos I and II, at 13, 14 (P. Kurtz* ed. 1973), reprinted from *Humanist Manifesto II*, Humanist, Sept.-Oct. 1973, at 4.
179 Kurtz*, *A Secular Humanist Declaration*, Free Inquiry, Winter 1980-81, at 3, 6. Its original signers include the president of the Fellowship of Religious Humanists. *Id.*
180 Huxley*, *The Coming New Religion of Humanism*, Humanist, Jan.-Feb. 1962, at 3, 5.
181 Provine*, *Book Review of Trial and Error: The American Controversy over Creation and Evolution*, Academe, Jan.-Feb. 1987, at 50, 52.
182 L. Gilkey*, *Maker of Heaven and Earth: A Study of the Christian Doctrine of Creation* 34 (1959).
183 R. Cross*, *The Emergence of Liberal Catholicism in America* 149 (1958).
184 W. Plaut*, *The Torah: A Modern Commentary* 6, 16 (1974).
185 S. Wine*, *Humanistic Judaism* (1978).
186 L. Spence*, *Myths and Legends of Babylonia and Assyria* 84 (1916).
187 R. Lull*, *Organic Evolution* 6 (rev. ed. 1948).
188 N. Gillespie*, *Charles Darwin and the Problem of Creation* 136-37 (1979).
189 R. Levins* & R. Lewontin*, *The Dialectical Biologist* 267 (1985).
190 Address of Dr. Colin Patterson*, American Museum of Natural History, tr. at 4 (Nov. 5, 1981).
191 R. Good*, *Features of Evolution in the Flowering Plants* 1 (1974).
192 Ayala*, *Teleological Explanations in Evolutionary Biology*, Philosophy of Science, Mar. 1970, at 1, 1.
193 N. Gillespie*, *Charles Darwin and the Problem of Creation* 124 (1979).
194 J. Moore*, *The Post-Darwinian Controversies* 220-69 (1979).
195 R. Numbers*, *Creation by Natural Law* 119-20 (1977).
196 Provine*, *Book Review of Trial and Error: The American Controversy over Creation and Evolution*, Academe, Jan.-Feb. 1987, at 50, 51.
197 *Id.*
198 M. Denton*, *Evolution: A Theory in Crisis* 353-54 (1985).
199 Gould*, *Evolution, Theology, and the Victorian Scientist*, 285 Nature 343, 343 (1980).
200 N. Gillespie*, *Charles Darwin and the Problem of Creation* 26-27 (1979).
201 J. Moore*, *The Post-Darwinian Controversies* 87 (1979).
202 *Id.* at 218-19.
203 M. Denton*, *Evolution: A Theory in Crisis* 100, 104 (1985).
204 L. Gilkey*, *Creationism on Trial: Evolution and God at Little Rock* 21-22 (1985).
205 NBC News* & Associated Press*, November National Poll at 15 (Nov.

24, 1981) (76% support for teaching both creation and evolution, and 10% additional support for teaching only creation, in public schools).

[206] Stacey* & Shupe*, *Religious Values and Religiosity in the Textbook Adoption Controversy in Texas 1981*, 25 Rev. of Religious Research 321, 326 (1984).

[206A] Public Policy Resources Laboratory* of Texas A. & M. University, *The Texas Poll*, Fall 1987, at 1, 19, 20 (61% of the 70% of the public believing that creation should be "taught along with evolution in public schools" stated that they were neither Fundamentalists nor Evangelicals).

[207] W. Stansfield*, *The Science of Evolution* 80-82 (1977).

[208] S. Austin, *Catastrophes in Earth History* (1984) (creationist author).

[209] Gould*, *Toward the Vindication of Punctuational Change*, in Catastrophes and Earth History: The New Uniformitarianism 9, 13-14 (W. Berggren* & J. Van Couvering* eds. 1984); Gould*, *Catastrophes and Steady State Earth*, Natural History, Feb. 1975, at 15, 16-17, 18.

[210] M. Shipley*, *The War on Modern Science* 384 (1927).

[211] Walsh*, *At AAAS Meeting, a Closing of Ranks*, 215 Science 380, 380 (1982).

[212] Saladin*, *Opposing Creationism: Scientists Organize*, Humanist, Mar.-Apr. 1982, at 59, 59.

[213] A. Lasen*, *Summary Report: Meeting on Creationism-Evolutionism* (NAS Oct. 19, 1981).

[214] Lewin*, *A Response to Creationism Evolves*, 214 Science 635, 635 (1981).

[215] *The ICR Position on Creationist Litigation and Legislation*, Acts & Facts, May 1981, at 1, 1.

[216] W. Rusch, A Brief Statement of the History and the Aims of the CRS 2 (unpub. statement by Creation Research Society 1982).

[217] *What Can We Learn from the Arkansas Decision?*, Bible-Science Newsletter, Feb. 1982, at 3.

[218] Myers, *Book Review*, Creation Social Science & Humanities Quarterly, Summer 1984, at 27, 28.

[219] Anderson* & Kilbourn*, *Creation, Evolution, and Curriculum*, 67 Science Education 45, 53-54 (1983).

[220] Chamberlin*, *The Method of Multiple Working Hypotheses*, 148 Science 754, 757-58 (1965).

[221] R. Hyman*, *Ways of Teaching* 77 (1970).

[222] J. Wiles* & J. Bondi*, *Curriculum Development: A Guide to Practice* 171, 172 (1972).

[223] Chamberlin*, *The Method of Multiple Working Hypotheses*, 148 Science 754, 756 (1965).

[224] Feyerabend*, *How To Be a Good Empiricist—A Plea for Tolerance in Matters Epistemological*, in The Philosophy of Science 12, 14 (P. Nidditch* ed. 1968) (Oxford U. Press).

[225] K. Popper*, *Objective Knowledge* 26 (1972).
[226] 1 I. Lakatos*, *The Methodology of Scientific Research Programmes* 1 (J. Worrall* & G. Currie* eds. 1978).
[227] A. de Grazia*, Quantavolution and Creation in Arkansas 4 (unpub. ms. 1982).
[228] P. Davis & E. Solomon*, *The World of Biology* 414 (1974) (Solomon* is an evolutionist, while Davis is a creationist biologist).
[229] R. Good*, *Features of Evolution in the Flowering Plants* 2 (1974).
[230] Stonehouse*, *Introduction,* to M. Pitman, Adam and Evolution 9, 12 (1984).
[231] Quoted in *Scientists Abandon Evolution*, Contrast, Mar.-Apr. 1982, at 1, 3 (Provine* describes himself as an Atheist).
[232] A. Thompson*, *Biology, Zoology, and Genetics: Evolution Model vs. Creation Model* 2, 271 (1983).
[233] T. Black*, *Straight Talk about American Education* 40, 276 (1982) (chancellor 1979-80, member 1969-80).
[234] Lecture by V. Sarich* at Bakersfield, California (May 18, 1986).
[235] Letter from Dr. W. Scot Morrow* to Dr. Major Rhodes* (Jan. 1, 1980) (he does regard the theory of creation as scientific).
[236] Alexander*, *Evolution, Creation, and Biology Teaching*, in Evolution versus Creationism 90, 91 (J. Zetterberg* ed. 1983).
[237] Anderson* & Kilbourn*, *Creation, Evolution, and Curriculum,* 67 Science Education 45, 53-54 (1983).
[238] V. Webster* *et al.*, *Life Science* 409, 436-37, 441-42, 444 (1980).
[239] *Id.*
[240] H. Schofield*, *The Philosophy of Education* 178, 181 (1972).
[241] C. Beck*, *Educational Philosophy and Theory: An Introduction* 190-91 (1974).
[242] Siegel*, *Critical Thinking as an Intellectual Right*, in Children's Intellectual Rights 39, 46 (D. Moshman* ed. 1986).
[243] H. Schofield*, *The Philosophy of Education* 182 (1972).
[244] J. Coleman*, *The Adolescent Society* 3 (1961).
[245] Chall*, *Middle and Secondary School Textbooks*, in The Textbook in American Society 24, 26 (J. Cole* & T. Sticht* eds. 1981).
[246] T. Roszak*, *Unfinished Animal* 99-100 (1975).
[247] G. Skoog*, Coverage of Evolution in Secondary School Biology Textbooks: 1900-1982, at 12 (unpub. ms. Oct. 16, 1982).
[248] E. Klinckmann*, *Biology Teachers' Handbook* 16 (2d ed. 1970).
[249] Kastrinos*, *Survey of the Teaching of Biology in Secondary Schools*, 98 School & Society 241, 242 (1970).
[250] E. Klinckmann*, *Biology Teachers' Handbook* 16 (2d ed. 1970).
[251] Klein*, *Preface*, to L. Sunderland, Darwin's Enigma 5, 5 (1985).
[252] G. Kerkut*, *Implications of Evolution* 148 (1960).
[253] Patterson*, *Book Review*, 29 Systematic Zoology 216, 217 (1980).

254 Corner*, *Evolution*, in Contemporary Botanical Thought 95, 97 (A. MacLeod* & L. Cobley* eds. 1961).
255 Bonner*, *Book Review*, 49 Am. Scientist 240 (1961).
256 A. Cairns-Smith*, *Genetic Takeover and the Mineral Origins of Life* 56 (1986).
257 Lambert*, Millar* & Hughes*, *Teaching the classic case of natural selection*, 79 Rivista di Biologia (Biology Forum) 117, 117-18 (1986).
258 Harper*, *Darwinism and Indoctrination*, 59 School Science Rev. 258, 258 (1977).
259 W. Provine*, Theories of Creationism and Evolution from a Historical Perspective (unpub. lecture before Sigma Xi Chapter at Corning, N.Y., Nov. 17, 1981). *E.g.*, Schafersman*, *Letter*, Geotimes, Aug. 1981, at 11, 11.
260 Patterson*, *An Engineer Looks at the Creationist Movement*, 89 Proc. Iowa Academy of Sciences 57 (1982).
261 Letter from Professor John W. Patterson* [of Iowa State University] to Mr. Kevin Wirth (Feb. 7, 1984).
262 Strike*, *The Status of Creation-Science: A Comment on Siegel and Hahn*, 63 Phi Delta Kappan 555, 556 (1982).
263 Gentry, *Extinct Radioactivity and the Discovery of a New Pleochroic Halo*, 213 Nature 487 (1967); Gentry, *Fossil Alpha-Recoil Analysis of Certain Variant Radioactive Halos*, 160 Science 1228 (1968).
264 Letter from Frank E. Myers* (Editor) to Robert V. Gentry (June 7, 1966) (on letterhead of J. Applied Physics and Applied Physics Letters, rejecting ms. and attaching reviewer comments that are quoted).
265 Reviewer response on *Science* form (n.d.).
266 Board of Educ. of Island Trees Union Free Sch. Dist. v. Pico, 457 U.S. 853 (1982) (plurality opinion)
267 Goldstein*, *On Being Adult and Being an Adult in Secular Law*, 105 Daedalus 69, 70 (Fall 1976).
268 T. Emerson*, *The System of Freedom of Expression* 624 (1970).
269 385 U.S. 603 (1967).
270 319 U.S. 642 (1943).
271 391 U.S. 563, 568 (1968).
272 79 C.J.S. *Schools and School Districts* §485, at 428
273 Shelton*, *Legislative Control over Public School Curriculum*, 15 Willamette L. Rev. 473, 504-05 (1979).
274 Austin Analytical Consulting*, Opinion Poll for Biology Teachers question 8 (1986).
275 482 U.S...., 96 L. Ed. 2d 510, 521 (1987).
276 Emerson* & Haber*, *The Scopes Case in Modern Dress*, 27 U. Chi. L. Rev. 522, 527 (1960).
277 463 U.S. 783 (1983).
278 C. Antieau*, A. Downey* & E. Roberts*, *Freedom from Federal Establishment* 200 (1964).
279 366 U.S. 420, 442 (1961).

[280] 413 U.S. 756, 771-72 (1973).
[281] 472 U.S. 38 (1985).
[282] Choper*, *The Religion Clauses of the First Amendment*, 41 U. Pitt. L. Rev. 673, 684 (1980).
[283] Board of Educ. v. Allen, 392 U.S. 236, 244-45 (1968).
[284] Wolman v. Walter, 433 U.S. 229, 248 (1977) (majority opinion in that Part VI).
[285] Dolby*, *Science and Pseudo-Science: The Case of Creationism*, 22 Zygon 195, 205-06 (1987). He does not support teaching the theory of creation at the elementary level.
[286] [Hooker], *Review of The Origin of Species*, Gardeners' Chronicle, Dec. 31, 1859, at 1051-52, reprinted in D. Hull*, *Darwin and His Critics* 81, 84-85 (1973).
[287] 1 *Holmes-Pollock Letters* 57-58 (M. Howe* ed. 1941).
[288] Hsu*, *Reply*, 15 Geology 177, 177 (1987); Hsu*, *Darwin's Three Mistakes*, 14 Geology 532, 534 (1986) (italics added).
[289] Gould*, *Is a new and general theory of evolution emerging?*, 6 Paleobiology 120-21 (1980).
[290] Saunders*, *Book Review*, New Scientist, Feb. 21, 1985, at 44, 44.
[291] Cracraft*, *Book Review of Beyond Neo-Darwinism*, 1 Cladistics 300, 303 (1985).
[292] Macbeth*, *How To Defuse a Feud*, Kronos, Summer 1982, at 1, 3-4.
[293] S. Løvtrup*, *Darwinism: The Refutation of a Myth* 422 (1987).
[294] Smith*, *Two Evolutions*, in On Nature 42 (L. Rouner* ed. 1984) (proponent of "great origins thesis").
[295] C. Darwin*, *The Origin of Species* 490 (1st ed. 1859, repr. 1964).

Credits

Appreciation is expressed for permission to use illustrations, including but not limited to the following:

Darwin's memorial and marker (from his tomb) on the dust jacket and frontispiece, courtesy of and ©1987 the Dean and Chapter of Westminster Abbey (photographer Malcolm Crowthers, London).

Author's picture on the dust jacket, by Eric N. Richards (Atlanta, Georgia).

Figures 2.5, 3.1, 8.3, 9.6, from G. Hunter, *A Civic Biology* (1914).

Figure 3.5, from Bowden, *The ape-man fallacy*, 73 Rivista di Biologia 416 (1980), ©1980 Univ. of Perugia.

Figure 6.6, ©1986 Professor Robert V. Gentry.

Figure 8.5, from Watson & Crick, *Molecular Structure of Nucleic Acids*, Nature, Apr. 25, 1953, at 737, ©1953 Nature.

Figure 9.2, from Luken, *The Scientific Method in Biology*, 17 J. College Science Teaching 274, 276 (1988), ©1988 National Science Teachers Association.

Figure 10.4, from O'Hear, *Popper and the philosophy of Science*, New Scientist, Aug. 22, 1985, at 43, ©1985 New Scientist (illustration by Ingram Pinn).

Appreciation is expressed to hundreds of authors and publishers for permission to reprint quotations from their publications, in which all rights are reserved by them, including but by no means limited to the following:

Alexander, *Evolution, Creation, and Biology Teaching*, in Evolution versus Creationism 90, 91 (J. Zetterberg ed. 1983).
©1983 Oryx Press and National Association of Biology Teachers and R. Alexander.

Alfvén & Mendis, *Interpretation of observed cosmic microwave background radiation*, 266 Nature 698 (1977),
©1977 Nature.

Amato, *Spectral variation on a universal theme*, 130 Science News 166, 166 (1986),
©1986 Science Service, Inc.

Anon., *Hoyle on evolution*, 296 Nature 105 (1981),
©1981 Nature.

Anon., *Unorthodox assessments*, 300 Nature 566 (1982),
©1982 Nature.

Anon., *What future for Biogenesis?*, 216 Nature 635 (1967),
©1967 Nature.

Axelrod, *Early Cambrian Marine Fauna*, 128 Science 7 (1958),
©1958 American Association for the Advancement of Science.

Barber, *Resistance by Scientists to Scientific Discovery*, 134 Science 596 (1961),
©1961 American Association for the Advancement of Science.

Bartels, *Commentary: It's Good Enough for Science, but Is It Good Enough for Social Action?*, Science, Technology & Human Values, Fall 1985, at 69, 72-73,
©1985 John Wiley & Sons, Inc.
Bird, *Freedom of Religion and Science Instruction in Public Schools*, 87 Yale L.J. 515, 519-20 (1978),
©1978 Yale Law Journal Co. and Fred B. Rothman & Co.
Bock, *Book Review*, 164 Science 684 (1969),
©1969 American Association for the Advancement of Science.
Boss, *Collapse and Formation of Stars*, Scientific Am., Jan. 1985, at 40.
©1985 Scientific American, Inc.
P. Bridgman, *The Way Things Are* 129 (1959),
©1959 Harvard University Press.
W. Broad & N. Wade, *Betrayers of the Truth* (1982),
©1982 W. Broad & N. Wade, reprinted by permission of Simon & Schuster, Inc.
J. Brooks & G. Shaw, *Origins and Development of Living Systems* 359-60 (1973),
©1973 Academic Press, Inc.
Brush, *Should the History of Science Be Rated X?*, 183 Science 1164 (1974),
©1974 American Association for the Advancement of Science.
Burbidge, *Was there really a Big Bang?*, 233 Nature 36 (1971),
©1971 Nature.
Burbidge, *Redshifts and distances*, 286 Nature 307 (1980),
©1980 Nature.
Burton, *The Human Side of the Physiologist*, 1 Physiologist 2 (1975),
©1975 American Physiological Society.
A. Cairns-Smith, *Genetic Takeover and the Mineral Origins of Life* (1986),
©1986 Cambridge University Press.
Cannon, *The Bases of Darwin's Achievement: A Revaluation*, 5 Victorian Studies 109 (1961),
©1961 Trustees of Indiana University.
Clemmey & Badham, *Oxygen in the Precambrian Atmosphere*, 10 Geology 141, 141-42, 145 (1982),
©1982 Geological Society of America.
Crawford, *Photon decay in curved space-time*, 277 Nature 633 (1979),
©1979 Nature.
R. Cross, *The Emergence of Liberal Catholicism in America* 149 (1958),
©1958 Harvard University Press.
Davies, *Chance or choice: is the Universe an accident?*, 80 New Scientist 506 (1978),
©1978 New Scientist.
De Vaucouleurs, *The Case for a Hierarchical Cosmology*, 167 Science 1203 (1970),
©1970 American Association for the Advancement of Science.
Dickerson, *Chemical Evolution and the Origin of Life*, Scientific Am., September 1978, at 70, reprinted in *Evolution* 30 (E. Mayr ed. 1978),
©1978 Scientific American, Inc.
P. Ehrlich & R. Holm, *The Process of Evolution* 310 (1963),
©1963 McGraw-Hill Book Co.
Ellis, *Alternatives to the Big Bang*, 22 Ann. Rev. Astronomy & Astrophysics 157 (1984),
©1984 Annual Reviews, Inc.
T. Emerson, *The System of Freedom of Expression* (1970),

©1970 Random House, Inc.

Erbich, *On the Probability of the Emergence of a Protein with a Particular Function*, 34 Acta Biotheoretica 53 (1985),
©1985 Martinus Nijhoff Publishers, by permission of Kluwer Academic Publishers.

Forey, *Neontological Analysis Versus Palaeontological Stories*, in Problems of Phylogenetic Reconstruction 119, 124 (K. Joysey & A. Friday eds. 1982),
©1982 Systematics Association.

Gale, *The Anthropic Principle*, Scientific Am., Dec. 1981, at 154,
©1981 Scientific American, Inc.

Glenister & Witzke, *Interpreting Earth History*, in Did the Devil Make Darwin Do It? Modern Perspectives on the Creation-Evolution Controversy 55 (D. Wilson ed. 1983),
©1983 Iowa State University Press.

S. Gould, *Ontogeny and Phylogeny* 126-27, 130 (1977),
©1977 Harvard University Press.

P. Grassé, *The Evolution of Living Organisms* 170 (1977),
©1977 Academic Press, Inc. and 1972 Editions Albin Michel Bandes.

Guth & Steinhardt, *The Inflationary Universe*, Scientific Am., May 1984, at 116.
©1984 Scientific American, Inc.

Herbert, *Lucy: The trouble with dating an older woman*, 123 Science News 5, 5 (1983),
©1983 Science Service, Inc.

Horgan, *Big Bang Bashers*, Scientific Am., Sept. 1987, at 22,
©1987 Scientific American, Inc.

Hoyle, *The Big Bang in Astronomy*, 91 New Scientist 521 (1981),
©1981 New Scientist.

Hughes, *The Fact and the Theory of Evolution*, 44 Am. Biology Teacher 25 (1982),
©1979 National Association of Biology Teachers.

Hull, *Thermodynamics and Kinetics of Spontaneous Generation*, 186 Nature 693 (1960),
©1960 Nature.

H. Jerison, *Evolution of the Brain and Intelligence* 153-55, 213 (1973),
©1973 Academic Press, Inc.

Jukes & Holmquist, *Evolutionary Clock: Nonconstancy of Rate in Different Species*, 177 Science 530 (1972),
©1972 American Association for the Advancement of Science.

Kaplan, *The Problem of Chance in Formation of Protobionts by Random Aggregation of Macromolecules*, 1 Chemical Evolution and the Origin of Life 319, 319 (R. Buvet & C. Ponnamperuma eds. 1971),
©1971 Elsevier Science Publishers B.V.

E. Klinckmann, *Biology Teachers' Handbook* 16-17 (1970),
©1970 John Wiley & Sons, Inc.

I. Lakatos, *The Methodology of Scientific Research* (J. Worrall & G. Currie eds. 1978),
©1978 Cambridge University Press.

Levine, *The Early Atmosphere: A New Picture*, Science Activities, Feb.-Mar. 1986, at 7, 10-11.
©1986 Helen Dwight Reid Educational Foundation, published by Heldref Publications.

Manly, *Tests of the Theory of Natural Selection: An Overview*, 15 J. Royal Society of New Zealand 411, 411, 425 (1985),

©1985 Royal Society of New Zealand.
Margon, *The Origin of the Cosmic X-Ray Background*, Scientific Am., Jan. 1983, at 104,
©1983 Scientific American, Inc.
Marx, *The Oldest Fossil Bird: A Rival for Archaeopteryx?*, 199 Science 284 (1978),
©1978 American Association for the Advancement of Science.
Mayr, *Evolution*, Scientific Am., Sept. 1978, at 47,
©1978 Scientific American, Inc.
Mayr, *Introduction*, to C. Darwin, The Origin of Species xii-xiii (1st ed. 1859, repr. 1964),
©1964 Harvard University Press.
E. Mayr, *The Growth of Biological Thought* 217-18 (1982),
©1982 Harvard University Press.
Narlikar, *Was there a big bang?*, New Scientist, July 2, 1981, at 19,
©1981 New Scientist.
Nissenbaum, *Scavenging of Soluble Organic Matter from the Prebiotic Oceans*, 7 Origins of Life 413, 413, 415 (1976),
©1976 Reidl Publishing Co. and by permission of Kluwer Academic Publishers.
Nissenbaum, Kenyon & Oro, *On the Possible Role of Organic Melanoidin Polymers as Matrices for Prebiotic Activity*, 6 J. Molecular Evolution 253 (1975),
©1975 Springer-Verlag.
D. Oldroyd, *Darwinian Impacts* (1980),
©1980 Humanities Press International, Inc.
Opik, *About Dogma in Science, and Other Recollections of an Astronomer*, 15 Ann. Rev. Astronomy & Astrophysics 1 (1977),
©1977 Annual Reviews, Inc.
R. Oram, *Biology: Living Systems* 732 (3d ed. 1979),
©1979 Merrill Publishing Co.
Oxnard, *Human Fossils: New Views of Old Bones*, 41 Am. Biology Teacher 264 (1979),
©1979 National Association of Biology Teachers.
Patterson, *Cladistics and classification*, 94 New Scientist 303 (1982),
©1982 New Scientist.
Patterson, *Significance of Fossils in Determining Evolutionary Relationships*, 12 Ann. Rev. Ecology & Systematics 195 (1981),
©1981 Annual Reviews, Inc.
Popper, *Letter*, 87 New Scientist 611 (1980).
©1980 New Scientist.
Quinn, *The Philosopher of Science as Expert Witness*, in Science and Reality 32 (J. Cushing, C. Delaney & G. Gutting eds. 1984),
©1984 University of Notre Dame Press.
Raloff, *They Call It Creation-Science*, Science News, Jan. 16, 1982, at 44, 46,
©1982 Science Service, Inc.
Riddiford & Penny, *The scientific status of modern evolutionary theory*, in Evolutionary Theory: Paths into the Future 1 (J. Pollard ed. 1984),
©1984 John Wiley & Sons, Inc.
J. Rifkin, *Algeny* (1983),
©1983 Viking Penguin Inc.
Sagan, *Discussion of K. Harada* and *Simulated Natural Experiments*, in The Origins

of Prebiological Systems and of Their Molecules 195-96, 374-75 (S. Fox ed. 1965), ©1965 Academic Press, Inc.

H. Schofield, *The Philosophy of Education*, 178, 181 (1972), ©1972 Unwin Hyman Ltd.

Scott, *Update on Genesis*, New Scientist, May 2, 1985, at 30, ©1985 New Scientist.

Scriven, *Explanation and Prediction in Evolutionary Theory*, 130 Science 477 (1959), ©1959 American Association for the Advancement of Science.

Shapiro, *The Improbability of Prebiotic Nucleic Acid Synthesis*, 14 Origin of Life 565, 565 (1984), ©1984 Reidl Publishing Co. and by permission of Kluwer Academic Publishers.

Shea, *Primate Morphometrics*, 224 Science 148 (1984). ©1984 American Association for the Advancement of Science.

Simpson, *The World into Which Darwin Led Us*, 131 Science 966 (1970), ©1970 American Association for the Advancement of Science.

Sparkes, *What is this thing called science?*, 89 New Scientist 156 (1981), ©1981 New Scientist.

Temussi, Paolillo, Ferrara, Benedetti & Andini, *Structural Characterization of Thermal Prebiotic Polypeptides*, 7 J. Molecular Evolution 105 (1976), ©1976 Springer-Verlag.

Tryon, *What made the world?*, New Scientist, March 8, 1984, at 14, ©1984 New Scientist.

Wald, *The Origin of Life*, Scientific Am., Aug. 1954, at 46, ©1954 Scientific American, Inc.

Watkins, *Against "Normal Science,"* in Criticism and the Growth of Knowledge 36 (I. Lakatos & A. Musgrave eds. 1970), ©1970 Cambridge University Press.

Wolf, *Non-cosmological redshifts of spectral lines*, 326 Nature 363 (1987), ©1987 Nature.

A. Whitehead, *the Function of Reason* 53-54, 58-59 (1929), ©1957 Princeton University Press.

S. Zuckerman, *Beyond the Ivory Tower: The Frontiers of Public and Private Science* 77, 81, 85 (1971), ©1971 Taplinger Publishing Co.

Author Index to Volume II

Subject Index to Volume II

THE AUTHOR

W.R. Bird, an Atlanta attorney and Yale Law School graduate, argued the test case before the Supreme Court of the United States on "evolution and creation-science" in public schools.* He has published legal articles on that subject in the *Yale Law Journal* and the *Harvard Journal of Law and Public Policy,* as well as a book and other legal articles on constitutional law, and a chapter and legal articles on nonprofit organization law.

He is an adjunct professor at a major law school, teaching its constitutional law course covering the church and state provision of the first amendment; and has litigated or filed amicus curiae briefs in many other constitutional cases and was a speaker at the Bicentennial Conference on the Religion Clauses of the First Amendment in Philadelphia. He won one of the twenty largest judgments in history in another case.

His legal education included membership on the Board of Editors of the *Yale Law Journal,* and the Egger Prize of Yale Law School for one of the two best student publications. Before that, he graduated *summa cum laude* from Vanderbilt University, where he was the first student to be exempted from the freshman year and enter as a sophomore.

He is a member of the prestigious American Law Institute (its second youngest member ever), of the American Bar Association and Association of Trial Lawyers of America, and of the bar in four states. He is listed in *Who's Who in the World, Who's Who in the South and Southwest,* and *Who's Who in American Law,* and is married with one child.

---

*The issues and terms in *Edwards v. Aguillard* were established by the Louisiana law that was under challenge, which required "balanced treatment for creation-science and evolution," and which defined creation-science as "scientific evidence[]." That terminology is not reflective of the author's own beliefs.